D1398803

RAREFIED
GAS DYNAMICS

Volume I

Advances in
Applied Mechanics

Editors:

H. L. DRYDEN

TH. VON KÁRMÁN

Managing Editor:

G. KUERTI

Case Institute of Technology, Cleveland, Ohio

Associate Editors:

F. H. VAN DEN DUNGEN

L. HOWARTH

RAREFIED
GAS DYNAMICS

PROCEEDINGS OF THE FOURTH INTERNATIONAL SYMPOSIUM
ON RAREFIED GAS DYNAMICS, HELD AT THE INSTITUTE
FOR AEROSPACE STUDIES, UNIVERSITY OF TORONTO, 1964

Edited by

J. H. de Leeuw

INSTITUTE FOR AEROSPACE STUDIES, UNIVERSITY OF TORONTO, TORONTO, CANADA

Volume I

1965

NEW YORK   LONDON

ACADEMIC PRESS

Library
I.U.P.
ndiana, Po⸝

533.2 Inℓℓ
4ᵗʰ 1964, V. 1, C. 1

COPYRIGHT © 1965, BY ACADEMIC PRESS INC.

ALL RIGHTS RESERVED.
NO PART OF THIS BOOK MAY BE REPRODUCED IN ANY FORM,
BY PHOTOSTAT, MICROFILM, OR ANY OTHER MEANS, WITHOUT
WRITTEN PERMISSION FROM THE PUBLISHERS.

ACADEMIC PRESS INC.
111 Fifth Avenue, New York, New York 10003

United Kingdom Edition published by
ACADEMIC PRESS INC. (LONDON) LTD.
Berkeley Square House, London W.1

LIBRARY OF CONGRESS CATALOG CARD NUMBER: 60-16990

PRINTED IN THE UNITED STATES OF AMERICA

Fourth International Symposium

Rarefied Gas Dynamics

Presented at the

UNIVERSITY OF TORONTO, JULY 1964

Under the sponsorship of

U.S. Air Force Office of Scientific Research
U.S. Office of Naval Research
National Aeronautics and Space Administration
Institute for Aerospace Studies, University of Toronto

Symposium Chairman

G. N. PATTERSON

Advisory Committee

EDMOND A. BRUN	D. W. HOLDER	RONALD F. PROBSTEIN
RAYMOND L. CHUAN	W. P. JONES	S. A. SCHAAF
F. M. DEVIENNE	H. H. KURZWEG	L. I. SEDOV
IMMANUEL ESTERMANN	H. W. LIEPMANN	R. E. STREET
HAROLD GRAD	W. PETRIE	F. R. THURSTON
	W. J. PRICE	

Papers Committee

J. M. BURGERS	F. C. HURLBUT	F. S. SHERMAN
H. K. CHENG	J. LAUFER	L. SIROVICH
J. H. DE LEEUW	J. A. LAURMANN	J. N. SMITH, JR.
(Chairman)	L. LEES	J. R. STALDER
J. B. FENN	V. C. LIU	L. TRILLING
J. B. FRENCH	G. J. MASLACH	M. VAN DYKE
C. G. GOODWIN	J. L. POTTER	D. R. WILLIS

Preface

In 1958 the First International Symposium on Rarefied Gas Dynamics was held at Nice. Since that first meeting international symposia in this subject area have been held biennially: at Berkeley in 1960 and at Paris in 1962. The Fourth International Symposium on Rarefied Gas Dynamics took place in Toronto, July 14–17, 1964, under the auspices of the U.S. Air Force Office of Scientific Research, the U.S. Office of Naval Research, the National Aeronautics and Space Administration, and the Institute for Aerospace Studies of the University of Toronto.

The Fourth Symposium attracted scientists and engineers from many parts of the world and 73 papers were presented during the meeting as compared to 55 in the previous one. This clearly indicates that the interest and active research in the subject area of rarefied gas dynamics, already evident from the previous symposia, has continued to grow.

These volumes constitute the Proceedings of the Fourth Symposium and in all but a few cases contain the entire text of the papers that were presented. The division of the Proceedings into sections has been somewhat arbitrary. In a few cases the section topics are not mutually exclusive and a number of papers could have been placed equally well in a different section. It is hoped that the editor's grouping of the papers is a convenient one for the reader.

The discussions following the presentation of the papers at the meeting were recorded in an attempt to make the Proceedings more valuable by including them. Considerable effort was expended in transcribing these records and the aid of the participants in the discussions in this effort is gratefully acknowledged. Nevertheless it was regretfully decided not to make the discussions part of the Proceedings. In the first place it became rapidly apparent that the already large size of these Proceedings made inclusion of more material difficult. Secondly, a preliminary editing showed almost all the questions to be requests for clarification of the oral presentations that were adequately answered in the written manuscripts.

The success of the Symposium depended on the efforts of a large group of individuals. Principal among these was Dr. G. N. Patterson, the director of the Institute for Aerospace Studies, who acted as symposium chairman, and who in addition was largely responsible for the physical organization of the meeting. A large editorial committee of eminent scientists reviewed the papers submitted for presentation and so greatly lightened the task of the editor. Their names are listed together with those of the members of the Advisory Committee on page v of these Proceedings.

Excellent support in the organization of the meeting was also received from the staff and students of the Institute for Aerospace Studies and thanks are due to the secretarial staff of the Institute for their enthusiastic and competent work.

Toronto, Canada   J. H. DE LEEUW

Contents of Volume I

Section 1

KINETIC THEORY

Section 2

SHOCK STRUCTURE

Section 3

TRANSITION FLOW—THEORY

Section 4

TRANSITION FLOW — EXPERIMENTAL

Section 5

FREE MOLECULE AND INTERNAL FLOW

Contents of Volume II

RAREFIED
GAS DYNAMICS

Volume I

KINETIC THEORY

Steady-State Oscillations in a Gas

HAROLD WEITZNER

Courant Institute of Mathematical Sciences, New York University, New York

The linearized one-dimensional Krook equation is solved for the case of a half-space of gas bounded by an oscillating wall. This situation corresponds to the commonly studied problem of the propagation of sound in a gas. The question of when a sound wave is observable is considered. Unless two conditions hold the sound wave will be lost in a larger, irregular disturbance. First, the observation must be taken many mean free paths from the wall. Second, the wave train is observable only for a limited length, and the number of wavelengths seen is of the order of the collision frequency over the oscillation frequency.

I. Introduction

Besides some experimental work on the propagation of sound in rarefied gases (Greenspan, 1950, 1956), there is an extensive literature on the theoretical aspects of this problem (Chapman and Cowling, 1952; Wang Chang and Uhlenbeck, 1952; Grad, 1949; Sirovich, 1963; Sirovich and Thurber, 1963; Pekeris *et al.*, 1963; and many others). The theoretical methods used all involve truncating a series of moment equations and obtaining a dispersion relation. Since this truncation procedure automatically eliminates an essential part of the linearized steady-state Boltzmann equation, namely the continuous spectrum,[1] the range of validity of these methods is open to question. Here, we solve the sound propagation problem exactly for an approximate kinetic equation, the linearized Krook equation, and we do find that the roots of the dispersion relation do not always determine the behavior of the wave motion in a gas (if any regular wave motion exists at all).

We solve the problem of a half-space of gas bounded by a wall oscillating

---

[1] The continuous spectrum in question does not come from the collision term but from the derivative term $v \, \partial f / \partial x$.

with small amplitude at a fixed frequency. We consider the system only in steady state when the transients have disappeared. We find the ordinary hydrodynamic type of sound mode only many mean free paths from the wall and we are able to find only a limited number of spatially coherent oscillations before the wave train is lost in larger incoherent oscillations. The number of wavelengths observable is of the order of the collision frequency over the frequency of oscillation. Thus, if the latter ratio is not large enough, then no coherent oscillation is observable at any distance from the wall.

We solve the problem by applying a Laplace transform in space to the linearized Krook equation and we specify the distribution function of particles leaving the wall. We solve for the particles incident on the wall uniquely, by requiring that the solution be well behaved at infinity. After obtaining the answer we consider various asymptotic limits and find the results described above. We also show that for any fixed ratio of collision frequency to oscillation frequency there is no regular wave pattern sufficiently far from the wall and there is only irregular decay to equilibrium. We rely heavily on an earlier paper (Weitzner, 1963) on the time dependent problem. We refer to the equations of this paper as, e.g., Eq. I-12, and we use its notation throughout. Since we are only interested in qualitative conclusions, for simplicity we take the Krook equation which is one-dimensional in velocity space as well as physical space. Cercignani (1962) has considered this problem at zero frequency using the generalized eigenfunction technique of Van Kampen (1955) and Case (1959). The careful reader will note that essentially the same elements appear in both methods and neither is significantly "simpler" than the other. We consider the methods used here sounder and more direct than the eigenfunction techniques.

The following section contains the bulk of the treatment of this problem. In an appendix we treat some more technical aspects of the problem. We obtain expressions for the particle distribution function striking the wall and the mass flow and energy at the wall in terms of the given distribution function of particles leaving the wall. Thus if we want some special relations among the moments at the wall then we must introduce coefficients of accommodation into the given data. Finally we consider the special case of specular reflection and obtain a fairly explicit answer.

II. Analysis

We start from the nondimensionalized, linearized, one-dimensional Krook equation and we assume that all perturbed variables have time dependence $e^{-i\omega t}$, so that

$$-i\omega g(x, v) + v\frac{\partial g}{\partial x} = -g(x, v) + f_0(v)\left[n(x) + vu(x) + \frac{v^2 - 1}{2} T(x)\right] \quad (1)$$

where $g(x, v)$ is the perturbed distribution function and $n(x)$, $u(x)$, $T(x) + n(x)$ $= e(x)$, are its zeroth, first, and second moments, and $f_0(v)$ is the Maxwell distribution $\exp(-v^2/2)/\sqrt{2\pi}$. We assume that

$$g(0, v) = \tilde{g}(v) \tag{2}$$

and we seek a solution of Eq. (1) in the domain $x \geq 0$ that takes the boundary value Eq. (2). We require that the solution be bounded at infinity. For such a solution, the Laplace transform in x must exist and if K is the transform variable; then the transform must be analytic for Re $K > 0$. If we take a Laplace transform then we obtain Eqs. I-11a, I-11b, I-11c, but with the changes

$$p \rightarrow -i\omega$$
$$ik \rightarrow K$$
$$\tilde{g}(v) \rightarrow v\tilde{g}(v) \tag{3}$$
$$N \rightarrow U$$
$$U \rightarrow E.$$

The solution to these modified equations is given by Eqs. I-12 to I-15. The variable z of I is given by

$$z = \frac{i\omega - 1}{K}. \tag{4}$$

We note that z and K are essentially the same independent variable. We write formulas in terms of z or K or both as it is convenient, but we must recall they are related by Eq. (4). This apparently awkward procedure greatly facilitates the use of material from I, and simplifies the formulas.

We see that the form of the solution is (see Eq. I-12)

$$n(K) = \frac{N(K, z)}{D(K, z)} = \frac{N\left(K, \dfrac{i\omega - 1}{K}\right)}{D\left(K, \dfrac{i\omega - 1}{K}\right)}. \tag{5}$$

The functions

$$F(z) = \int_{-\infty}^{\infty} \frac{f_0(v)\, dv}{v - z}, \qquad G(z) = \int_{-\infty}^{\infty} \frac{v\tilde{g}(v)\, dv}{v - z}$$

that appear in $N(K, z)$ and $D(K, z)$ are now defined by the integrals for all nonreal z. Thus these functions are discontinuous across the line Im $z = 0$. In what follows we take no analytic continuations of Eq. (5) and the defining relations for $F(z)$ and $G(z)$, but we use the actual formulas as given. For a

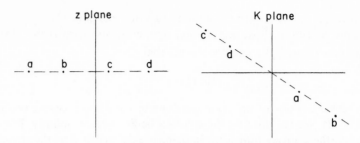

FIG. 1. Lines of discontinuity of $n(K)$ represented in the z and K planes.

general $\tilde{g}(v)$, $n(K)$ is not analytic for Re $K > 0$ and in Fig. 1 we plot the line of discontinuity in the z plane and in the K plane.

In order to have an acceptable solution to the problem we must eliminate the discontinuity of $n(K)$ across the line in Fig. 1 where Re $K > 0$. We show that given an arbitrary $\tilde{g}(v)$, $v > 0$ there is a unique $\tilde{g}(v)$, $v < 0$ such that Eq. (5) represents a function analytic in Re $K > 0$. We note that besides eliminating the cut we must also eliminate the poles coming from any roots of $D(K, z)$, Re $K > 0$. We see below that we shall be able to do both. The position of the singularities of $n(K)$ corresponds to the spectrum of the equation and we try to eliminate that part of the spectrum that generates exponentially growing modes. To eliminate the cut we need only require

$$\lim_{\substack{\mathrm{Im}\,z \to 0^+ \\ \mathrm{Re}\,z < 0}} n\left(\frac{i\omega - 1}{z}, z\right) = \lim_{\substack{\mathrm{Im}\,z \to 0^- \\ \mathrm{Re}\,z < 0}} n\left(\frac{i\omega - 1}{z}, z\right), \qquad (6)$$

since Eq. (5) is the solution to the problem, if any exists. In order to show that a solution exists we must show also that $g(K, v)$ has no singularities for Re $K > 0$. A straightforward and elementary calculation using Eqs. I-11a 11b, 11c, 12 shows that if $n(K)$ satisfies Eq. (6) then $g(v, K)$ has no singularities in Re $K > 0$. We show that Eq. (6) reduces to the classic Hilbert problem for arcs in complex variables and we follow the solution as outlined in Mushkelishvili (1953). In the reduction to a Hilbert problem it becomes necessary to locate the zeros of $D(K, z)$ and to obtain other properties. Thus, we study $D(K, z)$ at this point.

We consider $D(K, z)$ only in the upper half of the z plane and we can infer its properties in the lower half-plane by an appropriate complex conjugation. We may factor $D(K, z)$ as

$$D(K, z) = [K - K_0(z)][K - K_+(z)][K - K_-(z)] \qquad (7)$$

where $K_j(z)$ are analytic functions of z in the upper and in the lower half-planes. Further,

$$K_j(z^*) = K_j(z)^*. \qquad (8)$$

While Eq. (8) is not the most felicitous choice of relations between $K_j(z)$ in the upper and lower half-plane, we use it to follow the notation of I. The usefulness of considering K and z as independent variables is contained in Eq. (7) and the availability of information on $K_j(z)$ as contained in I. The condition that $D(K, z)$ vanish is just that $(i\omega - 1)/z = K_j(z)$ or that

$$i\omega - 1 = zK_j(z) \tag{9}$$

for some j. Thus we are interested in the curves

$$\text{Re } zK_j(z) = -1 \tag{10}$$

as for each value of z such Eq. (10) holds, there is an $\omega = \text{Im } zK_j(z)$ for which the dispersion relation has a root. From the asymptotic expansions of $K_j(z)$, Eq. I-18, we obtain

$$zK_0(z) = -1 - \frac{3(x^2 - y^2 - 2ixy)}{|z|^4} + O\left(\frac{1}{z^4}\right) \tag{11a}$$

$$zK_\pm(z) = -1 \pm \frac{\sqrt{3}(x - iy)}{|z|^2} + O\left(\frac{1}{z^3}\right). \tag{11b}$$

From the asymptotic expansion Eq. (11a) we infer the existence of two curves, one near the line $x = +y$ at infinity and the other near the line $x = -y$ at infinity such that Re $zK_0(z) = -1$. Such a curve cannot terminate at infinity; the harmonic function $[(\text{Re } zK_0(z) + 1)]$ would vanish on the boundary of a domain and hence would be identically zero; thus it must end on the real axis. Direct numerical computation shows that there are exactly two points on the real axis for which Re $zK_0(z) = -1$. Thus we may draw the plot of the contour lines Re $zK_0(z) = -1$ as in Fig. 2. We use the legend of Fig. 2 below

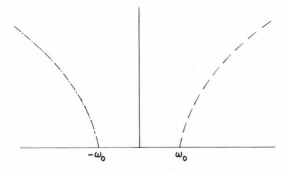

FIG. 2. Contour lines of $zK_0(z) + 1$ in the z plane.

KEY: — — —, $zK_i(z) + 1$ imaginary and Im $zK_i(z) > 0$; —·—·—, $zK_i(z) + 1$ imaginary and Im $zK_i(z) < 0$.

in Figs. 3 and 4. No other such curves may leave the real axis, and Im $zK_0(z)$ must be monotone on each of the two curves; for otherwise there would be a double point and another curve on which Re $zK_0(z) = -1$, an impossibility. Thus we see that for $-\omega_0 < \omega < \omega_0$ there is a unique root of $K - K_0(z)$ for Im $z > 0$. On the curve in the first quadrant of Fig. 2 Im $zK_0(z) > 0$ and in the second quadrant Im $zK_0(z) < 0$. In a similar manner we rely

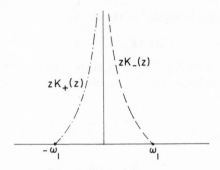

FIG. 3. Contour lines of $zK_\pm(z) + 1$ in the z plane.

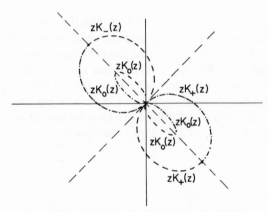

FIG. 4. Contour lines of $zK_i(z) + 1$ in the K plane.

on the asymptotic expansions Eq. (11b) and the numerical work of I to obtain a similar picture for $K_\pm(z)$. Again the values of Im $zK_\pm(z)$ are monotone on the respective curves and all values from $-\omega_1$ to 0 for $K_+(z)$ and 0 to $+\omega_1$ for $K_-(z)$ occur. We now transcribe all this information to the K plane in which we will ultimately work. The dashed lines of Fig. 4 are the map of the real and imaginary axes of the z plane. The curves have all the symmetries implied by the figure. Thus for $-\omega_0 < \omega < \omega_0$, $K - K_0((i\omega - 1)/K)$ has one root for Re $K > 0$ and for $-\omega_1 < \omega < \omega_1$ $[K - K_+((i\omega - 1)/K)]$

$[K - K_-((i\omega - 1)/K)]$ has one root for $\mathrm{Re}\ K > 0$.[2] For the same ranges of ω there is also a root for $\mathrm{Re}\ K < 0$. The roots for which $\mathrm{Re}\ K > 0$ correspond to unbounded disturbances in the gas. We show that it is possible to eliminate these and obtain an acceptable solution to the problem.

We may express $n(K)$ as

$$n(K) = n(K, z) = \frac{A(K, z) + K^2 \displaystyle\int_{-\infty}^0 \frac{v\tilde{g}(v)\,dv}{v - z}}{D(K, z)} \tag{12}$$

where

$$A(K, z) = N(K, z) - K^2 \int_{-\infty}^0 \frac{v\tilde{g}(v)\,dv}{v - z} \tag{13}$$

depends only on U, E, and the distribution function of particles leaving the wall ($v > 0$), and we have exhibited the explicit dependence on the particles striking the wall in Eq. (12). We define

$$H(z) = \int_{-\infty}^0 \frac{v\tilde{g}(v)\,dv}{v - z} \tag{14}$$

so that $H(z)$ is an analytic function of z except on the slit $\mathrm{Re}\ z < 0$, $\mathrm{Im}\ z = 0$. Since we require the distribution function of particles striking the wall to be well behaved we see that $H(z)$ goes to zero as $|z|$ goes to infinity and for $|z|$ small $H(z)$ is bounded. Thus, the condition that $n(K)$ have no branch cut for $\mathrm{Re}\ K > 0$, Eq. (6), becomes

$$\frac{A^+\left(\dfrac{i\omega - 1}{z}, z\right) + \left(\dfrac{i\omega - 1}{z}\right)^2 H^+(z)}{D^+\left(\dfrac{i\omega - 1}{z}, z\right)} = \frac{A^-\left(\dfrac{i\omega - 1}{z}, z\right) + \left(\dfrac{i\omega - 1}{z}\right)^2 H^-(z)}{D^-\left(\dfrac{i\omega - 1}{z}, z\right)} \tag{15}$$

where Eq. (15) applies for $\mathrm{Re}\ z < 0$, $\mathrm{Im}\ z = 0$, and the $\pm$ refers to $\lim \mathrm{Im}\ z \to 0^{\pm}$. We may rewrite Eq. (15) as

$$H^+(z) = \frac{D^+(K, z)}{D^-(K, z)} H^-(z) + \frac{D^+(K, z)A^-(K, z) - D^-(K, z)A^+(K, z)}{K^2 D^+(K, z)} \tag{16}$$

where we have again used the mixed K and z notation. We see that Eq. (16) is exactly the form of a Hilbert problem. From the desired properties of $H(z)$ we see that we seek a solution that tends to zero at infinity, that is analytic in the slit plane, and that is bounded for $|z|$ small.

[2] For the present problem the values of the constants are $\omega_0 = 3.2$, $\omega_1 = .55$. The root K_0 corresponds to the temperature relaxation mode and the root $K_{\pm}$ to the sound mode. The actual values of ω_0 and ω_1 are, of course, strongly model dependent and we do not consider the actual values very meaningful for physical problems.

Following Mushkelishvili (1953), we define

$$\tilde{\Gamma}(z) = \frac{1}{2\pi i} \int_{-\infty}^{0} \frac{dt}{t-z} \log \frac{D^+\left(\dfrac{i\omega-1}{t}, t\right)}{D^-\left(\dfrac{i\omega-1}{t}, t\right)} \tag{17}$$

so that

$$\exp[\tilde{\Gamma}(z)^+] = \frac{D^+\left(\dfrac{i\omega-1}{z}, z\right)}{D^-\left(\dfrac{i\omega-1}{z}, z\right)} \exp[\tilde{\Gamma}(z)^-]. \tag{18}$$

For Eq. (17) to be meaningful we must choose the branch of the logarithm so that as t goes to plus infinity and D^+/D^- tends to one, $\log D^+/D^-$ tends to zero. In preparation for solving the inhomogeneous equation (16) and in order to solve the homogeneous equation completely we must determine the behavior of $\Gamma(z)$ for $|z|$ small. While we know from Eq. (17) that

$$\tilde{\Gamma}(z) = \frac{1}{2\pi i} \log \left. \frac{D^+\left(\dfrac{i\omega-1}{t}, t\right)}{D^-\left(\dfrac{i\omega-1}{t}, t\right)} \right|_{t=0} \log(-z) + O(1), \tag{19}$$

the result has no content until we determine the branch of the log at $t = O$. We have all the necessary information in Figs. 2 and 3. Consider, for instance the factor of D^+ or D^-, $(i\omega - 1) - tK_0(t)$. As t varies from plus infinity to zero the real part changes sign for any ω. The imaginary part changes sign once for the factor of D^+ or the factor of D^- if $|\omega| < \omega_0$, and not at all otherwise. Thus the phase of the one factor has changed by $\pm 2\pi$ relative to the other. By analogous arguments we conclude that

$$\tilde{\Gamma}(z) = \begin{cases} 2\log(-z) + O(1), & |\omega| < \omega_0, \quad |\omega| < \omega_1 \\[2ex] \log(-z) + O(1), & \begin{cases} |\omega| < \min(\omega_0, \omega_1) \\ |\omega| > \max(\omega_0, \omega_1) \end{cases} \\[2ex] O(1), & |\omega| > \min(\omega_0, \omega_1). \end{cases}$$

We define

$$\Gamma(z) = \tilde{\Gamma}(z) - M \log(-z) \tag{20}$$

where

$$M = \begin{cases} 2, & |\omega| < \max(\omega_0, \omega_1) \\ 1, & |\omega| > \max(\omega_0, \omega_1), \quad |\omega| < \min(\omega_0, \omega_1) \\ 0, & |\omega| > \min(\omega_0, \omega_1). \end{cases} \tag{21}$$

Further, near infinity

$$\exp[\Gamma(z)] = \frac{1}{(-z)^M} \exp\left\{1 + \frac{\alpha_1}{z} + \frac{\alpha_2}{z^2} + \cdots + O\left(\frac{1}{z^n}\right)\right\}$$

where

$$\alpha_n = \frac{-1}{2\pi i} \int_{-\infty}^0 t^{n-1}\, dt \log \frac{D^+\left(\frac{i\omega - 1}{t}, t\right)}{D^-\left(\frac{i\omega - 1}{t}, t\right)} \tag{22a}$$

so that

$$\exp[\Gamma(z)] = \frac{1}{(-z)^M}\left\{1 + \frac{\alpha_1}{z} + \frac{\alpha_1^2 + 2\alpha_2}{2z^2} + O\left(\frac{1}{z^3}\right)\right\}. \tag{22b}$$

Hence

$$z^m \exp[\Gamma(z)], \qquad 0 \le m < M,$$

all constitute acceptable solutions to the homogeneous equation derived from Eq. (16) and the usual arguments show that there are no other such solutions. A specific solution to Eq. (16) is

$$H_0(z) = \frac{\exp[\Gamma(z)]}{2\pi i} \int_{-\infty}^0 \frac{A^-\exp[-\Gamma^-(t)] - A^+\exp[-\Gamma^+(t)]}{\left(\frac{i\omega - 1}{t}\right)^2} \frac{dt}{t - z} \tag{23}$$

so that the general solution is

$$H(z) = H_0(z) + \sum_{m=0}^{M-1} \gamma_m{}^M z^m \exp[\Gamma(z)]. \tag{24}$$

We see that there are exactly enough arbitrary constants in Eq. (24) to make the numerator of $n(K)$ in Eq. (5) vanish when the denominator vanishes at the M roots of $D(K, z)$ with Re $K > 0$. Thus the constants $\gamma_m{}^M$ are completely specified. Thus we have completed the first part of the problem and Eqs. (12)–(14) give the Laplace transform of the solution to the problem with $H(z)$ given by Eqs. (23) and (24). In the appendix we obtain more explicit expressions for the particle distribution function of particles leaving wall and the mass flow and energy transfer at the wall. For the remainder of this section we assume that the distribution function of particles leaving the wall is the correct one. We now proceed to the interpretation of the result.

Let us consider the simpler of the limits in question. We hold ω fixed and we seek an expansion of $n(x)$ for large x. We have

$$n(x) = \frac{e^{-i\omega t}}{2\pi i} \int_C e^{Kx} \frac{N(K, z)}{D(K, z)}\, dK \tag{25}$$

where we may deform the contour of integration into that shown in Fig. 5 which is in the left half-plane, but to the right of all the poles in the left half-plane. An elementary computation shows that

$$\frac{N(K)}{D(K)} = A_0 + A_1 K + A_2 K^2 + \cdots + A_n K^n + O(K^{n+1})$$

for $|K|$ small. Thus we may integrate Eq. (25) by parts repeatedly and we find that

$$n(x) = e^{-i\omega t} O\left(\frac{1}{x^n}\right) \qquad \text{for any } n. \tag{26}$$

The exact exponent n depends on the number of moments of the prescribed distribution function at the wall which exist. As the number of moments that

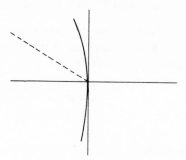

FIG. 5. Contour of integration C.

exist tends to infinity so does n. For the limit of large x no better estimate than Eq. (26) is possible.

Suppose the roots of $D(K, z)$ in the left half-plane are at K_m ($0 < m \leq M$). Then we may write $n(x)$ as

$$n(x) = \frac{e^{-i\omega t}}{2\pi i} \left[\int_C dK e^{Kx} \left(\frac{N(K)}{D(K)} - \sum_{m=1}^{M} \frac{N(K_m)}{(K - K_m)D'(K_m)} \right) \right.$$
$$\left. + \int_C dK e^{Kx} \sum_{m=1}^{M} \frac{N(K_m)}{(K - K_m)D'(K_m)} \right]. \tag{27}$$

We may evaluate the second integral explicitly and since the first integrand has no poles in the left half-plane (only a branch cut), we may integrate by parts repeatedly and find

$$n(x) = e^{-i\omega t} \sum_{m=1}^{M} e^{K_m x} \frac{N(K_m)}{D'(K_m)} + e^{-i\omega t} O\left(\frac{1}{x^n}\right). \tag{28}$$

In order that the mode associated with a given root K_m be observable we require that x be large and also that the exponential has not damped appreciably for such values of x. To see the result concretely let us consider the case of small ω so that we may expand the roots $K_m(\omega)$ using Eqs. (4), (9), and (11), and

$$n(x, t) = -e^{-i\omega t}\left[+ \frac{(3U - Q)}{6\sqrt{3}} \frac{e^{-i\pi/4}}{\sqrt{\omega}} \exp[-\sqrt{\omega/6}(1 - i)x] \right.$$
$$\left. + \frac{(\sqrt{3}E + \overline{Q})}{6(3 - \sqrt{3})} \exp(i\omega x/\sqrt{3} - \omega^2 x/3\sqrt{3}) + O\left(\frac{1}{x^n}\right) \right]$$

(29)

where

$$Q = \int v^3 g(v)\, dv, \qquad \overline{Q} = \int v^4 g(v)\, dv.$$

We note that if $3U - Q$ is not zero then there is a large term of order $1/\sqrt{\omega}$ which decays more rapidly than the other term which corresponds to the sound wave. However, for specular reflection $3U - Q = 0$ and in general $3U - Q$ vanishes if and only if

$$\int (v^3 - 3v)g(v)\, dv = 0$$

or if and only if there is no heat flow at the wall. It should be no surprise that if there is heat flow at the wall then the relaxation of the temperature to equilibrium should be strongly observable. In order that the sound wave predominate we must require that x is large and $\omega^2 x$ is not too large. Dimensionally we require (in terms of the mean free path λ, actual distance x', frequency ω', and collision frequency ν)

$$x'/\lambda \gg 1 \tag{30a}$$

$$\frac{\omega'}{\nu} \frac{\omega' x'}{v_{th}} = O(1). \tag{30b}$$

Equation (30a) requires that we be many mean free paths from the wall and Eq. (30b) states that the number of periods of the wave that are observable $(\omega' x'/v_{th})$, is of the order of the collision frequency over the oscillation frequency. In the Krook model hydrodynamic modes exist only if $\omega'/\nu \leq O(1)$ and within this range of values we would expect the damping rate in Eq. (28) to be of the same order of magnitude as in Eq. (30b) so that Eq. (30a) and Eq. (30b) should remain qualitatively correct restrictions for the observability of a hydrodynamic mode even if ω'/ν is not small. Thus in general we would expect to see these modes only several mean free paths from the wall and we would see only a number of periods of order ν/ω'. If ω'/ν is not small then at most a few oscillations should be observable and it would be difficult to ensure that one sees such phenomena experimentally. In Greenspan's experiments (1950, 1956) we recall that the largest experimental value of ω'/ν was about 1. Thus one does not yet have sufficient data to verify the behavior described here. We note finally that in the limit of small ω and with no heat flow at the wall, the amplitude of the hydrodynamic oscillation depends on a fourth moment of the distribution function at the wall as well as the second moment.

Appendix

Starting from the explicit solution for $H(z)$, we perform several transformations that enable us to give more complete answers to various questions. We obtain a more explicit form for the distribution function of particles striking the wall. We also obtain expressions for the particle flow and energy flow across the wall. We then show how to rewrite the Laplace transform of $n(x)$, $n(K)$, so as to exhibit explicitly the fact that it is analytic for Re $K > 0$. Finally we consider the special case of specular reflection at an oscillating wall and solve this problem.

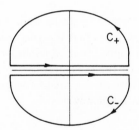

FIG. 6. Contours of integration $C_{\pm}$.

We begin with Eq. (23) for $H_0(z)$ and Eq. (24) for $H(z)$. We wish to write Eq. (23) as the sum of two integrals and then deform both contours from $(-\infty, 0)$ to $(0, +\infty)$. In order to include the behavior at infinity properly, we consider first

$$\int_{C_-} \frac{A(t) \exp[-\Gamma(t)]}{K^2(t)} \frac{dt}{t - z}$$

over the contour C_- of Fig. 6, where the contour of integration of $C_{\pm}$ is a semicircle of radius R plus a section of the real axis. Since for $|t|$ large

$$\frac{A(t)}{K^2(t)} = -\frac{\beta_1}{t} - \frac{\beta_2}{t^2} + O\left(\frac{1}{t^3}\right) \tag{A.1}$$

where

$$\beta_1 = \int_0^\infty v\tilde{g}(v)\, dv + U\, \frac{2i\omega - 1}{(i\omega - 1)^2} \tag{A.2}$$

$$\beta_2 = \int_0^\infty v^2 g(v)\, dv + \frac{E}{i\omega - 1}, \tag{A.3}$$

we have

$$\int_{-R}^0 \frac{A^-(t)\exp[-\Gamma^-(t)]\, dt}{K^2(t)(t-z)} = -\int_0^R \frac{A^-(t)\exp[-\Gamma(t)]\, dt}{K^2(t)(t-z)}$$
$$- 2\pi i\, \frac{A(z)\exp[-\Gamma(z)]\eta(-\operatorname{Im} z)}{K^2(z)}$$
$$+ \begin{cases} O\!\left(\dfrac{1}{R}\right), & M = 0 \\[2ex] \pi i\beta_1 + O\!\left(\dfrac{1}{R}\right), & M = 1 \\[2ex] -2R\beta_1 - \pi i[\beta_2 + (z-\alpha_1)\beta_1] + \\[1ex] \qquad\qquad + O\!\left(\dfrac{1}{R}\right), & M = 2, \end{cases} \tag{A.4}$$

where $\eta(x)$ is the Heaviside step function. Similarly

$$\int_{-R}^0 \frac{A^+(t)\exp[-\Gamma^+(t)]\, dt}{K^2(t)(t-z)}$$
$$= -\int_0^R \frac{A^+(t)\exp[-\Gamma(t)]\, dt}{K^2(t)(t-z)} - 2\pi i\, \frac{A(z)\exp[-\Gamma(z)]\eta(\operatorname{Im} z)}{K^2(z)} \tag{A.5}$$
$$- \begin{cases} O\!\left(\dfrac{1}{R}\right), & M = 0 \\[2ex] \pi i\beta_1 + O\!\left(\dfrac{1}{R}\right), & M = 1 \\[2ex] 2R\beta_1 - \pi i[\beta_2 + \beta_1(z-\alpha_1)] + O\!\left(\dfrac{1}{R}\right), & M = 2. \end{cases}$$

Hence, combining Eqs. (A.4) and (A.5) we find

$$H(z) + \frac{A(z)}{K^2(z)} = \frac{e^{\Gamma(z)}}{2\pi i}\left[\int_0^\infty \frac{dt\, e^{-\Gamma(t)}[A^+(t) - A^-(t)]}{(t-z)K^2(t)} + \sum_{m=0}^{M-1} \delta_m{}^M z^m\right]. \tag{A.6}$$

The left-hand side of Eq. (A.6) is just the numerator of $n(K)$. Hence, we choose the constants $\delta_m{}^M$ so that the bracket on the right-hand side of Eq. (A.6) vanishes at the roots of $D(K, z(K))$ with $\operatorname{Re} K > 0$. An elementary computation shows that

$$\frac{1}{2\pi i} \frac{A^+(t) - A^-(t)}{K^2(t)} \bigg|_{t>0} = t\tilde{g}(t) + \frac{e^{-t^2/2}}{\sqrt{2\pi}} \frac{t}{i\omega - 1}\left[tU\left(1 + \left(\frac{t^2 - 1}{2}\right) \cdot \left(\frac{i\omega}{i\omega - 1}\right)\right)\right.$$

$$\left. + E\left(\frac{t^2 - 1}{2}\right)\right]$$

$$= t\tilde{g}(t) + B(t).$$

Thus we have expressed the numerator of $n(K)$ in terms of the given function $\tilde{g}(v)$, $v > 0$ and the as yet undetermined constants U and E. We may then obtain $\tilde{g}(v)$ for $v < 0$ from Eq. (A.6) and

$$v\tilde{g}(v) = -B(v)$$

$$+ \frac{\{\exp[\Gamma^+(v)] - \exp[\Gamma^-(v)]\}}{2\pi i}\left\{\int_0^\infty \frac{dt\,\exp[-\Gamma(t)]}{t - v}[t\tilde{g}(t) + B(t)]\right.$$

$$\left. + \sum_{m=0}^{M-1} \delta_m{}^M t^m\right\}, \qquad v < 0. \quad \text{(A.7)}$$

We may readily determine U and E by taking the asymptotic expansion of Eq. (A.6) for large z and equating coefficients of $1/z$ and $1/z^2$ on both sides of the equation. We find

$$U\frac{\omega^2}{(i\omega - 1)^2} = -\int_0^\infty dt\, e^{-\Gamma(t)}\left(\frac{A^+ - A^-}{2\pi i K^2(t)}\right), \qquad\qquad M = 0$$

$$= -\delta_0{}^1 \qquad\qquad M = 1 \quad \text{(A.8)}$$

$$= +\delta_1{}^2 \qquad\qquad M = 2,$$

$$-E\frac{i\omega}{(i\omega - 1)} = \alpha_1 U\frac{\omega^2}{(i\omega - 1)^2} - \int_0^\infty t\,dt\, e^{-\Gamma(t)}\left(\frac{A^+ - A^-}{2\pi i K^2(t)}\right) \qquad M = 0$$

$$= -\delta_0{}^1\alpha_1 + \int_0^\infty dt\, e^{-\Gamma(t)}\left(\frac{A^+(t) - A^-(t)}{2\pi i K^2(t)}\right) \qquad M = 1 \quad \text{(A.9)}$$

$$= \alpha_1\delta_1{}^2 + \delta_0{}^2 \qquad\qquad M = 2.$$

The constants $\delta_j{}^i$ are linear in E and U, hence Eqs. (A.8) and (A.9) become two linear equations for U and E in terms of the given function $\tilde{g}(v)$, $v > 0$.

We presumably chose $H(z)$ in such a way that $n(K) = (K^2(z)H(z) + A(z))/D(K, z)$ had no singularities for $\operatorname{Re} K > 0$. Starting from Eq. (A.6) we may express $n(K)$ so as to exhibit its singularities explicitly. From Eqs. (6) and (A.6) we know that $e^{\Gamma(z)}/D(K, z)$ must be a function with poles and at most a cut on the positive real z axis. We find an explicit representation for this ratio that exhibits these properties and thus we have such a representation for $n(K)$ as well.

We may rewrite

$$
\begin{aligned}
\log \Gamma(z) &= \frac{1}{2\pi i} \int_{-\infty}^{0} \frac{dt}{t-z} \log \frac{t^3 D^+\left(\dfrac{i\omega-1}{t}, t\right)}{t^3 D^-\left(\dfrac{i\omega-1}{t}, t\right)} \\
&= \frac{1}{2\pi i} \int_{-\infty}^{0} \frac{dt}{t-z} \log\left(t^3 D^+\left(\frac{i\omega-1}{t}, t\right)\right) \\
&\quad - \int_{-\infty}^{0} \frac{dt}{t-z} \log\left(t^3 D^-\left(\frac{i\omega-1}{t}, t\right)\right).
\end{aligned}
$$

We note that $t^3 D^{\pm}((i\omega - 1)/t, t)$ goes to one as $|t|$ goes to infinity and $t^3 D^{\pm}$ is nonzero and bounded at $t = 0$. Hence we may treat the integrals separately. Let us consider

$$
\int_{c_+'} \frac{dt}{t-z} \log\left(t^3 D^+\left(\frac{i\omega-1}{t}, t\right)\right)
$$

over the contour of Fig. 7, where the zeros of $D^{\pm}(K, z)$ are excluded. The

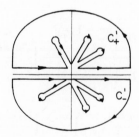

FIG. 7. Contours of integration $C_{\pm}'$.

integral at infinity vanishes and the integrals along the branch cuts are elementary so that finally taking a similar integral along C_-' for D^- we have

$$
\log \tilde{\Gamma}(z) = \log z^3 D(K, z) - \sum_{m=1}^{2M} \log(z_m - z) + 2M \log(-z) \quad \text{(A.10)}
$$

$$
+ \frac{1}{2\pi i} \int_{0}^{\infty} \frac{dt}{t-z} \log \frac{D^-\left(\dfrac{i\omega-1}{t}, t\right)}{D^+\left(\dfrac{i\omega-1}{t}, t\right)}
$$

where the summation in Eq. (A.10) is over *all* the roots of $D(K, z)$. Hence

$$e^{\Gamma(z)} = (-1)^M z^{3+M} \frac{D(K, z)e^{\Delta(z)}}{\prod\limits_{m=1}^{2M} (z_m - z)}$$

where

$$\Delta(z) = \frac{1}{2\pi i} \int_0^\infty \frac{dt}{t - z} \log \frac{D^-\left(\dfrac{i\omega - 1}{t}, t\right)}{D^+\left(\dfrac{i\omega - 1}{t}, t\right)} \tag{A.11}$$

and the branch of the log is such that as $t \to \infty$ log $\to 0$. Finally we may write

$$n(K) = (-1)^M (i\omega - 1)^2 \frac{z^{M+1}e^{\Delta(z)}}{\prod\limits_{m=1}^{2M} (z_m - z)} \left\{ \int_0^\infty \frac{dt e^{-\Gamma(t)}}{t - z} \left(\frac{A^+ - A^-}{2\pi i K^2(t)} \right) + \sum\limits_{m=0}^{M-1} \gamma_m{}^M z^m \right\} \tag{A.12}$$

and the constants are chosen so that there are no poles for Re $K > 0$. Thus we see that $n(K)$ has singularities only along a cut and for the zeros of $D(K, z)$ with Re $K < 0$.

Before proceeding to the case of specular reflection we obtain a simple relation between $\Gamma(z)$ and $\Gamma(-z)$. Let us consider

$$\log \tilde{\Gamma}(z) + \log \tilde{\Gamma}(-z)$$

$$= \frac{1}{2\pi i} \left\{ \int_{-\infty}^0 \frac{dt}{t - z} \log \frac{D^+\left(\dfrac{i\omega - 1}{t}, t\right)}{D^-\left(\dfrac{i\omega - 1}{t}, t\right)} - \int_0^\infty \frac{dt}{t - z} \log \frac{D^+\left(\dfrac{i\omega - 1}{-t}, -t\right)}{D^-\left(\dfrac{i\omega - 1}{-t}, -t\right)} \right\}.$$

Now

$$\frac{D^+\left(\dfrac{i\omega - 1}{-t}, -t\right)}{D^-\left(\dfrac{i\omega - 1}{-t}, -t\right)} = \frac{D^-\left(\dfrac{i\omega - 1}{t}, t\right)}{D^+\left(\dfrac{i\omega - 1}{t}, t\right)}$$

so that we may combine the two integrals and

$$\log \tilde{\Gamma}(z) + \log \Gamma(-z) = \frac{1}{2\pi i} \int_{-\infty}^\infty \frac{dt}{t - z} \log \left(\frac{D^+\left(\dfrac{i\omega - 1}{t}, t\right)}{D^-\left(\dfrac{i\omega - 1}{t}, t\right)} \right). \tag{A.13}$$

In Eq. (A.13) we must recall that although it is written as an integral from $-\infty$ to $+\infty$ the branches of the logs coincide at $\pm\infty$, *not* at zero. Hence by using the contours of Fig. 7 again we find

$$\log \tilde{\Gamma}(z) + \log \tilde{\Gamma}(-z) = \log z^3 D\left(\frac{i\omega - 1}{z}, z\right)$$

$$- \sum_{m=1}^{2M} \log(z_m - z) + 2M \log(-z)$$

and finally

$$\exp[\Gamma(z) + \Gamma(-z)] = (-1)^M \frac{z^3 D\left(\dfrac{i\omega - 1}{z}, z\right)}{\displaystyle\prod_{m=1}^{2M} (z_m - z)}. \qquad (A.14)$$

With this identity we may proceed to the case of specular reflection.

If we assume the gas to be bounded by a wall oscillating so that its position is given by $x_w = \varepsilon e^{-i\omega t}$ and its velocity by $v_w = -i\omega\varepsilon e^{-i\omega t}$, then the appropriate linearized boundary condition is

$$\tilde{g}(-v) = \tilde{g}(v) + 2i\omega\varepsilon \frac{\partial f_0}{\partial v}. \qquad (A.15)$$

Hence U is automatically determined and

$$U = -i\omega\varepsilon.$$

Again, we start from Eq. (A.6) which we write in the form

$$H(z) + \frac{A(z)}{K^2(z)} = e^{\Gamma(z)} J(z) \qquad (A.6')$$

where $J(z)$ is analytic in the plane with the exception of a slit from 0 to $+\infty$. An elementary computation shows that

$$H(z) + \frac{A(z)}{K^2(z)} - \left(H(-z) + \frac{A(-z)}{K^2(z)}\right)$$

$$= i\omega\varepsilon\left\{+\frac{2zF'(z)}{(i\omega - 1)} - \frac{z^2 F''(z)i\omega}{(i\omega - 1)^2} + 2zF'(z)\right\}$$

$$= \frac{(i\omega)^2}{i\omega - 1}\varepsilon\left\{2zF'(z) - \frac{z^2 F''(z)}{(i\omega - 1)}\right\}.$$

Hence

$$e^{\Gamma(z)} J(z) - e^{\Gamma(-z)} J(-z) = -\frac{\omega^2}{i\omega - 1}\varepsilon\left\{2zF'(z) - \frac{z^2 F''(z)}{(i\omega - 1)}\right\}. \qquad (A.16)$$

Finally, on multiplying Eq. (A.16) by $\exp[-\Gamma(z) + \Gamma(-z)]$ and using Eq. (A.14), we find

$$e^{-\Gamma(-z)}J(z) - e^{-\Gamma(z)}J(-z)$$

$$= -(-1)^M \frac{\left(\prod_{m=1}^{2M}(z_m - z)\right)\omega^2\varepsilon}{z^3 D\left(\dfrac{i\omega - 1}{z}, z\right)(i\omega - 1)}\left\{2zF' - \frac{z^2 F''(z)}{i\omega - 1}\right\}. \quad \text{(A.17)}$$

$$\equiv L(z)$$

We note that $e^{-\Gamma(-z)}J(z)$ is analytic with a slit from 0 to $+\infty$ and $e^{-\Gamma(z)}J(-z)$ is analytic with a slit from $-\infty$ to 0. Thus we shall split the right-hand side of Eq. (A.17) into two such terms and then use a Wiener-Hopf type argument. We note that $L(z)$ is analytic except for a cut on the real axis. Also $L(z)$ is well-defined near $z = 0$ since $z^3 D((i\omega - 1)/z, z)$ tends to $(i\omega - 1)^3$. We shall need the asymptotic expansion of $L(z)$ below:

$$L(z) = O\left(\frac{1}{z}\right), \qquad\qquad M = 0$$

$$= -\frac{2\varepsilon z}{(i\omega - 1)^2} + O\left(\frac{1}{z}\right), \qquad M = 1$$

$$\qquad\qquad\qquad\qquad\qquad\qquad M = 2 \qquad\qquad \text{(A.18)}$$

$$= \frac{\varepsilon z^3}{(i\omega - 1)^2} + \frac{\varepsilon z}{(i\omega - 1)^2}\left\{\left(3 - \frac{1}{i\omega}\right)\left(1 - \frac{3}{i\omega}\right) - (z_1^2 + z_2^2)\right\} + O\left(\frac{1}{z}\right).$$

We may express

$$L(z) = 2P_M(z) + O\left(\frac{1}{z}\right) \qquad\qquad \text{(A.19)}$$

where $P_M(z)$ is the odd polynomial given in Eq. (A.18). Thus $L(z) - 2P_M(z) = O(1/z)$ so that

$$L(z) - 2P_M(z) = \frac{1}{2\pi i}\int_{-\infty}^{\infty}\frac{dt}{t - z}(L^+(t) - L^-(t)) \qquad\qquad \text{(A.20)}$$

$$L(z) - 2P_M(z) = \frac{1}{2\pi i}\int_{-\infty}^{0}\frac{dt}{t - z}(L^+(t) - L^-(t)) + \frac{1}{2\pi i}\int_{0}^{\infty}\frac{dt}{2\pi i}(L^+(t) - L^-(t)) \qquad \text{(A.21)}$$

$$L(z) - 2P_M(z) = -M_1(z) + M_2(z). \qquad\qquad \text{(A.22)}$$

Now $M_1(z)$ is analytic in the plane slit from $-\infty$ to zero and $M_2(z)$ is analytic in the plane slit from 0 to $+\infty$. Finally

$$e^{-\Gamma(-z)}J(z) - M_2(z) - P_M(z) = e^{-\Gamma(z)}J(-z) - M_1(z) - P_M(-z). \quad \text{(A.23)}$$

Now the function on the right is analytic with a slit from $-\infty$ to 0 and the one on the left is analytic with a slit from 0 to $+\infty$. Hence the functions are analytic everywhere with the possible exception of zero and infinity. It is clear from the definition of the two functions that they are bounded near zero and hence analytic there. With a little computation we might easily show that near infinity the right (or left) side of Eq. (A.23) is $O(1/z)$ if $M = 0$, a constant plus $O(1/z)$ if $M = 1$, an even polynomial of degree two plus $O(1/z)$ if $M = 2$. Since either side of Eq. (A.23) is analytic in the finite plane it follows that either side of Eq. (A.23) equals an even polynomial of degree equal to $2M - 2$, $Q_M(z)$, $(Q_0(z) = 0)$. Hence

$$e^{-\Gamma(-z)}J(z) = +M_2(z) + P_M(z) + Q_M(z)$$

so that

$$e^{\Gamma(z)}J(z) = (-1)^M \frac{z^3 D\left(\dfrac{i\omega - 1}{z}, z\right)}{\displaystyle\prod_{m=1}^{2M}(z_m - z)} \{M_2(z) + P_M(z) + Q_M(z)\}$$

and finally

$$n(K) = \frac{(-1)^M(i\omega - 1)^3}{K\displaystyle\prod_{m=1}^{2M}\left(z_m - \dfrac{i\omega - 1}{K}\right)}\left\{M_2\left(\frac{i\omega - 1}{K}\right) + P_M\left(\frac{i\omega - 1}{K}\right) + Q_M\left(\frac{i\omega - 1}{K}\right)\right\}.$$

$$\text{(A.24)}$$

Clearly the polynomial Q_M is chosen so that $n(K)$ has no roots in the right half-plane. We note that $n(K)$ is bounded at the origin even though there are apparent powers of $1/K$ present. We can now invert the K transform to yield

$n(x, t)$

$$= e^{-i\omega t}(-1)^M(i\omega - 1)^3 \left\{ \sum_{m=1}^{M} \frac{\exp\left[\left(\dfrac{i\omega - 1}{z_m}\right)_x\right](M_2(z_m) + P_M(z_m) + Q_M(z_m))}{z_m \displaystyle\prod_{\substack{j=1 \\ z_j \neq z_m}}^{2M}(z_j - z_m)} \right.$$

$$\left. + \frac{1}{2\pi i}\int_0^\infty dt \exp\left[\left(\frac{i\omega - 1}{t}\right)x\right] \frac{\left[L^+\left(\dfrac{i\omega - 1}{t}\right) - L^-\left(\dfrac{i\omega - 1}{t}\right)\right]}{t\displaystyle\prod_{m=1}^{2M}(z_m - t)} \right\}. \quad \text{(A.25)}$$

In Eq. (A.25) the summation is over the M roots for which $\mathrm{Re}(i\omega - 1/zm) < 0$. In Eq. (A.25) we have exhibited explicitly the abstract form shown in Eq. (28) for the special case of specular reflection.

ACKNOWLEDGMENTS

The author wishes to thank Professor Harold Grad and Dr. Clifford Gardner for fruitful discussions. This work was supported by Grant No. AF-AFOSR-62-266 with the Air Force Office of Scientific Research.

REFERENCES

Case, K. M. (1959). *Ann. Phys. (N.Y.)* **7**, 349.
Cercignani, C. (1962). *Ann. Phys. (N.Y.)* **20**, 219.
Chapman, S., and Cowling, T. G. (1952). "The Mathematical Theory of Non-Uniform Gases." Cambridge Univ. Press, London and New York.
Grad, H. (1949). *Commun. Pure and Appl. Math.* **2**, 331.
Greenspan, M. (1950). *J. Acoust. Soc. Am.* **22**, 568.
Greenspan, M. (1956). *J. Acoust. Soc. Am.* **28**, 544.
Mushkelishvili, N.I. (1953). "Singular Integral Equations." Noordhoff, Groningen.
Peckeris, C. L., Alterman, Z., Finkelstein, L., Frankowski, K. (1962). *Phys. Fluids* **5**, 1608.
Sirovich, L. (1963). *Phys. Fluids* **6**, 10.
Sirovich, L., and Thurber, J. (1963). *In* "Rarefied Gas Dynamics" (J. A. Laurmann, ed.), pp. 159-180. Academic Press, New York.
Van Kampen, N. G. (1955). *Physica* **21**, 949.
Wang Chang, C. S., and Uhlenbeck, G. E. (1952). "On the Propagation of Sound in Monatomic Gases," Engr. Res. Inst., Univ. of Mich.
Weitzner, H. (1963). *Phys. Fluids* **6**, 484.

On the Propagation of Free Sound Waves in Rarefied Gas Dynamics

LAWRENCE SIROVICH
Division of Applied Mathematics, Brown University, Providence, Rhode Island

and

JAMES K. THURBER*
Graduate School of Mathematics, Adelphi University, Garden City, L.I., New York

A theory of sound propagation, employing general kinetic models, in an unbounded medium is presented. Numerical results for rigid sphere and Maxwell gas models are obtained. These are compared with already existing theories.

I. Introduction

It is well known that under normal conditions sound propagation in a gas is adequately described by the Navier-Stokes equations. These investigations of sound propagation go back to Stokes and Kirchoff (see Truesdell, 1953, for early references). The accuracy of conventional gas dynamics becomes doubtful, however, in the case of rarefied gas dynamics (or equivalently in the case of highly oscillatory phenomena). For an examination of this problem there is no recourse but to turn to kinetic theory and the Boltzmann equation.

The first analytical attempt at solving this problem via kinetic theory was made by Wang Chang (1948). She based her treatment on the Chapman-Enskog theory. Essentially she examined the dispersion relation resulting from the Burnett equations and from the next higher approximation which was called the super-Burnett equations. In light of present-day knowledge it can be said that this work only slightly extends the theory based on the Navier-Stokes equations.

A more far-reaching attempt at the problem was initiated by Wang Chang and Uhlenbeck (1952). In this second attack the Boltzmann equation was dealt with directly. In short, the Boltzmann equation for a Maxwell potential

---

Present address: Applied Mathematics Department, Brookhaven National Laboratories, Upton, New York.

gas was linearized about equilibrium and the distribution function was expanded in moments. This resulted in an infinite system of coupled equations in the moments. Wang Chang and Uhlenbeck effected a series of truncations of this system and analyzed the resulting dispersion relations. They found that successive truncations provide successive terms in the power series representation of the roots of the dispersion relations. Since this gives an expansion in the ratio of wave frequency to collision frequency, this procedure cannot be relied on to provide results appropriate to rarefied gas dynamics. In fact successive truncations can be identified with the results obtained from the Chapman-Enskog procedure.

Pekeris and his co-workers (1960) took up the work of Wang Chang and Uhlenbeck (1952), and with the aid of high-speed computers they were able to solve the dispersion relations corresponding to truncations involving up to 483 moments. In another investigation (Pekeris et al., 1962) they extended the procedure to a gas composed of rigid spheres. In this instance truncations corresponding to up to 105 moments were considered. The results of Pekeris et al. can be regarded as the finest results available to date. Yet the already mentioned power series nature of this procedure restricts the validity of the resulting data.

The failure of the above treatments to describe sound propagation in a rarefied media becomes apparent on comparison with experiment. Greenspan (1950, 1956) performing experiments with the noble gases obtained data on sound characteristics down to a Knudsen number (for this problem this is the ratio of mean-free-path to wavelength) of $O(1)$. In a later work Meyer and Sessler (1957) obtained data down to a Knudsen number of $O(10)$. These experiments yield data which are in good mutual agreement.

On comparing the work of Pekeris et al. (1960, 1962) with the above mentioned experimental work one finds that the theory becomes poor at a Knudsen number of $O(1)$ and becomes increasingly worse with increasing values of this parameter.

In this and a companion paper (Sirovich and Thurber, 1964) a fresh attack on this problem is made. A kinetic theory approach is also taken, now however, by means of kinetic models instead of the full Boltzmann equation. One of the most elementary models is the single relaxation model (see Bhatnager et al., 1954), which was used by the authors Sirovich and Thurber (1961, 1963) in an earlier investigation of sound propagation. As was pointed out in the latter reference and as can be seen in Figs. 1–4, this model is only capable of giving a qualitative theory. One essential reason for this is the fact that this model leads to a Prandtl number of 1 instead of the more correct value of 2/3. A procedure for obtaining more elaborate models for Maxwell potential gases has been given by Gross and Jackson (1959), and the extension for arbitrary molecular force laws as well as mixtures has been given by Sirovich (1962).

In this investigation we will employ these extended kinetic models. As is shown in Sirovich and Thurber (1965) these lead to results for sound propagation which are in excellent agreement with the existing experimental data through the entire Knudsen range.

In examining sound propagation two different physical situations naturally arise. There is the case of forced sound waves which describes the motion generated by an oscillating piston for instance. In particular this is the situation employed in experiment and the analysis of this situation is given in Sirovich and Thurber (1965). The other case is that of free soundwaves, i.e., the situation that arises when one examines the evolution of an initial disturbance in an unbounded media. This is the problem which is examined in this paper.

A general formulation of the sound problem is given here. In particular numerical results for 3, 5, 8, and 11 moments formulations are given for both a rigid sphere gas and a Maxwell potential gas, these cases being the limits of hard and soft interactions in a neutral gas. However, the analytical expressions can be used for arbitrary models involving any number of moments. In addition, the appendices contain information, formulas, and analysis which should be of value in any study employing general kinetic models.

II. Formulation of the Problem

In order to make the present paper self-contained we include the following brief exposition.

A gas slightly removed from equilibrium is considered. The distribution function f is written as

$$f = f^0(1 + g) \tag{2.1}$$

where the Maxwellian

$$f^0 = \frac{\rho_0}{(2\pi R T_0)^{3/2}} \exp\left(-\frac{\xi^2}{2RT_0}\right) \tag{2.2}$$

is the equilibrium distribution. The usual definitions hold; ρ_0, T_0, u_0 are equilibrium values of density, temperature, and velocity, respectively, and $\xi^2 = \xi_1{}^2 + \xi_2{}^2 + \xi^2$ is the square of the molecular speed. Ignoring terms quadratic in g we obtain the linearized Boltzmann equation

$$\left(\frac{\partial}{\partial t} + \xi_1 \frac{\partial}{\partial x}\right) g = \frac{1}{m} \int f_*{}^0 [g] B(0, U) \, d\varepsilon \, d\theta \, d\xi_* \tag{2.3}$$

with

$$[g] = g_*{}' + g' - g_* - g$$

and

$$U = |\xi_* - \xi|.$$

With the exception of ξ_* all symbols have the customary interpretation (see Chapman and Cowling, 1952); the symbol ξ_* here denotes the struck particle. Note that Eq. (2.3) is restricted to one-dimensional motions.

Equation (2.3) is next made dimensionless with respect to an unspecified frequency $v = 1/\tau$ as follows:

$$ t' = vt, \qquad x' = \frac{xv}{(RT_0)^{1/2}}, \qquad \xi' = \frac{\xi}{(RT_0)^{1/2}}, \qquad B' = \frac{\rho_0 Bv}{m}. \qquad (2.4) $$

After effecting this transformation the repetitive primes are removed, and the dimensionless equation is

$$ \left(\frac{\partial}{\partial t} + \xi \frac{\partial}{\partial x}\right) g = L(g) = \int \omega_*[g]B \, d\varepsilon \, d\theta \, d\xi_* \qquad (2.5) $$

with

$$ \omega = \frac{\exp(-\xi^2/2)}{(2\pi)^{3/2}}. \qquad (2.6) $$

Wang Chang and Uhlenbeck (1952) proved that the eigenfunctions of L are of the form

$$ f_{rl}(\xi)P_l\left(\frac{\xi_1}{\xi}\right) $$

where P_l are the Legendre polynomials. Furthermore they proved that for the special case $B = B(\theta)$ (satisfied by Maxwellian molecules) the orthonormal eigenfunctions of L (with respect to the weight function ω) are

$$ \psi_{rl} = \frac{S^r_{l+\frac{1}{2}}(\tfrac{1}{2}\xi^2)\xi^l P_l(\xi_1/\xi)}{\left[\dfrac{2^{l+1}\Gamma(r + l + (\tfrac{3}{2}))}{\pi^{1/2}r!(2l + 1)}\right]^{1/2}} \qquad (2.7) $$

where $S^r_{l+\frac{1}{2}}(\xi^2/2)$ are Laguerre polynomials (see Magnus and Oberhettinger, 1952).

For purposes of exposition as well as computation it is advantageous to reduce the double index occurring in Eq. (2.7) to a single one. One method of accomplishing this is by ordering the polynomials ψ_{rl} (of degree $2r + l$) according to degree. Formulas for this transformation are given in Appendix A. Independently of the specific choice of ordering we can take the subscripts as

$$ r = r(i), \qquad l = l(i) $$

i.e., so that they depend on a single index. Then we write

$$ \psi_{r(i)l(i)} = \psi_i $$

Library
I.U.P.
Indiana, Pa.

and expand the perturbed distribution function g in ψ_i, so that

$$g = \sum_{i=1}^{\infty} a_i \psi_i \tag{2.8}$$

with the coefficients a_i given by

$$a_i = \int \omega g \psi_i \, d\xi. \tag{2.9}$$

Adopting the ordering of Appendix A, the first five terms in the expansion of Eq. (2.8), are

$$\sum_{i=1}^{5} a_i \psi_i = \rho + \xi_1 u + \left(\frac{\xi^2}{2} - \frac{3}{2}\right)T + \frac{3}{2}\left(\xi_1{}^2 - \frac{\xi^2}{3}\right)p_{11} + \left(1 - \frac{\xi^2}{5}\right)\xi_1 S_1$$

where ρ, u, T, p_{11}, and S_1 are the dimensionless density, velocity, temperature, stress, and heat conduction perturbations.

The expansion of g is substituted into the linear Boltzmann equation, Eq. (2.5), and the latter is transformed into an infinite system of coupled equations (see Sirovich, 1963)[1]

$$\frac{\partial}{\partial t} a_i + A_{i\mu} \frac{\partial}{\partial x} a_\mu = B_{i\mu} a_\mu \tag{2.10}$$

with

$$A_{ij} = \int \psi_i \xi_1 \psi_j \, d\xi \tag{2.11}$$

and

$$B_{ij} = \int \psi_i L(\psi_j) \, d\xi. \tag{2.12}$$

This system has been deeply investigated (Sirovich, 1963a, b, c) and certain asymptotic solutions of it have been found (Sirovich, 1963b, c).

For Maxwell molecules the matrix B_{ij} is diagonal and we can write the system as

$$\frac{\partial}{\partial t} a_i + A_{i\mu} \frac{\partial}{\partial x} a_\mu = \lambda_i a_i \tag{2.13}$$

where the λ_i are the eigenvalues of L. To investigate sound propagation Wang Chang and Uhlenbeck (1952) truncate this into a finite system. This is accomplished by considering the first N equations (according to the ordering of Appendix A) and setting all but the first N a_i's to zero.

To study the nature of plane wave solutions Wang Chang and Uhlenbeck develop the associated dispersion relation of this finite system and then solve

---

[1] The summation convention is assumed for Greek but not Latin subscripts.

for the roots. Actually they consider only the boundary-value problem in their report. The initial-value problem was later considered in a paper by Sirovich (1963a) for the same system as well as the comparable finite systems gotten from Eq. (2.10). An important feature of these calculations is that the results appear as power series in inverse powers of the collision frequency. Therefore the results obtained can be considered reliable only for sound frequency small with respect to the collision frequency for the boundary value problem or wavelength large with respect to the mean free path for the initial value problem.

III. The Construction of Kinetic Models

In this section we effect an entirely different "truncation" scheme. The method used is due to Gross and Jackson (1959) who developed the scheme to generalize the Bhatnager-Gross-Krook model (1954). Several minor modifications of this procedure can be found in Sirovich (1962) and the subsequent discussion follows the latter reference.

For arbitrary molecular models the contribution of the linearized Boltzmann integral is

$$L(g) = \sum_{v,\,\mu=1}^{\infty} B_{v\mu} a_\mu \psi_v. \qquad (3.1)$$

We define the Nth order approximation L^N to L as follows:

$$L^N(g) = \sum_{v,\,\mu=1}^{N} B_{\mu v} a_\mu \psi_v + \lambda \sum_{\mu=N+1}^{\infty} a_i \psi_i. \qquad (3.2)$$

The value of λ need not be chosen by any definite rule, but for definiteness we will take

$$\lambda = B_{N+1,\,N+1}. \qquad (3.3)$$

An immediate transformation of Eq. (3.2) is gotten by adding

$$0 = \lambda \sum_{i=0}^{N} a_i \psi_i - \lambda \sum_{i=0}^{N} a_i \psi_i$$

to Eq. (3.2). This yields

$$L^N(g) = \sum_{v\mu}^{N} (B_{\mu v} - \delta_{\mu v}\lambda) a_\mu \psi_\mu + \lambda g$$

and the approximate Boltzmann equation is

$$\left(\frac{\partial}{\partial t} + \xi_1 \frac{\partial}{\partial x} - \lambda\right) g = \sum_{\mu v}^{N} (B_{\mu v} - \lambda \delta_{\mu v}) a_\mu \psi_\mu. \qquad (3.4)$$

The value λ as given by Eq. (3.3) is negative (Chapman and Cowling, 1952) and it is appropriate at this point to use it for the normalizing frequency ν of Eq. (2.4). Therefore we can finally write

$$\left(\frac{\partial}{\partial t} + \xi_1 \frac{\partial}{\partial x} + 1\right)g = \sum_{\mu, \nu = 1}^{N} a_\mu \beta_{\mu\nu} \psi_\nu \tag{3.5}$$

with

$$\beta_{\mu\nu} = \frac{B_{\mu\nu} - \lambda \delta_{\mu\nu}}{|\lambda|}. \tag{3.6}$$

As an example, if $N = 3$ we get

$$\left(\frac{\partial}{\partial t} + \xi_1 \frac{\partial}{\partial x} + 1\right)g = \rho + \xi_1 u + T\left(\frac{\xi^2}{2} - \frac{3}{2}\right), \tag{3.7}$$

the linearized form of the " Krooked " equation.

A discussion of equations such as Eq. (3.5) can be found in the cited literature. We note here that in contrast to the straightforward truncation discussed in the preceding section we now find that the differential operator is kept intact and further that, although only a finite matrix of the collision operator is faithfully preserved, the remainder of the collision term is qualitatively preserved. Several other features will be mentioned in the course of the discussion.

IV. The Initial-Value Problem

We now introduce plane wave solutions by means of the initial-value problem. Accordingly we consider Eq. (3.5) subject to the initial data

$$g(t = 0) = g_0(x, \xi)$$

of the perturbed distribution function. This problem is formally solved by means of a Laplace transform in time,

$$\int dt \, e^{-\sigma t},$$

and a Fourier transform in space,

$$\int dx \, e^{ikx}.$$

Performing these transformations leads to

$$(\sigma + ik\xi_1 + 1)g = \sum_{\mu, \nu}^{N} a_\mu \beta_{\mu\nu} \psi_\nu + g_0. \tag{4.1}$$

The transform of a variable has been denoted by the same letter as the variable itself. The wave number k is of course real and σ at this stage is complex with Re $\sigma > 0$. We may therefore divide by the coefficient of g in Eq. (4.1) to obtain g, and from this obtain the a_i's. Specifically,

$$a_j = \sum_{\mu\nu}^{N} a_\mu \beta_{\mu\nu} \gamma_{\nu j} + \int \frac{\omega g_0 \psi_j \, d\xi}{\sigma + 1 + ik\xi} \tag{4.2}$$

with

$$\gamma_{\nu j} = \frac{1}{k} \int \frac{\omega \psi_\nu \psi_j \, d\xi}{i\xi + ((\sigma + 1)/k)}. \tag{4.3}$$

In Appendix B the γ_{ij} are evaluated explicitly in terms of known functions. Examples of this matrix can be found in Sirovich and Thurber (1963).

It is convenient to rewrite Eq. (4.2) as

$$a_j = \sum C_{j\mu} a_\mu + v_j$$

with

$$v_j = \int \frac{\omega g_0 \psi_i}{\sigma + 1 + ik\xi_1} \, d\xi \tag{4.4}$$

and

$$C_{j\mu} = \sum_{\nu=1}^{N} \beta_{\mu\nu} \gamma_{\nu j}. \tag{4.5}$$

In matrix notation

$$\mathbf{a} = \mathbf{Ca} + \mathbf{v}.$$

Solving for $\mathbf{a}$, we get

$$\mathbf{a} = (\mathbf{1} - \mathbf{C})^{-1}\mathbf{v} \tag{4.6}$$

and we also now invert the Laplace transform, to obtain

$$a(k, t) = \frac{1}{2\pi} \int_\uparrow e^{\sigma t}(\mathbf{1} - \mathbf{C})^{-1}\mathbf{v} \, d\sigma. \tag{4.7}$$

The vertical arrow denotes a Bromwich path in the right half of the complex σ-plane, which is to the right of the poles of $(\mathbf{1} - \mathbf{C})^{-1}$. Regarding k as a parameter (which is real) Eq. (4.7) gives the evolution of an initial disturbance which is initially sinusoidal with wave number k. The evaluation of the integral in Eq. (4.7) naturally depends on the singularities of $(\mathbf{1} - \mathbf{C})^{-1}$, i.e., on the "dispersion relation"

$$D = \det(\mathbf{1} - \mathbf{C}) = 0. \tag{4.8}$$

We now consider this relation.

V. The Dispersion Relation

Each term of the dispersion relation, Eq. (4.8), is explicitly evaluated in Appendices B and C. In general each entry contains the error function of a complex variable multiplied by a Gaussian in the same variable. Some general remarks on the distribution of zeros of the dispersion relation are given in Sirovich and Thurber (1963). As is shown there, one finds a great many more modes of propagation than only that mode which we associate with sound. This is in agreement with the predictions of the Boltzmann equation itself (Sirovich, 1963). In this paper only the characteristics of the sound mode will be considered.

Appendix D shows that it is sufficient to consider only $k > 0$, and moreover that roots occur in conjugate pairs. This reduces the amount of analysis but aside from an asymptotic analysis very little in the way of quantitative results can be obtained by hand computation.

Because of this, Eq. (4.8) was programmed for machine solution. Although several interesting features presented themselves in the machine calculation we will not go into these. The values corresponding to sound propagation were found, and each such calculation was made independent of all others. This of course prevented accumulated error. Only two molecular models were considered, that of rigid spheres and Maxwell molecules. In order to carry out these computations it is necessary to know the eigenvalues λ_i, Eq. (2.13), for Maxwell molecules, and the cross sections B_{rl}, Eq. (2.12). A large block of the former have been computed by Alterman et al. (1962). For convenience a portion of these are listed in Appendix E. It will be noted that these are given in order of increasing magnitude. The distinguished moments in our model equations are chosen according to this procedure. For a discussion of the reasons for this see Sirovich (1963a). Although no list of B_{rl} for rigid spheres is available, Mott-Smith (1954) has given a formula for these cross sections. Using this formula, a large block of B_{rl} have been computed and are to be found in Appendix F. For each of the two gases four kinetic models were investigated. These correspond to 3, 5, 8, and 11 moment models in the sense of Eq. (3.4). As is well known rigid spheres and Maxwell molecules represent the limits of hard and soft potentials for a simple gas. Furthermore, the 11 moment model is sufficient to give correctly the viscosity and heat conduction to the fourth approximation in the sense of Chapman and Cowling (1952).[2]

In presenting the results it is clear from the analysis given in Sections II and

[2] This remark applies only to the rigid sphere gas since the transport coefficients are given exactly by the eigenvalues for Maxwell molecules.

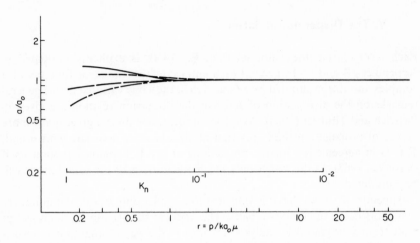

FIG. 1. Maxwell potential gas: free sound wave speeds, convergence of models.
KEY: — 11-moment model   – – 8-moment model
— - — 5-moment model   - - - 3-moment model

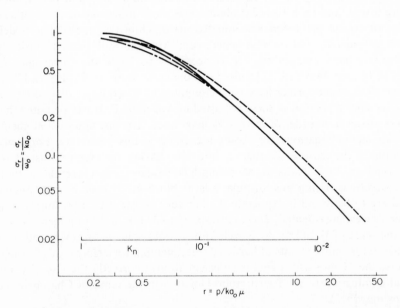

FIG. 2. Maxwell potential gas: free sound wave attenuation rates, convergence of models.
KEY: — 11-moment model   – – 8-moment model
— - — 5-moment model   - - - 3-moment model

III that the speed of propagation as well as the attenuation rate are functions of the wave number, k, above. However in keeping with the customary practice we shall use instead the parameter

$$r = \frac{3k}{2\sqrt{\gamma}} \qquad (5.1)$$

for Maxwell molecules, where γ denotes the ratio of specific heats, in this case equal to $5/3$. The reason for this is that one may easily rewrite r as

$$r = \frac{pk}{a_0\mu} \qquad (5.2)$$

where p is the pressure, a_0 the adiabatic speed of sound, μ the absolute viscosity, and k the dimensional wavenumber. In the plots for rigid spheres the same parameter as appears in (5.2) will be used.[3] For some purposes it is convenient to also exhibit the associated Knudsen number K_n,

$$K_n = \frac{\text{mean free path}}{\text{wavelength}}. \qquad (5.3)$$

Basing the mean free paths on the rigid sphere definition (see Chapman and Cowling, 1952) one easily has

$$K_n = \frac{8}{r5\pi\sqrt{2\pi\gamma}}. \qquad (5.4)$$

In Fig. 1 we have plotted the attenuation rate

$$\frac{\text{Re}\,\sigma}{\omega_0} = \frac{\sigma_r}{\omega_0} \qquad (5.5)$$

where

$$\omega_0 = a_0 k \qquad (5.6)$$

is an equivalent frequency. With the exception of the 3-moment model the convergence is good. The former model, i.e., the BGK single relaxation model, necessarily yields results different from all others. This is due to the fact that it has a Prandtl number of 1, whereas all others have the correct value of $2/3$. In Fig. 2 the sound speed ratio

$$a/a_0$$

is plotted, and in this case the convergence of the models is not quite as good. Ultimately this ratio must vanish for all the curves, since it can be shown that

---

[3] In this case $r = k\,1.4732/\sqrt{\gamma}$ in keeping with the fourth approximation to the rigid sphere viscosity found in Chapman and Cowling (1952).

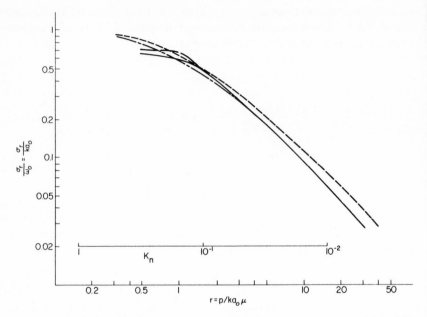

FIG. 3. Rigid sphere gas: free sound wave attenuation rates, convergence of models.
KEY: —   11-moment model   – –   8-moment model
     – – –   5-moment model   - - -   3-moment model

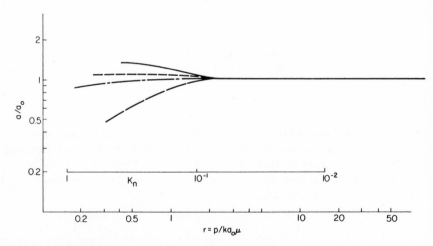

FIG. 4. Rigid sphere gas: free sound wave speeds, convergence of models.
KEY: —   11-moment model   – –   8-moment model
     – – –   5-moment model   - - -   3-moment model

the speed, a, vanishes as $k \to \infty$ (Sirovich and Thurber, 1963). Figures 3 and 4 contain the same information for the rigid sphere gas, and the same remarks again apply.

No experimental information exists with which to compare these curves, and it is unlikely that any such experiment might be devised. On the other hand for the case of forced sound waves considerable experimental information exists. As is shown in Sirovich and Thurber (1964), the experimental data and theoretical curves for the higher moment models are in exceptional agreement. For this reason we may regard the present model equations as a standard against which other equations can be compared.

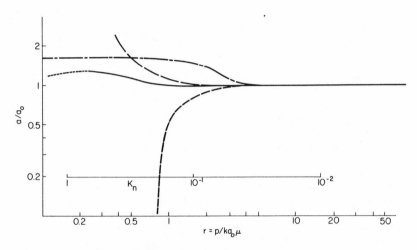

FIG. 5. Free sound wave speeds, comparison of Theories.
KEY: — 11-moment model (max potential)   – – Burnett
     – - – 13-moment theory (Grad)   - - - Navier-Stokes

In Figs. 5 and 6 we have plotted the attenuation rates and speed ratios of the Navier-Stokes, Burnett, and "13 moments" (of Grad) theories. For comparison the comparable curves for the 11-moment Maxwell gas model have also been plotted. Regarding Fig. 5 it is seen that the "13-moment" speed ratio has the limit of $a/a_0 = 1.64$ (see Grad, 1949). The Burnett speed becomes infinite and the Navier-Stokes speed vanishes at $r = 0.8$. All this is in contrast to the 11-moment model which reaches a maximum and then vanishes slowly. On Fig. 6 we see that both the Burnett and "13 moments" attenuation rates vanish. In reference to the latter it may be shown that any finite moments equation as given by Grad (1949) has a bounded σ_r and hence σ_r/ω_0 vanishes as $k \to \infty$. As can be seen the Navier-Stokes attenuation curve follows the 11-moments model closely until $r = 0.8$. As already mentioned

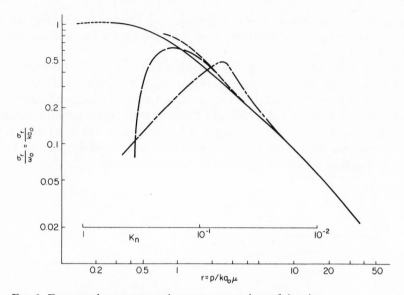

FIG. 6. Free sound wave attenuation rates, comparison of theories.
KEY: — 11-moment model (max potential)   – – Burnett
– – – 13-moment theory (Grad)   - - - Navier-Stokes

propagation ceases at this point. In the continuum regime, $K_n < 10^{-1}$, all curves except those of the " 13 moments " theory are in good agreement.

ACKNOWLEDGMENTS

J. K. Thurber is grateful to the Office of Naval Research for support under Nonr 3360(01). L. Sirovich is grateful to the Office of Naval Research for support under Nonr 562(07). This work was initiated by the authors under Atomic Energy Contract AT(30-1)-1480 while the authors were at New York University.

In addition, both authors are grateful to the Atomic Energy Commission for their liberal allocation of computer time.

Appendix A. Reduction of the Two-Dimensional Array to a One-Dimensional Array

The Maxwellian eigenfunctions ψ_{rl} in a natural way take two subscripts. For expositional purposes and for actual computation it is more convenient to deal with only a one-dimensional array. This is easily accomplished by introducing a subscript i and writing

$$r = r(i), \qquad l = l(i) \tag{A.1}$$

and therefore

$$\psi_{r(i)l(i)} = \psi_i.$$

Of course this may be accomplished in a variety of ways. A natural reduction is the following: All ψ_{rl} are first ordered according to the degree of the polynomial, $2r + l$, and then subordered in ascending values of l.

To accomplish this transformation let p denote the parity function of ψ_i, i.e.,

$$p = 0, \quad \psi_i \text{ odd},$$

$$p = 1, \quad \psi_i \text{ even}.$$

Then one may show

$$p = \frac{1 + \operatorname{sgn}\{i - [\sqrt{i}]^2 - [\sqrt{i}]\}}{2}. \tag{A.2}$$

The degree of the polynomial is then given by

$$n(i) = 2\left[\frac{-1 + \sqrt{4i + 1}}{2}\right] + \left(\frac{1 + (-1)^p}{2}\right). \tag{A.3}$$

The remainder of the transformation is then given by

$$r(i) = -i + \left[\frac{n}{2}\right]\left(\left[\frac{n}{2}\right] + 2\right) + \left(\frac{1 + (-1)^p}{2}\right)\left[\frac{n + 1}{2}\right]$$

$$l(i) = n + i - \left[\frac{n}{2}\right]\left(\left[\frac{n}{2}\right] + 3\right) - \left(\frac{1 + (-1)^p}{2}\right)\left[\frac{n + 1}{2}\right]. \tag{A.4}$$

in the above the brackets, [ ], represent "the greatest integer" symbol.

In the numerical calculation for reasons mentioned in the text the polynomials are again reordered. This time in terms of the magnitude of the diagonal entries.

Although the reduction to one subscript is in many respects very convenient some features are lost through it, or rather more difficult to trace. One of these, in particular, has a bearing on the dispersion relation to be discussed in Appendix D.

From Eq. (3.6) we have that

$$\beta_{\mu\nu} = \frac{B_{\mu\nu} - \lambda\delta_{\mu\nu}}{|\lambda|}. \tag{A.5}$$

As one can easily see

$$B_{ij} = \int \psi_i L(\psi_j)\, d\xi. \tag{A.6}$$

Returning to the original double subscript

$$B_{r(i)l(i);\, r'(j),\, l'(j)} = \int \psi_{r(i)l(i)} L(\psi_{r'(j)l'(j)}) \, d\xi. \tag{A.7}$$

Mott-Smith (1954) has shown that

$$B_{rlr'l'} = 0 \quad \text{for} \quad l \neq l'. \tag{A.8}$$

This condition is difficult to depict when the reduction to the one-dimensional array is performed. We shall need the following consequence of Eq. (D.8) in Appendix D,

$$\sum_v \beta_{\mu v} \psi_v = \sum_{rl'} \frac{B_{rl:\, r'l'} - \lambda \delta_{rr'} \delta_{ll'}}{|\lambda|} \psi_{r'l'} \tag{A.9}$$

is either even or odd. From Eq. (A.8), the definition of the Kronecker delta, and the fact that the degree of ψ_{rl} is $2r + l$, we see that the above summation, Eq. (A.9), is either odd or even depending on whether l is odd or even.

Appendix B. Evaluation of

$$D_{rl;\, \bar{r}l} = k \int_{-\infty}^{\infty} \frac{\omega \psi_{rl} \psi_{\bar{r}l}}{1 + \sigma - ik\xi_1} \, d\xi = \int_{-\infty}^{\infty} \frac{\omega \psi_{rl} \psi_{\bar{r}l}}{\lambda - i\xi_1} \, d\xi. \tag{B.1}$$

To facilitate the evaluation of this integral we introduce a compact notation. The Barnes symbol $(\ )_n$ is defined as

$$(b)_n = b(b + 1) \cdots (b + n - 1) \tag{B.2}$$

for positive integers n, and

$$(b)_0 = 1.$$

In particular

$$n! = (1)_n.$$

In terms of this symbol Legendre polynomials, P_n, are given by (see Magnus and Oberhettinger, 1954)

$$P_n(z) = \frac{(2n)!}{2^n n! n!} \sum_{k=0}^{[n/2]} z^{n-2k} \frac{(-)^k (n - 2k + 1)_{2k}}{4k \, k!(n + \frac{1}{2} - k)_k} \tag{B.3}$$

where $[a]$ represents the greatest integer less than or equal to a. Introducing the binomial coefficient,

$$C_n^{\,m} = \frac{m!}{n!(m - n)!} \tag{B.4}$$

we can express Sonine polynomials, $S_m{}^n$, by (Magnus and Oberhettinger, 1954)

$$S_m{}^n(x) = \frac{(-1)^n}{n!} \sum_{r=0}^n C_r{}^n(m + n - r + 1)_r(-)^r x^{n-r}. \tag{B.5}$$

It is convenient to group together a number of quantities into the following two symbols:

$$C_{rl;\tilde{r}\tilde{l}} = \frac{(-)^{r+\tilde{r}}(2l)!(2\tilde{l})!}{r!\tilde{r}!2^{l+\tilde{l}}(l!\tilde{l}!)^2} \sqrt{\frac{(1)_r(1)_{\tilde{r}}(2l+1)(2\tilde{l}+1)}{2^{l+\tilde{l}+2}(\tfrac{1}{2})_{r+l+1}(\tfrac{1}{2})_{\tilde{r}+\tilde{l}+1}}} \tag{B.6}$$

$$\Gamma_{rl;\tilde{r}\tilde{l}}^{jk;\tilde{j}\tilde{k}} = (-1)^{j+\tilde{j}+k+\tilde{k}}C_j{}^r C_{\tilde{j}}{}^{\tilde{r}} \times$$

$$\times \frac{(\tilde{r}+\tilde{l}+\tfrac{3}{2}-\tilde{j})_{\tilde{j}}(\tilde{r}+\tilde{l}+\tfrac{3}{2}-\tilde{j})_j(l-2k+l)_{2k}(\tilde{l}-2\tilde{k}+1)_{2\tilde{l}}}{4^{k+\tilde{k}}2^{r-j+\tilde{r}-\tilde{j}}(l+\tfrac{1}{2}-\tilde{k})(l+\tfrac{1}{2}-k)_k k!\tilde{k}!}. \tag{B.7}$$

The product of normalized eigenfunctions which occurs in Eq. (B.1) can now be written as

$$\psi_{rl}\psi_{\tilde{r}\tilde{l}} = C_{rl;\tilde{r}\tilde{l}} \sum_{j,\tilde{j},k,\tilde{k}=0}^{r,\tilde{r},[l/2],[\tilde{l}/2]} \Gamma_{rl;\tilde{r}\tilde{l}}^{jk;\tilde{j}\tilde{k}}(\xi^2)^{r-j+\tilde{r}-\tilde{j}+k-\tilde{k}}(\xi_1)^{l+\tilde{l}-2(k+\tilde{k})} \tag{B.8}$$

Clearly, $D_{rl;\tilde{r}\tilde{l}}$ may be represented in terms of the integrals

$$I_{m,n} = \int_{-\infty}^{\infty} \frac{\omega(\xi^2)^m(\xi_1)^n}{\lambda - i\xi_1}\,d\xi. \tag{B.9}$$

We shall further write

$$I_{0,n}' = I_n. \tag{B.10}$$

As is easily seen, the latter quantities satisfy the following recursive relation:

$$I_n = iA_{n-1} - i\lambda I_{n-1} \tag{B.11}$$

where

$$A_n = 0, \qquad\qquad n \text{ odd}$$
$$A_0 = 1$$
$$A_n = 1 \cdot 3 \cdot \cdots \cdot (n-1), \qquad n \text{ even.}$$

Alternately,

$$A_n = 2^{n/2}(\tfrac{1}{2})_{[n/2]} \sin^2 \frac{\pi(n+1)}{2}. \tag{B.12}$$

Since the ξ_2 and ξ_3 integrations in Eq. (B.9) are easily carried out $I_{m,n}$ can be represented in terms of I_r as follows:

$$I_{m,n} = \sum_{p+q+r=m} \frac{m!A_{2q}A_{2r}I_{n+2p}}{p!q!r!}. \tag{B.13}$$

The recursive equation, Eq. (B.10), may be solved and yields

$$I_n = (-i\lambda)^n I_0 + i \min(n, 1) \sum_{k=0}^{[(n-1)/2]} (-i\lambda)^{n-2k+1} A_{2k}. \qquad (B.14)$$

We now have

$$D_{rl;\tilde{r}\tilde{l}} = C_{rl;\tilde{r}\tilde{l}} \sum_{j, \tilde{j}, k, \tilde{k}=0}^{r, \tilde{r}, [l/2], [\tilde{l}/2]} \Gamma_{rl;\tilde{r}\tilde{l}}^{jk;\tilde{j}\tilde{k}} I_{r-j+\tilde{r}-\tilde{j}k+\tilde{k},\, l+\tilde{l}-2(k+\tilde{k})} \qquad (B.15)$$

which in addition to Eq. (B.14), furnishes the desired result in terms of I_0. In Appendix C,

$$M(\lambda) = \lambda I_0(\lambda) \qquad (B.16)$$

is evaluated and this completes the calculation.

The asymptotic form of $D_{rl;\tilde{r}\tilde{l}}$ for large arguments is obtained by substitution of

$$I_0 \sim \lambda \sum_{n=0} (-)^n \frac{A_{2n}}{\lambda^{2n}} \qquad (B.17)$$

into Eq. (B.14). The asymptotic form is derived in Appendix C.

A large block of the $D_{r,l,\tilde{r}l}$ as well as their asymptotic form is to be found in Table I of Sirovich and Thurber (1963).

Appendix C. Evaluation of

$$M(\lambda) = \lambda \int_{-\omega}^{\infty} \frac{\omega \, d\xi_1}{\lambda - i\xi_1}. \qquad (C.1)$$

Since

$$\lambda = \frac{1+\sigma}{k} \qquad (C.2)$$

represents a complex quantity, the integral in Eq. (C.1) defines two different analytic functions depending on whether Re $\lambda \lessgtr 0$. In both instances, however,

$$\frac{dM}{d\lambda} = \int_{-\infty}^{\infty} \frac{\omega \, d\xi_1}{\lambda - i\xi_1} - \lambda \int_{-\infty}^{\infty} \frac{\omega \, d\xi}{(\lambda - i\xi_1)^2}. \qquad (C.3)$$

This leads to

$$\frac{d}{d\lambda}\left(\frac{\exp(-\lambda^2/2)M}{\lambda}\right) = -\exp(-\lambda^2/2). \qquad (C.4)$$

Integrating Eq. (4) and denoting by $0^{\pm}$ the limit as we approach the origin with

Re $\lambda \gtrless 0$, we obtain

$$\frac{\exp(-\lambda^2/2)M^{\pm}}{\lambda} = -\int_{0^{\pm}}^{\lambda} \exp(-\mu^2/2)\,d\mu + \text{const} \tag{C.5}$$

with the path of integration lying in the appropriate half-plane.

The constant in Eq. (C.5) is obtained by returning to Eq. (C.1) from which we get

$$\frac{M^{\pm}}{\lambda}\bigg|_{\lambda=0^{\pm}} = \pm\sqrt{\pi/2}. \tag{C.6}$$

We therefore have

$$M = \begin{cases} M^+(\lambda) = \sqrt{\dfrac{\pi}{2}}\,\lambda\,\exp(\lambda^2/2)[1 - \Phi(\lambda/\sqrt{2})], & \text{Re } \lambda > 0 \\[3mm] M^-(\lambda) = -\sqrt{\dfrac{\pi}{2}}\,\lambda\,\exp(\lambda^2/2)[1 + \Phi(\lambda/\sqrt{2})], & \text{Re } \lambda < 0 \end{cases} \tag{C.7}$$

where

$$\Phi(x) = \sqrt{\frac{2}{\pi}} \int_0^{\sqrt{2}x} \exp(-t^2/2)\,dt \tag{C.8}$$

is the error function.

From the asymptotic theory of the error function (see Magnus and Oberttinger, 1954),

$$M^{\pm}(\lambda) = 1 - \frac{1}{\lambda^2} + \frac{1\cdot 3}{\lambda^4} - \frac{1\cdot 3\cdot 5}{\lambda^6} + \cdots$$

$$+ (-1)^n \frac{1\cdot 3\cdot 5\cdot \ldots \cdot(2n-3)}{\lambda^{2n-2}} + O\left(\frac{1}{\lambda^{2n}}\right)$$

$$|\arg \lambda| < \frac{3\pi}{4} - \varepsilon \tag{C.9}$$

where $\varepsilon > 0$ is small,

$$M^{\pm} = (-)^{\frac{1}{2}\pm\frac{1}{2}}\sqrt{2\pi}\lambda\,\exp(\lambda^2/2) + 1 - \frac{1}{\lambda^2} + \frac{1\cdot 3}{\lambda^4} + \cdots \tag{C.10}$$

with

$$\frac{\pi}{4} + \varepsilon < |\arg \lambda| < \frac{5\pi}{4} - \varepsilon.$$

The expansion for small λ is obtained from

$$\varphi\left(\frac{\lambda}{\sqrt{2}}\right) = \sqrt{\frac{2}{\pi}}\left(\lambda - \frac{\lambda^3}{2\cdot 3} + \frac{\lambda^5}{2^1\cdot 2^2\cdot 5} - \frac{\lambda^7}{3!2^3 7} \pm \cdots\right). \tag{C.11}$$

Appendix D. Properties of the Matrix
and Dispersion Relations

In the following series of lemmas we prove several general properties which relate to the dispersion relation found in Section V. We therefore focus attention on

$$C = \sum_{v} \beta_{\mu v} \gamma_{v j} \qquad (D.1)$$

with

$$\gamma_{v j} = \frac{1}{k} \int \frac{\omega \psi_v \psi_j \, d\xi}{i \xi_1 + \lambda} \, d\xi. \qquad (D.2)$$

Lemma 1. *Each element of $\gamma_{v j}$ can be written as*

$$\frac{i^n F(\lambda)}{k} \qquad (D.3)$$

where F is a real function of λ which is $\begin{Bmatrix} even \\ odd \end{Bmatrix}$ and $n = \begin{Bmatrix} 1 \\ 0 \end{Bmatrix}$.

This follows directly from Eqs. (B.13)–(B.15) of Appendix B.

Corollary. *The summation of Eq. (D.1) (i.e, the matrix elements)*

$$\sum_{v} \beta_{\mu v} \gamma_{v j}$$

also has one parity.

This follows immediately from the remarks made at the close of Appendix A. It was shown there that this summation is either odd or even from which the result follows.

A consequence is that the diagonal entries of the matrix in Eq. (D.1) are real.

Lemma 2. *A determinant for which the parities of any row may be gotten by multiplying the preceding row by i (and hence any determinant which may be put in this form) has itself a single parity. That is, the expanded determinant is a real function multiplied by 1 or i.*

The lemma is true for a two-by-two determinant. Expanding an n by n determinant (which satisfies the hypothesis) along the first column, we obtain $n, (n - 1)$ by $(n - 1)$ determinants. The first determinant satisfies the hypothesis of the lemma, the second may be given the same form by extracting an i from the first row. The third can be given the same form by interchanging the first and second rows. In fact it is clear that this may be done for each of the determinants. On invoking the inductive hypothesis the lemma is proven.

It is clear from Eqs. (D.1) and (D.3) that the matrix in Eq. (D.1) satisfies the hypothesis of Lemma 2. Then since the diagonal elements are real, so does the determinant, (4.8),

$$D = D(k, \lambda) = \det(1 - C) \tag{D.4}$$

Therefore we have proven:

Result 1. If $D(k, \lambda) = 0$, then

$$D(k, \lambda^*) = 0. \tag{D.5}$$

Thus, since $\lambda = (1 + \sigma)/k$, Eq. (D.5) expresses the fact that roots of the dispersion relation occur in conjugate pairs.

Lemma 3. *D is of even degree in k and λ.*

The only elements of C odd in k and λ are those of imaginary parity. But D is a real function; hence the terms of imaginary parity must occur to an even power and the lemma is proven.

Finally we prove:

Result 2. If $D(-k, -\lambda) = 0$, then

$$D(k, \lambda) = 0 \tag{D.6}$$

To be specific let us assume

$$k > 0, \qquad \text{Re } \lambda > 0$$

From Appendix C we have

$$M(-\lambda) = M^-(\lambda). \tag{D.7}$$

Exhibiting this explicitly in the hypothesis we write

$$D(-k, -\lambda) = D[-k, -\lambda; M^-(-\lambda)] = 0.$$

But from the functional forms for M^+ and M^- given in Appendix C, we have

$$M^-(-\lambda) = M^+(\lambda) \tag{D.8}$$

Using this with Lemma 3 we have

$$D[-k, -\lambda; M^-(-\lambda)] = D[k, \lambda; M^+(\lambda)] \tag{D.9}$$

which proves the statement in Eq. (D.6).

Since $\lambda = (1 + \sigma)/k$, we have therefore that positive and negative values of k lead to the same value for σ. This therefore justifies our restriction to $k > 0$.

Appendix E. Maxwell Eigenvalues

The expression for the eigenvalues for Maxwell molecules, λ_{rl}, was first given by Wang-Chang and Uhlenbeck (1952) in terms of a quadrature. Mott-Smith (1954) then developed infinite series and asymptotic expressions for λ_{rl} and Alterman *et al.* (1962) numerically computed a very large block of these eigenvalues. For convenience, in Table I we list a partial list from the latter reference. In accordance with our needs these are listed in the order of increasing magnitudes.

TABLE I

$\lambda_{rl}/\lambda_{02}$

r	l	$\lambda_{rl}/\lambda_{02}$	r	l	$\lambda_{rl}/\lambda_{02}$	r	l	$\lambda_{rl}/\lambda_{02}$
0	0	0.	5	2	1.73098	4	6	2.55245
0	1	0.	3	3	1.76308	0	7	2.69640
1	0	0.	7	1	1.77672	1	7	2.70979
1	1	0.66667	6	2	1.83018	2	7	2.72655
2	0	0.66667	4	3	1.85333	3	7	2.74642
0	2	1.	2	4	1.86334	4	7	2.76876
2	1	1.	0	4	1.87313	0	8	2.91932
1	2	1.16667	1	4	1.91062	1	8	2.93035
3	1	1.22814	5	3	1.93709	2	8	2.94320
4	0	1.22814	6	3	2.01478	3	8	2.95803
2	2	1.34222	3	4	2.02884	0	9	3.12640
4	1	1.40369	4	4	2.09168	1	9	3.13577
5	0	1.40369	5	4	2.15326	2	9	3.14613
3	2	1.49147	0	5	2.18283	3	9	3.15772
0	3	1.5	1	5	2.20659	0	10	3.32065
5	1	1.54745	2	5	2.24145	1	10	3.32877
6	0	1.54745	3	5	2.28236	2	10	3.33744
1	3	1.57036	4	5	2.32615	1	11	3.51135
4	2	1.61932	5	5	2.37099	2	11	3.51879
2	3	1.66702	0	6	2.45323	0	12	3.67871
6	1	1.66980	1	6	2.47033	0	13	3.84535
7	0	1.66980	2	6	2.49363	1	13	3.85100
			3	6	2.51254			

Appendix F. Rigid Sphere Cross Sections

In order to carry out any calculation involving rigid spheres it is necessary to have knowledge of the " cross sections"

$$B_{rl;\,r'l'} = \int \psi_{rl} L(\psi_{r'l'}) \, d\xi = B_{rl;\,r'l'}. \tag{F.1}$$

Mott-Smith (1954) has obtained the following formula for $B_{rl;\,r'l}$:

$$B_{rl;\,r'l} = -\frac{\sigma^2 \pi}{\sqrt{2}} \frac{(2l+1)(2l)! \displaystyle\sum_{n=0}^{\min(r,\,r')} \sum_{m=0}^{l} \frac{\Gamma(l-m+r+r'-2n-\frac{1}{2})}{(l-m)!(r-n)!(r'-n)!} B_m{}^n}{2^{r+r'+3l}(l+\frac{3}{2})[\Gamma(r+l+\frac{3}{2})\Gamma(r'+l'+\frac{3}{2})]^{1/2}} \tag{F.2}$$

with

$$B_m{}^n = \frac{(m+2n+1)!}{(2n+1)!m!} - \frac{2^{m-1}(m+n+1)!}{n!m!}; \qquad m, n \neq 0, 0$$

$$B_0{}^0 = 0. \tag{F.3}$$

The quantity σ represents the diameter of the rigid sphere.

A large block of the $B_{rl;\,sl}$ have been numerically computed and Table II contains

$$\frac{B_{rl;\,sl}}{B_{02;\,02}}.$$

TABLE II

$l = 0$

$s \backslash r$	0	1	2	3	4	5	6	7	8
0	0.	0.	0.	0.	0.	0.	0.	0.	0.
1		0.	0.	0.	0.	0.	0.	0.	0.
2			−0.66667	−0.15430	0.01818	0.00433	0.00130	0.00044	0.00016
3				−1.10714	0.28200	0.03712	0.00982	0.00324	0.00120
4					−1.45288	0.39006	0.05495	0.01557	0.00550
5						−1.74397	0.48438	0.07148	0.02127
6							−1.99892	0.56863	0.08683
7								−2.22791	0.64521
8									−2.43721

$l = 1$

$s \backslash r$	0	1	2	3	4	5	6	7
0	0.	0.	0.	0.	0.	0.	0.	0.
1		−0.66667	0.12599	0.01286	0.00274	0.00075	0.00024	0.00008
2			−1.07143	0.25030	0.03057	0.00758	0.00237	0.00083
3				−1.40303	0.35867	0.04817	0.01307	0.00444
4					−1.68819	0.45419	0.06480	0.01868
5						−1.94075	0.53969	0.08036
6							−2.16905	0.61755
7								−2.37853

$l = 2$

$s \backslash r$	0	1	2	3	4	5	6	7
0	−1.	0.13363	0.01114	0.00206	0.00050	0.00014	0.00005	0.00002
1		−1.22024	0.24256	0.02629	0.00593	0.00171	0.00056	0.00020
2			−1.47433	0.34443	0.04289	0.01092	0.00351	0.00127
3				−1.71982	0.43686	0.05914	0.01628	0.00562
4					−1.94952	0.52098	0.07460	0.02169
5						−2.16361	0.59818	0.08920
6							−2.36377	0.66967
7								−2.55181

TABLE II (*continued*)

l	s \ r	0	1	2	3	4	5	6
l = 3	0	−1.5	0.22728	0.02094	0.00420	0.00111	0.00034	0.00011
	1		−1.64187	0.33299	0.03732	0.00873	0.00262	0.00089
	2			−1.82502	0.42449	0.05337	0.01381	0.00453
	3				−2.01665	0.50737	0.06879	0.01908
	4					−2.20584	0.58362	0.08343
	5						−2.38887	0.65445
	6							−2.56468
l = 4	0	−1.81746	0.28511	0.02751	0.00580	0.00160	0.00051	0.00018
	1		−1.95626	0.39733	0.04519	0.01082	0.00333	0.00116
	2			−2.11310	0.48704	0.06137	0.01603	0.00533
	3				−2.27649	0.56603	0.07650	0.02128
	4					−2.44032	0.63809	0.09073
	5						−2.60160	0.70499
	6							−2.75895
l = 5	0	−2.04365	0.31961	0.03134	0.00677	0.00193	0.00063	
	1		−2.19480	0.44098	0.05027	0.01216	0.00380	
	2			−2.34576	0.53334	0.06693	0.01754	
	3				−2.49686	0.61222	0.08217	
	4					−2.64679	0.68298	
	5						−2.79446	
l = 6	0	−2.22122	0.34009	0.03327	0.00726	0.00210		
	1		−2.38307	0.46987	0.05319	0.01289		
	2			−2.53527	0.56648	0.07043		
	3				−2.68229	0.64728		
	4					−2.82556		

TABLE II (continued)

l	r \ s	0	1	2	3	4	5	6
$l=7$	0	−2.37148	0.35244	0.03401	0.00741	0.00216		
	1		−2.53898	0.48883	0.05459	0.01317		
	2			−2.69343	0.58975	0.07235		
	3				−2.83969	0.67139		
	4					−2.9802		
$l=8$	0	−2.50540	0.36009	0.03404	0.00734			
	1		−2.67412	0.50135	0.05499			
	2			−2.82965	0.60599			
	3				−2.97585			
$l=9$	0	−2.62874	0.36506	0.03369	0.00716			
	1		−2.79574	0.50978	0.05475			
	2			−2.95073	0.61737			
	3				−3.09647			
$l=10$	0	−2.74466	0.36845	0.03312				
	1		−2.90823	0.51563				
	2			−3.06135				
$l=11$	0	−2.85493	0.37089	0.03247				
	1		−3.01426	0.51984				
	2			−3.16460				
$l=12$	0	−2.96065	0.37275					
	1		−3.11544					
$l=13$	0	−3.06251	0.37424					
	1		−3.21277					
$l=14$	0	−3.16099						
$l=15$	0	−3.25646						

REFERENCES

Alterman, Z., Frankowski, K., and Pekeris, C. L. (1962). *Astrophys. J. Suppl. Ser.* **7**, 291.

Bhatnagar, P. L., Gross, E. P., and Krook, M. (1954). *Phys. Rev.* **94**, 511.

Chapman, S., and Cowling, T. G. (1952). "The Mathematical Theory of Non-Uniform Gases." Cambridge Univ. Press, London and New York.

Grad, H. (1949). *Commun. Pure Appl. Math.* **2**, 331.

Greenspan, M. (1950). *J. Acoust. Soc. Am.* **22**, 568.

Greenspan, M. (1956). *J. Acoust. Soc. Am.* **28**, 644.

Gross, E. P., and Jackson, E. A. (1959). *Phys. Fluids* **2**, 432.

Magnus, W., and Oberhettinger, F. (1954). "Formulas and Theorems for the Functions of Mathematical Physics." Chelsea, New York.

Meyer, E., and Sessler, G. (1957). *Z. Physik* **149**, 15.

Mott-Smith, H. M. (1954). "A New Approach in the Kinetic Theory of Gases." Lincoln Lab. Group Rept. V-2, Lexington, Massachusetts.

Pekeris, C. L., Alterman, Z., and Finkelstein, L. (1960). *In* "Symposium on the Numerical Treatment of Ordinary Differential Equations, Integral and Integro-Differential Equations of P.I.C.C.," p. 389. Birhauser-Verlag, Basel.

Pekeris, C. L., Alterman, Z., Finkelstein, L., and Frankowski, K. (1962). *Phys. Fluids* **5**, 1608.

Sirovich, L. (1962). *Phys. Fluids* **5**, 908.

Sirovich, L. (1963a). *Phys. Fluids* **6**, 10.

Sirovich, L. (1963b). *Phys. Fluids*, **6**, 218.

Sirovich, L. (1963c). *Phys. Fluids* **6**, 1428.

Sirovich, L., and Thurber, J. K. (1961). "Sound Propagation according to Kinetic Models." AFOSR-1380, MF-17, Courant Inst. Math. Sci., New York Univ.

Sirovich, L., and Thurber, J. K. (1963). *In* "Rarefied Gas Dynamics." (J. A. Laurmann, ed.), Vol. 1, p. 159. Academic Press, New York.

Sirovich, L., and Thurber, J. K. (1965). *J. Acoust. Soc. Am.* In press.

Truesdell, C. (1953). *J. Ratl. Mech. Anal.* **2**, 693.

Wang Chang, C. S. (1948). "On the Dispersion of Sound in Helium." Applied Physic Lab., The Johns Hopkins University, CM-467, UMH-3-F.

Wang Chang, C. S., and Uhlenbeck, G. E. (1952). "On the Propagation of Sound in Monatomic Gases." Eng. Res. Inst. Univ. Mich., ONR Contract N6ONR-23222.

Forced Sound Propagation in Gases of Arbitrary Density[1]

RODNEY J. MASON, JR.

Graduate School of Aerospace Engineering, Cornell University, Ithaca, New York

The steady-state sound disturbances induced in a monatomic gas by an oscillating plane boundary are examined. Kinetic source terms are developed to represent the effect of particle reflections from the moving boundary. Linearized model equations are employed. Specular reflection and an $\exp(-i\omega t)$ time dependence are assumed. The equations are solved with the aid of Fourier transforms. An exact solution is obtained for a model equation which relaxes to a Cauchy distribution. The second model equation relaxes to the Maxwellian velocity distribution but must be solved by approximate techniques. Both solutions exhibit the Navier-Stokes form in the continuum regime and a "free molecule" form when collisions are absent. The Maxwellian solution is in acceptable quantitative agreement with all available data.

I. Introduction

The survey article by Sherman and Talbot (1960) indicated the need for a fully kinetic solution to the problem of forced sound propagation in gases. The kinetic solution would be required to assume the Navier-Stokes form in the continuum regime so as to agree with the measurements of Greenspan (1956). But in the free molecular limit it should take on the "free streaming" form predicted and substantiated by Meyer and Sessler (1957). Kinetic studies of sound propagation have been conducted by several authors including Wang Chang and Uhlenbeck (1952), Bhatnagar *et al.* (1954) and Sirovich and Thurber (1963). Questions regarding boundary conditions were avoided by all these workers who did initial value problems in an unbounded gas rather than the semi-infinite problem to which measurements refer.

We shall solve the more pertinent problem of forced oscillations in a semi-

[1] The study was supported by the Air Force Office of Scientific Research.

infinite monatomic gas. Our approach has analogs in the bounded plasma problems solved by Landau (1946) and Platzman and Buchsbaum (1962).

In Section II linearized kinetic source terms are developed to represent the effect of specular and diffuse isothermal particle reflections from the moving boundary. To simplify the mathematics in place of the more rigorous Boltzmann equation we utilize the BGK model kinetic equation (due to Bhatnagar *et al.*). This equation is modified in Section III so as to relax to a Cauchy type distribution which approximates the Maxwellian. With the aid of the specular source term we solve this equation exactly. The solution agrees quantitatively with the Navier-Stokes predictions in the continuum regime, and qualitatively with the Meyer and Sessler results under free molecular conditions.

We solve the conventional BGK equation in Section IV, by employing a combination of numerical and approximate, analytic techniques, which are motivated, in part, by our experience with the Cauchy solution. The Maxwellian result is in acceptable quantitative agreement with experiment throughout the continuum, transition and free molecular regimes.

II. The Kinetic Source Terms

The problem of sound propagation in a semi-infinite gas is simplified considerably if we convert it to a full-space problem by imposing an artificial symmetry. The physical system consists of an oscillating boundary at $x = 0^+$ and gas extending to $x = +\infty$. To create the symmetry we reflect this arrangement about the origin. The resulting system has two boundaries oscillating *in opposite* directions at $x = 0^\pm$, and two bodies of gas which carry mirror-image disturbances to $x = \pm\infty$. The one-dimensional, linearized, first order disturbances in the new full-space will be governed by the kinetic equation

$$\frac{\partial f}{\partial t} + u \frac{\partial f}{\partial x} = \left(\frac{\partial f}{\partial t}\right)_{\text{col}} + \left(\frac{\partial f}{\partial t}\right)_{s} \tag{1}$$

where the velocity distribution is assumed to be slightly perturbed, $f = n_0 f_0 + f_1$, about a uniform state $n_0 f_0$, and f_1 is the first order perturbation. The collision term is $(\partial f / \partial t)_{\text{col}}$, and $(\partial f / \partial t)_s$ is the source term representing the influence of the boundaries on the gas.

For sound production the displacements of the two oscillating boundaries are small. Hence to first order it is appropriate to apply the boundary condition on the particle velocities at the origin. The source term therefore contains a delta function at $x = 0$. In the case of specular reflection each particle striking the boundaries has its velocity reversed and increased by twice the boundary velocity. If $-n_0 u f_0(u) - u f_1(u, x = 0^+)$, $u < 0$, is the flux distribution (an intrinsically positive quantity) of particles striking the right boundary, the specularly reflected flux distribution is $n_0 u f_0(-u + 2v^+(t))$ $+ u f_1(-u + 2v^+(t), 0^+)$, $u > 0$ where $v^+(t)$ is the right boundary velocity. The isotropy of $n_0 f_0$ in velocity space, and the imposed artificial symmetry of the problem permits us to write this reflected flux in the right half plane as $n_0 u f_0(u - 2v^+(t)) + u f_1(u - 2v^+(t), 0^-)$, $u = 0$. The specular source term for $u > 0$ must provide the difference between the reflected particle flux into $u > 0$ and the incident flux of particles with $u > 0$ from the left half plane, so that multiplying this difference by $\delta(x)$ which locates the source at the origin, we obtain

$$\left(\frac{\partial f}{\partial t}\right)_s = \{n_0 f_0(u - 2v^+(t)) - n_0 f_0$$
$$+ f_1(u - 2v^+(t), 0^-) - f_1(u, 0^-)\} u\, \delta(x), \qquad u > 0. \qquad (2)$$

Consideration of the particles in $u < 0$ yields a similar expression. When these two expressions are expanded to first order in $v^+(t)$, the terms in f_1 cancel for each velocity range, and the specular source term becomes simply

$$\left(\frac{\partial f}{\partial t}\right)_s = -2n_0 v^+(t) u \frac{\partial f_0}{\partial u} \delta(x), \qquad u \gtrless 0. \qquad (3)$$

Alternatively, when diffuse isothermal reflection occurs at the boundaries, the reflected distribution is Maxwellian, based on the uniform background temperature and centered about the boundary speed. The reflected number density must be adjusted to equate the incident and reflected particle fluxes in the frame of the moving boundary. In $u > 0$ this reflected flux distribution is

$$n_0 u \left(1 + \frac{v^+(t) - 2s^-(0^+)}{2c}\right) f_0(u - v^+(t))$$

$$c = \int\limits_{-\infty}^{\infty} \int\limits_{u=0}^{\infty} \int u f_0\, d^3v, \qquad n_0 s^-(0^+) = \int\limits_{-\infty}^{\infty} \int\limits_{u=-\infty}^{0} \int u f_1(u, 0^+)\, d^3v. \qquad (4)$$

Again a similar result is obtained for the particles in $u < 0$. We avail ourselves of the imposed symmetry, take the difference between the reflected and incident particle fluxes and expand to first order in $v^+(t)$ to find that for diffuse isothermal reflection

$$\left(\frac{\partial f}{\partial t}\right)_s = -n_0 v^+(t) \left\{\frac{\partial f_0}{\partial u} \mp \frac{1}{2c} f_0\right\} u\, \delta(x) \mp \left\{\frac{n_0 s^-(0^+)}{c} f_0 + f_1(u, 0^\mp)\right\} u\, \delta(x) \qquad (5)$$

where the upper signs apply for $u > 0$, and the lower for $u < 0$. The second bracket contains terms dependent on f_1. These represent the ability of the boundary to convert any incident first order distribution to the Maxwellian form. This second bracket vanishes in the free molecular limit since there are no particle collisions to reflect disturbances and produce an *incident* f_1. It appears that omission of this term even in the transition regime may yield accurate results for diffuse isothermal reflection since $|s^-(0^+)| \ll |v^+(t)|$ until collisions are numerous.

In view of its relative simplicity we shall employ only the specular source term in our subsequent study of forced sound propagation.

III. Cauchy Solution

A. Density Transform

The linearized BGK model kinetic equation replaces the Boltzmann collision integral with an algebraic operator, which effectively acts to relax the total velocity distribution, f, to the locally perturbed state $(n_0 + n_1)f_0(\bar{v} - \bar{v}_1, a_0^2 + a_1^2)$, where $n_0 f_0(u, a_0^2)$ is the uniform background distribution of Eq. (1) and n_1, $\bar{v}_1$, and $a_1^2 = kT_1/m$ are the first order perturbations of density, mean velocity, and mean thermal speed. Usually, $n_0 f_0$ is chosen as the Maxwellian on physical grounds. However, mathematically, the linearized BGK operator will properly represent relaxation if $n_0 f_0$ is any uniform state resembling the Maxwellian in that it integrates to n_0, has the mean thermal speed $a_0^2 = kT_0/m$ and possesses a finite fourth moment. For the present we assume that $n_0 f_0$ possesses these properties, but is otherwise arbitrary.

We expand the modified BGK operator to first order in the perturbation quantities n_1, $\bar{v}_1$ and a_1^2; then placing it in Eq. (1) along with the specular source term of Eq. (3) we obtain for one-dimensional disturbances

$$\frac{\partial f_1}{\partial t} + u \frac{\partial f_1}{\partial x} = -v\left(f_1 - n_1 f_0 + n_0 u_1 \frac{\partial f_0}{\partial u} - n_0 a_1^2 \frac{\partial f_0}{\partial a_0^2} \right)$$

$$- 2n_0 v^+(t) \frac{\partial f_0}{\partial u} u \, \delta(x) \tag{6}$$

$$n_1 = \int f_1 \, d^3v, \qquad n_0 u_1 = \int u f_1 \, d^3v,$$

$$n_0 a_1^2 + n_1 a_0^2 = \tfrac{1}{3} \int (u^2 + v^2 + w^2) f_1 \, d^3v \tag{7}$$

where v is positive and proportional to a velocity-independent collision frequency.

We let $v^+(t) = \exp(-i\omega t)$ with ω the oscillation frequency of the boundary, and assume this exponential time dependence for all perturbation quantities.

Operating with $\int \exp(-ikx)\, dx$ we transform all the terms in Eqs. (6) and (7). We factor the time dependence. Then Eq. (6) becomes upon transformation

$$(-i\omega + \nu + iku)f_1 = \nu\left(n_1 f_0 - n_0 u_1 \frac{\partial f_0}{\partial u} + n_0 a_1{}^2 \frac{\partial f_0}{\partial a_0{}^2}\right)$$

$$- 2n_0 v_p \frac{\partial f_0}{\partial u} u \tag{8}$$

where the subscript "1" will now refer to time-independent transformed quantities. We take the zeroeth moment of Eq. (8) to eliminate u_1 in terms of n_1. Then we divide the resultant equation by $(-i\omega + \nu + iku)$, integrate both sides over all velocity space and solve for n_1. The result is given by

$$n_1 = \frac{i2n_0 v_p \mathscr{S}}{1 - \varepsilon} + \frac{\partial \mathscr{T}/\partial a_0{}^2}{1 - \varepsilon} n_0 a_1{}^2 \tag{9}$$

$$\mathscr{T} = -\frac{iv}{k}\int \frac{g_0\, du}{u - u_p}, \qquad \mathscr{S} = \frac{1}{k}\int \frac{(u - iv/k)\, \partial g_0/\partial u}{u - u_p}\, du \tag{10}$$

with $u_p = (\omega + iv)/k$, $\varepsilon = \mathscr{T} + iv\mathscr{S}$, and $g_0 = \iint f_0\, dv\, dw$. Similarly, after eliminating u_1 from Eq. (8) and dividing by $(-i\omega + \nu + iku)$ we integrate the product of $(u^2 + v^2 + w^2)/3$ and the resultant expression for f_1 over all velocity space. This integral is then used with the Fourier transform of $n_0 a_1{}^2 + n_1 a_0{}^2$ in Eq. (7) to produce

$$n_0 a_1{}^2 = \frac{i2n_0 v_p(2a_0{}^2 k^2 \mathscr{S}^* - \omega)}{k^2(3 - 2\mathscr{T}^*)} + \frac{(\omega^2 - (3 - 2\varepsilon^*)a_0{}^2 k^2)}{k^2(3 - 2\mathscr{T}^*)} n_1 \tag{11}$$

$$\mathscr{T}^* = -\frac{iv}{k}\int \frac{g_0{}^*\, du}{u - u_p}, \qquad \mathscr{S}^* = \frac{1}{k}\int \frac{(u - iv/k)\, \partial g_0{}^*/\partial u}{u - u_p}\, du \tag{12}$$

with $\varepsilon^* = \mathscr{T}^* + iv\mathscr{S}^*$, $\mathscr{F}^* = \mathscr{T}^* + a_0{}^2\, \partial \mathscr{T}^*/\partial a_0{}^2$, and $g_0{}^* = (1/a_0{}^2)\iint v^2 f_0\, dv\, dw$. Finally, combining Eq. (9) and Eq. (10) we obtain the exact density transform

$$n_1 = i2n_0 v_p \frac{\text{NUM}(k)}{\text{DEN}(k)} \tag{13}$$

$$\text{NUM}(k) = (2a_0{}^2 k^2 \mathscr{S}^* - \omega)\frac{\partial \mathscr{T}}{\partial a_0{}^2} + \mathscr{S}k^2(3 - 2\mathscr{F}^*) \tag{14}$$

$$\text{DEN}(k) = (1 - \varepsilon)k^2(3 - 2\mathscr{F}^*) - (\omega^2 - (3 - 2\varepsilon^*)a_0{}^2 k^2)\frac{\partial \mathscr{T}}{\partial a_0{}^2}. \tag{15}$$

The uniform background distribution $n_0 f_0$ must be stated explicitly before the transform integrals $\mathscr{T}$, $\mathscr{S}$, etc., can be evaluated. In Section IV we will see that use of the Maxwellian requires that the transform integrals be expressed in terms of a special function (the plasma dispersion function of Fried and Conte, 1961) so that they give rise to a highly complicated transform for the density. Inversion of this transform will of necessity proceed by approximate techniques. Therefore, to gain initial insight in this section we let

$$n_0 f_0 = \frac{8b^5 n_0}{5\pi^2(u^2 + v^2 + w^2 + b^2)^4}, \qquad b^2 = 3a_0^2 \qquad (16)$$

which permits us to find an exact solution to Eq. (6). This Cauchy-type distribution satisfies the physical requirement of isotropy in velocity space. The fourth power dependence of the denominator is chosen since higher powers introduce unnecessary complexity, while lower powers fail to permit adiabatic oscillations in the continuum, i.e., $n_0 u_1^3$ can diverge for these distributions. The one-dimensional form of Eq. (16) is $g_0(u) = \iint f_0 \, dv \, dw$. Comparing this to the one-dimensional Maxwellian we find that the Cauchy number exceeds the Maxwellian out to $u/a_0 = 0.85$; then there are less Cauchy particles until $u/a_0 \approx 6.0$, after which the Cauchy number remains in excess.

The transform integrals may now be computed. The integral becomes, for example,

$$\mathscr{T} = -\frac{iv}{k}\left(\frac{8b^5}{3\pi}\right) \int_{-\infty}^{+\infty} \frac{du}{(u^2 + b^2)^3 (u - (\omega + iv)/k)}\bigg\}, \qquad v > 0, \qquad (17)$$

which may be evaluated by contour integration in complex u space. We close the contour with a semicircular arc at infinity in the upper half plane. The arc makes no contribution. The integral equals $2\pi i$ times the sum of the residues in the *upper half plane*. We see there is always a third order pole at $u = ib$. Note that thus far $\mathscr{T}$ has been defined for real k only (the initial Fourier transform uses real k values). When $k > 0$ there is a first order pole at $u = (\omega + iv)/k$ in the upper half plane which contributes a residue. For $k < 0$ this pole resides in the lower half plane and, therefore, does not contribute. Thus computing over the residues we find that $\mathscr{T}$ has, in fact, two branches:

$$\mathscr{T} = \mathscr{T}_+(k) = \frac{\delta(8k^2 + 9\gamma k + 3\gamma^2)}{3(k + \gamma)^3}, \qquad k \text{ real}, \quad > 0$$

$$\mathscr{T} = \mathscr{T}_-(k) = \frac{\delta(8k^2 - 9\gamma k + 3\gamma^2)}{3(-k + \gamma)^3}, \qquad k \text{ real}, \quad < 0 \qquad (17a)$$

where $\delta = v/b$ and $\gamma = (v - i\omega)/b$.

The inversion of Eq. (13) is facilitated if we speak of complex k. We therefore note that although the $\mathscr{T}_\pm$ are originally defined for real k, we may take the fractional representations of Eq. (17a) as the analytic continuations of the integral branches throughout the entire complex plane. Then from Eq. (17a) we have for arbitrary complex k, for example, $\mathcal{T}_+(k) = \mathcal{T}_-(-k)$. Similar considerations apply to the remaining transform integrals $\mathcal{S}$, ε, $\mathcal{T}^*$, etc. We note that the double branch character of functions possessing the form of our transform integrals has been discussed by both Sirovich and Thurber (1963) and Platzman and Buchsbaum (1962).

We now evaluate all the remaining transform integrals, analytically continue them to complex k, substitute our results in Eqs. (13) and (14) and obtain after considerable algebraic rearrangement the exact Cauchy density transform:

$$n_1 = \frac{i2n_0 v_p N_\pm(\xi)}{\omega D_\pm(\xi)}, \qquad \pm \text{ for } \text{Re}(k) \gtrless 0 \tag{18}$$

$$\begin{aligned} N_+(\xi) = N_-(-\xi) = {} & 45\xi^5 + (171 + 105P)\xi^4 \\ & + (252 + 85P)R\xi^3 + (180 + 25P)R^2\xi^2 \\ & + 63R^3\xi + 9R^4 \end{aligned} \tag{19}$$

$$\begin{aligned} D_+(\xi) = D_-(-\xi) = {} & 9\xi^7 + (63 + 21P)\xi^6 + (189 + 129P + 17P^2)\xi^5 \\ & + (315 + 342P + 98P^2 + 5P^3)\xi^4 \\ & + (315 + 183P + 35P^2)R\xi^3 + (189 + 39P + 5P^2)R^2\xi^2 \\ & + 63R^3\xi + 9R^4 \end{aligned} \tag{20}$$

with $P = iv/\omega$, $R = 1 + P$, and $\xi = (ibk)/\omega$.

B. Dispersion Relation and Transform Inversion

The steady-state density disturbances caused by the oscillating boundaries in our "Cauchy gas" are given by the Fourier inversion of Eqs. (18)–(20), which is

$$n_1(x) = \frac{in_0 v_p}{\pi\omega}\left\{ \int_{k=-\infty}^{0} \frac{N_-(\xi)}{D_-(\xi)} e^{ikx}\, dk + \int_{0}^{\infty} \frac{N_+(\xi)}{D_+\xi()} e^{ikx}\, dk \right\} \tag{21}$$

where $\xi = (ibk)/\omega$ and $n_1(x)$ is now the inverted transform of n_1. The inversion integral must be split into two parts owing to the different transform branches applying in $\text{Re}(k) \gtrless 0$. Upon separation into partial fractions, Eq. (21) becomes

$$n_1(x) = \frac{n_0 v_p}{c_0} \sum_{i=1}^{7} \frac{A(\xi_i)}{2\pi i}\left\{ \int_{k=-\infty}^{0} \frac{(-1)e^{ikx}\, dk}{k - (-k_i)} + \int_{k=0}^{\infty} \frac{e^{ikx}\, dk}{k - k_i} \right\} \tag{22}$$

$$A(\xi_i) = \frac{i2\sqrt{5}N_+(\xi_i)}{27\prod_{i \neq j}(\xi_i - \xi_j)}, \qquad \xi_i = \frac{ibk_i}{\omega}, \qquad b = \sqrt{3}a_0, \tag{23}$$

where $c_0 = \sqrt{5/3}a_0$ is the continuum sound speed and the $k_i(\propto \xi_i)$ are the roots in k space of the dispersion relation $D_+(\xi, P) = 0$ with $P = iq = iv/\omega$ for a specified value of q. We note from Eq. (20) that the zeros of D_- are simply the negative of the zeros of D_+ so that only the latter need be studied to determine all the properties of Eq. (21).

The Cornell CDC 1604 computer has been used to trace out the seven roots of the D_+ dispersion relation over the range $10^{-2} \leqslant q \leqslant 10^{+3}$. The k_i root trajectories are plotted in Fig. 1. Note that there are at most three zeros in the first k quadrant. Since there are no D_+ zeros in the fourth quadrant, by Eq. (20) there will be no D_- zeros in the second k quadrant. Further discussion will be devoted to the dispersion roots in Section III, C.

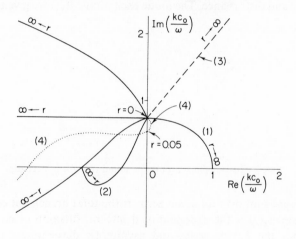

Fig. 1. Cauchy root trajectories.

We now invert each bracketed pair of integrals in Eq. (22) by integrating over the twin quarter pie contours of Fig. 2. (Alternatively, the tables, e.g., Erdelyi (1954) could be consulted, but the contour inversion is more instructive.) The branch cut along the line $\text{Re}(k) = 0$ separates the right and left half planes where the negative and positive range integrands apply, respectively. Since the quarter circle arcs at infinity make no contribution, each $k = 0 \to +\infty$ integral reduces to $2\pi i$ times the residue at k_i (if this root is in the first quadrant) plus an additional contribution from the return path along the branch cut $k = i\infty \to 0$. In contrast the $k = -\infty \to 0$ integrals yield only a branch cut contribution since we have established that none of the zeros, $-k_i$, reside in the second quadrant. Our Eq. (22) density solution is therefore

$$n_1(x) = \frac{n_0 v_p}{c_0} \sum_l A(\xi_l) e^{ik_l x}$$

$$+ \frac{n_0 v_p}{c_0} \sum_{j=1}^{7} \frac{A(\xi_j)}{2\pi i} \left(e^{ik_j x} E_1(ik_j x) + e^{-ik_j x} E_1(-ik_j x) \right) \quad (24)$$

$$E_1(z) = \int_z^\infty \frac{e^{-t}}{t} \, dt = -\gamma - \log_e z - \sum_{n=1}^{\infty} \frac{(-1)^n z^n}{n \cdot n!} \quad (25)$$

$$E_1(z) \sim e^{-z} \left(\frac{1}{z} - \frac{1}{z^2} + \frac{2!}{z^3} - \frac{3!}{z^4} + \cdots \right) \quad (26)$$

where $\gamma = 0.577 \ldots$ is Euler's constant. The index l runs over all the zeros of D_+ in the first k quadrant, and selects the modes contributing exponentially to the net sound disturbance. The mode excitations $A(\xi_i)$ are given by Eq. (23).

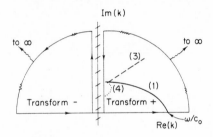

FIG. 2. Quarter pie contours for sound transform inversion.

The additional sum over all seven zeros is the total branch cut contribution. The function $E_1(z)$ is the exponential integral function of complex argument. It has the Taylor series and asymptotic development of Eqs. (25) and (26).

C. Discussion of Cauchy Results

Re-examining the Cauchy root trajectories of Fig. 1, we note that all the roots are far from the origin for large (continuum) values of $q = v/\omega$, except for the root labeled (1) in the first quadrant, and its mirror image (2) in the third. As q is decreased all the roots move toward the origin, so that as q goes to zero they all converge on the point $c_0 k/\omega = i5^{1/2}/3$. This free molecular point of accumulation is, however, a consequence of our choice of a model distribution $n_0 f_0$. If, for example, $n_0 f_0$ had two poles in the upper half u plane, instead of one at $u = ib$, there would be two accumulation points for the dispersion roots as q becomes small. Thus for quantitative predictions of the significant root trajectories for small q we see that the physically correct $n_0 f_0$ should be employed. This is presumably the Maxwellian. Using the Cauchy distribution, the most we can expect is overall qualitative accuracy.

Figure 1 shows us that from the continuum ($q \approx 10^3$) down to $q = 0.13$ D_+ possesses only two zeros in the first quadrant. The first, (1), is undamped in the continuum where it goes to $c_0 k/\omega = 1$. This corresponds to the "first mode" or "sound mode" of the Navier-Stokes theory of sound propagation. The second, (3), has its wave number equal to its attentuation rate for large q. It therefore identifies with Navier-Stokes "diffusion mode." Finally, for $q < 0.13$ yet a third mode, (4), moves into the first quadrant and yields for these small q an additional exponential contribution to the net density disturbance.

The nondimensional Cauchy sound mode and diffusion mode attenuation rates $\alpha = \mathrm{Im}(c_0 k_i/\omega)$ and wave numbers $\beta = \mathrm{Re}(c_0 k_i/\omega)$ are plotted in Figs. 3 and 4 along with the Cornell 1604 estimates for the α and β values predicted by the Navier-Stokes dispersion relation. This relation has been fully discussed elsewhere (see Sherman and Talbot, 1960). In the Navier-Stokes theory the various regimes for sound propagation are characterized by the parameter $r = P_0/(\mu\omega)$, where P_0 is the uniform background pressure, μ the viscosity and ω the circular oscillation frequency. For the presentations given in Figs. 3 and 4 we have chosen the Cauchy model collision parameter, v, so that $q = (20/7)r$. This brings the Cauchy α value into agreement with the Navier-Stokes attenuation (and measurement) in the continuum regime. Figure 3 shows us that the Cauchy α value departs from the Navier-Stokes value at $r \approx 30$. However, it is close to the cross hatched data curve (Sherman and Talbot, 1960) down to $r = 1.5$. Thereafter the Cauchy modes (1), (3), and (4) all exceed the measured decay rates.

A program was written for the Cornell computer using complex arithmetic to compute the exponential integral functions by Taylor series out to $|z| = 10$ and by asymptotic series thereafter. These functions were then used to compute the net branch cut contribution $n_1(x)$. The Cauchy branch cut curves are plotted in Fig. 5 for the range $0.087 \leqslant r \leqslant 350$. Note that the db scale in this and subsequent figures refers to 20 times the logarithm of the disturbance quantities. The branch cut contribution is weak in the continuum but grows as r decreases so that, as we shall see, it dominates the overall disturbance in the free molecular limit. Since the branch cut contribution survives when collisions have ceased to be active, it will henceforth be termed the *free streaming* mode. The attenuation rate of the free streaming mode is position dependent and varies most rapidly near the boundary at $x = 0^+$. For large x the decay is algebraic (for the Cauchy model), which follows from the asymptotic form of the exponential integral [see Eq. (23)].

The density excitation moduli, $|A(\xi_i)|$ (see Eq. (23)) of the three exponential modes have been plotted versus r in Fig. 6 along with the initial modulus of the free streaming disturbance. The modulus of the initial total disturbance

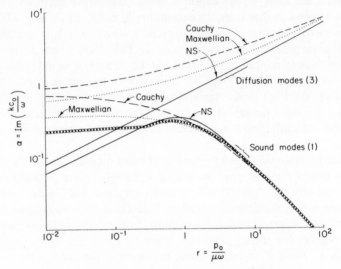

FIG. 3. Sound and diffusion mode attenuation rates.

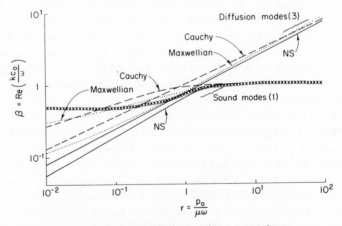

FIG. 4. Sound and diffusion mode wave numbers.

$|n_1(0)c_0/(n_0 v_p)|$ also appears. The sound mode dominates in the continuum but is surpassed at $r \approx 1.0$ by the diffusion mode. For small r all the modes are strongly excited, but owing to their relative phase differences the net density disturbance deviates only slightly from its continuum value throughout the whole r range.

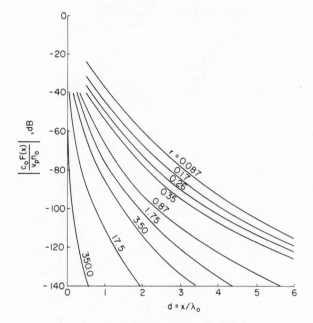

FIG. 5. Cauchy free streaming mode modulus.

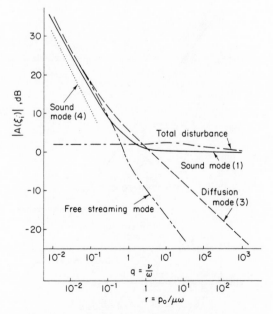

FIG. 6. Cauchy density excitation moduli.

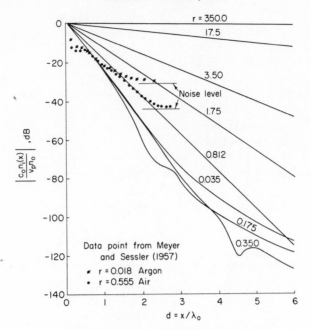

FIG. 7. Total Cauchy density disturbance.

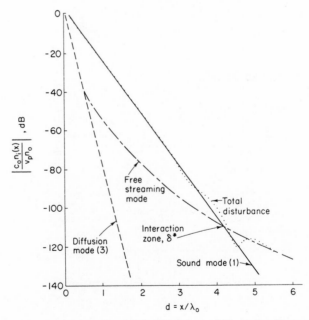

FIG. 8. Individual mode contributions to $r = 0.35$ net density curve.

Finally, the moduli of the total density disturbances $|n_1(x)c_0/(n_0 v_p)|$ of Eq. (24) were computed and appear in Fig. 7. On the logarithmic scale the net disturbance exhibits linear decay in the continuum regime where the exponential sound mode, (1), dominates. In the free molecular limit all the modes are excited nearly equally, but the exponential modes rapidly decay away with distance leaving just the free streaming disturbance. For the transition regime values ($r \approx 1$) the density plot exhibits peaks at a transition distance δ^*. This distance moves toward $x = 0^+$ as r decreases (and mean free path increases). At distances less than δ^* the sound is primarily exponential in character. Beyond δ^* the free streaming mode dominates. In Fig. 8 we have plotted separately the various terms responsible for the $r = 0.35$ net density curve. The process of conversion from exponential to free streaming decay is quite evident.

The data of Meyer and Sessler (1957) are plotted on Fig. 7 for comparison. If we assume that the Meyer and Sessler instruments responded primarily to density pulses (as tacitly assumed in their theory), then we see that the Cauchy curves are too rapidly damped for small r to give quantitative agreement, although the general form of the theoretical curves is acceptable. The transition peaks are predicted for very low sound levels. Unfortunately no measurements are currently available to verify their existence. Although the measurements of Heckl and Maidanik (1962) exhibit such "anomalous peaks," these peaks occur at a much more intense level than those predicted by the present theory, which employs a specular source term.

IV. Maxwellian Solution

A. Density Transform

A convenient property of the three-dimensional Maxwellian distribution

$$n_0 f_0(u, v, w) = \frac{n_0}{(2\pi a_0^2)^{3/2}} \exp\left[-\frac{(u^2 + v^2 + w^2)}{2a_0^2} \right] \tag{27}$$

is that its one-dimensional counterparts $g_0(u)$ and $g_0^*(u)$ [defined with Eqs. (10) and (12)] are equal. Consequently, we see that in the special case of the Maxwellian $\mathscr{T}^* = \mathscr{T}$, $\mathscr{S}^* = \mathscr{S}$, $\varepsilon^* = \varepsilon$ and $(\partial/\partial a_0^2)(\mathscr{T}^*) = (\partial/\partial a_0^2)(\mathscr{T})$. Thus for the Maxwellian the Eq. (13) transform simplifies slightly to become

$$n_1 = i2n_0 v_p \frac{\text{NUM}(k)}{\text{DEN}(k)} \tag{28}$$

$$\text{NUM}(k) = -\omega \frac{\partial \mathscr{T}}{\partial a_0^2} + \mathscr{S}k^2(3 - 2\mathscr{T}) \tag{29}$$

$$\mathrm{DEN}(k) = (1 - \varepsilon)k^2(3 - 2\mathscr{T}) - (\omega^2 - k^2a_0^2)\frac{\partial\mathscr{T}}{\partial a_0^2}. \tag{30}$$

The Maxwellian $\mathscr{T}$ transform integral is

$$\mathscr{T} = -\frac{iv}{k}\left\{\frac{1}{(2\pi a_0^2)^{1/2}}\int_{-\infty}^{+\infty}\frac{\exp(-u^2/2a_0^2)}{(u - (\omega + iv)/k)}\,du\right\}. \tag{31}$$

The semicircular contour used to evaluate Eq. (17) no longer serves since the integrand of Eq. (31) diverges for large imaginary u. But, $\mathscr{T}$ can be cast in the form

$$\mathscr{T} = \frac{-P}{\eta}\mathscr{Z}(\rho), \qquad \mathscr{Z}(\rho) = \frac{i}{(2\pi)^{1/2}}\int_{-\infty}^{+\infty}\frac{\exp(-t^2)\,dt}{t - \rho} \tag{32}$$

with

$$P = iv/\omega, \qquad \eta = ika_0/\omega, \qquad \rho = (\omega + iv)/(2^{1/2}a_0k). \tag{33}$$

As in the Cauchy case the integrals $\mathscr{T}$ and $\mathscr{Z}$ are initially defined for real k only. For $k > 0$ the pole at ρ is in the upper half t plane, and $\mathscr{Z}$ takes on the values of its upper branch $\mathscr{Z}_+$. For $k < 0$, ρ is in the lower half plane and $\mathscr{Z} = \mathscr{Z}_-$. For purposes of inversion ρ must take on arbitrary complex values so that we need the analytic continuations of the two integrals $\mathscr{Z}_\pm$. For this "continuation" $\mathscr{Z}_+$ must always include the residue due to the pole at ρ, even when ρ (for some k) passes into the lower half t plane. Similarly, k must continue to exclude this residue, if ρ moves into the upper half plane. Thus for arbitrary k the difference between the two $\mathscr{Z}$ branches must be simply $2\pi i$ times the residue at $t = \rho$, or

$$\mathscr{Z}_+(\rho) - \mathscr{Z}_-(\rho) = -(2\pi)^{1/2}\exp(-\rho^2) = K(\rho), \tag{34}$$

as pointed out with regard to a similar function by Landau (1946).

Quite fortunately, the positive branch $\mathscr{Z}_+$ satisfies the relation $\mathscr{Z}_+(\rho) = iZ(\rho)/2^{1/2}$, where $Z(\rho)$ is the "plasma dispersion function," which has been discussed and tabulated by Fried and Conte (1961). Noting from Eq. (33) that $\rho = iR/(2^{1/2}\eta)$ with $R = 1 + P$ and using the Fried and Conte results, we obtain the Taylor series and asymptotic representations

$$\mathscr{Z}_+(\eta) = \frac{K(\rho)}{2} + \frac{\pi^{1/2}}{2}\frac{R}{\eta}\sum_{n=0}^{\infty}\frac{(R^2/2\eta^2)^n}{(n + \frac{1}{2})!} \tag{35}$$

$$\mathscr{Z}_+(\eta) \sim \sigma_1\frac{K(\rho)}{2} - \frac{\eta}{R}\left(1 - \frac{\eta^2}{R^2} + \frac{3\eta^4}{R^4} - \frac{3\cdot 5\eta^6}{R^6} + \cdots\right)$$

$$\sigma_1 = \begin{cases} 0, & > 0 \\ 1, & \mathrm{Im}(\rho) = 0 \\ 2, & < 0. \end{cases} \tag{36}$$

The function $\mathscr{L}_-(\eta)$ is obtained from $\mathscr{L}_+(\eta)$ with the aid of Eq. (34).

We may conclude that the two $\mathscr{T}$ branches are $\mathscr{T}_\pm = -(P/\eta)\mathscr{L}_\pm(\eta)$. Similarly, the remaining transform functions may be expressed in terms of $\mathscr{L}_\pm(\eta)$. When this is done the exact Maxwellian density transforms of Eqs. (28) to (30) take on the form

$$n_1 = \frac{i2\eta_0 v_p}{\omega} \frac{N_\pm(\eta)}{D_\pm(\eta)} \tag{37}$$

$$N_\pm(\eta) = \frac{R^7}{2\eta^5} \left[(PR\eta + 6\eta^3) + (PR^2 + (11R - 5)\eta^2)\mathscr{L}_\pm(\eta) \right.$$

$$\left. + 4PR\eta\mathscr{L}_\pm^2(\eta) \right] \tag{38}$$

$$D_\pm(\eta) = \frac{R^7}{2\eta^5} \left[(6\eta^5 + P(R - 6)\eta^3 + PR\eta) \right.$$

$$+ P(11\eta^4 + (R^2 - 10R - 5)\eta^2 + R^2)\mathscr{L}_\pm(\eta)$$

$$\left. + P^2(4\eta^3 - 4R\eta)\mathscr{L}_\pm^2(\eta) \right] \tag{39}$$

$$N_\pm(\eta) \sim 3R^4 + R^2(5R - 14)\eta^2 + \cdots \tag{40}$$

$$D_\pm(\eta) \sim 3R^4 + PR^2(5R + 14)\eta^2 + P(5R^2 - 17R - 87)\eta^4 + \cdots, \tag{41}$$

where the $+$ (or $-$) expressions must be used when $\mathrm{Re}(k) > 0$ (or <0).

The asymptotic $N_\pm$ and $D_\pm$ are obtained from the exact expressions with the aid of Eq. (34) and the $\mathscr{L}_+$ function expansion of Eq. (36). They are accurate asymptotic representations if (a) $|\eta/R| \ll 1$, which occurs for moderate $\eta = ia_0 k/\omega$ and large (continuum) values of $R\, (= 1 + iv/\omega)$ and (b) k is sufficiently close to the real axis to keep ρ in the upper (or lower) half plane for $\mathrm{Re}(k) > 0$ (or <0). This second requirement assures that there is no necessity for terms containing $K(\rho)$ in Eq. (44) or (45).

B. Maxwellian Transform Inversion

Equation (37) has the inversion

$$n_1(x) = \frac{in_0 v_p}{\pi\omega} \left\{ \int_{k=-\infty}^{0} \frac{N_-(\eta)}{D_-(\eta)} e^{ikx}\, dk + \int_{k=0}^{\infty} \frac{N_+(\eta)}{D_+(\eta)} e^{ikx}\, dk \right\}. \tag{42}$$

As in the Cauchy case we may calculate Eq. (42) over the contours of Fig. 2. Again the two integrals in Eq. (42) reduce to $2\pi i$ times the residues at the zeros of D_- in the second k quadrant, and at the zeros of D_+ in the first quadrant plus a net branch cut contribution.

The denominators $D_\pm$ in the inversion integral are, however, transcendental for the Maxwellian distribution. Each branch possesses an infinite number of zeros. Now on physical grounds we may conclude that there are no second quadrant D_- zeros (there were none in the Cauchy solution), since these would imply the existence of exponential disturbances originating at $x = \pm\infty$ where there are no gas perturbing sources. Hence we consider just the D_+ zeros. To gain an approximate description of the Maxwellian sound propagation we have used the Cornell 1604 computer to trace out the exact trajectories of the two first quadrant D_+ zeros, which are least-damped in the continuum regime ($q \sim 10^3$). Initial estimates for the zero loci when $q \geqslant 50$ were obtained by solving for the two first quadrant zeros of the asymptotic quartic approximation to D_+, Eq. (41). The asymptotic roots at $q = 50$ were then used as starting values in an iterative scheme which followed the trajectories, as defined by the exact dispersion relation, while q was decreased in small steps to $q = 10^{-2}$.

As in the Cauchy problem these two first quadrant zeros are found to correspond to the Navier-Stokes sound, (1), and diffusion, (3), modes. The attenuation rates and wave numbers of these Maxwellian zeros have been plotted in Figs. 3 and 4 for comparison with previous results. We chose the Maxwellian collision parameter v such that $q = (6/7)r$, which brings the Maxwellian sound α value into agreement with the near continuum measurements. The Maxwellian sound, (1), curves are seen to lie closer to the cross hatched data display in these figures than either the Navier-Stokes or the Cauchy predictions. This agreement is meaningful, however, only in the range $r > 1.0$ where the sound mode is expected to dominate.

It should be pointed out that in the paper defining the Model equation by Bhatnagar et al. (1954) an error in the asymptotic, adiabatic sound dispersion relation placed the diffusion zero in the second quadrant. As a result the diffusion mode was not identified by those authors. The same error required them to predict a q/r value that is three times too large.

If we now assume that none of the remaining, neglected zeros are significant, Eq. (42) reduces to

$$n_1(x) \doteq \frac{n_0 v_p}{c_0} \sum_l A(\eta_l) e^{ik_l x} + F(x) \tag{43}$$

$$A(\eta_i) = \frac{i2(5/3)^{1/2} N_+(\eta_i)}{\dfrac{\partial}{\partial \eta}(D_+(\eta))_{\eta=\eta_i}} \tag{44}$$

$$A(\eta_i) \sim \frac{i2(5/3)^{1/2}(3R^4 + R^2(5R - 14)\eta_i^2)}{P(5R^2 - 17R - 87)\prod_{i=j}(\eta_i - \eta_j)} \tag{45}$$

$$F(x) = \frac{in_0 v_p}{\pi \omega} \int_{k=0}^{i\infty} \left(\frac{N_+(\eta)}{D_+(\eta)} - \frac{N_-(\eta)}{D_-(\eta)} \right) e^{ikx} \, dk. \tag{46}$$

The index l in Eq. (43) runs over the least-damped first quadrant zeros of D_+. We have dotted the equals sign in this equation since the need for more exponential modes is uncertain.

The exponential excitations, $A(\eta_i)$, fall out of the residue computation at the first order poles of the inversion integral Eq. (42). The asymptotic excitation expression, Eq. (45) is valid for large r when the approximate transform expressions Eqs. (40) and (41) apply. With the aid of the Cornell 1604 computer we have plotted the asymptotic and the exact Maxwellian excitation moduli, $|A(\eta_i)|$, in Fig. 9. These excitations agree qualitatively with the Cauchy predictions of Fig. 6 throughout the full r range.

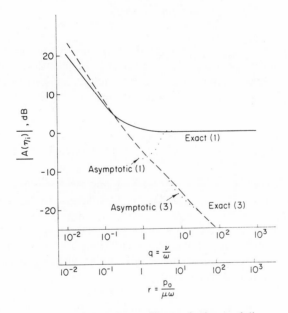

FIG. 9. Maxwellian excitation moduli.

The free streaming contribution $F(x)$ is the sum of the two branch cut integrals along the imaginary axis. An exact evaluation of Eq. (46) must be accomplished numerically, but an approximate estimate of $F(x)$, valid for large x may be determined using the saddle point method. To obtain this estimate we first take the difference of the two $N(\eta)$ branches defined in Eq. (38) and eliminate the function $\mathscr{L}_+(\eta)$ in terms of $\mathscr{L}_-(\eta)$ by means of Eq. (34). The same operations are performed on the $D(\eta)$ branches and we obtain

$$N_+(\eta) - N_-(\eta) = B_1 K(\rho) + B_2 K^2(\rho)$$

$$B_1 = \frac{R^7}{2\eta^5} \{PR^2 + (11R - 5)\eta^2 + 8PR\eta\mathscr{L}_-(\eta)\}$$

$$B_2 = \frac{R^7}{2\eta^5} \{4PR\eta\} \tag{47}$$

$$D_+(\eta) - D_-(\eta) = c_1 K(\rho) + c_2 K^2(\rho)$$

$$C_1 = \frac{R^7}{2\eta^5} \{P(11\eta^4 + (R^2 - 10R - 5)\eta^2 + R^2)$$

$$+ 8P^2\eta(\eta^2 - R)\mathscr{L}_-(\eta)\}$$

$$C_2 = \frac{R^7}{2\eta^5} \{4P^2\eta(\eta^2 - R)\}. \tag{48}$$

We now find a common denominator for the two fractions in the integrand of Eq. (46) and use Eqs. (47) and (48) to eliminate the plus functions in the new numerator in terms of the corresponding minus functions. Employing the substitutions $k = is$ and $v_1 = v - i\omega$ so that by Eq. (33) $\rho = v_1/(2^{1/2}a_0 s)$, we have

$$F(x) = \frac{n_0 v_p}{\omega} \left(\frac{2}{\pi}\right)^{1/2} \int_{s=0}^{\infty} \left(\frac{B_1 D_- - C_1 N_-}{D_+ D_-}\right) \exp\left(\frac{-v_1^2}{2a_0^2 s^2} - sx\right) ds$$

$$+ \frac{-2n_0 v_p}{\omega} \int_{s=0}^{\infty} \left(\frac{B_2 D_- - C_2 N_-}{D_+ D_-}\right) \exp\left(\frac{-v_1^2}{a_0^2 s^2} - sx\right) ds. \tag{49}$$

The exponential factor in the first integral has three saddle points at $s = (v_1^2/(a_0^2 x))^{1/3}$, corresponding to the three cube root branches. Throughout the range $\infty \geqslant r = (7/6)(v/\omega) \geqslant 0$ the saddle point yielding the smallest modulus for the exponential factor is

$$s_1 = \left|\frac{v_1^2}{a_0^2 x}\right|^{1/3} e^{i\varphi}, \qquad \varphi = -\frac{2}{3}\arctan\left(\frac{\omega}{v}\right). \tag{50}$$

We now deform the path of integration for the first integral so that it passes out along the ray from the origin to s_1, then through s_1 on the path of steepest descent, and finally along an arc to $s = +\infty$. Along this path the exponential factor dominates the integrand, since the bracketed term is slowly varying. Hence we may simply evaluate the bracket at s_1 and move it outside the integral sign. The remaining integral over the exponential factor is readily approximated with the standard Debye formula.

We perform a similar analysis for the second integral which has its saddle point at $s_2 = 2^{1/3}s_1$. Finally, expanding both bracket terms for large x (or small s_1) with the aid of the asymptotic $\mathscr{L}_\pm$ expansions and retaining only the leading term we obtain

$$F(x) \sim \frac{n_0 v_p}{c_0}\left(\frac{2 \cdot 5^{1/2}}{27}\right)R^2(R+2)^2\tau^{1/3}\exp\{-\tfrac{3}{2}\tau^{2/3}e^{i\varphi}\}e^{i\varphi/2} \tag{51}$$

where $\tau = 2\pi(5/3)^{1/2}|R|d$, $R = 1 + i(6/7)r$ and $d = x/\lambda_0$, while λ_0 is the continuum sound wave length. Equation (50) gives φ. We note that the leading term of the second integral is of exponentially lower order than the leading term of the first; hence the second integral makes no contribution to Eq. (51).

The modulus of the leading term in $F(x)$, Eq. (51), is plotted versus d in Fig. 10. As compared to the earlier Cauchy free streaming the Maxwellian streaming is stronger for small r and d, and considerably weaker for large r and d. We point out that Eq. (51) takes on the form predicted by Cook *et al.* (1953) for the free molecular limit ($r = 0$, $R = 1$).

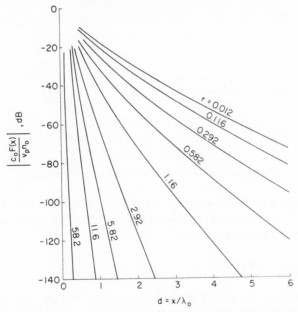

FIG. 10. Asymptotic Maxwellian free streaming mode modulus.

In Fig. 11 we plot the modulus of the overall approximate Maxwellian disturbance modulus, $|n_1(x)c_0/(n_0 v_p)|$, of Eq. (43) versus d. This includes only the first quadrant least-damped exponential modes examined in Figs. 3, 4, and 9, plus the leading term of the free streaming disturbance. We observe that beyond $d = 1.0$ a good estimate to $F(x)$ should be obtained from just the leading term. However, the over-all curves of Fig. 11 may still be in error due to our choice of exponential modes included. From Figs. 3 and 4 we know that the Maxwellian solution will be in good agreement with experiment while mode (1) dominates (which is for $r > 1.0$ by Fig. 9). The published data of Meyer and Sessler (1953) are plotted on Fig. 11 to show that the $0.05 \leqslant r \leqslant 1.0$

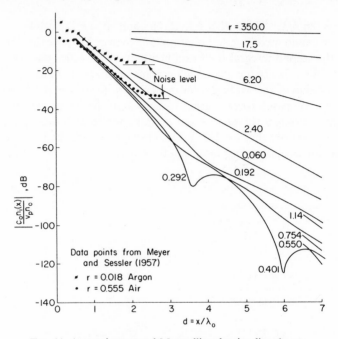

FIG. 11. Approximate total Maxwellian density disturbance.

agreement is also acceptable, although the data rise above our predictions for larger values. The exponential to free streaming transition peaks still occur, but again they are found at very low sound levels.

C. Free Molecular Solution

Final insight into the nature of the source terms and the free molecular solution may be gained by returning to the original kinetic transform equation, Eq. (8). Setting v to zero it may be solved directly to yield

$$f_1 = i2n_0v_p \frac{\partial f_0/\partial u}{k - \omega/u}, \qquad \omega = \omega_1 + i\gamma, \quad \gamma > 0. \tag{52}$$

The boundary oscillation frequency will be assumed to be slightly complex, corresponding to oscillations of slowly growing amplitude. The inverse transform of Eq. (52) is

$$
f_1(u, x) = \begin{cases} -2n_0 v_p \dfrac{\partial f_0}{\partial u} e^{i(\omega/u)x}, & x, u > 0 \\[2mm] 0, & x > 0, \quad u < 0, \end{cases} \tag{53}
$$

since only when $u > 0$ does the pole at ω/u reside in the upper half k plane, and contribute a residue.

As a check we multiply Eq. (53) by u and integrate over all velocities (i.e., take the first moment). Setting x to zero we have $n_0 u_1(x = 0^+) = n_0 v_p$, as required. Taking the zeroeth moment we get

$$
n_1(x) = -2n_0 v_p \int_{u=0}^{\infty} \frac{\partial f_0}{\partial u} e^{i(\omega/u)x} \, du, \quad x > 0. \tag{54}
$$

Let f_0 be Maxwellian. Then Eq. (54) is the limiting form of the formally complete density solution of Eq. (42). The integral in Eq. (54) has been examined by Abramowitz (1953). His analysis indicates that the leading asymptotic dependence of Eq. (54) at large x is given by Eq. (51) with $r = 0$ ($R = 1$), as expected.

ACKNOWLEDGMENTS

The author wishes to acknowledge the assistance and patient guidance given him in this work by his major advisor, Professor Donald L. Turcotte, at Cornell University. He is also most grateful to Miss Surena Morrisey and Miss Alice Anthony for their aid in preparing the manuscript.

REFERENCES

Abramowitz, M. (1953). *J. Math. and Phys.* **32**, 188.

Bhatnagar, P. L., Gross, E. P., and Krook, M. (1954). *Phys. Rev.* **94**, 511.

Cook, R. K., Greenspan, M., and Thompson, Jr., M. D. (1953). *J. Acoust. Soc. Am.* **25**, 192.

Erdelyi, A. (1954). "Tables of Integral Transforms," Vol. I, p. 8 (The Bateman Manuscript Project). McGraw-Hill, New York.

Fried, B. D., and Conte, S. D. (1961). "The Plasma Dispersion Function." Academic Press, New York.

Greenspan, M. (1956). *J. Acoust. Soc. Am.* **28**, 644.

Heckl, M. A., and Maidanik, G. (1962). "Sound Propagation in Rarefied Gases." Bolt, Birenak and Newman Rept. No. 940. ONR contract Nonr 3697 (00).

Landau, L. (1946), *J. Phys. (USSR)* **10**, 25.

Meyer, E. and Sessler, G. (1957). *Z. Physik.* **149**, 15.

Platzman, P. M., and Buchsbaum, S. J. (1962). *Phys. Rev.* **128**, 1004.

Sherman, F. S., and Talbot, L. (1960). *In* "Rarefied Gas Dynamics" (F. M. Devienne, ed.), pp. 161–191. Pergamon, New York.

Sirovich, L., and Thurber, J. K. (1963). *In* "Rarefied Gas Dynamics" (J. A. Laurmann, ed.), Vol. I, pp. 159–180. Academic Press, New York.

Wang Chang, C. S., and Uhlenbeck, G. E. (1952). "On the Propagation of Sound in Monatomic Gases." Eng. Res. Inst. Univ. Mich. ONR contract N6 onr-23222.

Propagation of an Initial Density Discontinuity[1]

GEORGE BIENKOWSKI[2]
Firestone Flight Sciences Laboratory, California Institute of Technology,
Pasadena, California

The propagation of an initial one-dimensional density discontinuity is studied. The solution for times much shorter than the mean free time between collisions (i.e., collisionless), and the solution for times much longer than the mean free time (i.e., Euler) are functions of the same similarity variable x/t. They differ only in the details of the profiles.

A method for evaluating the first effect of collisions is developed as an expansion in time with coefficients as functions of the similarity variable. The solutions are obtained in detail for both the Krook collision model and the *exact* collision integral for inverse fifth-power repulsion.

The Krook model is found to agree qualitatively with the "exact" solution except in the region of eventual shock formation for high initial density ratios. In that region the Krook model tends to overestimate the effect of collisions. The first effect of collisions in general alters the free molecular solution in the proper direction toward the Navier-Stokes result. The "first collision" solution appears to be valid up to times of the order of a mean free time between collisions on the high pressure side.

In order to delineate the region of transition from this "first collision" solution to the Navier-Stokes regime, the linearized Navier-Stokes equations are solved by Laplace transforms. The results indicate that at least in the linearized case the Navier-Stokes equations become valid for times in excess of ten mean free times between collisions. The "wave" and "contact surface" regions, however, do not become separated until about 50 mean free times, and interaction between them does not cease until some time in excess of 100 mean free times. The Euler solution is not approached until about 1000 mean free times have elapsed.

A crude approximation of the non-linear case where the "shock" and contact surface have separated is obtained on the assumption of no interaction

[1] This research was supported by the Advanced Research Projects Agency under Contract No. DA-31-ARO(D)-33. Part of the work was done while the author was a National Science Foundation Fellow.
[2] *Present address:* Gas Dynamics Laboratory, Princeton University, Princeton, New Jersey.

between the two. This solution appears valid for times in excess of 100 mean free times on the high pressure side, while the Euler solution becomes reasonable only after 1000 mean free times.

One concludes that a calculation of the initial effect of collisions combined with a solution of the Navier-Stokes equations should adequately describe the propagation of an initial density discontinuity, and that the major part of the formation of the distinct shock, contact surface, and expansion wave regions takes place within the Navier-Stokes regime.

I. Introduction

In problems of steady external flow around bodies, the influence of interparticle collisions is nonuniform, being dominant far from the body and negligible near the body, while at least one boundary condition has to be applied in each region. To study the effect of collisions, it is therefore more desirable to look at an initial value problem, where the effect of collisions is proportional to the elapsed time expressed in units of the mean free time between collisions. Furthermore, to eliminate the uncertainties of gas-solid interface interactions a problem with no solid boundaries can be chosen. One such problem that can yield useful information as to the effects of collision is the sudden release of a gas discontinuity. Conceptually one can imagine two semi-infinite regions of gas of different thermodynamic states (both in equilibrium) separated by a diaphragm until it is broken at time $t = 0$. This is just the idealized shock-tube problem. Collisions alter the initial collisionless profile into one containing shock and contact layers which are thin compared to the separation between them. The initial formation of these "discontinuities" is of great fluid dynamic interest.

This particular problem is chosen for the additional reason that both limiting solutions are similarity solutions of the same variable. If a diaphragm is removed at time $t = 0$, the collisionless and the Euler solutions are both functions of x/t alone. This fact can be of great help in analyzing the effect of collisions. Since the two solutions satisfy the same boundary conditions at plus and minus infinity, they can only vary as to their detailed form in between. The transition solution can be considered in a plane determined by the coordinates x/t and t, where the coordinate t is now a direct measure of the effect of collisions.

The solution of any initial value problem is in principle possible because of the characteristic form of the Boltzmann equation. In practice, however, the calculation of the collision integral along the characteristic requires knowing the value of the distribution function along all the other characteristics, and integration over several variables. In general these integrations cannot be accomplished even with high speed computers. Secondly, certain convergence difficulties, even with approximate collision models, are expected to limit this approach to times of the order of a few mean free times, as shown by Willis (1960)[3]. Alternative approaches such as moment methods (Lees, 1959; Krook, 1959), discrete velocity methods (Broadwell, 1963; Hamel and Wachman, 1964), or Monte Carlo methods (Haviland and Lavin, 1962) might also be used. The difficulties associated with these methods or the models necessary to make them tractable make it more desirable to study first the initial effect of collisions and the Navier-Stokes regime with a minimum of *ad hoc* assumptions. The region in between, though difficult to bridge, is not expected in this problem to contain any new physical phenomena.

The region of the initial effect of collisions is important because the choice of collision model is most likely to have the greatest consequences here. Under special initial conditions the exact collision integral required to determine the initial effect of collisions can be sufficiently simplified to make numerical calculation feasible. Thus, a real comparison is possible between this "exact" calculation and one based on the Krook model (Bhatnagar *et al.*, 1954).

For the case of a very small initial density discontinuity the entire problem can be linearized. The long time solution can be obtained on the basis of the linearized Navier-Stokes equations without regard to the separation between the shock and contact surface. The remaining gap between this solution and the "first collision" solution is narrowed and can be understood to be the "transition" regime, and not simply inaccuracies in the method of solution of the Navier-Stokes equations.

The general theory of the response of gases to the release of an initial density discontinuity is formulated in Section II, A. The calculation of the first effect of collisions based on both the Krook and the exact collision term (for Maxwellian molecules) is discussed in the rest of Section II. The long time collision dominated solution based on the linearized Navier-Stokes equations is discussed in Section III. Some conclusions are drawn in Section IV.

II. Short-Time Solution

A. Formulation of the Problem

1. Equation and Initial Conditions. A uniform gas in the half space $x > 0$ has the density ρ_+ and temperature T_+. The half space $x < 0$ is filled with the same gas but at density ρ_- and temperature T_-. The imaginary

[3] Chu (1964) has been able to obtain a convergent numerical solution for the problem up to 30 mean free times on the low pressure side under the assumption of the Krook model and a one-dimensional ($\gamma = 3$) gas.

diaphragm separating the two regions is withdrawn at time $t = 0$. The subsequent motion is governed by the following kinetic equation:

$$\frac{\partial f}{\partial t}(v_x, v_y, v_z, x, t) + v_x \frac{\partial f}{\partial x}(v_x, v_y, v_z, x, t) = J(v_x, v_y, v_z, x, t), \quad (2.1)$$

where f is the distribution function and J is a term representing the net gain per unit time of particles in the velocity space around v_x, v_y, v_z, as a result of collisions.

In general, J is a complicated integral function of f regardless of whether the Boltzmann collision integral or some model term is used. Thus integration along the single characteristic or particle path yields a complicated nonlinear integral equation. Presently only limiting solutions for times very short and very long with respect to the mean "free" time are available. The short-time solution is obtained by dropping the collision term and solving the differential equation for f. The long-time solution is obtained by equating the collision term locally to zero everywhere, yielding a Maxwellian distribution function, with parameters determined by defining the mean quantities ρ, u, and T.

2. Euler Limit. This long time solution is the well known idealized shock tube solution and is discussed, for example by Glass (1958) and Patterson (1948). The solution is obtained by matching the velocity and pressure behind a shock propagating into the low pressure region to the velocity and pressure obtained behind the expansion fan propagating into the high pressure region. The density and temperature are discontinuous at the contact front, which moves with the flow velocity. The solution is a function of a single variable x/t, because there can be no separate length or time scale in the problem.

3. Collisionless Limit. The short time (collisionless) solution is not as well known (first studied by Keller, 1948), but is very easy to obtain. For an initial value problem such as we are considering, the collisionless Boltzmann equation without body forces has the simple solution

$$f(v_x, v_y, v_z, x, t) = f(v_x, v_y, v_z, x - v_x t, 0). \quad (2.2)$$

The shift in coordinate $(x - v_x t)$ is an expression of the fact that without collisions or body forces particle paths are straight lines. The relation between f at t and f at zero time expresses the fact that the distribution density is unaltered along particle paths.

If the gas on either side of the diaphragm is initially at rest and at equilibrium, it seems reasonable to specify the initial distribution function as a different Maxwellian for $x > 0$ and $x < 0$. For these initial conditions integration to obtain the moments can be done immediately. A lack of a characteristic time or length scale again insures that the solutions are functions of the variable x/t alone. Some of the lower physically significant moments are:

$$\rho_0\left(\frac{x}{t}\right) = \frac{\rho_-}{2}\left[1 - \text{erf}\left(\frac{x}{t\sqrt{2RT_-}}\right)\right] + \frac{\rho_+}{2}\left[1 + \text{erf}\left(\frac{x}{t\sqrt{2RT_+}}\right)\right], \quad (2.3)$$

$$\rho_0 v_0\left(\frac{x}{t}\right) = \frac{\rho_-\sqrt{2RT_-}}{2\sqrt{\pi}}\exp\left(-\frac{x^2}{2RT_-t^2}\right) - \frac{\rho_+\sqrt{2RT_+}}{2\sqrt{\pi}}\exp\left(-\frac{x^2}{2RT_+t^2}\right), \quad (2.4)$$

where R is k/m, the gas constant, where k is the Boltzmann constant, and m the molecular mass.

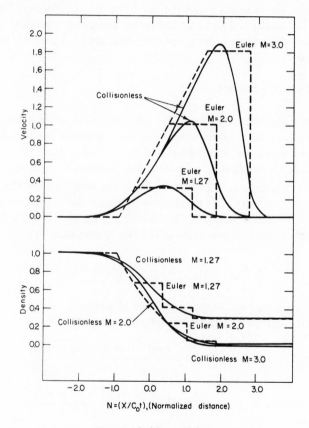

FIG. 1. Limiting solutions.

4. Comparison of Limiting Solutions. Figure 1 is a comparison of the Euler and collisionless solutions for the case of uniform initial temperature. The

velocity and density profiles are shown for three initial density ratios $\rho_+/\rho_- =$ 0.298, 0.0201, 0.375 $\times$ 10^{-3}, which correspond to shock Mach numbers in the Euler limit of $M_s = 1.27$, 2.00 and 3.00, respectively. The similarity between the Euler and collisionless solutions is remarkable. The "collisionless" velocity profile is much steeper on the low density side than on the high density side, although not in as pronounced a way as the Euler solution. The "collisionless" density profile looks in many respects like the best mean smooth curve through the discontinuous Euler profile. These similarities suggest that the broad aspects of the solution for this initial value problem are determined by the kinematics rather than the details of the interaction or noninteraction between particles. Conservation of mass and momentum guarantee that the integrals under the curves have to be identical for the two solutions. The additional fact that the mean molecular speed and the speed of sound are of the same order guarantees that the (x/t) scale for both solutions is similar.

B. Initial Effect of Collisions

1. Coordinate Transformation. The fact that both asymptotic solutions (for $t \to 0$ and $t \to \infty$) are functions of (x/t) only suggests the transformation to a new coordinate system proportional to x/t, and t, where now t will be a direct measure of the effect of collisions. We define new variables $N = x/c_0 t$ and $\tau = t/\tau_{f_0}$ where c_0 is $\sqrt{2RT_-}$ and τ_{f_0} is the reciprocal of the collision frequency at $x \to -\infty$. By nondimensionalizing the other variables as $\bar{f} = (m)c_0{}^3/\rho_- \cdot f$ and $\bar{J} = mc_0{}^3\tau_{f_0}/\rho_- \cdot J$ and $\bar{v}_x, \bar{v}_y, \bar{v}_z = v_x/c_0, v_y/c_0, v_z/c_0$, respectively, we obtain a new form of the Boltzmann equation:

$$\tau \frac{\partial f}{\partial \tau}(\mathbf{v}, N, \tau) + (v_x - N)\frac{\partial f}{\partial N}(\mathbf{v}, N, \tau) = \tau J(\mathbf{v}, N, \tau) \qquad (2.5)$$

where the bars have been dropped for ease of notation.

The initial conditions in the new variables can be stated as

$$f(v_x, v_y, v_z, N \to -\infty, 0) = \frac{\exp(-(v_x{}^2 + v_y{}^2 + v_z{}^2))}{(\pi)^{3/2}} \qquad (2.6)$$

$$f(v_x, v_y, v_z, N \to \infty, 0) = \frac{\rho_r \exp(-(v_x{}^2 + v_y{}^2 + v_z{}^2)/T_r)}{(\pi T_r)^{3/2}} \qquad (2.7)$$

where $\rho_r = \rho_+/\rho_-$ and $T_r = T_+/T_-$.

2. Formal Solution. If we look for solutions valid near $\tau = 0$, we find we can obtain a solution for f as a power series in τ with coefficients as functions

of N. The solution then becomes

$$f(v_x, v_y, v_z, N, \tau) = \sum_{n=0}^{\infty} f_n(v_x, v_y, v_z, N)\tau^n \qquad (2.8)$$

and

$$J(v_x, v_y, v_z, N, \tau) = \sum_{n=0}^{\infty} J_n(v_x, v_y, v_z, N)\tau^n \qquad (2.9)$$

where

$$f_n(v_x, v_y, v_z, N) = (v_x - N)^n \int_{\pm\infty}^{N} \frac{J_{n-1}(v_x, v_y, v_z, N^1)\, dN^1}{(v_x - N^1)^{n+1}},$$

$$n \geqslant 1 \quad \text{for} \quad (N - v_x) \gtrless 0, \qquad (2.10)$$

and

$$f_0(v_x, v_y, v_z, N) = f(v_x, v_y, v_z, N \to \mp\infty, 0) \quad \text{for} \quad v_x \gtrless N. \quad (2.11)$$

3. First Order Term. Setting aside the questions of validity we look at the solution for $f_1(v_x, v_y, v_z, N)$ as the evaluation of the slope $(\partial f/\partial \tau)_{\tau \to 0}$. This coefficient represents the initial effect of collisions. Since one purpose of this paper is to study the validity of the " Krook's " collision model, the " nearly collision free " region is of the greatest importance, because the limitations of the model are likely to be most stringent there. This first order perturbation away from the collisionless solution coupled with some approximate Navier-Stokes solution for large times should also go a long way towards determining the transition from the collisionless to the collision-dominated regime in this initial value problem.

We are interested mainly in the moments of f_1 and not f_1 itself. If we confine ourselves to moments no higher than the heat flux, we notice that in this one-dimensional problem integrations over the transverse velocities v_y and v_z can be carried out in advance. Since only 1 and $(v_y^2 + v_z^2)^2$ enter into the integrations over v_y and v_z we can define new functions

$$FN_n = \int\!\!\!\int_{-\infty}^{\infty} f_n \, dv_y \, dv_z, \qquad (2.12)$$

and

$$FT_n = \int\!\!\!\int_{-\infty}^{\infty} f_n(v_y^2 + v_z^2) \, dv_y \, dv_z, \qquad (2.13)$$

as well as JN and JT similarly defined.

Now FN_1 is related to JN_0, while FT_1 is related to JT_0 only. The perturbation moments can in turn be defined in terms of single integrals of FN_1 and FT_1 over v_x. Suppose the physically meaningful variables are considered also as expansions in τ analogous to the expansion of the distribution function:

$$\text{density:} \quad \rho = \rho_0(N) + \rho_1(N)\tau + \cdots$$
$$\text{velocity:} \quad v = v_0(N) + v_1(N)\tau \cdots \tag{2.14}$$
$$\text{etc.}$$

where zeroth order quantities are the collisionless solutions determined by Eqs. (2.3) and (2.4) and nondimensionalized. The expressions for the first order density and velocity are

$$\rho_1(N) = MN_1{}^0, \tag{2.15}$$
$$v_1(N) = (MN_1{}^1 - \rho_1 v_0)/\rho_0,$$

where

$$MN_1{}^n = \int_{-\infty}^{\infty} v_x{}^n FN_1 \, dv_x, \tag{2.16}$$

with a similar definition of $MT_1{}^n$ needed in the higher moments.

It can be verified easily that these moments for positive values of n are finite and well behaved as long as f_1 has only integrable singularities. The behavior of f_1 near $v_x = N$ (where singularities can exist) is analyzed in detail by Bienkowski (1964). It is shown that for the Krook model f_1 has a logarithmically infinite slope while for the "exact Maxwellian molecule collision term," f_1 has a square root singularity. The moments for both cases are therefore finite.

C. Solution with the Krook Collision Term

1. The Krook Collision Model. In order to avoid the complexities of the collision integral it is often replaced by a model term first suggested by Bhatnagar *et al.* (1954). This model can best be considered as an *ad hoc* assumption where certain assumed free parameters in the collision term are related to macroscopic properties by requiring the conservation of mass, momentum and energy as well as the best fit of the approach to equilibrium results. The fact that only one free constant appears means that only a single collision "time" (relaxation constant) can be defined. This constant can be chosen to match correctly one of the transport properties such as viscosity, or conductivity but not both. The model inherently fixes the value of the Prandtl number in the continuum limit.

2. First Order Perturbation Solution. The "first collision" solution, f_1, can be evaluated in terms of the integral over functions involving only the density, ρ_0, velocity, v_0, and temperature T_0, based on the collisionless solution. The

moments can be calculated directly from Eqs. (2.15) and (2.16) with JN_0 expressed as follows:

$$JN_0 = c\rho_0(N)\left[\frac{\rho_0(N)}{(\pi T_0(N))^{1/2}}\exp\left(-\frac{(v_x - v_0(N))^2}{T_0(N)}\right) - FN_0(v_x, N)\right], \quad (2.17)$$

and a similar expression for JT_0. The collision frequency has to be chosen proportional to ρ_0 to facilitate later comparison to the results obtained by the use of the exact collision integral for Maxwellian particles. The value of the constant is chosen as $c = \pi/4$ in order to make the fourth moment equation (for the stress) take the correct form for Maxwellian molecules where $v = \pi/4\,\mu/p$ is taken as a definition of collision frequency, with μ the viscosity. This choice, however, forces the coefficient of the collision term in the heat flux moment equation to be incorrect by the factor $3/2$.

D. Solution with "Exact" Collision Term

1. Exact Collision Integral. In the "exact" form of the Boltzmann equation the collision term has the general form

$$J(\mathbf{v}, \mathbf{r}, t) = \iiint \{f(\mathbf{v}^1, \mathbf{r}, t)f(\mathbf{v}_1{}^1, \mathbf{r}, t) - f(\mathbf{v}, \mathbf{r}, t)f(\mathbf{v}_1, \mathbf{r}, t)\}$$
$$\cdot |\mathbf{v} - \mathbf{v}_1| b\, db\, d\varepsilon\, d^3\mathbf{v}_1 \qquad (2.18)$$

where b and ε are the parameters of collision, $\mathbf{v}, \mathbf{v}_1$ are the velocities of the particles before collision and $\mathbf{v}^1, \mathbf{v}_1{}^1$, are the velocities after collision. To calculate J_0 in the present expansion appears straightforward since f_0 is known. However, this calculation is not in general feasible, since J_0 itself is a fivefold integral, while the perturbation moments require three more velocity integrations and one space integration over N^1.

The particular choice of initial conditions as an initial density discontinuity with the same temperature on both sides yields such a simple form for f_0, that regardless of the particle interaction model, J_0 can be evaluated by two numerical integrations, while the moments require only two additional numerical integrations (as in the Krook model). By choosing Maxwellian molecules (fifth power repulsion particle interaction) another integration in the term linear in $(1 - \rho_r)$ can be evaluated analytically.

By substituting our f_0 into the expression for JN_0, with the proper normalizations to correspond to our nondimensional coordinates we obtain an expression of the form

$$JN_0(v_x, v_y, v_z, N) = A\left(\frac{1 - \rho_r}{2}\right) + B\left(\frac{1 - \rho_r}{2}\right)^2 \qquad (2.19)$$

where A and B are complicated sevenfold integrals. JT_0 has an identical form except for an additional factor $(v_y{}^2 + v_z{}^2)$ in the integrands contained in A and B factors.

Regardless of the actual numerical value of the integral its dependence on the initial density ratio is only quadratic, whereas the Krook model depends on $(1 - \rho_r)$ in a much more complicated way. An expansion of the Krook model in $(1 - \rho_r)$ would necessarily yield higher order terms. One would suspect therefore that the Krook model cannot be an equally valid representation for the collision process for the entire range of initial density ratios. Furthermore from this form as well as physical consideration in the justification of the Krook model its accuracy would be expected to improve as $(1 - \rho_r) \to 0$.

2. Evaluation of Zeroth Order Collision Integral. Since the two terms A and B in Eq. (2.19) can be evaluated separately we look at a typical term in the factor A, as an example. Three integrations can be carried out immediately by a change of variables. Additional integrations can be carried out analytically for either hard spheres or Maxwellian molecules. Because of the implicit assumption of velocity independent collision frequency in the Krook model for more meaningful comparison to the Krook model solution we shall consider the case of Maxwellian molecules only. In that case the term $gb\,db$ where g is the magnitude of the relative velocity can be replaced by $\sqrt{2mK}\,ada$ where $a = b(g^2 2mK)^{1/4}$ and K is the proportionality constant in the fifth power repulsion law. This simplification allows evaluating three more integrations in the linear terms and two more in the quadratic terms without resort to numerical means.

Using Jeans' (1954) evaluation of the velocities after collision, and carrying out the integrations over all but the collision parameter a we obtain as a typical linear term in the factor A:

$$\exp(-v_x{}^2)\frac{\sqrt{\pi}}{2}\int_0^\infty \left[1 + \operatorname{erf}\left(\frac{N - v_x(1 - \sigma)}{\sqrt{\sigma(2 - \sigma)}}\right)\right] da^2(\sigma) \qquad (2.20)$$

where $\sigma = \cos^2\theta_0$ and θ_0 is the half angle between asymptotes of collision.

Since the relation between da^2 and $d\sigma$ is only an expression of the geometry of inverse fifth power particle interaction it can be determined independently of the problem under consideration. This just leads to the transformation of the integral

$$\int_0^\infty I(\sigma(a^2))\,da^2 = \int_0^{1/2} I(\sigma)WC(\sigma)\,d\sigma \qquad (2.21)$$

where I is any integrand and $WC(\sigma)$ is a numerically evaluated function dependent only on the choice of fifth power interaction law. The details of the preceding calculations are contained in Bienkowski (1964). Near $N = v_x$ it can be shown that JN_0 behaves as

$$JN_0 = \frac{C_3 \text{ sign}(N - v_x)}{\sqrt{|N - v_x|}} + \text{h.o.t.} \cdots .$$ (2.22)

The collision integral, therefore, for Maxwellian molecules behaves very differently near $v_x = N$ than does the Krook model. This behavior is physically explainable and reasonable. The Krook model by assuming spherical symmetry in the scattered particles restricts any peculiarities around $v_x = N$ to come from the loss term alone. In the Maxwellian molecule collision integral (as for any power law interaction) the change in ff_1 through a collision is finite even for a very small deflection in a collision for $v_x \to N$, while the number of such collisions is approaching infinity. Thus near $v_x - N = 0$ the collision integral diverges.

This divergence is not real, as it is a result of the breakdown of the validity of the Boltzmann equation in the region of $v_x \to N$. In this regime (near the initial discontinuity) the lack of a cutoff for interactions violates the binary collision assumption. Physically this can be considered as a result of the unrealistic initial conditions for the Boltzmann equation. The instantaneous removal of the diaphragm is inconsistent with the Boltzmann equation, as no times shorter than the duration of an average "collision" can be treated by the theory. Conceptually the divergent results can be eliminated by introducing a "thin adjustment layer" (of the order of a collision time) into the initial conditions to replace the discontinuity. Fortunately this need not be done in detail as the physically meaningful results, the moments, are finite because of the integrable nature of the singularity.

E. "First Collision" Results

The macroscopic properties of density, pressure, temperature, velocity, stress and heat flux were calculated numerically by quadratures for both the Krook model and the "exact" Maxwellian molecule case, under the assumption of equal initial temperature on the two sides of the diaphragm, for three density ratios.

The density profiles for collisionless flow ρ_0, the Euler solution ρ_e, and the first collision perturbation ρ_1 for both collision models for shock Mach number $M_s = 3.00$ is presented in Fig. 2. Figures 3 and 4 are similar plots of velocity for $M_s = 1.27$ and $M_s = 3.00$, respectively, Since this property is normalized by the density the regions of low density are not attenuated and can thus be of great importance. Figure 5 is a similar plot of the temperature for $M_s = 1.27$.

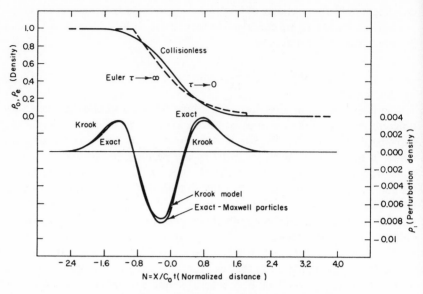

FIG. 2. Density profiles ($M_s = 3.00$, $\rho_r = 0.375 \times 10^{-3}$).

It is apparent that for all the evaluated macroscopic properties the qualitative appearance of the "first collision" term is very similar for both the Krook and the "exact Maxwellian" model. Quantitatively, however, the

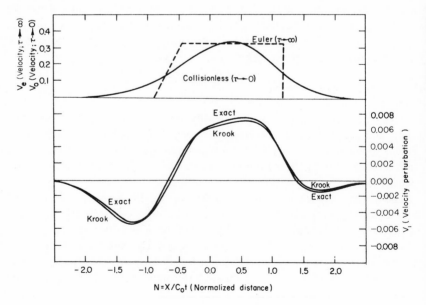

FIG. 3. Velocity profiles ($M_s = 1.27$, $\rho_r = 0.298$).

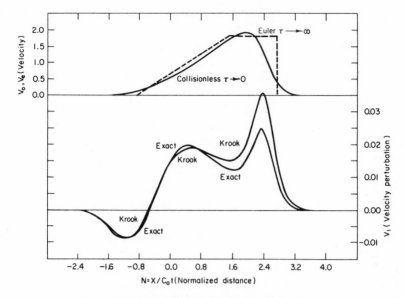

Fig. 4. Velocity profiles ($M_s = 3.00$, $\rho_r = 0.375 \times 10^{-3}$).

discrepancy between the two solutions is not constant either for different moments or at different positions ($N = x/c_0 t$). Because of the single free parameter in the Krook model the accuracy of the different moments cannot

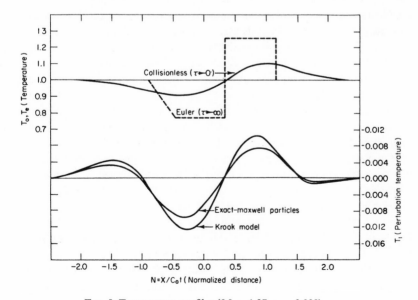

Fig. 5. Temperature profiles ($M_s = 1.27$, $\rho_r = 0.298$).

be expected to be the same. The qualitative agreement is therefore surprisingly good. In view of the greatly different type of singularity of the distribution function obtained by the two methods, the great qualitative agreement between the macroscopic moments is an indication of the insensitivity of the macroscopic properties to the details of the collision process, as long as the basic conservation laws are satisfied. The macroscopic properties including moments which have v_t^2 in the integrand appear to have a greater difference between the Krook and the exact solution than do those with moments of the v_x velocity only. This is most noticeable in the lower Mach number case by comparing velocity and temperature profiles, where the difference between the two solutions for the velocity is much smaller than for the temperature. This suggests that possibly the spherical symmetry inherent in the Krook collision model represents thermalization incorrectly by assuming it to be equal in all directions around the mean velocity.

Another important discrepancy between the Krook and the exact solution is the apparent dependence of the difference between these solutions in the low density region on the initial density ratio. The velocity profiles in Fig. 4 indicate that the discrepancy is growing with Mach number. Comparison between the Euler and collisionless solution (Fig. 1) shows that, whereas on the high density side the two velocity profiles are fairly close regardless of the Mach number, in the region near the eventual shock formation the discrepancy grows with Mach number. Since the Euler solution is based on local equilibrium, the close proximity to it of the collisionless solution suggests that in the high density region the assumption of near equilibrium inherent in the justification of the Krook model may be reasonably correct. Near the shock formation region, however, this assumption becomes less and less reasonable as the eventual shock Mach number is increased.

In general we can conclude that at least for the problem where the initial temperature is the same on both sides of the diaphragm the Krook model gives a reasonable gross description of the initial effect of collisions. Since the Krook model is known to be correct (within the limitations of the one free parameter) as equilibrium is approached, its use for numerical studies in the transition range of problems similar to this one seems justified. The limitations of the validity in the eventual shock formation region and the apparent incorrect thermalization suggest that the use of the model in problems with collisions between streams of greatly differing velocities and temperatures may be unjustified, or at least less accurate.

A look at Figs. 2–5 is sufficient to convince one that the first effect of collisions in its broad aspects does tend to alter the solution in the right direction toward the Euler regime. The details may not be right everywhere, and this first perturbation is incapable of representing the entire process of transition. The major effect, however, of steepening gradients in the wave regions is evident. Even what appears as an incorrect velocity perturbation in the "contact surface" regime, becomes reasonable when one remembers that the Navier-Stokes results of Goldworthy (1959) give an induced velocity in that region.

III. Linearized Navier-Stokes Solution

A. Formulation of the Problem

As time progresses from the initial release of the imaginary diaphragm discussed in Section II, A, collisions increase in their importance until after a sufficient number of mean free times they become dominant. The proper equations then become the Navier-Stokes equations, except possibly in the region of very high gradients within the shock wave. Unfortunately a general solution of the nonlinear Navier-Stokes equations is not feasible except possibly by numerical integration, or in a regime where distinct shock wave, contact surface and expansion wave exist. If however, the Navier-Stokes equations are linearized with respect to the initial density ratio an exact solution can be obtained by Laplace transform techniques. Comparison of this solution to the corresponding linearized first collision results allows a determination of the time span of the transition and its possible importance. It is useful therefore to investigate in detail the solution of the linearized equations for this problem, while keeping in mind that certain strictly *non-linear* phenomena will not be obtainable in this way.

We linearize and nondimensionalize the Navier-Stokes equations and combine the equations into a single equation:

$$\gamma \frac{\partial^5 \varphi}{\partial \tilde{t} \, \partial \tilde{x}^4} - (\gamma + \tfrac{4}{3}\mathrm{Pr}) \frac{\partial^4 \varphi}{\partial \tilde{t}^2 \, \partial \tilde{x}^2} - \tfrac{4}{3}\mathrm{Pr} \frac{\partial^3 \varphi}{\partial \tilde{t} \, \partial \tilde{x}^2} + \tfrac{4}{3}\mathrm{Pr} \frac{\partial^3 \varphi}{\partial \tilde{t}^3} + \frac{\partial^4 \varphi}{\partial \tilde{x}^4} = 0 \qquad (3.1)$$

where φ represents any of the perturbation properties $\tilde{\rho}$, $\tilde{T}$, or $\tilde{v}$ defined as

$$\rho = \bar{\rho}\left(1 + \frac{1 - \rho_r}{2} \tilde{\rho}\right), \quad T = \bar{T}\left(1 + \frac{1 - \rho_r}{2} \tilde{T}\right), \quad \text{and} \quad v = a_0\left(\frac{1 - \rho_r}{2}\right)\tilde{v}, \quad (3.2)$$

while

$$\tilde{t} = 3a_0^2 \bar{\rho} t / 4\bar{\mu} \quad \text{and} \quad \tilde{x} = 3a_0 \bar{\rho} x / 4\bar{\mu}. \qquad (3.3)$$

Barred quantities represent average values, a_0 is the sound speed ($a_0 = \sqrt{\gamma/2}c_0$), $\rho_r = \rho_+ / \rho_-$ as before, and $\mathrm{Pr} = \bar{\mu} C_p / \bar{\kappa}$ the Prandtl number where μ is the viscosity, κ the conductivity, and C_p the specific heat at constant pressure.

It is readily seen that this equation is fourth order in $\tilde{x}$ and third order in $\tilde{t}$. Thus three initial conditions and four boundary conditions are needed. The problem as originally stated is formulated as an initial value problem in infinite space, with a step function in density, uniform temperature and zero initial velocity as initial conditions. The boundary conditions are $\tilde{\rho} = 1$, $\tilde{T} = 0$ at $\tilde{x} \to -\infty$ and $\tilde{\rho} = -1$, $\tilde{T} = 0$ at $\tilde{x} \to \infty$.

A solution can be obtained by Laplace transformation in $\tilde{t}$ followed by solution of the ordinary equation in $\tilde{x}$. The mathematics can be further simplified by noticing the symmetry around $\tilde{x} = 0$ in this linearized case. Since $\tilde{\rho}$ and $\tilde{T}$ have to be antisymmetric while $\tilde{v}$ has to be symmetric we can reduce the problem to a half space for $\tilde{x} > 0$ with appropriate boundary conditions at $\tilde{x} = 0$. If we further define a new variable $\tilde{\rho}' = \tilde{\rho} + 1$, we can treat the problem as having all zero initial conditions with $\tilde{\rho}'(0, t) = 1$ and $\tilde{T}(0, t) = 0$ as well as $\tilde{\rho}' = \tilde{T} = 0$ as $x \to \infty$.

B. Laplace Transform Solution

The transformed equation and boundary conditions are particularly simple and yield immediately

$$\bar{\varphi}(x, s) = A(s) \exp(-\lambda_1(s)x) + B(s) \exp(-\lambda_2(s)x) \qquad (3.4)$$

where λ_1 and λ_2 are the roots with positive real parts of a biquadratic equation for λ. The expressions for λ_1 and λ_2 and the constants A and B were evaluated explicitly for arbitrary Prandtl number but their complicated form makes inversion difficult. For the special case of $Pr = \frac{3}{4}$ the form of the solution is greatly simplified. Since the variation of the solution with Prandtl number is not expected to be great and the basic physical phenomena are certainly going to be only weakly dependent on the exact numerical value of Pr, the solution for $Pr = \frac{3}{4}$ is calculated, even though this value is not consistent with the other assumptions. The constants λ_1 and λ_2 now become

$$\lambda_1(s) = \sqrt{s} \qquad \text{and} \qquad \lambda_2(s) = s/\sqrt{\gamma s + 1}, \qquad (3.5)$$

and a typical transformed variable becomes

$$\bar{\varphi}_T = \left[\frac{\gamma - 1}{\gamma s} + \gamma\left(s + \frac{1}{\gamma - 1}\right)^{-1}\right]\left[\exp\left(\frac{-sx}{\sqrt{\gamma s + 1}}\right) - \exp(-\sqrt{sx})\right]. \quad (3.6)$$

C. Inversion of Transforms

1. The Method of Inversion. The inversion of transforms of the type in Eq. (3.6) cannot be accomplished exactly. For short times standard techniques of expanding in $1/s$ yield a valid solution. For long times methods very similar to that used by Clarke (1960) yield asymptotic series that can be used to

evaluate the solution. The essential feature of this method is that it properly takes the limit $\tilde{t} \to \infty$ while keeping $\tilde{x}/\tilde{t}$ finite.

2. The Short Time Solution. The short-time solution of the Navier-Stokes equations is of course of little physical value as the equations themselves are not valid in that region. It is, however, of some interest to look at the nature of this solution in order to notice its greatly different behavior from the collisionless result, which *is* valid in that region.

Straightforward evaluation of leading terms in the expansion in $1/s$ of the Laplace transforms yields the result for the temperature for instance:

$$\tilde{T}(x, t) = \text{erfc}\left(\frac{\tilde{x}}{2\sqrt{\gamma\tilde{t}}}\right) - \text{erfc}\left(\frac{\tilde{x}}{2\sqrt{\tilde{t}}}\right). \tag{3.7}$$

The obvious variable in the short time Navier-Stokes solution is the diffusive type of variable $\tilde{x}/\sqrt{\tilde{t}}$ rather than the correct short time similarity variable $\tilde{x}/\tilde{t}$ arising in the collisionless solution. Thus the Navier-Stokes solution cannot possibly correctly represent the initial response to the release of the density discontinuity.

3. Large Time Solution. The large time solution of the Navier-Stokes equation is of much greater physical interest. It should correctly represent the emergence of a wave from the initially fully viscous type of solution. It should indicate the time at which the wave and contact surface become distinct, and when they cease to influence each other.

The large time solution is a result of the addition of two contributions. One can be identified as the "contact" surface solution as this is what it represents in the limit $t \to \infty$. The other one can be identified as the "wave" solution as this is its meaning for very large times. The "contact surface" solution has the form:

$$\varphi_c \sim A \, \text{erfc}\left(\frac{\sqrt{\tilde{t}}\tilde{N}}{2}\right) + \frac{B \exp(-\tilde{t}\tilde{N}^2/4)}{\sqrt{\tilde{t}}} \tag{3.8}$$

where $\tilde{N} = \tilde{x}/\tilde{t} = \sqrt{2/\gamma}N$, and A is of order unity for the temperature and density, zero for the velocity, while B is an asymptotic series in $1/\tilde{t}$ of order unity or less for all properties. A and B are evaluated explicitly but the details are omitted here.

The "wave" solution in turn has the form

$$\varphi_w \sim C \, \text{erfc}\left[\sqrt{\frac{\tilde{t}}{2\gamma}}(\tilde{N} - 1)\right] + \frac{D \exp[(\tilde{t}/2\gamma)(\tilde{N} - 1)^2]}{\sqrt{\tilde{t}}}, \tag{3.9}$$

where C is a constant and D is an asymptotic series in $\tilde{t}(\tilde{N} - 1)^2/8$. Both, however, are of order unity. The form of the "wave" solution away from the wave ($\tilde{N} = 1$) position is in principle different. The leading terms are identical, and the deviations occur in the region where the contribution of this solution is negligible. C and the first three terms of D have been evaluated explicitly.

It is interesting to notice that a large time solution near the wave can be obtained from physical considerations, along the lines suggested by Whitham (1959), by replacing the time derivative $\partial/\partial \tilde{t}$ by $-\partial/\partial \tilde{x}$ in all but the ($\partial/\partial \tilde{t} + \partial/\partial \tilde{x}$) term in the equation. The leading terms turn out to be identical in form to those obtained by our technique, but the coefficients in the terms higher than the first are not correct. For instance in the expression for the temperature the leading coefficient of the exponential term is $\gamma/4$ instead of $3\gamma/8$. The basic behavior of the solution, however, is qualitatively the same.

D. Results

In the linearized case we now have a reasonable means of determining the transition between the "first collision" and the Navier-Stokes results.

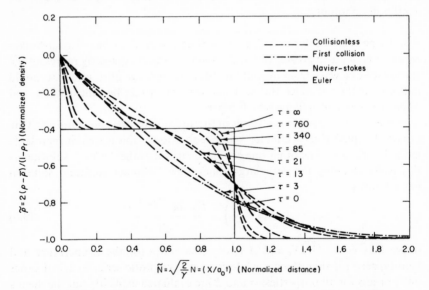

FIG. 6. Time history of density profiles—linearized ($M_s = 1.00, \rho_r \rightarrow 1.00$).

Figures 6–8 represent the density, temperature, and velocity profiles at several times. The collisionless solution is shown for $\tau = 0$. The first collision results are shown for $\tau = 3$, although this is somewhat beyond the expected range of validity, to indicate clearly the direction of perturbation. The Navier-Stokes solutions are not shown for times shorter than $\tau = 13$ because their extent

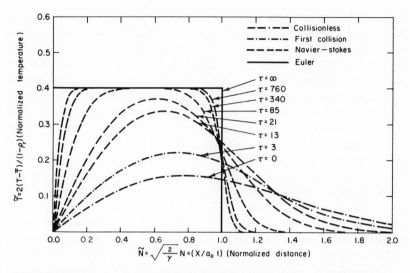

FIG. 7. Time history of temperature profiles—linearized ($M_s = 1.00, \rho_r \to 1.00$).

in $\tilde{N} = (\tilde{x}/\tilde{t})$ exceeded that of the collisionless solution, whereas the "first collision" results indicate that collisions tend to decrease this extent.

Comparison of the $\tau = 0$, $\tau = 3$, and $\tau = 13$ results indicates that in general the change is everywhere monotonic in this region, although once in the

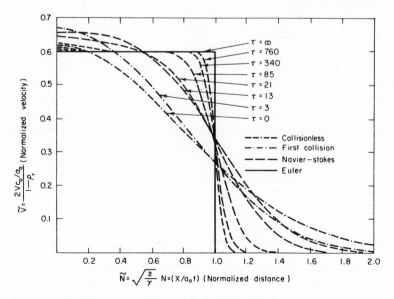

FIG. 8. Time history of velocity profiles—linearized ($M_s = 1.00, \rho_r \to 1.00$).

Navier-Stokes regime the solution may start changing in a different way. Notice that for all three properties separation between the "contact surface" and wave region occurs someplace between $\tau = 21$ and $\tau = 85$, and probably closer to $\tau = 85$. For times longer than this, the solution is apparently very close to that obtained by treating the "contact surface" and the wave regions completely separately with no interaction. There is, however, still a noticeable asymmetry in the wave region, especially for the temperature profile (Fig. 7) at $\tau = 85$, indicating that the two regions still influence each other slightly. Notice that the "induced" velocity at $\tilde{N} = 0$ first rises in the "first collision" analysis and then falls in the Navier-Stokes analysis. A cross plot of the velocity versus time indicates that the cross-over point occurs at about $\tau = 5$. What is more interesting is the fact that for $\tau = 5$ the Navier-Stokes solution at $\tilde{N} = 0$ is essentially the solution for the "contact surface" growth without any interaction with the wave. This suggests that by the time the Navier-Stokes equations are valid the region near $\tilde{N} = 0$ is already independent of the wave, though the wave is still far from its "equilibrium" profile.

The startling property of the results presented in Figs. 6–8 is the apparent smooth transition from the collisionless flow to the Euler limit. The remaining gap between τ of order unity and τ of order 10 cannot introduce really new phenomena although the mathematical treatment of that region is very difficult.

IV. Discussion

A. Validity of Solutions

1. First Collision Solution. No rigorous means of determining the range of validity of the first collision solution has been found. Some plausibility criteria are discussed by Bienkowski (1964). The important result is that even at $\tau \approx 1$ the first order perturbation in τ is only about 10 per cent of the collisionless solution. Some additional justification can also be obtained for the Krook model results in the fact that the next order term is still negligible at that time. Though not rigorous these justifications suggest that the first collision results can probably be believed up to times of the order of one mean free time.

It is interesting to note here that the initial effect of collisions is rather slow. After an average of one collision per particle the profiles are altered away from the collisionless results by only a few per cent.

2. Linearized Navier-Stokes Solution. Aside from the usual limitations of the Navier-Stokes equations the linearized solution is limited to an infinitesimally small initial density discontinuity. An evaluation of the nonlinear convective terms by using the linearized solution leads to secular terms. This means that for any finite initial density jump, the nonlinear convective terms eventually become important.

If we choose as a limit to the validity of the linearized solution a time when the nonlinear convective terms become of the same order as the linear viscous terms, we obtain the approximate criterion:

$$(1 - \rho_r)\tilde{\tau} < 10. \tag{4.1}$$

This suggests that for some value of ρ_r the linearization can be valid to times of the order of $\tilde{\tau} = 100$. Since $\tilde{\tau} > 100$ the wave and contact surface have separated, the nonlinear effects can be incorporated at least qualitatively in steepening the "shock" wave, while the effect on the contact surface and expansion wave remains minor. The complete solution can then be at least qualitatively understood. Unfortunately, this criterion limits the shock Mach number to be less than about 1.05.

3. Transition Region. The stress-velocity gradient and heat flux-temperature gradient relations have the same form in both continuum and collisionless cases [except for the time dependence of the coefficients in the latter (Narashima, 1962)]. This suggests that we look at the ratios of stress to rate

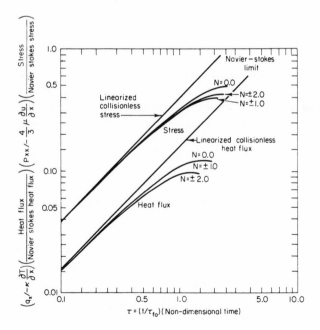

FIG. 9. Stress-strain rate ratio and heat flux—temperature gradient ratio versus time—linearized ($M_s = 1.00$, $\rho_r \to 1.00$).

of strain, and heat flux to temperature gradient as functions of time. These two quantities evaluated on the basis of the first collision perturbation in the linearized case are presented in Fig. 9. Its form suggests that the assumption of a time dependent viscosity (or heat conductivity) of the form

$$\mu = \mu_{N.S.}(1 - \exp(-a\tau)), \qquad (4.2)$$

where $\mu_{N.S.}$ is the usual viscosity and a is a constant, could be useful means of obtaining a complete solution within the Navier-Stokes formalism. It further verifies the fact that for a obtained here from the "first collision" solution the Navier-Stokes results should become valid for $\tau \geqslant 10$.

B. Nonlinear Solution

The nonlinear modifications to the linearized Navier-Stokes solution discussed in Section III can be qualitatively understood. In the expansion wave, and contact surface region, the modification should be primarily a result of property variation, but the phenomena should still be diffusive, with scales in $\tilde{x}$ growing as $\sqrt{\tilde{\tau}}$. In our variable, the scales in $\tilde{N}$ around each region should decrease as $1/\sqrt{\tilde{\tau}}$. In the "shock wave" region, however, the convective terms should eventually balance the diffusive terms and yield a constant thickness in $\tilde{x}$, or a thickness in $\tilde{N}$ decreasing as $1/\tilde{\tau}$. It would be very difficult to obtain a solution where all the regions are merged, but for sufficiently large times an approximation incorporating the above stated ideas can be used for comparative purposes. That regime could be treated by the inner-outer expansion technique (Kaplun and Lagerstrom, 1957), but because three regions are involved, the complexity would be great while the expected extension of the validity of results is quite limited. Thus only the case of no interaction between shock, contact surface, and expansion wave were considered.

Figure 10 represents a typical plot of the expected temperature profiles at various times as a function of $N = x/c_0 t$. In addition to the limiting cases of collisionless and Euler solutions, profiles at $\tau = 1$ and $\tau = 3$ are obtained by adding the first collision solution, although the validity of the solution at $\tau = 3$ is doubtful. A crude approximation to the Navier-Stokes solution is evaluated for $\tau = 100$ and $\tau = 50$. This approximation consists of neglecting all interaction between the shock, the contact surface and the expansion wave. The shock, however, is modified to be the equilibrium shock profile for a steady normal shock (Gilbarg and Paolucci, 1953). The contact surface is modified to include the heat conduction and viscosity as done by Goldworthy (1959). The expansion wave is very crudely calculated by modifying a linearized solution for a wave front.

At $\tau = 50$ the "noninteracting" Navier-Stokes approximation is at the absolute limit of its possible validity, because the region separating the shock and contact surface is very small compared to their thicknesses. The process of transition appears more or less direct and no really new phenomena can be expected to occur between $\tau = 3$ and $\tau = 50$. The mathematical forms of the two limiting solutions are, however, vastly different. Inclusion of interaction in the Navier-Stokes solution would reduce the gap of uncertainty even further, and together with the first collision results would probably be adequate to describe the complete process of propagation of an initial density discontinuity.

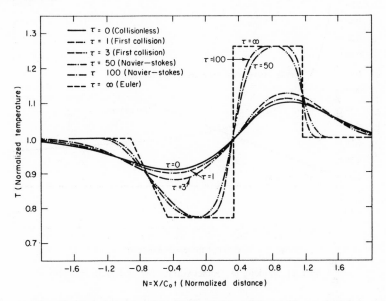

FIG. 10. Temperature profiles at several times ($M_s = 1.27$, $\rho_r = 0.298$).

Notice in Fig. 10 that the $1/\tau$ decay of the " shock wave " thickness does not introduce as great an asymmetric deviation from the linearized solution as would be expected. This results from the fact that the *local* mean free time should be used as a scaling factor. Although the " shock wave " thickness decays as $1/\tau$ the proportionality constant is much smaller than the constant in $1/\sqrt{\tau}$ decay of the contact surface thickness. Thus for the times shown, $\tau = 50$ and 100, the two thicknesses are not as greatly different as might at first be expected.

Another interesting result can be obtained by crossplotting the velocity at the " contact surface " versus time. The contact surface here is defined as the point to the right of which the total mass of gas is equal to the amount that was to the right of the diaphragm initially. This reduces to the conventional definition in the Euler limit, but still defines a "contact surface" at any time. Figure 11 represents the velocity at such a position (which is itself a function of time) obtained on the "first collision" basis and also from Goldworthy's (1959) solution. The crossing point is around $\tau = 8$ which corresponds to about 4 *local* mean free times. Allowing for some "transition" from one to the other solution, 10 local mean free times appears as a reasonable criterion for the validity of the Navier-Stokes formalism.

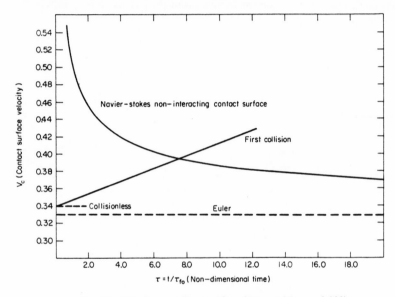

FIG. 11. Velocity at contact surface ($M_s = 1.27, \rho_r = 0.298$).

All the results presented suggest that most of the transition from the collisionless to the Euler solution takes place within the Navier-Stokes regime, although the fully "viscous" solution may be needed. This suggests that comparison of any molecular analysis to the high Reynolds number limit of essentially inviscid, or "boundary layer" flow is meaningless as a determination of the "transition" regime. For the problem under consideration, collisions have the initial effect of steepening gradients in certain regions (with respect to the time normalized space coordinate), but the major part of the formation of the shock, or its emergence from the fully "viscous" flow takes place within the Navier-Stokes regime.

REFERENCES

Bhatnagar, P. L., Gross, E. P., and Krook, M. (1954). *Phys. Rev.* **94**, 511.

Bienkowski, G. (1964). GALCIT Memo. No. 70.

Broadwell, J. E. (1963). Space Technology Lab. Rept. 9813–6001–RUOOO.

Chu, C. K. (1964). Columbia University, Plasma Research Lab. Rept. 11.

Clarke, J. F. (1960). College of Aeronautics, Cranfield, England, Rept. 124.

Gilbarg, D. and Paolucci, D. (1953). *J. Ratl. Mech. Anal.* **2**, 617.

Glass, I. I. (1958). Univ. of Toronto, Inst. Aerophys. Rev. 12.

Goldworthy, F. A. (1959). *J. Fluid Mech.* **5**, 164.

Hamel, B. B., and Wachman, M. (1964). General Electric Space Sci. Lab. Rept. R64SD53; also in this volume, p. 370.

Haviland, J. K., and Lavin, M. L. (1962). *Phys. Fluids* **5**, 1399.

Jeans, J. H. (1954). "The Dynamical Theory of Gases," 4th ed. Dover, New York.

Kaplun, S. and Lagerstrom, P. A. (1957) *J. Math. and Mech.* **6**, 585.

Keller, J. B. (1948) *Communs. Pure Appl. Math.* **1**, 275.

Krook, M. (1959). *J. Fluid Mech.* **6**, 523.

Lees, L. (1959). GALCIT Memo. 51.

Narasimha, R. (1962). *J. Fluid Mech.* **12**, 294.

Patterson, G. H. (1948). Naval Ordnance Lab. Memo. 9903.

Whitham, G. B. (1959). *Communs. Pure Appl. Math.* **12**, 113.

Willis, D. R. (1960). Royal Inst. Technol., Stockholm, Gas Dynamics Tech. Note 4.

Numerical Experiments in Kinetic Theory[1]

DONALD G. ANDERSON AND HILLIARD K. MACOMBER
Harvard University, Cambridge, Massachusetts

Most nonlinear problems in kinetic theory can be treated only through approximation procedures whose accuracy is unknown. To assess the accuracy of certain of these procedures, approximate and exact solutions of Krook's kinetic equation have been obtained for two steady, one-dimensional problems: Couette flow with heat transfer and the structure of a plane shock wave. Solutions have been obtained for a wide range of the characteristic dimensionless parameters.

I. Introduction

The Navier-Stokes equations are known to be inadequate in transition regions such as boundary, initial, and shock layers. In principle, the Boltzmann equation provides a more adequate description of such transition regions. However, this equation can be solved only through approximation procedures whose accuracy is unknown. One of the purposes of the present research is to gain some insight into the accuracy of certain of these procedures.

Krook (1955) has pointed out that if the effects of molecular collisions are described by the simplest of the hierarchy of Statistical Models, many problems become amenable to numerical treatment. This provides an opportunity to assess the accuracy of approximation procedures through a comparison of approximate and exact solutions.

Any approximation procedure consists essentially of two steps: (i) the prescription of the velocity dependence of the distribution function by an approximate form containing a finite number of space and time dependent parameters and (ii) the selection of a finite number of moment equations to determine the parameters.

We have obtained exact (Anderson, 1963) and approximate (Macomber,

[1] The work presented in this paper was supported by the National Science Foundation.

1965) solutions of two model problems: Couette flow with heat transfer and the structure of a plane shock wave. Investigation of other problems, approximation procedures, and models is continuing. The calculations involved and the full range of the results obtained are much too elaborate to record here. We shall merely outline the calculations and present graphically a selected sample of the results obtained thus far.

II. Krook Kinetic Equation

Consider a monatomic gas with no internal degrees of freedom. In the absence of external forces, the steady one-dimensional Krook kinetic equation can be written:

$$u \frac{\partial f}{\partial x} = v(x)[F - f]. \tag{1}$$

The mean collision frequency $v(x)$ depends on the law of force between molecules and is usually prescribed as a function of number density and temperature. F is the Maxwellian distribution function:

$$F(\mathbf{u}; n, \mathbf{q}, T) = n(m/2\pi kT)^{3/2} \exp[-m(\mathbf{u} - \mathbf{q})^2/2kT], \tag{2}$$

m is the molecular mass, and k is Boltzmann's constant. n, $\mathbf{q}$, and T are the local number density, flow velocity, and kinetic temperature defined in the usual way. With the statistical model the distribution function is completely determined by these moments.

The collision frequency $v(x)$ can be removed from the kinetic equation by defining a new independent variable τ proportional to $\int^x v(t) \, dt/U$, where U is some characteristic velocity. Solutions obtained as functions of τ are universal in the sense that they are independent of any particular prescription for $v(x)$. The strategy adopted here is to compare approximate and exact universal solutions. The transformation from τ to x can be determined by a simple quadrature once the law of force between molecules is specified.

III. Couette Flow with Heat Transfer

A. Exact Formulation

The configuration and notation for the Couette flow problem are presented schematically in Fig. 1 (left). The Krook kinetic equation (1) must be solved subject to boundary conditions imposed at $x = x_0$ and $x = x_1$. For this purpose it is convenient to define half range distribution functions $f^+ = f$ for $u > 0$ and $f^- = f$ for $u < 0$. We assume that molecules which strike a plate accommodate perfectly to the plate velocity and temperature and are emitted with a Maxwellian velocity distribution. Thus the boundary conditions may be written:

$$f^+(\mathbf{u}, x_0) = F(\mathbf{u}; n_0, q_0\hat{y}, T_0),$$

$$^-(\mathbf{u}, x_1) = F(\mathbf{u}; n_1, q_1\hat{y}, T_1).$$

(3)

| COUETTE FLOW | SHOCK WAVE |

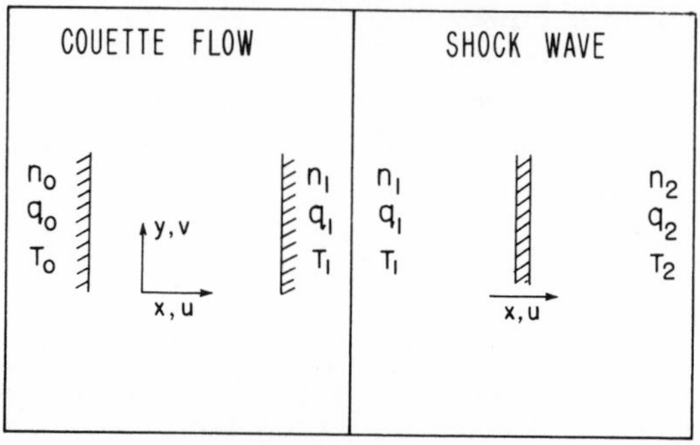

FIG. 1. Schematic diagrams of problem configurations.

Without loss of generality we may choose $q_0 = 0$, $q_1 \geqslant 0$, and $T_0 \geqslant T_1$. It is convenient to define dimensionless variables n/n_0, T/T_0, and q/u_0, where $u_0 = \sqrt{kT_0/m}$. A new independent variable τ is defined by

$$\tau = \lambda \int_{x_0}^{x} v(t)\, dt/u_0;$$

(4)

$$\lambda = u_0 \Big/ \int_{x_0}^{x_1} v(t)\, dt$$

(5)

is a Knudsen number for the problem.

The problem is characterized by three dimensionless parameters: the Knudsen number λ, the temperature ratio T_1/T_0, and the velocity ratio q_1/u_0. The ratio n_1/n_0 is determined as part of the solution of the problem through the condition that the flow velocity normal to the plates vanish.

The kinetic equation (1), which now reads

$$\lambda \frac{u}{u_0} \frac{\partial f}{\partial \tau} + f = F,$$

(6)

can be formally integrated to express f as a functional of n, q, and T. Imposition of the boundary conditions (3) yields expressions for the half-range distribution functions, e.g.,

$$f^+(\mathbf{u}, \tau) = F(\mathbf{u}; n_0, 0, T_0) \exp\left(-\frac{\tau u_0}{\lambda u}\right)$$

$$+ \frac{u_0}{\lambda u} \int_0^\tau \exp\left[-\frac{(\tau - t)u_0}{\lambda u}\right] F(\mathbf{u}; n, q\hat{y}, T) \, dt. \tag{7}$$

Substitution of these expressions in the integrals defining n, q, and T yields a set of singular nonlinear integral equations. Exact solution of the problem involves solving these equations for n, q, T, and the quantity n_1/n_0. Subsequently, other moments such as the components of the stress tensor and heat flux vector can be obtained by quadrature.

B. Approximation Procedures

We prescribe the velocity dependence of the distribution function by an approximate form containing space dependent parameters. The prescription should take account of the half-range character of the problem which is induced by the boundary conditions (3). At the boundaries the distribution function is discontinuous on the plane $u = 0$ in velocity space.

Krook (1959) has proposed half-range approximate forms based on "modified Maxwell functions." We have obtained solutions based on a number of such forms. For concreteness and brevity we consider here only the specific approximate form:

$$f^+ = (A_{00}^+ + A_{01}^+ u + A_{02}^+ u^2)F(\mathbf{u}; n_0, 0, T_0)$$
$$+ (A_{10}^+ + A_{11}^+ u)F(\mathbf{u}; n_1, q_1\hat{y}, T_1), \tag{8}$$
$$f^- = (A_{00}^- + A_{01}^- u)F(\mathbf{u}; n_0, 0, T_0)$$
$$+ (A_{10}^- + A_{11}^- u + A_{12}^- u^2)F(\mathbf{u}; n_1, q_1\hat{y}, T_1),$$

where the parameters $A_{ij}^{\pm}$ are unspecified functions of τ.

To determine the ten parameters $A_{ij}^{\pm}$, we utilize ten half-range moment equations. A half-range moment equation is obtained by multiplying the kinetic equation (6) through by a polynomial in the molecular velocity components and integrating over the velocity half space $u > 0$ or $u < 0$. To ensure conservation of mass, momentum, and energy we demand that eight of the ten required equations be based on the polynomials 1, u, v, and $\mathbf{u}^2$. For $q_1 = 0$ the two half-range moment equations based on v are nugatory because of the axial symmetry in velocity space; hence in this case only six half-range moment equations are required to ensure conservation. For our specific example the additional half-range moment equations required are based on the polynomial uv for $q_1 > 0$ and on the polynomials u^2 and $u(v^2 + w^2)$ for $q_1 = 0$.

Any half-range moment can be expressed as a linear combination of the parameters by substituting one of the forms (8) in the integral defining the moment. When all moments involved in the ten half-range moment equations are so expressed, a set of ordinary differential equations for the parameters is obtained. These equations must be solved subject to the boundary conditions

$$A_{ij}^+(0) = \delta_{i0}\delta_{j0}, \qquad A_{ij}^-(1) = \delta_{i1}\delta_{j0} \tag{9}$$

where δ_{ij} is the Kronecker delta; and the quantity n_1/n_0 must be determined so that the flow velocity normal to the plates is zero.

C. Computational Aspects

The exact problem reduces to that of solving a set of three singular, nonlinear integral equations for n, q, and T. Simultaneously, the quantity n_1/n_0 must be determined from a fourth such equation. The kernel function

$$G_n(q) = \frac{1}{\sqrt{2\pi}} \int_0^\infty du \, u^{n-2} \exp[-u^2/2 - q/u] \tag{10}$$

which appears in the equations has been studied by Abramowitz (1953). $G_n(q)$ is a special case of the kernel function studied by the present authors in connection with the shock wave equations. The problem is replaced by a discrete analog in which the dependent variables are represented by truncated Chebyshev polynomial expansions, and the integral operators are replaced by quadrature formulae. The logarithmic singularity of the kernel is retained in the discrete analog since it is an important feature of the problem. The resulting finite set of nonlinear transcendental equations for the Chebyshev expansion coefficients is solved iteratively by methods which will be described elsewhere. Experiments suggest that about four significant figures have been obtained.

For $\lambda \geqslant 1$ the iterative solution of the equations presents no great difficulty. However, as λ decreases the iterative process becomes increasingly ill-conditioned and slowly convergent, because the equations become identities in the limit $\lambda \to 0$. Thus for very small λ the equations must be reformulated.

Solutions have been obtained for nine values of λ between 10.0 and 0.1; for $T_1/T_0 = 1.0$, 0.7, 0.4, and 0.1; and for $q_1/u_0 = 0.0$, 0.4, 1.0, and 5.0. For any given set of parameters it is not clear whether various linearized analyses which have been considered (e.g., Willis, 1962) might apply. The "nonlinearity" of the problem is a rather complicated function of the full set of characteristic parameters.

Derived moments such as the components of the stress tensor and heat flux vector have been calculated for selected sets of the characteristic parameters. In particular, the three nonzero conserved moments were computed to check the accuracy of the results. Attempts to correlate the solutions in terms of effective viscosities and thermal conductivities were unsuccessful in the range of Knudsen numbers considered.

The approximation procedure, in the case considered, results in a two-point boundary-value problem for a set of ten ordinary differential equations. This problem is solved iteratively by Newton's method. As in the case of the exact solution some difficulty is experienced in obtaining solutions for $\lambda < 1$. Indeed, in the limit $\lambda \to 0$ the problem becomes a singular perturbation problem. Solutions accurate to three significant figures have been obtained for eleven values of λ between 100.0 and 0.5, and for values of T_1/T_0 and q_1/u_0 as given above.

D. Comparison of Solutions

Figures 2 through 9 show approximate and exact curves of the dimensionless number density, flow velocity, and temperature for three problems: heat transfer, Couette flow, and Couette flow with heat transfer. The values

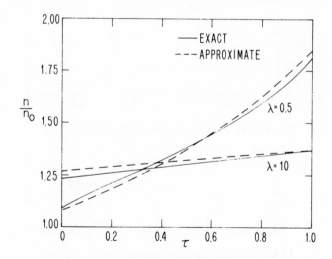

FIG. 2. Density profiles for heat transfer ($T_1/T_0 = 0.4$).

of the characteristic parameters involved are: $T_1/T_0 = 0.4$ for heat transfer; $q_1/u_0 = 1.0$ for Couette flow; and $T_1/T_0 = 0.4$, $q_1/u_0 = 1.0$ for Couette flow with heat transfer—all for $\lambda = 10.0$ and 0.5.

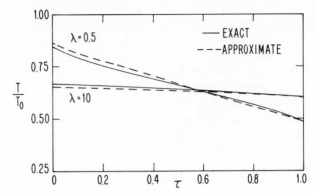

FIG. 3. Temperature profiles for heat transfer ($T_1/T_0 = 0.4$).

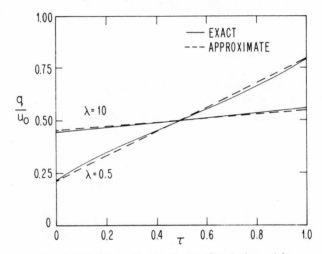

FIG. 4. Velocity profiles for Couette flow ($q_1/u_0 = 1.0$).

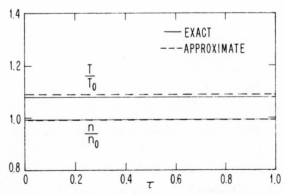

FIG. 5. Density and temperature profiles for Couette flow ($\lambda = 10.0$, $q_1/u_0 = 1.0$).

The approximate solutions shown have the right general character. The errors are of the order of a few per cent, and are relatively uniformly distributed with respect to τ. The accuracy decreases with λ as might be anticipated from the bimodal character of the approximate forms (8). Heat transfer

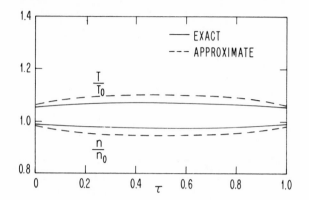

FIG. 6. Density and temperature profiles for Couette flow ($\lambda = 0.5$, $q_1/u_0 = 1.0$).

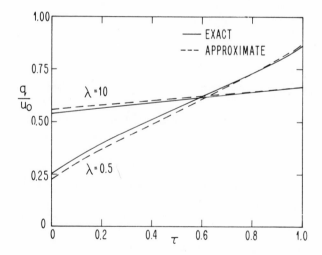

FIG. 7. Velocity profiles for Couette flow with heat transfer ($T_1/T_0 = 0.4$, $q_1/u_0 = 1.0$).

and Couette flow are more symmetrical in velocity space than Couette flow with heat transfer. The approximate solutions are correspondingly more accurate; this may be due to the inherent velocity symmetry of the approximate form (8). It is interesting to note that the conserved moments required

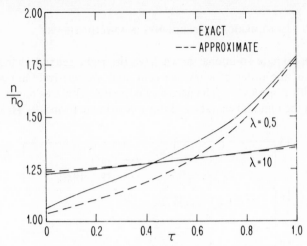

FIG. 8. Density profiles for Couette flow with heat transfer ($T_1/T_0 = 0.4$, $q_1/u_0 = 1.0$).

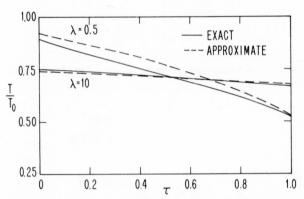

FIG. 9. Temperature profiles for Couette flow with heat transfer ($T_1/T_0 = 0.4$, $q_1/u_0 = 1.0$).

TABLE I

CONSERVED MOMENTS

			Shear stress		Energy flux	
λ	T_1/T_0	q_1/u_0	Exact	Approx.	Exact	Approx.
10.0	0.4	0.0	0.0	0.0	0.913	0.911
0.5	0.4	0.0	0.0	0.0	0.549	0.545
10.0	1.0	1.0	-0.377	-0.376	-0.377	-0.376
0.5	1.0	1.0	-0.209	-0.208	-0.209	-0.208
10.0	0.4	1.0	-0.377	-0.376	0.536	0.535
0.5	0.4	1.0	-0.209	-0.208	0.340	0.340

for the calculation of skin friction and heat transfer coefficients and given in Table I are significantly more accurate than the profiles themselves. This accords with the work of Willis (1963).

IV. Shock Wave

A. Exact Formulation

The configuration and notation for the shock wave problem are presented schematically in Fig. 1 (right). In a frame of reference moving with the shock wave, the problem is steady and one-dimensional. Far from the shock wave the flow tends to equilibrium and thus

$$f(\mathbf{u}, -\infty) = F(\mathbf{u}; n_1, q_1\hat{x}, T_1),$$

$$f(\mathbf{u}, +\infty) = F(\mathbf{u}; n_2, q_2\hat{x}, T_2). \tag{11}$$

The upstream and downstream equilibrium conditions are related by the Rankine-Hugoniot relations, and the problem is characterized by a single dimensionless parameter, the Mach number M.

A new independent variable τ is defined by

$$\tau = \int_0^x v(t) \, dt/q_1. \tag{12}$$

As in Section III, A the kinetic equation can be formally integrated to yield expressions for the half-range distribution functions, e.g.,

$$f^+(\mathbf{u}, \tau) = \frac{q_1}{u} \int_{-\infty}^{\tau} \exp\left[-(\tau - t)\frac{q_1}{u}\right] F(\mathbf{u}; n, q\hat{x}, T) \, dt. \tag{13}$$

Substitution of these expressions in the integrals defining n, q, and T yields a set of singular, nonlinear integral equations. Conservation of mass implies $nq = n_1 q_1$. This relation is used to express n in terms of q, and to eliminate one of the integral equations. Exact solution of the problem involves solving the remaining two equations for q and T.

B. Approximation Procedures

We prescribe the velocity dependence of the distribution function by an approximate form containing a finite number of τ-dependent parameters. Krook (1959) has proposed approximate forms which generalize that of Mott-Smith (1951). We have obtained solutions based on a number of these forms and extensions thereof. For concreteness and brevity we consider here only the three approximate forms:

Bimodal: $f = (A_{10} + A_{11}u + A_{12}u^2)F(\mathbf{u}; n_1, q_1\hat{x}, T_1)$

$\qquad\qquad + (A_{20} + A_{21}u)F(\mathbf{u}; n_2, q_2\hat{x}, T_2),$ (14)

Trimodal I: $f = A_{11}uF(\mathbf{u}; n_1, q_1\hat{x}, T_1) + A_{21}uF(\mathbf{u}; n_2, q_2\hat{x}, T_2)$

$\qquad\qquad + F(\mathbf{u}; n, q\hat{x}, T),$ (15)

Trimodal II: $f = (A_{11}u + A_{12}u^2 + A_{13}u^3)F(\mathbf{u}; n_1, q_1\hat{x}, T_1)$

$\qquad\qquad + (A_{21}u + A_{22}u^2)F(\mathbf{u}; n_2, q_2\hat{x}, T_2)$

$\qquad\qquad + F(\mathbf{u}; n, q\hat{x}, T).$ (16)

The parameter A_{ij} are unspecified functions of τ.

To determine n, q, T, and the parameters A_{ij}, we utilize appropriate sets of moment equations. To ensure conservation of mass, momentum, and energy we demand that three of the moment equations be based on the polynomials 1, u, and $\mathbf{u}^2$. These three moment equations are used in their integrated forms expressing constancy of the moments involved. To these conservation relations we add moment equations based on the polynomials u^2 and $u\mathbf{u}^2$, thus defining a complete set of equations for the Bimodal form (14).

The trimodal forms (15) and (16) involve the local number density n, flow velocity q, and temperature T. Substitution of these forms in the integrals defining n, q, and T yields algebraic *compatibility conditions* for the parameters involved in the forms. To the conservation relations and compatibility conditions we add the moment equation based on the polynomial u^2; for the form (16) we also add the moment equation based on $u\mathbf{u}^2$. We thus define complete sets of equations for the trimodal forms.

Any moment can be expressed in terms of the τ-dependent functions involved in a form by substituting the form in the integral defining the moment. Expressing each moment involved in the equations for a form in this way yields a complete set of equations for the τ-dependent functions. The algebraic equations of the set are used to eliminate some of the τ-dependent functions. The resulting set of ordinary differential equations must be solved subject to the following boundary conditions:

Bimodal: $A_{ij}(-\infty) = \delta_{i1}\delta_{j0}, \qquad A_{ij}(+\infty) = \delta_{i2}\delta_{j0};$

Trimodal I, II: $A_{ij}(\pm\infty) = 0.$ (17)

C. Computational Aspects

The exact problem reduces to that of solving three singular, nonlinear integral equations for n, q, and T. We use the law of conservation of mass,

$nq = n_1q_1$, to eliminate n and one of the integral equations from the problem. The kernel function

$$H_n(p, q) = \frac{1}{\sqrt{2\pi}} \int_0^\infty du\ u^{n-2} \exp[-(u - p)^2/2 - q/u] \tag{18}$$

which appears in the equations has been studied in quite some detail and its properties will be reported elsewhere shortly (Anderson and Macomber, 1964). The problem is replaced by a discrete analog in which the dependent variables are represented by truncated Chebyshev polynomial expansions with argument $\tanh[(z - \tau_0)/\delta]$, and the integral operators are replaced by quadrature formulas. τ_0 and δ are adjustable parameters of the representation which are determined by certain numerical considerations. The resulting finite set of nonlinear transcendental equations for the Chebyshev expansion coefficients is solved iteratively by methods which will be described elsewhere. Liepmann *et al.* (1962) have considered basically the same problem but have adopted a different computational procedure and obtained somewhat different results.

From a numerical point of view the shock wave problem is a rather peculiar one. The iteration proceeds satisfactorily in its early stages, though the process is ill-conditioned and slowly convergent. After about ten or fifteen iterations the process becomes stationary and the solution is not improved by further iteration. Extensive experimentation suggests that this difficulty is due to the invariance of the equations under translation of the coordinate system; to obtain a unique solution the value of one of the dependent variables must be specified at $\tau = 0$. Because one iteration requires approximately one-half minute on the IBM 7094, various devices for alleviating this difficulty have been investigated in simpler model problems. None of these devices have proved successful in the original problem. For this reason the solutions obtained thus far probably contain only two to three significant figures. Results have been obtained for $M = 1.2, 1.5, 2.0, 3.0, 5.0, 7.0,$ and 10.0

The approximation procedure, in the cases considered, results in one or two autonomous ordinary differential equations. The numerical solution is easily obtained in the one-equation case. In the two-equation case numerical integration in the phase plane is required. Solutions accurate to five significant figures have been obtained for $M = 1.5, 3.0,$ and 5.0.

D. Comparison of Solutions

Figures 10 through 15 show approximate and exact normalized velocity and temperature profiles for two Mach numbers, 1.5 and 5.0. The origin of coordinates is taken as that point at which the normalized velocity and temperature profiles intersect. It should be noted that the independent variable is τ rather than x; this makes the profiles more symmetrical and affects their relative positions. It is found that if the characteristic velocity

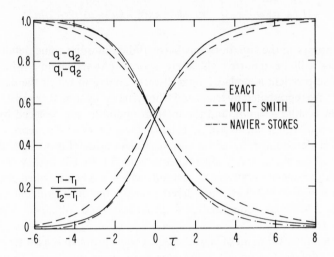

FIG. 10. Shock wave velocity and temperature profiles ($M = 1.5$).

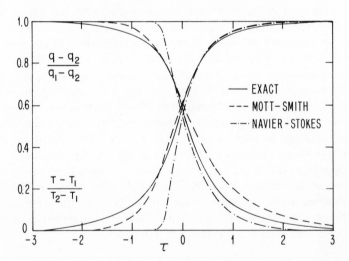

FIG. 11. Shock wave velocity and temperature profiles ($M = 5.0$).

involved in the definition of τ is taken as $\sqrt{kT_2/m}$ rather than q_1, the profiles for $M = 5.0$ and $M = 10.0$ are essentially identical. This suggests that the limiting profiles as $M \to \infty$ are essentially those obtained for $M = 10.0$.

All graphs show the exact profiles. Figures 10 and 11 show profiles based on the approximate form of Mott-Smith (1951) and the u^2 moment equation as well as Navier-Stokes profiles based on the application of the Chapman-

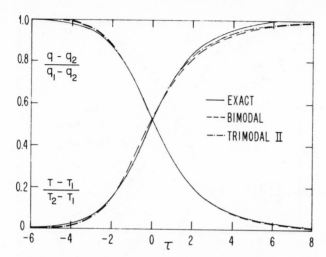

FIG. 12. Shock wave velocity and temperature profiles ($M = 1.5$).

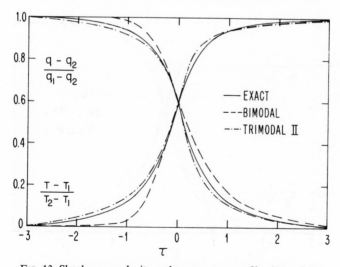

FIG. 13. Shock wave velocity and temperature profiles ($M = 5.0$).

Enskog procedure to the Krook equation. The Mott-Smith profiles are relatively inaccurate for either Mach number. The Navier-Stokes and exact profiles agree quite well at $M = 1.5$ but poorly at $M = 5.0$; the discrepancy in the velocity profiles downstream is considerably greater than that reported by Chahine (1962).

Figures 12 and 13 show profiles based on the Bimodal and Trimodal II

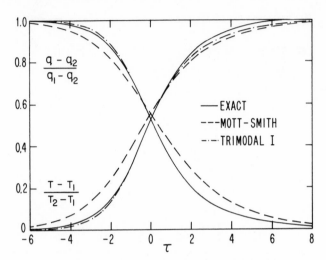

Fig. 14. Shock wave velocity and temperature profiles ($M = 1.5$).

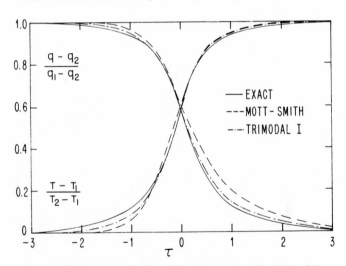

Fig. 15. Shock wave velocity and temperature profiles ($M = 5.0$).

approximation procedures described in Section IV, B. Both procedures result in a pair of ordinary differential equations and are of comparable complexity. The agreement with the exact profiles for $M = 1.5$ is quite good, in fact better than at $M = 5.0$. This is perhaps surprising since both procedures are generalizations of that of Mott-Smith. Figures 14 and 15 show Mott-Smith profiles and profiles based on the Trimodal I approximation procedure. Both procedures involve the solution of a single ordinary differential equation, and hence are of comparable complexity. However, the Trimodal I profiles are considerably more accurate than the Mott-Smith profiles. In general, trimodal approximation procedures are more accurate than those of a bimodal character.

V. Conclusion

Approximate and exact solutions of the Krook kinetic equation have been obtained for two steady, one-dimensional problems. Comparison of these solutions provides some insight into the accuracy of certain approximation procedures. The comparison suggests that relatively simple procedures can yield acceptably accurate results—at least in the context of the Krook equation. A modicum of justification is thereby obtained for the extension of such procedures to more complicated problems whose exact solution is not feasible.

ACKNOWLEDGMENT

The authors are grateful to Professor Max Krook for suggesting the problem and for helpful criticism of the manuscript.

REFERENCES

Abramowitz, M. (1953). *J. Math. and Phys.* **32**, 188.
Anderson, D. G. (1963). Numerical Experiments in Kinetic Theory, Ph.D. Thesis, Harvard University, Cambridge, Massachusetts.
Anderson, D. G., and Macomber, H. K. (1964). To be published.
Chahine, M. T. (1963). *In* "Rarefied Gas Dynamics" (J. Laurmann, ed.), Vol. I, p. 260. Academic Press, New York.
Krook, M. (1955). *Phys. Rev.* **99**, 1896.
Krook, M. (1959). *J. Fluid Mech.* **6**, 523.
Liepmann, H. W., Narasimha, R., and Chahine, M. T. (1962). *Phys. Fluids* **5**, 1313.
Macomber, H. K. (1965). Moment Methods for Non-linear Problems in Kinetic Theory, Ph.D. Thesis, Harvard University, Cambridge, Massachusetts.
Mott-Smith, H. M. (1951). *Phys. Rev.* **82**, 885.
Willis, D. R. (1962). *Phys. Fluids* **5**, 127.
Willis, D. R. (1963). *In* "Rarefied Gas Dynamics" (J. Laurmann, ed.), Vol. I, p. 209. Academic Press, New York.

An Analysis of Some Rarefied Gas Phenomena from the Molecular Approach[1]

WALTER J. SCHAETZLE

University of Alabama, Tuscaloosa, Alabama

The study of gas dynamics from the macroscopic approach loses much of the physical picture of collisions between molecules, and between molecules and surfaces. This approach deals with gas dynamics by directly considering the collisions between molecules, collisions between molecules and surfaces, and the distance molecules travel between collisions. The molecular movement is traced by a large digital computer through the tabulation of the individual molecule numbers, momentums in two dimensions, and energies. The procedure is very similar to the Monte Carlo techniques used by many rarefied gas flow investigators. The simplified boundary conditions associated with the technique allow the disclosure of much information lost in the oversimplification of the differential equations and the boundary conditions normally required in rarefied gas dynamics to obtain results.

In this paper the technique is applied to the compressible flow over the leading edge of a flat plate at a slightly supersonic velocity. Some of the effects observed include the leading edge slip effects, and a step velocity normal to the plate. These and other rarefied gas flow phenomena resulting from this problem are discussed.

I. Introduction

An analysis of rarefied gas flow fields is made by a study of the collisions of the individual molecules. This is basically done by assuming a molecular distribution over the flow field and then determining the resulting conditions at individual points in the field through the use of basic kinetic theory. If the new value disagrees with the assumed value, it is replaced by a modified value. This process continues until the entire flow field is in equilibrium with the

[1] All large computer runs were made on the IBM 7094 computer at and through the courtesy of Marshall Space Flight Center.

112

boundary conditions. The conditions assigned are free stream values outside the field and the manner in which molecules reflect from surfaces. Basically the solutions result from counting molecules and their properties as they move through the flow field and represent the compressible gas version of previous work by the author (Schaetzle, 1962, 1963).

The primary advantage of the technique in solving problems is that every phase of the flow field is determined from the physical reaction of molecules. As a result rarefied gas phenomena, such as a normal step velocity at a surface, can be explained through this intimate relation with the individual molecule reactions. Also, the boundary conditions associated with this type of analysis are very basic and place only very limited restrictions on any gas flow problem.

In most closed analytical solutions the differential equations and boundary conditions must be simplified to a degree where the rarefied gas problem loses much of its meaning. An example where these conditions produced impractical results is the transition flow through a tube. The Navier-Stokes equations were correctly modified to handle flow with slip boundary conditions at the surfaces. However, the boundary conditions imposed included the free stream velocity at the entrance along with the Knudsen slip velocity conditions (Schaaf, 1961). The results included a slip velocity of over 80 per cent of free stream velocity at the entrance. It might be noted that free molecular flow with diffuse reflection results in a slip velocity of only 50 per cent of free stream velocity. The result came about because the acquirable solution required oversimplified boundary conditions. If the boundary conditions could have been set up at the tube entrance the solution would have given excellent results. Continuum solutions give excellent results in most cases, but have definite limitations in certain rarefied gas flow problems.

The main problem solved in this paper is the compressible flow over the leading edge of a flat plate. The boundary conditions imposed are the free stream molecular distribution in front and above the plate and diffuse reflection of molecules from the plate. The free stream velocity is prescribed by a modified Mach number (free stream velocity divided by average molecule velocity) of 1.15. The area analyzed reaches 4.5 mean free paths in front of the plate, 8 mean free paths along the plate and 10 mean free paths above the plate. The results include the tangential and normal velocity distributions in this region. The normal velocity distribution includes a step v eocity at the plate surface, while the tangential velocities show a slight increase after the initial velocity drop at the leading edge. The major difficulty was the limitation on available computer time.

The physical phenomena from the above results and previous results of the author are analyzed into basic molecular flow concepts. These include the tangential velocity jump, the normal step velocity, and the Knudsen layer.

II. Method of Analysis

The technical analysis is similar to the analysis in Schaetzle (1962, 1963) except compressible flow parameters are included. A detailed analysis is given in these references so only an outline of the procedure is given. The concept is to set up a molecular distribution flow field in a volume with specific boundary conditions. In this case the conditions are the free stream conditions at specific distances forward and above the flat plate. In the flow field the conditions are first assumed. Then through an integration over the flow field volume around a point, the conditions at the point are determined by the properties of the molecules moving past the point. If these values disagree with the assumed value, a new value is determined as a function of the previously assumed value and the calculated value. This process continues until the entire flow field is in equilibrium with the surrounding boundary conditions. This results in a relaxation technique very similar to the heat conduction relaxation technique for odd shaped configurations as discussed in Jakob (1949).

A. The Integration

The integration determines the number of molecules and their properties which pass a point as a function of the entire flow field. In order to physically determine the number of molecules which pass a point and their properties, such as energy, momentum, etc., an area element dA is considered at the point. The numbers and properties are then determined by the quantity passing through the area element. In the flow field the area element is allowed to rotate so all molecules enter perpendicular to the element, but on a surface the element is held fixed parallel to the surface. In the flow field the probability of interaction must be equal from all directions but on a surface the probability of interaction is a function of the direction of the approaching molecules.

The integration is based on molecules having a collision and then passing through dA without another collision. On this basis the number of molecules, the x-momentum and the energy passing through dA are, respectively:

$$\frac{dN}{dA} = \iiint\limits_{-\infty}^{+\infty} dx\, dy\, dz \iiint\limits_{-\infty}^{+\infty} du\, dv\, dw [N_c(x, y, c)]$$

$$\times \left[\exp\left(-\frac{\sqrt{x^2 + y^2 + z^2}}{l(x, y, u, c)} \right) \right] \left[\frac{d\Omega(x, y, z, u, c)}{4\pi} \right] \qquad (1)$$

$$\frac{dM_x}{dA} = \iiint\limits_{-\infty}^{+\infty} dx\, dy\, dz \iiint\limits_{-\infty}^{+\infty} du\, dv\, dw\, C_x[N_c(x, y, u, c)]$$

$$\times \left[\exp\left(-\frac{\sqrt{x^2 + y^2 + z^2}}{l(x, y, u, c)}\right)\right]\left[\frac{d\Omega(x, y, z, u, c)}{4\pi}\right] \qquad (2)$$

$$\frac{dE}{dA} = \iiint\limits_{-\infty}^{+\infty} dx\, dy\, dz \iiint\limits_{-\infty}^{+\infty} du\, dv\, dw\, C^2[N_c(x, y, u, c)]$$

$$\times \left[\exp\left(-\frac{\sqrt{x^2 + y^2 + z^2}}{l(x, y, u, c)}\right)\right]\left[\frac{d\Omega(x, y, z, u, c)}{4\pi}\right]. \qquad (3)$$

In the solution, these equations are numerically integrated.

The collision parameter $N_c(x, y, u, c)$ represents the molecules which collide in the volume element. The molecules entering the element have come from 480 elements, each of which can have an individual molecule distribution. After the collisions in the element a Maxwellian distribution is assumed for the molecules after collision. However, the properties in the element are based on the 480 different distributions. The properties of the molecules after collision are based on the conservation of number, momentum, and energy. In the numerical integration, the molecules having a collision in the element are divided into 15 groups of molecules as a function of the individual molecule velocities.

The mean free path l is allowed to vary as a function of density, the relative velocity between the starting point and ending point, and the individual molecule velocities.

The solid angle Ω is a function of location, individual molecule velocities and relative velocity V. Schaetzle (1962) gives a detailed analysis of the solid angle variations.

The molecular distributions, the mean free path variations, the probabilities of collision, etc. are determined directly from the elementary kinetic theory in Loeb (1934), Chapman (1960), and Jeans (1960).

B. Definitions

The properties at a point are defined as

$$\rho = \frac{dN}{dA}\Big/\bar{c} \qquad (4)$$

$$V = \frac{dM_x}{dA}\Big/\frac{dN}{dA} \qquad (5)$$

$$V_y = \frac{dM_y}{dA} \bigg/ \frac{dN}{dA} \tag{6}$$

$$E = \frac{dE}{dA} \bigg/ \frac{dN}{dA}. \tag{7}$$

The definition for density is in accord with the classical volume element definition, but the values for velocity and energy show some variation for a noncontinuum fluid. For a continuum fluid the definitions are in complete agreement as a $\bar{c}$ could be used to divide the numerator and denominator of each term. It might be noted that probes inserted into the fluid would detect the above quantities.

C. Boundary Conditions

The boundary conditions include the free stream molecule velocity distribution and the plate reflections. The stream conditions are given a Maxwellian distribution with an imposed free stream velocity. The molecules colliding with a surface are reflected with a diffuse reflection at the plate temperature. The plate temperature is taken as in equilibrium with the energy level of the incoming molecules, that is, adiabatic recovery is assumed. The number of incoming and reflected molecules is equal.

D. Error Analysis

The primary errors are a function of the finite element size and the limited number of velocity elements in the numerical integrations. Also causing appreciable errors are the finite integrations, the approximated variation in density, and the limit on the flow field size due to computer size limitations.

The volume elements varied from cubical 0.05 free stream mean free paths near the point of consideration to cubical 0.25 free stream mean free paths at distances of more than 1 mean free path from the point of consideration. The errors due to the finite size (Schaetzle, 1960) are less than 2 per cent in the overall problem.

The velocity distribution is divided into 15 increments with the maximum velocity increment at 2.05 times the average molecule velocity. At high-stream velocities the molecules moving upstream are appreciably effected. The error with these molecules may be as high as 50 per cent as a modified Mach number of 1.2; however, less than 5 per cent of the molecules move upstream at this velocity so the overall error is still less than 2.5 per cent. The effect is felt in the last problem.

The integrations extended 10 mean free paths upstream from the leading edge, 5 mean free paths downstream from this point, 4 mean free paths above and below this point and 5 mean free paths to either side of this point. Less than 1 per cent of the molecules were lost due to the integration limits.

The density between the collision point and the property recording point is assumed to be the average between the two points. In some cases and especially for the velocity jump this causes appreciable error. However, most molecules come from the immediate area of the recording point and the solid angle effect is as large as the mean free path effect, so that the over-all error is still less than 5 per cent.

Owing to computer size limitations the flow field was limited in size. This prohibits the field from changing at the boundaries. However as the primary changes occur directly at the leading edge the effect of the flow boundaries on this area is small and for this reason, only the results near the leading edge are included. The results indicate that the limits used are very reasonable.

The combination of over-all errors is determined to be less than 5 per cent of the free stream velocity over the entire field and the errors directly over the leading edge of the flat plate are less than 3 per cent of the free stream velocity.

III. Computer Conversion and Limitations

The problem was converted to a form suitable for the digital computer by first integrating over the velocity distribution and z-axis at seven modified Mach numbers. This data is stored in the computer and all additional integrations are made with this data, using approximations for changes in density and energy. With the use of this technique the computer time is approximately reduced by a factor of 30. Even with this reduction the final computer time was 15 minutes per iteration for the utilized flow area. This is an increase by a factor of 4 over the incompressible cases previously run.

The convergence was fairly rapid and after twelve iterations, the velocities were fluctuating by less than one per cent. The energy level and density had slightly higher fluctuations. However, it should be noted that the starting assumption had energies and densities twice as high as the final ones. Considering this the convergence was satisfactory.

IV. Results

The results using the described technique are given in Figs. 1 through 6. The figures are limited primarily to velocities, however, some effect of the density and energy changes will be noted.

Figures 1 and 2 give the tangential velocity profiles in the incompressible flow regime at a free stream modified Mach number of 0.2. These figures are

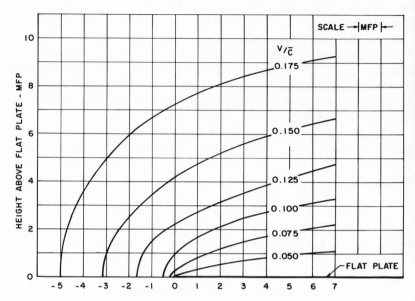

FIG. 1. Constant tangential velocities with $V_0/\bar{c} = 0.2$.

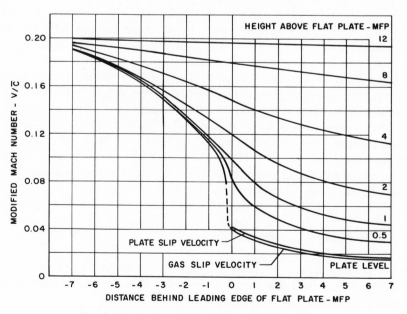

FIG. 2. Tangential velocity profiles with $V_0/\bar{c} = 0.2$.

identical to the curves in Schaetzle (1963), and are presented primarily for comparison with the compressible flow case. Figure 1 gives constant velocity lines and Fig. 2 gives the velocity variation at various heights above the plate. The steepness of the velocity drop should be noted. This drop could be a miniature shock wave, however the small thickness should be noted. The change in velocity 0.5 mean free paths above the plate shows more resemblance to a shock wave.

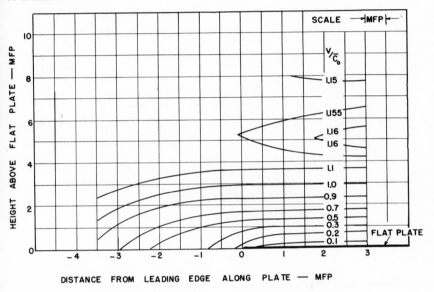

FIG. 3. Constant tangential velocities with $V_0/\bar{c} = 1.15$.

Figures 3 through 6 give the tangential and normal velocity profiles for a free stream modified Mach number of 1.15. The velocity profiles in Fig. 3 tend to flatten out appreciably compared to those in Fig. 1. Also there is a slight increase in velocity from about 0.5 to 2.0 mean free paths above the plate behind the leading edge. The effect is attributed to the pressure increase at the leading edge which immediately decays. The decay rate could not be calculated as the length of the calculated flow field was too limited. Future calculations are expected to clearly define this parameter.

Figure 4 gives the velocity profiles normal to the plate. It should be noted that these velocities reach a maximum of 11 per cent of the free stream velocity. These are also attributed to the density buildup at the plate edge. It might also be noted that the normal velocity at the plate edge does not reach zero. This is discussed later.

Figure 5 gives the tangential flow field at the plate and 0.5 mean free paths above the plate. Both profiles closely resemble a miniature shock and do not

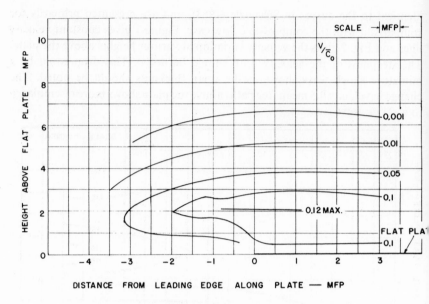

FIG. 4. Constant normal velocities with $V_0/\bar{c} = 1.15$.

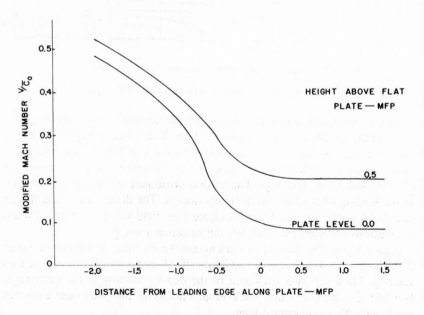

FIG. 5. Tangential velocity profiles with $V_0/\bar{c} = 1.15$.

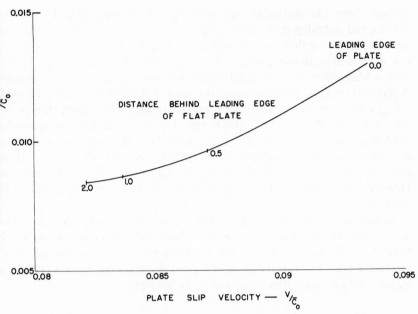

FIG. 6. Tangential velocity versus normal velocity for $V_0/\bar{c} = 1.15$.

show the steepness exhibited by the plate level profile in Fig. 2. This is attributed to the backflow of the density buildup.

Figure 6 gives the tangential and normal velocities on the plate surface. At first glance a normal velocity adjacent to the surface seems impossible, since the mass flow is zero in the normal direction, however, a study of the

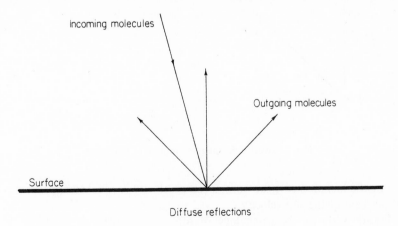

FIG. 7. Normal jump velocity schematic.

reaction from the molecular view indicates this occurs. Consider the incoming and outgoing molecules in Fig. 7. The incoming molecules arrive at the plate with a random velocity and twice the slip velocity. The slip velocity is converted to random energy and the molecules leave in a cosine distribution with a Maxwellian velocity distribution but with a higher random velocity. A physical analysis clearly indicates the normal momentum leaving the plate is higher than the normal momentum approaching the plate. According to the special definition of velocity in this report (Eq. 5), the velocity is equal to the total momentum flux divided by the mass flux. It should be noted this definition basically agrees with Grad (1958), Eq. 17.2. This results from the derivation of Boltzmann's equation which is initiated through the Hamiltonian equations. These equations are basically the conservation of momentum.

At first glance this violates the continuity equation, but the normal continuity equation is derived for a continuous fluid. This is not a continuous fluid. Now if continuity is applied to the incoming and reflected molecules separately, the mass flow is still zero, as the densities in both directions vary. This satisfies the zero mass flow condition at the boundary.

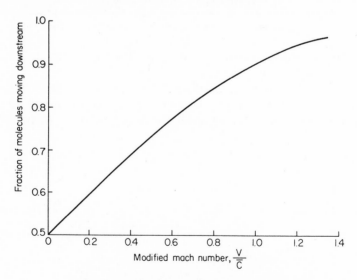

FIG. 8. Relative downstream motion of molecules.

For the included case the normal jump velocity is equal to approximately 10 per cent of the slip velocity.

Figure 8 shows the percentage of molecules moving downstream as a function of modified Mach number up to a value slightly over 1.2. This basically shows the percentage of upstream molecules providing the properties at each point.

Haviland (1963) and Chahine (1963) and a number of other authors give the flow solution through a normal shock. Drawing a line through the center of the shock and letting either side disappear sets up a flow pattern with a discontinuity. Slicing the velocity jump in Figs. 2 and 5 creates the same discontinuity. A similar thing occurs in the Knudsen layer next to a surface. Now if the surface of each of discontinuities is penetrated by the same fraction of an effective mean free path, the percentage of discontinuity compared to the normal flow is approximately the same. Basically a shock wave is therefore very similar to the Knudsen layer.

In general the molecular approach will give a solution to gas dynamic problems, but, like the Monte Carlo method, require computers 100 to 10,000 times faster than present day models. However, analyzing gas dynamics from the molecular approach gives a clear physical insight to the gas dynamic phenomena.

List of Symbols

A	Area	m	Mass of a molecule
c	Individual molecule velocity	N	Number of molecules
$\bar{c}$	Random average molecule velocity	V	Velocity parallel to the plate
$\bar{c}_0$	Random free stream average molecule velocity	V_0	Free stream velocity
		V_y	Velocity normal to the plate
E	Energy	u, v, w	Molecule velocities in x, y, and z directions
l	Mean free path		
M	Momentum	Ω	Solid angle
M	Modified Mach number (velocity divided by average molecule velocity)		

REFERENCES

Chahine, M. T. (1963). *In* "Rarefied Gas Dynamics" (J. A. Laurmann, ed.), Vol. I, p. 260. Academic Press, New York.

Chapman, S., and Cowling, T. G. (1960). "The Mathematical Theory of Nonuniform Gases." Cambridge Univ. Press, London and New York.

Grad, H. (1958). *In* "Handbuch der Physik" (S. Flugge, ed.). Springer, Berlin.

Haviland, J. K. (1963). *In* "Rarefied Gas Dynamics" (J. A. Laurman, ed.), Vol. I, p. 274. Academic Press, New York.

Jakob, M. (1961). "Heat Transfer," Vol. I, p. 366. Wiley, New York.

Jeans, J. H. (1960). "Introduction to Kinetic Theory." Cambridge Univ. Press, London and New York.

Loeb, L. B. (1934). "The Kinetic Theory of Gases." McGraw-Hill, New York.

Schaaf, S. A., and Chambre, P. L. (1959). *In* "Fundamentals of Gas Dynamics" (H. W. Emmons, ed.), p. 687. Princeton Univ. Press, Princeton, New Jersey.

Schaetzle, W. J. (1962). A Molecular Approach to Rarefied Gas Dynamics, Doctoral Dissertation, Washington University, St. Louis.

Schaetzle, W. J. (1963). *In* "Rarefied Gas Dynamics" (J. A. Laurmann, ed.), Vol. I, p. 136. Academic Press, New York.

Steady Expansions at High-Speed Ratio Using the BGK Kinetic Model

JOHN W. BROOK AND RICHARD A. OMAN
Research Department, Grumman Aircraft Engineering Corporation, Bethpage, L.I., New York

Numerical calculations of axially symmetric and two-dimensional steady expansions of a monatomic gas have been carried out using an approximate Boltzmann equation with a Krook collision term. The calculations are performed for a variety of stagnation temperatures and sonic Reynolds numbers. At large distances from the sonic line, the velocity and density profiles follow the results predicted by inviscid flow theory, but the temperature "freezes" at a value dependent primarily on the sonic Reynolds number and stagnation temperature. A somewhat anomalous dependence of the final temperature on the particular initial distribution function used in the iterative procedure is also found. Transport data for argon have been used in the calculations.

I. Introduction

Freely expanding gas flows require an improvement of our understanding of the basic flow structure for more reliable use in a number of practical applications. These include formation and analysis of high-intensity molecular beams with nozzle sources, interaction of rocket exhaust plumes with surrounding structure and instrumentation in a high vacuum environment, and dissipation of gas sources in space. Although the first application originally led to this work, the present results have already proven useful in design analyses of several space vehicle problems.

We are interested in the processes that can best be described as departures from thermodynamic (as opposed to chemical) equilibrium. A particular aspect of these flows which makes them interesting from a theoretical point of view is the fact that a single flow can span the entire range of Knudsen numbers from continuum to free molecular. Furthermore, these flows can be formulated analytically without the need to consider surface interactions in

125

the analysis. The reasonable approximation of spherical or cylindrical symmetry (cf. Sherman, 1962) enables one to construct a manageable mathematical problem which retains the major features of the real flows.

We have chosen to employ the Bhatnagar-Gross-Krook model of the Boltzmann equation for a monatomic gas (Bhatnagar *et al.*, 1954) hereinafter called the Krook model. We feel that the Krook model is presently the only practical method for displaying the qualitative behavior of the important properties of the real flow in a tractable form.

Flow Structure

Before moving to the discussion of our method, a few comments concerning the general characteristics to be expected in high Mach number, low-density expansions should be helpful. The first point to be realized is that further changes in stream velocity in the subsequent flow will be small with respect to the velocity of the fluid anywhere within the range of interest, because the velocity is already quite close to the thermodynamic limit. If we limit our attention to steady flows, and employ conservation of mass to relate the density and velocity distributions, we find that (to a good asymptotic approximation) $\rho \sim r^{-\nu}$, where $\nu = 1$ or 2 depending on whether the flow is cylindrically or spherically symmetric. This result is not dependent on the local collision frequency and holds quite well throughout the expansion.[1] We therefore see that there can be little flexibility in the kinetic effects on the first two moments of the distribution function, the density, and the stream velocity. The effect on the temperature, however, is quite different.

We expect the temperature to approach some asymptotic value (i.e., to "freeze") as collisions become less frequent, and thereby to depart from the equilibrium or near-equilibrium temperature distribution.

The goal of this paper is to demonstrate the departure of the stream temperature from its near-equilibrium behavior and to furnish approximate criteria for predicting the onset of freezing and for predicting the asymptotic values of the temperature.

II. Description of Krook Model

For the analysis of the present problem, we employ the kinetic model of the Boltzmann equation first proposed by Bhatnagar *et al.* (1954), commonly called the Krook model. This model is discussed in detail elsewhere (e.g.,

---

[1] It can be shown that a "free-molecule expansion" due to angular dispersion of individual molecular velocities always diverges much less rapidly than a Prandtl-Meyer expansion at the corresponding speed ratio.

Fishman, 1959; Kogan, 1958; and Narasimha, 1961) and we will not elaborate upon those discussions here. It suffices to say that the model possesses at least the minimum requirements of a meaningful kinetic equation: it has the required five collisional invariants, it has an H-theorem, and it reduces to the equilibrium (Maxwellian) distribution in the long time limit of the spatially homogeneous case. Rott (1964) has also shown that the Krook model can be derived from the Boltzmann equation by a particular iterative procedure. The model equation also presents a significant computational saving compared with the full Boltzmann equation.

Quantitatively, the results derived from the Krook model are subject to an inherent uncertainty. For instance, it is known that the Chapman-Enskog procedure, when applied to this model, yields a Prandtl number of 1 (Narasimha, 1961), rather than the correct value for a monatomic gas (roughly $\frac{2}{3}$). Also, the collision frequency used in the Krook model is independent of the molecular velocity, which may produce appreciable errors in certain situations. However, for qualitative purposes, particularly when nonlinearity is important, the Krook model will probably reproduce most of the important features of any given flow. The only existing nonlinear solution of the model equation appears to be the work of Chahine (1962) concerning the structure of strong shock waves. Here it is shown that the expected breakdown of the Navier-Stokes equations does indeed take place (Liepmann et al., 1962). Furthermore, maximum slope shock thicknesses based on the kinetic equation are very close to those calculated from the corresponding Navier-Stokes equations (with $Pr = 1$) for all Mach numbers. However, shock thickness based on the area under the temperature profile are from 1.5 to about 4 times larger (for $M_\infty = 3$ and 10, respectively) than the corresponding Navier-Stokes thicknesses. A similar qualitative result would probably be shown by an exact solution of the Boltzmann equation.

As a final note, we mention that the above solution of the plane shock problem, while being among the simplest of kinetic problems, consumed a considerable amount of computing time even with the use of the Krook model.

III. Mathematical Formulation

The problem we consider is an idealized model of the steady expansion of a monatomic gas with either spherical or cylindrical symmetry. In a spherical or cylindrical coordinate system the convective operator of the Boltzmann equation contains terms involving derivatives of the velocity distribution function with respect to the (thermal) velocity components. If one removes the singular part of these terms, the rest are of higher order in the local speed ratio and the convective term can be approximated by[2]

$$\tilde{v}_r \frac{d}{dr}(\tilde{r}^\nu f) = \tilde{A}n(\tilde{r}^\nu F - \tilde{r}^\nu f) \tag{1}$$

or, defining $\varphi = \tilde{r}^\nu f$ and $\Phi = \tilde{r}^\nu F$, we get

$$\tilde{v}_r \frac{d\varphi}{d\tilde{r}} = \tilde{A}n(\Phi - \varphi) \tag{2}$$

where f is the number density of molecules in phase space, the product An is the collision frequency (assumed independent of $\mathbf{v}$), F is the local Maxwellian (equilibrium) velocity distribution function, $\tilde{v}_r$ is the component of velocity in the radial direction; $\nu = 2$ for spherical symmetry, and $\nu = 1$ for cylindrical symmetry: ($\tilde{}$) denotes dimensional quantities.

We express the Maxwellian as follows:

$$F = \frac{n}{(2\pi RT)^{3/2}} \exp -\left\{\frac{1}{2RT}[\mathbf{v} - \mathbf{u}]^2]\right\} \tag{3}$$

where n is the local number density of particles in physical space, T the local translational temperature, R the gas constant, and $\mathbf{u}$ the local mass velocity. By definition,

$$n = \int f \, d\mathbf{v} \tag{4}$$

$$n\mathbf{u} = \int \mathbf{v}f \, d\mathbf{v} \tag{5}$$

$$\tfrac{3}{2}nRT = \int \tfrac{1}{2}(\mathbf{v} - \mathbf{u})^2 f \, d\mathbf{v}. \tag{6}$$

Narasimha (1961) has discussed the choice of the parameter A. By carrying out the Chapman-Enskog expansion for the Krook model, he showed $A = mRT/\mu$, where m is the molecular mass and μ the coefficient of viscosity. If it is desired to match the viscosity, this relation can be employed.

Similarly, the heat conduction coefficient is found to depend upon A. However, the resulting Prandtl number does not have the correct value for a monatomic gas so that either the viscosity or the heat conduction coefficients

---

[2] The omitted convection terms are

$$\frac{(v_\theta^2 + v_\phi^2)}{r} \frac{\partial\varphi}{\partial v_r} - \frac{v_r}{r}\left[\frac{\partial\varphi}{\partial v_\phi} + \frac{\partial\varphi}{\partial v_\theta} + \nu\varphi\right] + \frac{v_\phi \cot\theta}{r} v_\theta \frac{\partial\varphi}{\partial v_\theta} - v_\theta \frac{\partial\varphi}{\partial v_\phi}$$

where (r, θ, ϕ) is the orthogonal spherical coordinate system, and v_θ and v_ϕ are the corresponding molecular velocity components. All terms involving v_ϕ are zero for the cylindrical case. We are grateful to F. S. Sherman and D. R. Willis for calling our attention to these terms, and to Y. P. Pao for communicating them to us.

can be matched, but not both. The collision frequency becomes p/μ, where p is the pressure. Narasimha also states that in low density flows, the choice $A = (5/4)p/\mu$ is more appropriate because it matches the number of collisions per unit volume per unit time, which is a more important quantity than the viscosity for these cases. Employing the latter dependency and introducing a reference length L_{ref} and a reference velocity V_{ref}, Eq. (6) becomes

$$\frac{d}{d\xi}(v_x\varphi) + \varphi = \Phi \tag{7}$$

where

$$\xi = \frac{3}{4}\frac{Re_{ref}}{M_{ref}^2}\int_{x_{ref}}^x \frac{p}{\mu}\,dx'$$

$$x = \tilde{r}/L_{ref}, \qquad v_x = \tilde{v}_r/L_{ref}, \qquad P = \tilde{P}/P_{ref}, \qquad \mu = \tilde{\mu}/\mu_{ref}$$

$$u = \tilde{u}/u_{ref}, \qquad Re_{ref} = \rho_{ref}V_{ref}L_{ref}/\mu_{ref}$$

$$M_{ref}^2 = (3/5)V_{ref}^2/RT_{ref}$$

P_{ref}, ρ_{ref}, T_{ref}, and μ_{ref} are the reference pressure, density, temperature, and coefficient of viscosity, respectively, at $r = L_{ref}$. Since any supersonic flow is generated by passage of the flow through a sonic region, we shall use the sonic conditions as reference quantities. The reference Mach number, M_{ref}, is then unity, and the reference Reynolds number, Re_{ref}, is redesignated Re^*. Similarly, other quantities at sonic velocity will be denoted by an asterisk. Defining the stretched variable ξ to be zero at $r = L_{ref} = L^*$, we find

$$\xi = \tfrac{3}{4}\,Re^*\int_1^x \frac{p}{\mu}\,dx'. \tag{8}$$

The solution of Eq. (7) can be formally represented as[3]

$$\varphi = \varphi_0{}^+ e^{-(\xi-\xi_0)/v_x} + H(v_x)\int_{\xi_0}^\xi \frac{\Phi(\xi', \mathbf{v})}{v_x}\exp-\left(\frac{\xi-\xi'}{v_x}\right)d\xi'$$

$$+ H(-v_x)\left\{\int_\infty^\xi \frac{\Phi(\xi', \mathbf{v})}{v_x}\exp-\left(\frac{\xi-\xi'}{v_x}\right)d\xi'\right.$$

$$+ \left.\left[\varphi_0{}^- - \int_\infty^{\xi_0}\frac{\Phi(\xi', \mathbf{v})}{v_x}\exp\frac{\xi'-\xi_0}{v_x}d\xi'\right]e^{-(\xi-\xi_0)/v_x}\right\} \tag{9}$$

[3] An analysis of the neglected convective terms (Brook, 1965) shows that the error in the integrands Eq. (9) due to the use of the approximate Eq. (1) is of the order

$$\frac{1}{Re^*}x^{-\kappa}$$

where κ is a positive number of order unity, which depends upon the viscosity-temperature relationship.

where $H(\pm v_x)$ is the Heaviside step function. The subscript 0 applies to quantities where the initial condition is applied. The initial condition is represented by prescribing the velocity distribution function at $x = x_0$ for positive $(\varphi_0{}^+)$ and negative $(\varphi_0{}^-)$ values of the velocity v_x. Thus, the first two terms of Eq. (9) refer to particles moving in the positive direction with respect to a fixed coordinate system and the other terms refer to particles moving in the negative direction ("back scattering"). Note that $\varphi_0{}^-$ is determined by setting the term in square brackets in Eq. (9) equal to zero and cannot be prescribed *a priori*. The choice of the initial distribution will be discussed in more detail later. The results presented in this paper have been computed neglecting the back scattering contributions, an assumption which is consistent with the assumption of high-speed ratio.

Chahine (1962) showed that the solution of the Krook equation for the normal shock problem could be found by a process of successive iteration on the formal integral solutions, Eq. (9). Since the integrands in Eq. (9) are in turn integrals of f [Eqs. (3)–(5)], the iteration procedure must be started by using a known solution. Chahine chose to use as the first iterate the Navier-Stokes shock profiles because, among other reasons, the iterative procedure proved unable to eliminate the singular behavior of the zeroth order or inviscid shock solution.

For the present calculation we have chosen to employ the inviscid (equilibrium) solution associated with a spherical or cylindrically symmetric steady source as the first iterate. In a spherical or cylindrical coordinate system, the Euler equation can be combined with the continuity equation to give the governing equation of the flow

$$\left(1 - \frac{u^2}{a^2}\right)\frac{du}{dr} + \frac{uv}{r} = 0 \tag{10}$$

where a is the local sound speed. Using the energy equation and introducing the variable $W = u/u^*$, we find Eq. (10) to be (for a monatomic gas)

$$\frac{1 - W^2}{1 - \frac{1}{2}W^2}\frac{dW}{dx} + \frac{Wv}{x} = 0. \tag{11}$$

The solution of Eq. (10) is

$$\frac{(4 - W^2)^{3/2}}{3^{3/2}W} = x^v. \tag{12}$$

Using Eq. (12) and the isentropic relations enables one to find the other flow properties.

Before proceeding further, let us return briefly to the model equation to define a useful property of the flow. We rewrite Eq. (6) in a different non-dimensional form:

$$\varepsilon v \frac{d\varphi}{dx} = \Phi - \varphi \tag{13}$$

where

$$v = \tilde{v}_r/u, \qquad x = \tilde{r}/L.$$

In the above, u is the *local* mass velocity, and L is a new characteristic length which depends on local flow gradients. The parameter ε can be expressed as

$$\varepsilon = \frac{4}{5}\frac{\mu u}{pL} = \frac{4}{5}\frac{\mu u}{pT}\frac{dT}{dx}, \tag{14}$$

if we choose $L = T/(dT/dx)$, which is appropriate in this case.

Solutions to Eq. (13) can be expected to remain near equilibrium ($\varphi \approx \Phi$) as long as values of ε are sufficiently small. We then see from Eq. (14) that nonequilibrium effects can be brought about by two causes. First, dT/dx can become large, (strong gradients) or second, μ/p can become large (infrequent collisions).

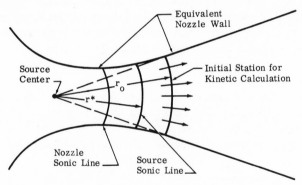

FIG. 1. Relationship between nozzle and source flows.

Referring back to Eq. (10), we see that for our source flow the value of du/dr at $u = a$ (the sonic line) becomes infinite and (as a result of the isentropic relations) so does dT/dx. Thus, for this flow the region near the sonic line will be a region of strong nonequilibrium effects, and it is not practical to choose our starting point x_0 in this vicinity. If we chose x_0 some distance downstream of the sonic line, the flow at this point can be considered to have been produced by a converging-diverging nozzle with the proper initial conditions at $x = x_0$. The relationship between a nozzle and the source flow is depicted in Fig. 1. Note that the interaction of particles with any wall must be considered specular to retain the assumed flow symmetry, and downstream recompressions, which may occur in some real nozzles, are not considered.

We substitute the flow properties determined from the inviscid solution [Eq. (12)] into Eq. (9) choosing $\varphi_0{}^+ = \Phi_0{}^+$.

Numerical Procedure

The integral solution of Eq. (7) represented formally by Eq. (9) must be evaluated numerically from the results of the previous iterations. Two basic iteration schemes have been employed: a simple substitution technique in which the output moments from the nth iteration become the input moments for the $(n + 1)$th iteration, and a method of the Newton-Raphson $(N - R)$ type in which the $(n + 1)$th input is predicted by a linear extrapolation of the difference between successive output values. The latter procedure has proved to be better, giving a more accurate solution within a given calculation time. Both procedures converge within the limits imposed by truncation and round-off errors, although they both require a large number of iterations to produce satisfactory accuracy. The $N - R$ procedure requires a simple error control to prevent instabilities in the first few predictions, but with this it is quite satisfactory in all respects. All of the results presented are from the $N - R$ method after 30 iterations. The differences between successive iterates for the temperature at the final step are always less than 0.1 % of the final value of the temperature for the cases shown, but we are unable to define the exact error in our values.

We express the phase space coordinates in terms of a radial (streamwise) and a tangential velocity component. The integration for each moment over the tangential component can be performed in closed form. We are then left with an integration over all values of the radial velocity component (v_x) and an integration over the transformed space variable (ξ). The former is performed by Hermite-Gauss quadrature, the latter by Simpson's rule.

The Hermite-Gauss quadrature, which is of the general form

$$\int_{-\infty}^{\infty} \exp(-y^2)w(y)\,dy \cong \sum_{i=1}^{n} A_i w(y_i),$$

is particularly well suited to this problem. With appropriate transformation the distribution function can be set up so that the mean velocity of the flow coincides with $y = 0$ in the above expression, and when the velocity coordinates are normalized by $T^{1/2}$, the distribution always has the same width in velocity space. The truncation error is therefore uniform over all values of the speed ratio.

When the flow is far from equilibrium, $w(y)$ for particles with positive velocities bears no direct relationship to $w(y)$ for those with negative ones and therefore w may be discontinuous at $v_x = 0$. The quadrature always fits a

smooth function through such a discontinuity. Since we have limited ourselves to cases in which the initial conditions are already at high-speed ratio,
and since $S \geqslant S_0$, we have ignored all contributions to the moments from
$v_x < 0$ by setting $w(-) = 0$. In Eq. (9), therefore, we have effectively set
$H(-v_x)$ equal to zero everywhere.

The interval size for the Simpson's rule integration was chosen by comparisons of the results for different intervals. We used a total of 320 integration
intervals to cover the indicated streamwise intervals. Estimated contribution
to the total error from this source is less than 3%, based on an error proportional to h^4.

We note that Chahine and Narasimha (1963) employed a series of Gauss
quadratures for the integration over velocity space using a total of 10,000
points, and they found two iterations sufficient. Using their running time, we
estimate in the present case (30 iterations, 320 steps) a running time on the
IBM 7094 of roughly 120 hours for each case. The 9-point Hermite-Gauss
quadrature enabled us to perform the equivalent calculation in an average
time of 5 minutes per case. Comparison of final asymptotic temperatures for
different orders in the quadrature are shown in Table I for the typical spherical
case of $S_0 = 3.0$, Re* = 10^4, and a stagnation temperature of $1000°K$.

TABLE I

COMPARISONS OF HERMITE-GAUSS INTEGRATIONS

No. of points	T_f/T^*	No. of iterations	$\triangle T_f/T_f$
7	0.0489	30	0.0076
8	0.0528	30	0.0082
9	0.0490	30	0.0066

There did not appear to be any significant change in rate of convergence
among the 3 cases. The difference between the 29th and 30th interates was
always very close to 0.0075 of the final value. The 5-point case (not shown)
showed early convergence characteristics similar to the others, but the later
stages showed apparently random oscillations within a total spread of about
5% in the final temperature. The $N - R$ method would not work for
the 5-point case, and simple substitution was used.

For calculational purposes we have used the Sutherland viscosity equation

$$\frac{\mu}{\mu^*} = \left(\frac{T}{T^*}\right)^{3/2} \left[\frac{T^*/50°K + 2.25}{T/50°K + 2.25}\right]$$

which agrees to within about 5% with the viscosity data for argon (Amdur
and Mason, 1958; Hilsenrath, et al., 1955) in the range $50°K \leqslant T \leqslant 1600°K$.

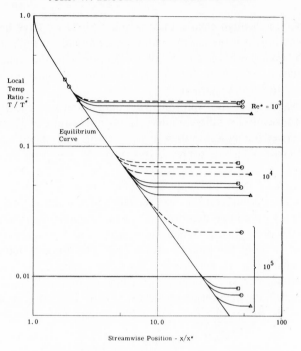

FIG. 2. Temperature distribution in a spherical source flow.
KEY: ————, $T_{st} = 1000°K$; – – – – –, $T_{st} = 3000°K$; ▢, $S_0 = 2.8$; ○, $S_0 = 3.0$; △, $S_0 = 3.5$.

IV. Results

The main features of the results as seen in Figs. 2 and 3 are consistent with the expectations previously discussed. The temperature follows the inviscid curve for some distance which is dependent on T_{st} and Re* (stagnation conditions), and then breaks away to a constant value in a relatively short transition distance. The density and velocity follow the inviscid curve to a degree which is well within the numerical accuracy of our calculations. The final values of the temperature show quite strong dependence on Re*, and on the particular type of temperature dependence of the collision cross section. A more surprising result is the change in final temperature that results from a small change in x_0, the point in the flow where the kinetic solution is started. This point appears anomalous, so we will discuss it first.

A. Sensitivity to Initial Conditions

We find that a small increase in x_0 (and therefore S_0) always produces a corresponding decrease in the final freezing temperature. This effect is present even for those cases which appear to follow the inviscid curve for long distances before freezing. We are operating in a regime where the back scattering is indeed very small and will diminish exponentially with S_0^2. This exponential decay is not observed in our tests of variations in S_0, so it appears unlikely that neglecting this part of the distribution can produce a significant error in the flow characteristics, although this cannot be stated with certainty. Furthermore, each case presented spans the same ratio of x_f to x_0. We therefore do not attribute the spread to differences in propagated error due to a longer span of the calculation.

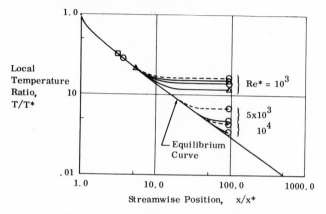

FIG. 3. Temperature distribution in a cylindrical source flow.
KEY: ————, $T_{st} = 1000°K$; – – –, $T_{st} = 3000°K$; □, $S_0 = 2.8$; ○ $= 3.0$; △ $= 3.5$.

The fact that the integrations over velocity space are closely approximated by our procedure seems apparent. We find that (1) the inviscid curve can be reproduced for any desired distance by simply employing a sufficiently high Re*, and (2) varying the order of the Hermite-Gauss quadratures from 9 to 7 results in the quite moderate changes shown in Table I, and indicates a very small error for the 9-point case. Furthermore, the spread of final temperatures with variations in S_0 is preserved in an unchanged form for all orders tested.

A change in the iteration procedure from the Newton-Raphson type used for the results presented to a simple substitution method resulted in an adverse change in convergence rate and quality of the final answers, but again the relative spread due to changes in S_0 was observed in the same form.

It appears that the observed changes in temperature distribution with changes in matching point can be explained on the basis of the importance of the exact form of the velocity distribution function. The errors introduced by approximating part of the convective term in Eq. (1) can affect the final nonequilibrium temperatures. Conclusive proof that this effect is in fact the source of the S_0 spreading is not at present available; only a systematic calculation using a characteristics method to handle the complete partial differential equation can resolve the difficulty.

Figure 4 shows values of ε calculated from the inviscid (i) solution, and Fig. 5 shows how the value of ε_i corresponding to the frozen temperature

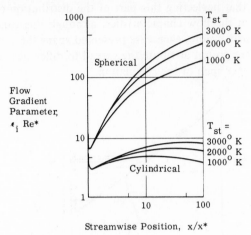

FIG. 4. Flow gradient parameter for inviscid source flows.

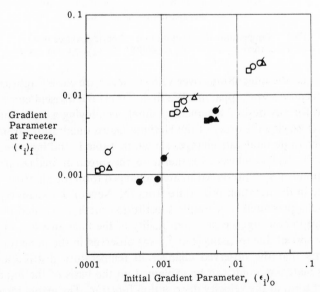

FIG. 5. Gradient parameter at Freeze versus initial gradient parameter (flagged symbols, 3000°K, unflagged 1000°K stagnation temperature. Filled symbols are cylindrical, unfilled spherical source flows.)

KEY: □, $S_0 = 2.8$, ○ = 3.0, △ = 3.5.

seems to depend on the value of $(\varepsilon_i)_0$. If the freezing process in our calculation were dependent only on local conditions, we would expect $(\varepsilon_i)_f$ to be nearly a constant.

B. Discussion of Results

If we accept the present hypothesis of the validity of the approximate Krook model in this application, we are drawn to several conclusions concerning the applications of noncontinuum expansions. First, however, we must recognize the need to verify these results by alternative methods.

Qualitative experimental agreement with our results as to the gross characteristics of expansion flows has been indicated by Reis and Fenn (1964) and recently by Scott and Phipps (1964). They all observed departures from the inviscid theory in the direction of higher temperatures, and the departures occurred further upstream for decreased stagnation density (pressure). Arguments supporting the insensitivity of ρ and u to collision frequency were given in part by Sherman (1962) and by Sibulkin and Gallaher (1963), and an order of magnitude analysis which indicated the observed ρ, u, and T behavior was given by Oman and Calia (1963).

The experimental work which seems to be the most helpful in an assessment of the behavior we have described is that of Becker and Henkes (1956), and that of Hagena and Henkes (1960). In these works measurements of molecular velocity distributions in various types of nozzle flows were presented. For pure argon flows Becker and Henkes show some data which have a slope of final Mach number versus Re* which is very close to that given by calculations with our method (although these cases are outside the range where back scattering can be ignored). Their values of final Mach number are higher than those we calculate (~ 6 vs. ~ 5), but part of this may be due to a measured stream velocity greater than the thermodynamic limit. Although Hagena and Henkes dealt with gases having a large number of internal degrees of freedom, their results show many of the characteristics we have predicted for the monatomic case. They show (for CO_2 in a converging nozzle) a temperature distribution that is nearly independent of downstream position at low stagnation pressures (ρ_{st} is proportional to Re*) and that becomes more like an equilibrium distribution of $T(x)$ at high ρ_{st}. Their data show the final temperature proportional to the logarithm of ρ_{st}^{-1} in the frozen regime, a behavior which is quite similar to our observations. For UF_6 the behavior is less clear cut, but the "freezing" character is no longer ρ_{st} dependent if it is present at all. When they employed a converging-diverging nozzle (with UF_6 only), the velocity distributions approach the thermodynamic limit in a coherent fashion, but the temperature distributions show an anomalous (to us) behavior, probably due to changes in exchange of energy between translational and internal states. However, there is a significant difference between the flows in the two types of nozzles, and much of this difference could be attributed to the rate of expansion in the early stages. The popular conclusion that converging-diverging nozzles are always inferior to converging types for molecular beams seems to us to be questionable, at least for high ρ_{st}.

We must bear in mind that the real flows described have many differences from the ideal symmetric cases we have treated. In addition to the obvious ones, we must recognize that the thermal velocity distributions are not necessarily isotropic, so different experimental methods for inferring the "temperature" will often yield different values.

V. Conclusions

The expected distributions of density $(\rho \sim r^{-\nu})$, velocity $(u/u_i \approx 1)$ and temperature (a freezing phenomenon which occurs at a point primarily dependent on Re*) have been shown in both the spherically and cylindrically symmetric cases. The exact value of the final (asymptotic) downstream temperature depends somewhat on the exact nature of the upstream flow as well as on the collision frequency effect embodied in the Reynolds number, although the former dependence seems to require further study. The velocity dependence of collision cross section is also important, yielding an earlier freezing point for stronger temperature dependence.

Other things being equal, higher densities in the stagnation region will always produce lower final temperatures and consequently higher final Mach numbers.

ACKNOWLEDGMENT

The authors would like to express their appreciation to Conrad Augustin for carrying out the computer programming.

REFERENCES

Andur, I., and Mason, E. A. (1958). *Phys. Fluids* **1**, 370.
Becker, E. W., and Henkes, W. (1956). *Z. Physik* **146**, 320.
Bhatnagar, P. L., Gross, E. P., and Krook, M. (1954). *Phys. Rev.* **94**, 511.
Brook, J. W. (1965). Ph.D. Thesis, Polytechnic Institute of Brooklyn, New York.
Chahine, M. T. (1962). *In* " Rarefied Gas Dynamics " (J. Laurmann, ed.), p. 260. Academic Press, New York.
Chahine, M. T., and Narasimha, R. (1963). "Evaluation of the Integral $\int_{0}^{\infty} v^n \exp[-(v-u)^2 -(x/y)\,dv$." Tech. Rept. No. 32–459, Jet Propulsion Laboratory, California Institute of Technology.

Fishman, F. J., Jr. (1959). Ph.D. Thesis, Harvard University, Cambridge, Massachusetts.

Hagena, O., and Henkes, W. (1960). *Z. Naturforsch.* **15a**, 851–858.

Hilsenrath, J. (1955). "Tables of Thermal Properties of Gases." *Nat. Bur. Std. Circ.* 564.

Kogan, M. N. (1958). *Prikl. Mat. Mekh.* **22**, 425.

Liepmann, H. W., Narasimha, R., and Chahine, M. T. (1962). *Phys. Fluids* **5**, 11.

Narasimha, R. (1961), Ph.D. Thesis, California Institute of Technology.

Oman, R. A., and Calia, V. S. (1963). "Interaction of High Energy Gas Molecules with Solid Surfaces. Part II, Progress in an Experimental Investigation of Molecular-Surface Interaction." Grumman Research Department Rep. RE-166.

Reis, V. H., and Fenn, J. B. (1964). *J. Chem. Phys.* **39**, 3240–3250.

Rott, N. (1964). *Phys. Fluids* **7**, 4.

Scott, J. E., and Phipps, J. A. (1964). *Bull. Am. Phys. Soc.* [*II*] **9**, 5 (Abstract G2).

Sherman, F. S. (1962). *In* "Rarefied Gas Dynamics" (J. Laurmann, ed.), Vol. II, pp. 228–260. Academic Press, New York.

Sibulkin, M., and Gallaher, W. H. (1963), *J. Am. Inst. Aeron. Astron.* **1**, 1452.

Section 2

SHOCK STRUCTURE

Exact Numerical Solution of the Complete BGK Equation for Strong Shock Waves[1]

M. T. CHAHINE
Jet Propulsion Laboratory, California Institute of Technology, Pasadena, California
and
R. NARASIMHA
Indian Institute of Science, Bangalore, India;
and California Institute of Technology, Pasadena, California

The numerical convergence of the iterative solution to the complete BGK equation is investigated. The previous numerical techniques are vastly improved, resulting in a considerable saving in computing time and smaller errors. Consequently the number of iterations is raised above 10. New shock profiles are computed for a range of Mach numbers and a special study of the development of the complete distribution function within the shock wave is carried out.

I. Introduction

The structure of plane normal shock waves in the Bhatnagar-Gross-Krook (BGK) collision model was discussed by Liepmann, *et al.* (1962) and Chahine (1963). In these papers, we reported the results of carrying out three iterations on the first five moments of the distribution function, using an iterative numerical scheme to generate the solution of the model Boltzmann equation starting from the Navier-Stokes (NS) solution. While the results indicated sufficiently rapid convergence to reveal the main features of shock structure, no special attempt was made in these papers to investigate the convergence as such.

[1] The present study was carried out in close association with Professor H. W. Liepmann. California Institute of Technology, Pasadena, California.

This paper presents the results of one phase of research carried out at the Jet Propulsion Laboratory, California Institute of Technology, under Contract No. NAS 7-100 sponsored by the National Aeronautics and Space Administration.

140

We believe we have obtained in this paper an exact numerical solution of the BGK equation for the flow through a shock wave. It must be mentioned, however, that the numbers we have obtained, i.e., for the density-slope thickness of the shock, cannot be strictly and directly compared with experimental results. The reason for this is that the equation solved is only a model of the Boltzmann equation, and it is expected, and indeed known, that the results will differ from those given by the full Boltzmann equation. (The Pr in the NS limit, for instance, is 1 for the model, but the exact value is $\frac{2}{3}$.) Nevertheless, from the reasonable success the model has previously achieved in dealing with gas kinetic problems (Liepmann *et al.* (1962), the results obtained here should be indicative of the correct results for a real gas. Their significance lies, moreover, in the fact that within the framework of the model, the solution we have obtained is exact, i.e., no further *ad hoc* assumptions or approximations of any kind are involved. Our chief purpose is to understand, as far as possible, the dynamics of the flow through the shock and the structure of the solution of the full Boltzmann equation.

To show that the iterative solution of the BGK equation is numerically convergent, the numerical techniques previously used were vastly improved by the use of the saddle-point method, which resulted in a more efficient numerical process. It required only 1/10 the computing time previously needed and introduced a smaller computational error, thereby allowing the number of iterations to be raised beyond 10. In Section II, we study in some detail the convergence properties of the scheme; in Section III, we present more complete results of the profiles and their corresponding shock thickness. In Section IV, we give preliminary results of the computations of the distribution function; in Section V, we give a brief discussion and some conclusions.

II. Iterative Solution

It has been shown previously that the basic BGK equation for the distribution of molecular velocities

$$v_x \frac{\partial f}{\partial x} = An[F - f] \tag{1}$$

may be integrated formally for $v_x \gtrless 0$, subject to the boundary conditions at $x = \pm\infty$ (see Fig. 1), to yield

$$f_\pm(v_x \gtrless 0, v_y, v_z, x) = \int_{\mp\infty}^{x} \frac{An}{v_x} F \exp\left\{-\int_{x'}^{x} \frac{An}{v_x} dx''\right\} dx'. \tag{2}$$

$1/An$ is the relaxation time which depends only on the local state of the gas;

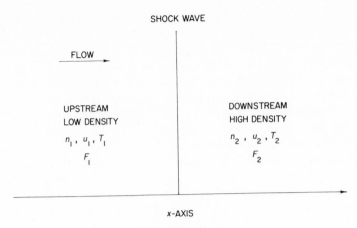

FIG. 1. Notations.

and $F(\mathbf{V}, x)$ is the local Maxwellian distribution function corresponding at every point to the number density

$$n(x) = \int_{-\infty}^{+\infty} f(\mathbf{V}, x)\, d\mathbf{V}, \qquad (3a)$$

mass flux

$$u(x)n(x) = \int_{-\infty}^{+\infty} v_x f(\mathbf{V}, x)\, d\mathbf{V}, \qquad (3b)$$

and temperature

$$3Rn(x)T(x) = \int_{-\infty}^{+\infty} [\mathbf{V} - \mathbf{u}(x)]^2 f(\mathbf{V}, x)\, d\mathbf{V}. \qquad (3c)$$

Equations (2) and (3) form a system of four equations with four unknowns f, n, u, and T, the solution of which can formally be obtained by iterations using a sequence of functions $n^j(x)$, $u^j(x)$, and $T^j(x)$. The iterative solution used in this paper is essentially the same as that suggested by one of the authors (R. Narasimha)[2] and used in Liepmann et al. (1962). The basic idea underlying this procedure is that the iterative solution depends in each step only on the lowest moments of the distribution function of the previous step and not on the detailed shape of the distribution function itself.

The essence of the iteration procedure can be described very briefly. We first prescribe some initial variation n^0, u^0, and T^0 (and not f^0) across the shock wave, and formulate the first approximation f^1 to the distribution function

[2] A similar method, starting however with the free molecule distribution function, was proposed by Willis (1960) for the piston problem.

from Eq. (2) to read

$$f_{\mp}{}^{1} = \int_{\pm\infty}^{x} \frac{A^{0}(x')n^{0}(x')}{v_x} F^{0}(\mathbf{V}, x') \exp\left\{-\int_{x'}^{x} \frac{A^{0}(x'')n^{0}(x'')}{v_x} dx''\right\} dx'. \qquad (4)$$

We integrate f^{1} to get new values of $n^{1}(x)$, $u^{1}(x)$, and $T^{1}(x)$, which form the new $F^{1}(\mathbf{V}, x)$; and using this in Eq. (4), we compute the next iterate.

In the present paper, we have used the Navier-Stokes solution to provide an initial input n^{0}, u^{0}, and T^{0} in $F^{0}(\mathbf{V}, x)$.

The processes and arguments by which u^{1}, n^{1}, and T^{1} are evaluated may be properly illustrated by considering as a specific but typical example the first moment $n^{1}(x)$, given by

$$n^{1}(x) = \int_{-\infty}^{+\infty} \int_{-\infty}^{+\infty} \left[\int_{-\infty}^{0} f_{-}{}^{1}\, dv_x + \int_{0}^{+\infty} f_{+}{}^{1}\, dv_x \right] dv_y\, dv_z. \qquad (5)$$

Equation (5) can be integrated immediately with respect to v_y, and v_z and reduced, using Eq. (4) to read

$$\frac{2n^{1}(x)}{n_1} = \int_{0}^{-\infty} \int_{x}^{+\infty} \frac{N^{0}(x')}{L^{0}(x')} \frac{1}{\eta} \exp\left\{-[\eta - S^{0}(x')]^{2} - \frac{h^{0}(x', x)}{\eta}\right\} dx'\, d\eta$$

$$+ \int_{0}^{+\infty} \int_{-\infty}^{x} \frac{N^{0}(x')}{L^{0}(x')} \frac{1}{\eta} \exp\left\{-[\eta - S^{0}(x')]^{2} - \frac{h^{0}(x', x)}{\eta}\right\} dx'\, d\eta \qquad (6)$$

where

$$\theta^{0}(x) = \frac{T^{0}(x)}{T_1}; \qquad L^{0}(x) = \frac{\Lambda^{0}(x)}{\Lambda_1} = \frac{\mu^{0}(T)/\mu_1}{N^{0}(x)\sqrt{\theta^{0}(x)}}$$

$$U^{0}(x) = \frac{u^{0}(x)}{u_1}; \qquad S^{0}(x) = \frac{u^{0}(x)}{\sqrt{2RT^{0}(x)}}$$

$$N^{0}(x) = \frac{n^{0}(x)}{n_1}; \qquad \eta = \frac{v_x}{\sqrt{2RT^{0}(x)}}$$

and

$$h^{0}(x', x) = \frac{\sqrt{\pi}}{2} [\theta^{0}(x')]^{-1/2} \int_{x'}^{x} \frac{[\theta^{0}(x'')]^{1/2}}{L^{0}(x'')} dx''$$

with x' and x denoting, respectively, the lower and upper limits of the integral with respect to x''. Consequently,

$$\frac{h^{0}(x', x)}{\eta} \geqslant 0 \qquad (7)$$

and the integrand is bounded and does not change sign. Hence, the integrand in Eq. (6) is always finite.

A. Numerical Technique[3]

Because Eq. (6) involves three integrations whose ranges are very large, direct evaluation of this integral is too time-consuming to be feasible on a computer whose maximum and minimum multiplication times are in the 2–10 μsec range. However, it is possible to adapt each term of this integral for machine computations by considering the physical nature of Eq. (6). At each stage, the iteration properly samples and weights the input (i.e., the previous iterate), and redistributes the flow quantities accordingly. It was shown by Liepmann et al. (1962) that the gradients in the Navier-Stokes shock are fairly small (relative to the local mean free path) in the downstream side of the shocks; hence, here the sampling distance is also small, and no strong deviations from the Navier-Stokes structure are expected. Upstream, however, the gradients and sampling distances (for velocities η of order S, which contribute most to the moments) are greater, and a larger part of the input is weighted in the iteration, so larger deviations might be expected. If the iteration is convergent, it will finally lead to the true solution, which by definition is properly weighted.

The authors (1964) developed a computational method in which the argument of the integral with respect to η is weighted against its contribution throughout the range of integration for any value of $x' \neq x$. The advantage of this arises from the fact that as η approaches either end point of the path of integration, the argument $-\{(\eta - S^0)^2 + h^0/\eta\}$ tends to $-\infty$. Thus the parts corresponding to large arguments furnish a contribution which becomes smaller as η approaches these limits; therefore, only the immediate vicinity of the saddle point is of significance. The evaluation of this saddle point is discussed in detail by Chahine and Narasimha (1964). Also the truncation of the path of integration with respect to η at a point where

$$\exp\left\{-(\eta - S^0)^2 - \frac{h^0(x', x)}{\eta}\right\} \leqslant 10^{-32}$$

leaves the calculation with substantial accuracy.

In the calculation process Eq. (3) is evaluated simultaneously for each given value of x using a Gaussian quadrature formula in each interval. A step-by-step integration is initiated by evaluating $h^0(x', x)$ at $x' = x + \Delta x'$, and the integrand is determined by interpolating the values of the other parameters N^0, L^0, S^0, at the required value of x'. Then, the integration with respect to η is carried out with increasing values of the step size as we move away from the saddle point. The same procedure is repeated for the following values of $x' = x + k \Delta x'$ until the integration with respect to x' is complete. The singularity when $x' = x$ and $\eta = 0$ was evaluated by taking very fine values

---

[3] Details of the various computational techniques will appear in Chahine (1965).

of $\Delta\eta$ and Δx in this vicinity, which ensured that the integral did not change when we went to finer steps.

Due to the predominant existence of $1/\eta$ in the integrand of Eq. (3a), the computational error introduced in calculating $N^j(x)$ is relatively large and varies from $\pm 5 \times 10^{-4}$ on the extreme high-density side to $\pm 10^{-7}$ on the extreme low-density side. The error introduced in evaluating U^j and T^j, however, is relatively smaller.

A study of the numerical behavior of N^j, U^j, and T^j as $x \to \infty$ confirms the physical interpretations advanced earlier in this section; namely, as x moves downstream, the sampling distance becomes very small. This also explains why any numerical error introduced tends to reproduce itself and even becomes amplified as the computational errors accumulate. For this reason, it was found necessary to terminate the evaluation of the shock profile on the high-density side when $N_2 - N^j(x) \leqslant 5 \times 10^{-4}$. On the low-density side, however, the shock profiles were terminated only at $N^j(x) - 1 \leqslant 10^{-7}$.

Conservation of mass requires that $un = $ constant, or $U^j N^j = 1$, all across the shock. This suggests two ways of obtaining the velocity U after each iteration. In the first method, we take $U^j = 1/N^j$, automatically conserving mass flux. In the second method, we evaluate U^j from Eq. (3b) by integrating over the distribution function. It was discovered that the convergence properties of the solution depended to some extent on whether the first or the second method was used for finding U^j, though the final results appear to agree within the computational errors. The results quoted here are obtained using $U^j = 1/N^j$, unless otherwise stated.

The succeeding iterations are performed in a manner similar to the one explained above, simply by replacing $n(x)$, $u(x)$, and $T(x)$ on the right-hand side of Eq. (6) by the results of the previous iteration. However, to pursue the iteration further requires a delicate study of the total error regarded as a buildup from round-off and truncation errors. This suggests that at some stage the residual errors and the generated errors be of such magnitude that continuation of the process is unprofitfible. In the present work, 21 iterations were carried out for $M_1 = 3.0$, with the results remaining accurate in their third decimal.

B. Convergence

Even if the present iterative process theoretically converges to a given limit, it does not follow that the results of the digital computations will approach this limit. The present iterative solution is necessarily a finite numerical process in which the concept of formal convergence hardly plays any role, though it is involved in the analytical arguments by which the process is established. Because of the complexity of Eq. (3), no analytical proof of convergence is presented in this paper; instead, it will be left to the numerical

TABLE I

RATE OF MASS-FLUX CONVERGENCE, Δ

X	Δ value after number of iterations $j =$:								
	1	2	3	4	5	6	10	13	16
$+0.75$	0.0401	0.0425	0.0290	0.0163	0.0072	0.0021	0.0005	0.0003	0.0001
-0.75	0.0540	0.0510	0.0450	0.0203	0.0088	0.0024	0.0009	0.0002	0.0001

results to indicate the rate and trend of convergence. Therefore, any conclusion about the convergence should not be made without taking into account the error introduced from the previous steps. One measure of the rate of convergence is the value of the mass-flux integral in Eq. (3b), which should be equal to a constant (namely, $n_1 u_1$) all across the shock. This criterion can be justified analytically by the fact that, in this iteration scheme, if the mass-flux converges then the density converges too. In connection with this, all the final results in the present paper fulfill the condition that

$$\Delta \equiv |1 - U^j(x)N^j(x)| \leqslant 10^{-4} \tag{8}$$

throughout the shock, thereby satisfying the conservation of mass to an order within the computational error. This condition was satisfied in the first iteration for $M_1 = 1.5$. However, at $M_1 = 3.0$ the rate of convergence is relatively slower than at $M_1 = 5.0$ and 10.0. The rate of convergence of the mass-flux integral can best be judged in Table I, computed for $M_1 = 10.0$ at the two points $X = \pm 0.75$ within the shock wave where the deviations Δ were largest.

A second measure of the rate of convergence is obtained by studying the maximum gradients of the computed moments. This proved to be a slower condition to satisfy than the mass-flux criterion (as can be noted in Fig. 4 which will be discussed in the following section).

III. Results

The iterative scheme discussed in the previous section was programmed on the IBM 7094. Each iteration was carried out over 60 values of x across the shock wave for a monatomic gas with a Prandtl number $\text{Pr} = 1.0$ and a viscosity $\mu \sim T^{0.816}$

The results of the new computation are summarized in Figs. 2 through 7 and discussed below. Of the shock waves computed, only the n and T profiles for $M_1 = 10.0$, 5.0, and 3.0 are shown in this paper, in Figs. 2 and 3. It should be noted here that there has been no sliding of the results on the x-axis (within the computational error). The profiles show that the BGK solution deviates from the Navier-Stokes on the high-density side as well as on the low-density side. The deviation on the high-density side is larger than had been thought previously and can probably be accounted for by the higher-order terms (like the Burnett) in the Chapman-Enskog expansion. The Burnett equations include terms proportional to the second derivatives of the flow quantities, and these may be expected to make noticeable contributions, especially in regions of high curvature in the shock profile. However, the deviations are more pronounced on the low-density side than on the high-density side,

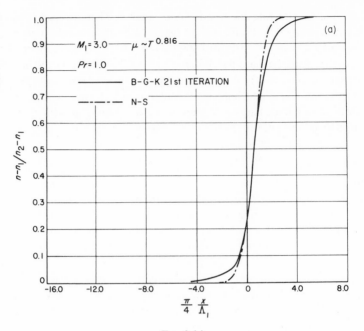

FIG. 2 (a).

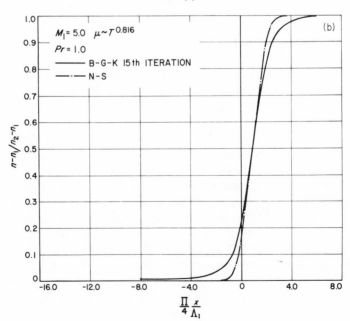

FIG. 2 (b).

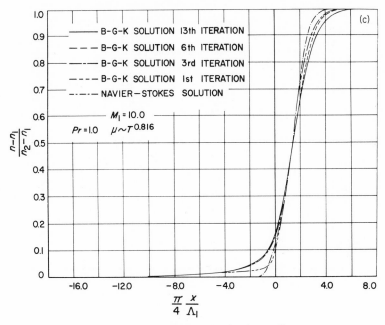

FIG. 2 (a, b, c). Shock-wave density profiles.

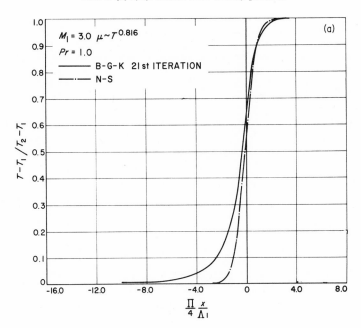

FIG. 3 (a).

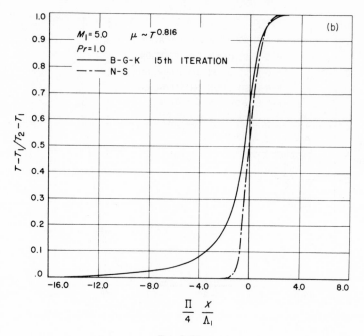

FIG. 3 (b).

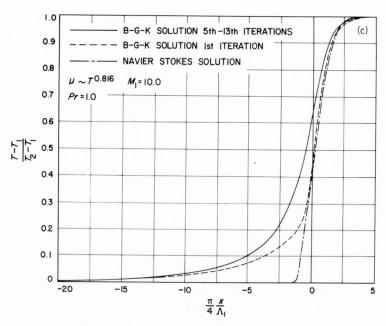

FIG. 3 (a, b, c). Shock-wave temperature profiles.

especially for the temperature. While there is definite asymmetry in both density and temperature profiles, we should note that the asymmetry in the density is very weak, as shown in Fig. 5.

The case of $M_1 = 1.5$ remains unchanged since the first iterative solution reproduces the NS well within the margin of computational errors in u, n, and T. The second and third iterates were, for all computational purposes, also unchanged. This served both as a check to the numerical techniques employed and as a confirmation of the validity of the NS solution for weak shock waves.[4]

The maximum slopes inside the shock, shown in Fig. 4, are computed from first-order differences with $\Delta x = \Lambda_1/4$, except for the Navier-Stokes gradients which were computed numerically from the solution of the initial input. These results show a gradual deviation from their Navier-Stokes values to limits reached in 20 iterations for $M_1 = 3.0$ and 15 iterations for $M_1 = 10.0$. As an obvious consequence to the fact that the iterative solution converges faster on the low-density side, the maximum temperature gradient, which occurs further upstream, converges faster than that of the density. In Fig. 4, case I corresponds to the solution for which $U^j = 1/N^j$, and case II corre-

[4] Tables of the NS solution for the structure of shock waves in a monatomic gas will be given in a forthcoming JPL report arranged by the authors.

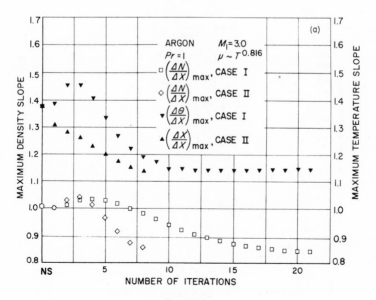

FIG. 4 (a).

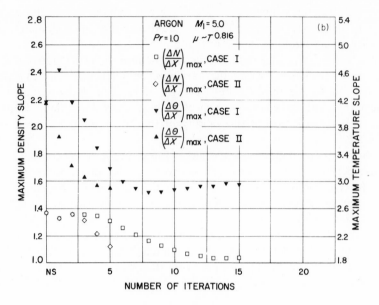

FIG. 4 (b).

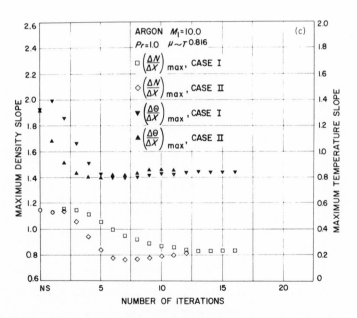

FIG. 4 (a, b, c). Convergence of profiles' maximum gradients. Case I refers to the method in which $U^j = 1/N^j$ and case II refers to the method in which U^j is evaluated from Eq. (3b).

sponds to the solution for which U^j is evaluated from Eq. (3b). It is interesting to note that the final result is approached from above for case I and from below for case II.

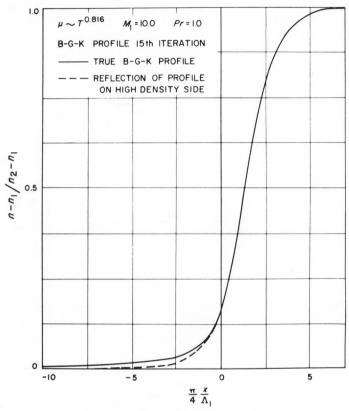

FIG. 5. Reflection of density profile on the high-density side for $M_1 = 10.0$.

Although the definition of a shock thickness is arbitrary, the maximum slope thickness is the most popular parameter describing the structure of a shock wave. In this paper, the maximum slope density thickness shown in Fig. 6 is based on the results of the final iteration and is obtained by numerically integrating $\partial f/\partial x$ in Eq. (1). The results show a good agreement between the BGK and the NS solutions at low Mach numbers, followed by a noticeable deviation at higher M_1.

Grad (1952) proposed another, and in some ways a truer, definition of shock thickness based on an integral of the shock profile. This parameter, known as the area thickness, is presented in Fig. 7 for both the BGK and the NS density profiles. By comparing Figs. 6 and 7, we can easily see that the deviation in the area thickness is proportionally larger and that $\delta_{area} \geqslant \delta_{max\ slope}$, as expected.

For the sake of completeness, we list in Table II the maximum slope and area thicknesses based on the temperature profile. We see a wider deviation here between the NS and BGK solutions than in the density profiles. This is rather obviously due to the greater asymmetry of the temperature profile, and to the occurrence of the temperature maximum slope further upstream than the point of maximum density slope (see Figs. 2 and 3).

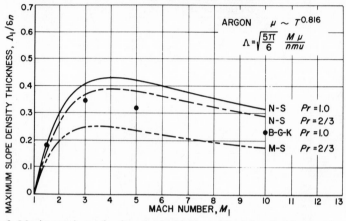

FIG. 6. Maximum-slope, density, shock thickness. The Mott-Smith curve is obtained from Muckenfuss (1962) by interpolation.

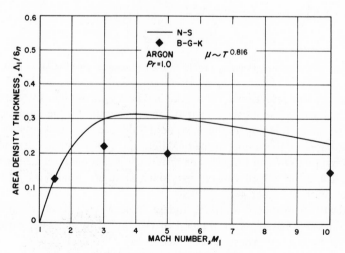

FIG. 7. Area shock thickness.

TABLE II

TEMPERATURE MAXIMUM SLOPE AND AREA THICKNESS FOR $\mu \sim T^{0.816}$ AND $\text{Pr} = 1.0$

	Λ_1/δ_T (max slope)		Λ_1/δ_T (area)	
M_1	NS	BGK	NS	BGK
1.5	0.178	0.178	0.140	0.140
3.0	0.406	0.34	0.316	0.175
5.0	0.427	0.30	0.339	0.129
10.0	0.342	0.21	0.268	0.0812

IV. Velocity Distribution Function

The numerical process discussed in Section II, together with the output of the final iteration, i.e., the jth, may be employed to solve for the distribution function $f_{\pm}(V, x)$ given by Eq. (2). The convergence of the distribution function was demonstrated numerically for $M_1 = 3.0$ and appeared to take place rapidly on the low density side of the shock while the high density side

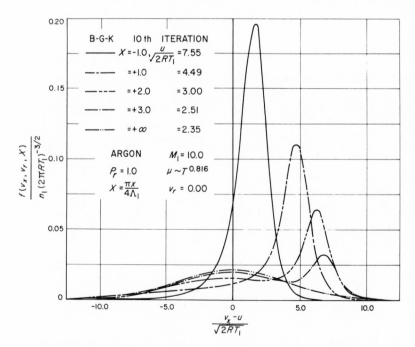

FIG. 8. Development of the distribution function across the shock wave for $M_1 = 10.0$.

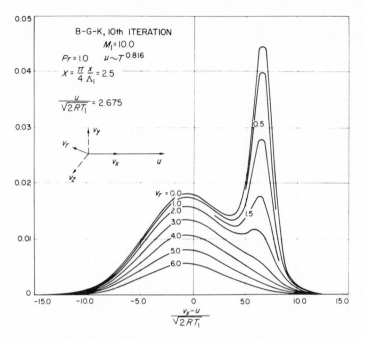

FIG. 9. Dependence of f on v_x and v_r at a specific x.

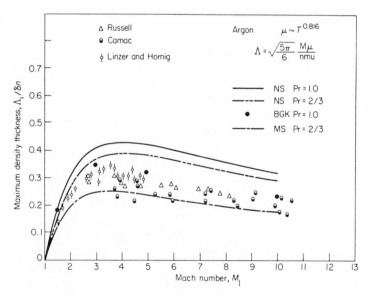

FIG. 10. Comparison between various experimental and theoretical maximum-density, slope, shock thicknesses.

gradually converged after 15 iterations. The manner in which this convergence was approached was orderly and in the final iterations seemed to affect mainly the regions of $f_{\pm}(\mathbf{V}, x)$ maxima, at each value of x.

Other properties of the distribution function are determined analytically by examining $f(\mathbf{V}, x)$. Since the integrands of Eq. (2) do not change signs along their respective range of integration, it can be easily shown that both

$$f_{\pm}{}^{j}(\mathbf{V}, x) \geqslant 0$$

for all values of $\mathbf{V}$ and x, which cannot be said for the Chapman-Enskog expansion or its further variations. Also, the distribution function is axisymmetrical in velocity space around the axis v_x with local maxima along the v_x axes only, or in other words,

$$\frac{\partial f}{\partial v_i} = 0; \quad \text{at} \quad v_i = 0$$

$$i = y, z$$

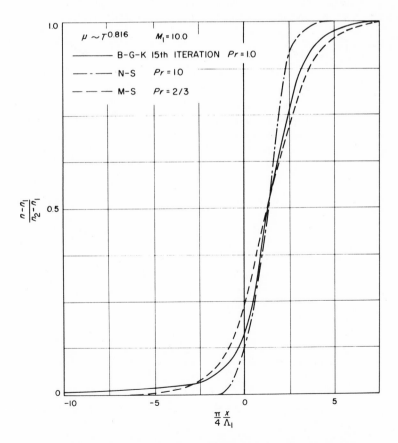

FIG. 11. Density profiles matched at the 0.5 point on the ordinate axis.

Along the v_x-axis, $\partial f / \partial v_x$ has a maximum of three zeros, as shown in Fig. 8. The dependence of f on v_x and v_r at a given x is shown in Fig. 9. More complete data and further analysis of f is presently underway and will be published in the near future.

V. Conclusions

We conclude that the iterative scheme described in the previous sections is fully capable of giving satisfactory results for the whole range of Mach numbers. Numerical convergence of the method seems to be conclusive, and in this paper we have been able to show numerical convergence of the mass-flux [Eq. (3b)] as well as that of the maximum gradients of the profiles for all computed Mach numbers. And for one case, $M_1 = 3.0$, we carried out the elaborate task of showing the convergence of the distribution function itself.

For weak shock waves, $M_1 = 1.5$, the first and all iterations of the BGK solutions are in complete agreement, within the order of computational errors, with the NS solution for predicting the structure of shock waves. For stronger

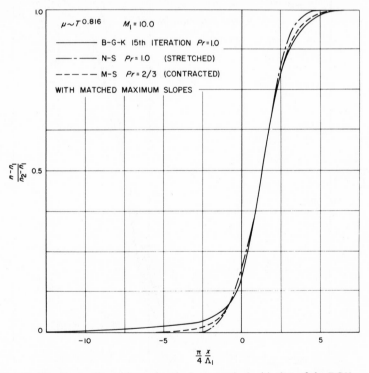

Fig. 12. Density profiles with maximum slope matched with that of the BGK.

shocks, in which there are larger deviations from equilibrium, the rate of convergence was slower; e.g., 15 iterations were required at $M_1 = 10.0$, and the final results show marked deviation from the NS solution.

The results for the density-slope shock thickness show a deviation of about 25% from the Navier-Stokes values. This is somewhat larger than had been previously thought, but brings closer to the general trend of the experimental results of Linzer and Hornig (1963), Camac (1964), and Russell (1965), as shown in Fig. 10. Figure 11 shows the BGK, Navier-Stokes, and Mott-Smith density profiles plotted on a common scale with the halfway point (on the density scale) being identical for all of them. Figure 12 shows the same profiles stretched or contracted along the abscissa to have the same maximum slope as the BGK solution. It is seen that the differences in the shape of the profiles for density are slight and would probably be rather difficult to pick up experimentally with present techniques. However, a similar plot of temperature profiles would show larger differences on the low density side.

Too much emphasis, however, cannot be placed on the precise numerical figures obtained from our computations, as they are concerned only with a model of the Boltzmann equation. Their significance lies, rather, in providing some insight into the probable structure of solutions of the full Boltzmann equation, and in possible applications of the model to more complicated situations.

Nomenclature

A Parameter in the BGK collision model, see Eq. (1)

F Maxwellian distribution function

f Molecular velocity distribution function

L Mean free path ratio, Λ/Λ_1

M Mach number

m Molecular mass

N Density ratio, n/n_1

n Number density

Pr   Prandtl number

R Boltzmann gas constant

S Speed ratio, $u/\sqrt{2RT}$

T Temperature

U Velocity ratio, u/u_1

u Mass velocity along the x-axis

V Molecular velocity (v_x, v_y, v_z)

v_r^2 $= v_y^2 + v_z^2$

X Nondimensional physical axis, $(\pi/4)\,(x/\Lambda_1)$

x Physical axis along the direction of flow

Δ See Eq. (8)

η Molecular velocity, $v_x/\sqrt{2RT}$

θ Temperature ratio, T/T_1

Λ $\sqrt{5\pi/6}\ (M\mu/nmu) = $ Maxwellian mean free path

μ Viscosity

Superscript

0   Initial input (Navier-Stokes)

1   First iteration

j jth iteration

Subscript

1   Conditions at $-\infty$ (ahead of the shock)

2   Conditions at $+\infty$ (behind the shock)

+   Corresponds to $v_x > 0$

−   Corresponds to $v_x < 0$

REFERENCES

Camac, M. (1964). AIAA Aerospace Science Meeting, New York, January 20–22, Preprint No. 64-35.

Chahine, M. T. (1963). *In* "Rarefied Gas Dynamics" (J. Laurmann, ed.), Vol. I, p. 26. Academic Press, New York. Also in "The Structure of Strong Shock Waves in the Krook Collision Model." Tech. Rept. No. 32-327, Jet Propulsion Laboratory, California Inst. of Technol., Pasadena, California.

Chahine, M. T. (1965). *Methods Computat. Phys.* **4**, 83

Chahine, M. T. and Narasimha, R. (1964). *J. Math. and Phys.* **43**, 163. Also in "Evaluation of the Integral $\int_0^\infty v^n \exp\{-(v-u)^2 - x/v\}\, dv$," Tech. Rept. No. 32-459, Jet Propulsion Laboratory, California Inst. of Technol. Pasadena, California.

Grad, H. (1952). *Communs. Pure Appl. Math.* **5**, 257.

Liepmann, H. W., Narasimha, R., and Chahine, M. (1962). *Phys. Fluids* **5**, 1313.

Linzer, M., and Hornig, D. F. (1963). *Phys. Fluids* **12**, 1661.

Muckenfuss, C. (1962). *Phys. Fluids* **5**, 1325.

Russell, D. (1965). This volume, p. 265. Academic Press, New York.

Willis, D. R. (1960). "Investigation of the Development of a Shock Wave for Times Smaller than the Average Collision Time KTH." *Division of Gas Dynamics TN4*, Stockholm.

Shock-Wave Structure in Highly Rarefied Flows

D. BATTAT
The College of Aeronautics, Department of Aerodynamics, Cranfield, Bedford, England

The Boltzmann equation is written in terms of two functions associated with the gain and loss of a certain type of molecule due to collisions. Its integral form is then applied to the problem of normal shock structure, and an iteration technique is used to determine the solution. The first approximation to the velocity distribution function of the Chapman-Enskog sequence, which leads to the Navier-Stokes equations, is used to initiate the iteration scheme. Expressions for the distribution function and the flow parameters pertinent to the first iteration are derived and show that the BGK model results can be obtained as a special case. This model is found to be valid in the continuum regime only, and is consequently limited to the study of strong shocks. In the present treatment the iteration is carried out on the distribution function and the analysis indicates that the method is equally valid for variations in both Mach and Knudsen numbers. Finally, the results of the first approximation are simplified, and expressed in a form suitable for numerical computation, and the range of their validity is discussed. The method should be equally suitable for other flow problems of linear or nonlinear nature.

I. Introduction

The problem of plane shock wave structure has been studied in the past by various methods. The structure of weak shocks in a continuum medium is well understood and several attempts to describe the stronger shocks have been made. However, the position of the shock problem in rarefied flows is still not clear and its simple geometry and freedom from solid boundaries still do not necessarily imply that the strong shock results are applicable in this case. The predictions of the so-called higher-continuum approximations have not been supported by the experimental work available on this problem, and these approaches have been meeting growing criticism. The usual definition, in the shock problem, of the Knudsen number based on the geometry of the shock thickness, is quite arbitrary and does not offer a measure of the degree of the flow rarefaction throughout a wide range. Indeed, the more diffuse the shock becomes, the more this arbitrariness tends to be significant.

The aim of the present work is to study the shock problem under conditions of increasing rarefaction and variable shock strength. The problem is approached through the kinetic theory and the full Boltzmann equation is used, without actually linearizing it. A solution by iteration is then adopted due to the success it has met in other problems and to its suitability for use in conjunction with the Boltzmann equation. To start the iteration scheme, which is performed on the velocity distribution function, the first approximation, in the Chapman-Enskog sequence leading to the Navier-Stokes equations, is considered in view of its relative simplicity and validity. In addition, the parameters appearing in this distribution function can be associated with the local degree of rarefaction.

Since this work was undertaken, Liepmann et al. (1962) and Chahine (1963) have studied the shock problem and computed profiles using the BGK model in an iteration scheme starting from the Navier-Stokes solution. This method is suitable for strong shocks, and can be obtained as a special case from the results of the present treatment. The study by Liepmann and associates, has, however, touched upon several aspects of interest to the present study and to the shock problem in general.

In Section II the integral form of the Boltzmann equation is transformed and suitably expressed for an iterative solution, and in Section III the equation is applied to the shock wave problem with its appropriate boundary conditions.

In Section IV the iteration technique is initiated using the Navier-Stokes approximation, and the first iteration to the distribution function is determined. In Section V the equations for the flow parameters are derived and brought into a form which can be solved numerically. A simplified form of these equations is also determined. The study is then concluded by a discussion.

II. General Formulation

Consider the steady state one-dimensional Boltzmann integrodifferential equation (subsequently B.E.) for the single particle velocity distribution function $f(c, x)$, in the absence of external forces,

$$u \frac{df}{dx} = \iint \{ f(c', x) f(c_1', x) - f(c, x) f(c_1, x) \} k_1(g, b) \, dk \, dc_1, \qquad (2.1)$$

in which $k_1(g, b)$ is a positive scalar function of the relative speed and the encounter variable and dk contains the geometrical variables specifying a collision and is independent of the velocities.

The function f, in the case of plane shock wave in a uniform stream, varies in a continuous manner as the flow progresses downstream and its form could be described to undergo continuous "stretching and distortion," consequently the function f is represented by

$$f(\mathbf{c}, x) = f^{(0)}(\mathbf{c}, x)[1 + \varphi(\mathbf{c}, x)]; \qquad (2.2)$$

$f^{(0)}$ is the local Maxwellian distribution function given by

$$f^{(0)}(\mathbf{c}, x) = n(x)[\beta(x)/\pi]^{3/2} \exp\{-\beta(x)[\mathbf{c} - \bar{u}(x)]^2\}; \qquad \beta(x) = m/2kT(x) \tag{2.3}$$

where n, $\bar{u}$, T are given by the actual local conditions, and the deviation function from Maxwellian, φ, to be determined, is such that f is a solution of the B.E. The function φ is not necessarily small, but when the random speed $C \to \infty$ the product $f^{(0)}\varphi \to 0$. Though $f^{(0)}$ is not a solution of the B.E., it clearly obeys the condition,

$$f^{(0)\prime}f_1^{(0)\prime} = f^{(0)}f_1^{(0)}.$$

Using the representation of Eq. (2.2), and assuming that the collision term can be separated, the B.E. becomes

$$u\frac{df}{dx} + f\iint f_1^{(0)}(1 + \varphi_1)k_1 \, d\mathbf{k} \, d\mathbf{c}_1 = f^{(0)}\iint f_1^{(0)}k_1 \, d\mathbf{k} \, d\mathbf{c}$$
$$\qquad\qquad ① \qquad ②$$
$$+ f^{(0)}\iint f_1^{(0)}(\varphi' + \varphi_1' + \varphi'\varphi_1')k_1 \, d\mathbf{k} \, d\mathbf{c}_1.$$
$$\qquad\qquad\qquad ③ \qquad ④ \qquad ⑤ \qquad (2.4)$$

Equation (2.4) can now be transformed (Chapman and Cowling, 1960; Waldmann, 1958), and an outline of the derivation is given.

With ψ and ε being polar angles specifying the direction of the unit vector $\mathbf{k}$ (apse line) about $\mathbf{g}$ as axis, and k_1 being a function of the relative speed g and the angle ψ between $\mathbf{g}$ and $\mathbf{k}$, parts 1 and 2 of Eq. (2.4) may be expressed as

$$(f^{(0)})^{-1}\int f^{(0)}f_1^{(0)}\left\{\iint k_1(g, \psi)\sin\psi \, d\psi \, d\varepsilon\right\}d\mathbf{c}_1 = (f^{(0)})^{-1}\delta_0(\mathbf{c}), \quad (2.5)$$

$$(f^{(0)})^{-1}\int \varphi_1\left\{f^{(0)}f_1^{(0)}\iint k_1(g, \psi)\sin\psi \, d\psi \, d\varepsilon\right\}d\mathbf{c}_1 = (f^{(0)})^{-1}\int \varphi_1\delta_1(\mathbf{c}, \mathbf{c}_1)d\mathbf{c}_1 \tag{2.6}$$

where $\delta_1(\mathbf{c}, \mathbf{c}_1)$ is a symmetrical function of $\mathbf{c}$, $\mathbf{c}_1$.

Regarding part 3 of Eq. (2.4), we first note the relations of $\mathbf{c}'$, $\mathbf{c}_1'$ in terms of $\mathbf{c}$, $\mathbf{c}_1$:

$$\mathbf{c}_1' = \mathbf{c}_1 - (\mathbf{g}\cdot\mathbf{k})\mathbf{k}; \qquad \mathbf{c}' = \mathbf{c} + (\mathbf{g}\cdot\mathbf{k})\mathbf{k}; \qquad \mathbf{g} = \mathbf{c}_1 - \mathbf{c}. \tag{2.7}$$

As $d\mathbf{c}_1 = d\mathbf{g}$, let $\mathbf{g} = g\mathbf{n}$, where $\mathbf{n}$ is a unit vector; then $d\mathbf{g} = g^2\, dg\, d\mathbf{n}$. Again let $\mathbf{R} = g\mathbf{k}$; then, similarly, $d\mathbf{R} = g^2\, dg\, d\mathbf{k}$. Next we change the variable, $\mathbf{R}$ to $\mathbf{K}$ where

$$\mathbf{K} = (\mathbf{g}\cdot\mathbf{k})\mathbf{k} = g\cos\psi\,\mathbf{k} = \cos\psi\,\mathbf{R};$$

then $d\mathbf{K} = \cos^3\psi\, d\mathbf{R}$ and $K = g\cos\psi$. A final change from $\mathbf{K}$ to $\mathbf{c}'$ can now be made.

The speed C_1 appearing in $f_1^{(0)}$ is expressed next in terms of C'. By making use of Eq. (2.7) and defining angles θ between $\mathbf{C}'$ and $\mathbf{K}$, and ε_1 between the planes of $\mathbf{C}'$ and $\mathbf{K}$ and $\mathbf{K}$ and $\mathbf{n}$, respectively, and then using a formula from spherical trigonometry, we obtain the relation

$$C_1^{\ 2} = C'^2 + 2KC'\sin\theta\tan\psi\cos\varepsilon_1 + K^2\tan^2\psi.$$

Finally, the orientation of $\mathbf{n}$ about $\mathbf{K}$ is given by the polar angles ψ and ε_1; thus $d\mathbf{n} = \sin\psi\, d\psi\, d\varepsilon_1$, and part 3 of Eq. (2.4) becomes

$$
\begin{aligned}
f^{(0)} &\iint \varphi' f_1^{(0)} k_1\, d\mathbf{k}\, d\mathbf{c}_1 \\
&= \int \varphi'\bigg\{ 2\pi f^{(0)} f^{(0)'} \int_0^{\pi/2} \exp(-\beta K^2\tan^2\psi) J_0(2i\beta|\mathbf{C}\wedge\mathbf{C}'|\tan\psi) \\
&\qquad\qquad \times k_1(K\sec\psi,\psi)\sec^3\psi\sin\psi\, d\psi\bigg\} d\mathbf{c}' \\
&= \int \varphi'\delta_2(\mathbf{c},\mathbf{c}')\, d\mathbf{c}' \qquad\qquad\qquad\qquad\qquad\qquad\qquad (2.8)
\end{aligned}
$$

where J_0 is Bessel's zero function, and as one can easily verify, $\delta_2(\mathbf{c},\mathbf{c}')$ is a symmetric function of $\mathbf{c}$, $\mathbf{c}'$. Changing $\mathbf{c}'$ to $\mathbf{c}_1$, we accordingly have

$$f^{(0)'} \to f_1^{(0)}; \qquad \varphi' \to \varphi_1; \qquad K \to g; \qquad \delta_2(\mathbf{c},\mathbf{c}') \to \delta_2(\mathbf{c},\mathbf{c}_1).$$

Part 4 of Eq. (2.4) is considered next, and in transforming this integral we use a new unit vector $\mathbf{k}_1$, whose direction is that of $\mathbf{g} - (\mathbf{g}\cdot\mathbf{k})\mathbf{k}$, and the polar angles giving its orientation about $\mathbf{g}$ as axis are $\pi/2 - \psi$ and $\varepsilon + \pi$. The transformation now proceeds as for part 3 of Eq. (2.4), where this time we put

$$\mathbf{K}_1 = \mathbf{c}_1' - \mathbf{c} = \mathbf{g} - (\mathbf{g}\cdot\mathbf{k})\mathbf{k} = \sin\psi\,\mathbf{R}_1$$

and finally the variable is changed from $\mathbf{K}_1$ to $\mathbf{c}_1'$. The speed C_1 in $f_1^{(0)}$ is now expressed in terms of C_1', and angles θ_1 and ε_2 are defined in a similar way to part 3 of Eq. (2.4). By using Eq. (2.7) again, we have

$$C_1^{\ 2} = C_1'^2 + K_1\cot^2\psi + 2C_1'K_1\sin\theta\cot\psi\cos\varepsilon_2,$$

and also $d\mathbf{n} = \cos\psi\, d\psi\, d\varepsilon_2$.

After integrating with respect to ε_2, putting $\psi' = \pi/2 - \psi$, and then identifying ψ' with ψ, part 4 of Eq. (2.4) becomes

$$f^{(0)} \iint \varphi_1' f_1^{(0)} k_1 \, d\mathbf{k} \, d\mathbf{c}_1$$

$$= \int \varphi_1' \Bigg\{ 2\pi f^{(0)} f_1^{(0)'} \int_0^{\pi/2} \exp[-\beta K_1{}^2 \tan^2 \psi]$$

$$\times J_0(2i\beta|\mathbf{C} \wedge \mathbf{C}_1'| \tan \psi) k_1(K_1 \sec \psi, \pi/2 - \psi) \sec^2 \psi \, d\psi \Bigg\} \, d\mathbf{c}_1'$$

$$= \int \varphi_1' \delta_3(\mathbf{c}, \mathbf{c}_1') \, d\mathbf{c}_1'$$

where $\delta_3(\mathbf{c}, \mathbf{c}_1')$ is a symmetrical function of $\mathbf{c}, \mathbf{c}_1'$.

Finally, changing $\mathbf{c}_1'$ to $\mathbf{c}_1$, we have

$$f_1^{(0)'} \to f_1^{(0)}; \qquad \varphi_1' \to \varphi_1; \qquad K_1 \to g; \qquad \delta_3(\mathbf{c}, \mathbf{c}_1') \to \delta_3(\mathbf{c}, \mathbf{c}_1).$$

Part 5 of Eq. (2.4) is represented for the present by

$$\Omega = f^{(0)} \iint f_1^{(0)} \varphi' \varphi_1' k_1 \, d\mathbf{k} \, d\mathbf{c}_1. \tag{2.10}$$

Combining these results, Eq. (2.4) will have the form

$$u \frac{df}{dx} + \frac{f}{f^{(0)}} \left[\delta_0(\mathbf{c}) + \int \varphi_1 \delta_1(\mathbf{c}, \mathbf{c}_1) \, d\mathbf{c}_1 \right]$$

$$= \delta_0(\mathbf{c}) + \int \varphi_1 \{\delta_2(\mathbf{c}, \mathbf{c}_1) + \delta_3(\mathbf{c}, \mathbf{c}_1)\} \, d\mathbf{c}_1 + \Omega. \tag{2.11}$$

The positive scalar $k_1(g, \psi)$ is given by

$$k_1(g, \psi) = \frac{gb}{\sin \psi} \left| \frac{\partial b}{\partial \psi} \right| = 4g \cos \psi \, \bar{k}_1(g, \psi) \tag{2.11}$$

where b is the encounter variable and $\bar{k}_1$ is the collision cross section defined by

$$\bar{k}_1(g, \psi) = \frac{b}{2 \sin 2\psi} \left| \frac{\partial b}{\partial \psi} \right|.$$

For hard sphere molecules, with a molecular diameter σ,

$$b = \sigma \sin \psi; \qquad \bar{k}_1 = \sigma^2/4.$$

Introducing $\bar{k}_1(g, \psi)$ in the integrals, letting $x = \pi - 2\psi$, and then substituting the resulting coefficients in Eq. (2.11), the B.E. is made dimensionless on multiplying throughout by the local $L\beta^{1/2}(x)$. One obtains the result

$$\lambda \mathfrak{C}_x \frac{df}{d\hat{x}} + f\left(K_0 + \int_{-\infty}^{\infty} \varphi_1 K_1 \exp(-\mathfrak{C}_1{}^2)\, d\mathfrak{C}_1\right)$$

$$= f^{(0)}\left(K_0 + \int_{-\infty}^{\infty} \varphi_1 K_2 \exp(-\mathfrak{C}_1{}^2)\, d\mathfrak{C}_1\right) + \frac{L\beta^{1/2}}{f^{(0)}} \Omega \quad (2.13)$$

where

$$K_0(\mathfrak{C}) = 2\pi^{-1/2} \Delta \int_{-\infty}^{\infty} \mathfrak{G} \exp(-\mathfrak{C}_1{}^2)\left\{\int_0^{\pi} \bar{k}_1(g, x) \sin x\, dx\right\} d\mathfrak{C}_1, \quad (2.14a)$$

$$K_1(\mathfrak{C}, \mathfrak{C}_1) = 2\pi^{-1/2} \Delta \mathfrak{G} \int_0^{\pi} \bar{k}_1(g, x) \sin x\, dx, \quad (2.14b)$$

$$K_2(\mathfrak{C}, \mathfrak{C}_1) = 2\pi^{-1/2} \Delta \mathfrak{G} \int_0^{\pi} \left\{\bar{k}_1\left(\frac{g}{\sin \frac{1}{2}x}, x\right) + \right.$$

$$\left. + \bar{k}_1\left(\frac{g}{\sin \frac{1}{2}x}, \pi - x\right)\right\} \frac{\exp(-\mathfrak{G}^2 \cot^2 \frac{1}{2}x}{\sin^4 \frac{1}{2}x}$$

$$\times J_0(2i|\mathfrak{C} \wedge \mathfrak{C}_1| \cot \frac{1}{2}x) \sin x\, dx, \quad (2.14c)$$

and

molecular velocity: $\mathfrak{C}_r(\mathfrak{C}_x, \mathfrak{C}_y, \mathfrak{C}_z) = \beta^{1/2}(x)\mathbf{c}(u, v, w),$

random velocity: $\mathfrak{C}(\mathfrak{U}, \mathfrak{V}, \mathfrak{W}) = \beta^{1/2}(x)\mathbf{C}(U, V, W),$

mean speed: $\overline{\mathfrak{A}}(x) = \beta^{1/2}(x)\bar{u}(x),$

Knudsen number: $\lambda(x) = \bar{l}(x)/L = \Delta/nL; \qquad \Delta = 1/\sqrt{2}\pi\sigma^2.$

The expression for the mean free path l is chosen arbitrarily, L is a typical length, and $\hat{x} = x/L$.

Equation (2.13) can now be integrated with respect to $\hat{x}$, yielding

$$f(\mathfrak{C}_r, \hat{x}) = f(\mathfrak{C}_r, \hat{x}_0) \exp\left(-\int_{\hat{x}_0}^{\hat{x}} \frac{D(\mathfrak{C}_r, x)}{\lambda(x)\mathfrak{C}_x}\, dx\right) + \int_{\hat{x}_0}^{\hat{x}} \exp\left(-\int_{\hat{x}'}^{\hat{x}} \frac{D(\mathfrak{C}_r, x)}{\lambda(x)\mathfrak{C}_x}\, dx\right)$$

$$\times f^{(0)} \frac{P(\mathfrak{C}_r, \hat{x}')}{\lambda(\hat{x}')\mathfrak{C}_x}\, d\hat{x}', \quad (2.15)$$

where

$$D(\mathfrak{C}_r, x) = K_0 + \int_{-\infty}^{\infty} \varphi_1 K_1 \exp(-\mathfrak{C}_1{}^2)\, d\mathfrak{C}_1 = K_0 + \overline{\varphi K_1}, \quad (2.16)$$

$$P(\mathfrak{C}_r, x) = K_0 + \int_{-\infty}^{\infty} \varphi_1 K_2 \exp(-\mathfrak{C}_1{}^2)\, d\mathfrak{C}_1 + L\beta^{1/2} \frac{\Omega}{f^{(0)}}$$

$$= K_0 + \overline{\varphi K_2} + \overline{\varphi K_4}, \quad (2.17)$$

and $\hat{x}_0$ is a fixed value of $\hat{x}$.

Equations (2.15)–(2.17) have been rendered dimensionless using the local flow parameters and they replace the normal integral form of the one-dimensional B.E. The functions D and P are, as we know, associated with the disappearance and production of molecules by encounters in dc about c, and here they are given in terms of various average weighting functions, themselves dependent on the actual form of the distribution function f, and on coefficients related to the particular collision cross section.

The determination of the coefficients K_0, K_1 and K_2 requires the specification of the type of encounter between the molecules, and the formulation of the problem is restricted now to hard sphere molecules. For this case the collision cross section $\bar{k}_1(g, \psi)$ is simply a constant equal to $\sigma^2/4$ and the integrations in Eq. (2.14) can be performed analytically, yielding

$$K_0(\mathfrak{C}) = (2\pi)^{-1/2}[\exp(-\mathfrak{C}^2) + (2\mathfrak{C} + \mathfrak{C}^{-1})(\tfrac{1}{2}\pi^{1/2})\operatorname{erf}\mathfrak{C}], \quad (2.18a)$$

$$K_1(\mathfrak{C}, \mathfrak{C}_1) = 2^{-1/2}\pi^{-3/2}\mathfrak{G}, \quad (2.18b)$$

$$K_2(\mathfrak{C}, \mathfrak{C}_1) = 2^{-1/2}\pi^{-3/2}[2\mathfrak{G}^{-1}\exp(\{|\mathfrak{C}_1 \wedge \mathfrak{C}|\mathfrak{G}^{-1}\})^2]. \quad (2.18c)$$

When the dimensionless random speed $\mathfrak{C}$ equals one, K_0 is very nearly equal to one also, a fact which will be useful later on when comparing the Krook model with the B.E.

Equations (2.15)–(2.17) express the B.E. in a form suitable for solution by an iterative process, but first they are applied to the normal shock wave problem.

III. Shock Wave Structure

Consider a normal shock wave in a uniform free stream and fix the coordinate system at its center. The B.E. (2.15) is now applied to this case noting that the boundary conditions at $\pm\infty$ are such that the distribution function is Maxwellian. The flow parameters n_1, $\bar{u}_1$, T_1 upstream at $-\infty$ and n_2, $\bar{u}_2$, T_2 downstream at $+\infty$ are given *a priori*, but satisfy the Rankine-Hugoniot conditions. The application of these boundary conditions to the B.E. necessitates the definition of four representations in the half spaces $x \gtrless 0$, $\mathfrak{C}_x \gtrless 0$ but as the boundaries are at infinity, two half range representations in the velocity space are sufficient. From Eq. (2.15) these are

$$f^{(+)}(\mathfrak{C}_r, \hat{x}) = \int_{-\infty}^{\hat{x}} \exp\left(-\int_{\hat{x}'}^{\hat{x}} \frac{D(\mathfrak{C}_r, x)}{\lambda(x)\mathfrak{C}_x}\, dx\right)\frac{f^{(0)}(\mathfrak{C}_r, \hat{x}')}{\lambda(\hat{x}')\mathfrak{C}_x} P(\mathfrak{C}_r, \hat{x}')\, d\hat{x}',$$
$$\mathfrak{C}_x > 0, \quad (3.1)$$

$$f^{(-)}(\mathfrak{C}_r, \hat{x}) = \int_{\infty}^{\hat{x}} \exp\left(-\int_{\hat{x}'}^{\hat{x}} \frac{D(\mathfrak{C}_r, x)}{\lambda(x)\mathfrak{C}_x}\, dx\right)\frac{f^{(0)}(\mathfrak{C}_r, \hat{x}')}{\lambda(\hat{x}')\mathfrak{C}_x} P(\mathfrak{C}_r, \hat{x}')\, d\hat{x}',$$
$$\mathfrak{C}_x < 0. \quad (3.2)$$

At large distances from the shock the local flow parameters $n(x)$, $\bar{u}(x)$, and $T(x)$ tend to the respective constant values at the boundary, the deviation from Maxwellian, φ, becomes increasingly small, and at the limit the distribution function is identical to the Maxwellian and the boundary conditions are satisfied.

The unknown local flow parameters are obtained from the relations

$$n(x) = \int_{-\infty}^{\infty} \iint_{0}^{0} f^{(-)} \, d\mathbf{c} + \int_{-\infty}^{\infty} \iint_{0}^{\infty} f^{(+)} \, d\mathbf{c}, \tag{3.3a}$$

$$n(x)\bar{u}(x) = \int_{-\infty}^{\infty} \iint_{0}^{0} u f^{(-)} \, d\mathbf{c} + \int_{-\infty}^{\infty} \iint_{0}^{\infty} u f^{(+)} \, d\mathbf{c}, \tag{3.3b}$$

$$3(k/m)n(x)T(x) = \int_{-\infty}^{\infty} \iint_{0}^{0} [\mathbf{c} - \bar{u}(x)]^2 f^{(-)} \, d\mathbf{c} + \int_{-\infty}^{\infty} \iint_{0}^{\infty} [\mathbf{c} - \bar{u}(x)]^2 f^{(+)} \, d\mathbf{c}, \tag{3.3c}$$

where, it should be noted, we have assumed that the solutions $n(x)$, $\bar{u}(x)$, $T(x)$ of the system (3.3) do actually exist and are differentiable and satisfy the boundary conditions.

In the integral equations (3.1) and (3.2) the distribution function f is basically the only unknown and a solution by iteration is proposed. First a guess of the function φ is made and the corresponding parameters, n, $\bar{u}$, and T are found from the solution of the equations of molecular transport of mass, momentum and energy (Patterson, 1956). With the knowledge of these zeroth approximations of φ and the flow parameters, the first iterate of f can, in principal, be found from Eqs. (3.1) and (3.2) and the corresponding n, $\bar{u}$, T are determined from Eq. (3.3). The first iterate of φ is then found from Eq. (2.2) and the process is carried on. The problem as such reduces to one of convergence of this process and the determination of a zeroth φ for the initiation of the iterative process. The problem of convergence is not dealt with in this paper, but a set of conditions somewhat similar to those obtained by Willis (1961) in his treatment of the linearized Couette flow could probably be derived. Alternatively, the study of the convergence could be made from the results of a computing machine.

IV. The First Approximation

To start the iteration procedure, a guess, and a correct one, of the distribution function must be made, and the Navier-Stokes approximation (subsequently NS) would appear to be the obvious choice to consider here, in view of the support it has had from recent experimental work. Let us therefore choose for the deviation function from Maxwellian, φ, the first approximation of the Chapman-Enskog solution of the B.E. (Chapman and Cowling, 1960). Its one-dimensional form is given by

$$\varphi_0(\mathfrak{C}, \hat{x}) = -(\theta/t_x)\mathfrak{U}(\mathfrak{C}^2 - \tfrac{5}{2}) - (\theta/t_{xx})(\mathfrak{U}^2 - \tfrac{1}{3}\mathfrak{C}^2), \tag{4.1}$$

where

$$\theta = \mu/p\beta^{1/2}L; \qquad t_x = [\tfrac{3}{2}(d \log T/d\hat{x})]^{-1}; \qquad t_{xx} = (2\beta^{1/2} \, d\bar{u}/d\hat{x})^{-1}. \tag{4.2}$$

The coefficient θ is, in this case, equal to the local Knudsen number multiplied by a factor of order unity. It is also possible (Sherman, 1958) to relate θ to the mean free time, and t_x and t_{xx} with characteristic times for $\bar{u}$ and T to undergo a change.

The corresponding distribution function f_0 for Eq. (4.1) leads, as we know, to the one-dimensional NS equations, with solutions $n_0(x)$, $\bar{u}_0(x)$, and $T_0(x)$ which we are considering here as known. These solutions together with Eq. (4.1) enable us to determine the zeroth approximation D_0 and P_0 from Eqs. (2.16), (2.17), and subsequently the first iteration of the distribution function from Eqs. (3.1), (3.2). In the following the index zero will be dropped, and terms in D and P involving the random speed component $\mathfrak{U}$ will be neglected as their contribution is comparatively small.

Upon substitution in D of φ_0, and the coefficients K_0 and K_1 from Eqs. (2.18a), (2.18b), and performing the integration involved, we obtain

$$D(\mathfrak{C}, \hat{x}) = K_0 + \overline{\varphi K_1} = (2\pi)^{-1/2}[\exp(-\mathfrak{C}^2)\{1 - (\theta/4t_{xx})\mathfrak{C}^{-2}\}$$
$$+ \{2\mathfrak{C} + \mathfrak{C}^{-1}[1 - (\theta/6t_{xx})]$$
$$+ (\theta/4t_{xx})\mathfrak{C}^{-3}\}\tfrac{1}{2}\pi^{1/2} \operatorname{erf} \mathfrak{C}]. \tag{4.3}$$

Similarly, and by using the coefficient K_2, Eq. (2.18c), the integration of the expression $\overline{\varphi K_2}$ of P, Eq. (2.17) can be performed analytically after few substitutions and gives

$$\overline{\varphi K_2}(\mathfrak{C}, \hat{x}) = (2\pi)^{-1/2}(\theta/6t_{xx})[\exp(-\mathfrak{C}^2)\{\mathfrak{C}^2 - 1 - \tfrac{3}{4}\mathfrak{C}^{-2}\}$$
$$+ \{2\mathfrak{C}^3 - \mathfrak{C} + \tfrac{1}{2}\mathfrak{C}^{-1} + \tfrac{3}{4}\mathfrak{C}^{-3}\}\tfrac{1}{2}\pi^{1/2} \operatorname{erf} \mathfrak{C}]. \tag{4.4}$$

The nonlinear part $\overline{\varphi K_4}$ of P is considered next, where Ω is given in Eq. (2.10), and in which we substitute $k_1 = g\sigma^2 \cos \psi$ and $d\mathbf{k} = \sin \psi \, d\psi \, d\varepsilon$. In addition, φ' and φ_1' are obtained from Eq. (4.1) where for φ', for example, we have

$$\varphi' = -\theta[(\mathfrak{U}'/t_x)(\mathfrak{C}'^2 - \tfrac{5}{2}) + (1/t_{xx})(\mathfrak{U}'^2 - \tfrac{1}{3}\mathfrak{C}'^2)].$$

Finally, the velocity components after the collision can be found in terms of the given initial components (Patterson, 1956), with $\delta = 2\psi$, and the integrations involved in $\overline{\varphi K_4}$ can now be performed. The determination of this part is long and tedious but an analytical result can be obtained and this is given in Appendix A.

Combining the results of K_0, $\overline{\varphi K_2}$, and $\overline{\varphi K_4}$, from Eqs. (2.18a), (4.4), and (A.1), respectively, we obtain

$$
\begin{aligned}
P(\mathbb{C}, \hat{x}) &= K_0 + \overline{\varphi K_2} + \overline{\varphi K_4} \\
&= 2\pi^{-1/2}[\exp(-\mathbb{C}^2)\{1 + (\theta/6t_{xx})(\mathbb{C}^2 - 1 - \tfrac{3}{4}\mathbb{C}^{-2}) \\
&\quad + (\theta^2/4)(N_{-4}\mathbb{C}^{-4} + N_{-2}\mathbb{C}^{-2} + N_0 + N_2\mathbb{C}^2 + N_4\mathbb{C}^4 + N_6\mathbb{C}^6)\} \\
&\quad + \{2\mathbb{C} + \mathbb{C}^{-1} + (\theta/6t_{xx})(2\mathbb{C}^3 - \mathbb{C} + \tfrac{1}{2}\mathbb{C}^{-1} + \tfrac{3}{4}\mathbb{C}^{-3}) \\
&\quad + (\theta^2/4)(N_{-5}\mathbb{C}^{-5} + N_{-3}\mathbb{C}^{-3} + N_{-1}\mathbb{C}^{-1} + N_1\mathbb{C} + N_3\mathbb{C}^3 \\
&\quad + N_5\mathbb{C}^5 + N_7\mathbb{C}^7)\}\tfrac{1}{2}\pi^{1/2}\,\mathrm{erf}(\mathbb{C})],
\end{aligned}
\tag{4.5}
$$

where the coefficients $N_{-5} \cdots N_7$ are functions of $\hat{x}$ and are given in Appendix A.

The dependance of the distribution function, Eqs. (3.1) and (3.2), on the molecular velocity is now known, but to determine its dependance on $\hat{x}$ we require the NS analytical solutions. However, as we are only interested in certain moments, the entire determination of the distribution function is not necessary.

It is noted that for the continuum case $\theta = \lambda \simeq 0$ and from Eqs. (4.3) and (4.5) $D = P = K_0$, where K_0, as we mentioned earlier, is of order unity when $\mathbb{C}$ is of order unity, and the distribution function (3.1), (3.2) reduces to that of the BGK model. The additional terms we have obtained in D and P are dependent on the Knudsen number and the velocity and temperature gradients and could all be regarded as corrections, becoming of importance as the flow medium becomes more rarefied.

As one would expect, if we consider the flow parameters appearing in Eqs. (3.1) and (3.2) as constant, the resulting distribution function will be Maxwellian, with uniform parameters. Regarding D and P, a close examination when $\mathbb{C} \to 0$, reveals no singularities.

V. The Flow Parameters

A. Derivation

The function D, Eq. (4.3) is very nearly unity when the dimensionless random speed $\mathbb{C}$ is equal to one, and this is true even for large values of θ/t_{xx} of order 10. We can therefore expand the exponential in Eqs. (3.1) and (3.2) as a power series in the neighborhood of this value of D, and consider only the first two terms of the expansion. The resulting distribution function is then used in Eq. (3.3) and the first approximation to the flow parameters is obtained, namely,

$$n^{(1)}(\hat{x}) = \int_{-\infty}^{\hat{x}} \frac{n(\hat{x}')}{\pi^{1/2}\lambda(\hat{x}')} J_0^{(+)}(\hat{x}, \hat{x}') \, d\hat{x}'$$

$$+ \int_x^{\infty} \frac{n(\hat{x}')}{\pi^{1/2}\lambda(\hat{x}')} J_0^{(-)}(\hat{x}, \hat{x}') \, d\hat{x}' = \mathfrak{F}_0^{(1)}(\hat{x}), \qquad (5.1a)$$

$$n^{(1)}(\hat{x})\bar{u}^{(1)}(\hat{x}) = \int_{-\infty}^{\hat{x}} \frac{n(\hat{x}')}{\pi^{1/2}\lambda(\hat{x}')\beta^{1/2}(\hat{x}')} J_1^{(+)}(\hat{x}, \hat{x}') \, d\hat{x}'$$

$$+ \int_x^{\infty} \frac{n(\hat{x}')}{\pi^{1/2}\lambda(\hat{x}')\beta^{1/2}(\hat{x}')} J_1^{(-)}(\hat{x}, \hat{x}') \, d\hat{x}' = \mathfrak{F}_1^{(1)}(\hat{x}), \qquad (5.1b)$$

$$(3k/m)n^{(1)}(\hat{x})T^{(1)}(\hat{x}) + n^{(1)}(\hat{x})(\bar{u}^{(1)})^2(\hat{x})$$

$$= \int_{-\infty}^{\hat{x}} \frac{n(\hat{x}')}{\pi^{1/2}\lambda(\hat{x}')\beta(\hat{x}')} [J_2^{(+)}(\hat{x}, \hat{x}') + I_0^{(+)}(\hat{x}, \hat{x}')] \, d\hat{x}'$$

$$+ \int_{\hat{x}}^{\infty} \frac{n(\hat{x}')}{\pi^{1/2}\lambda(\hat{x}')\beta(\hat{x}')} [J_2^{(-)}(\hat{x}, \hat{x}') + I_0^{(-)}(\hat{x}, \hat{x}')] \, d\hat{x}' = \mathfrak{F}_2^{(1)}(\hat{x}),$$

where $\qquad\qquad\qquad\qquad\qquad\qquad\qquad\qquad\qquad\qquad\qquad (5.1c)$

$$J_n^{(\pm)}(\hat{x}, \hat{x}') = \int_0^{\pm\infty} \exp\{-[\delta(\hat{x}, \hat{x}')/\mathbb{C}_x] - [\mathbb{C}_x - \bar{\mathfrak{U}}(\hat{x}')]^2\}$$

$$\times M_1(\mathbb{C}_x, \hat{x}, \hat{x}')\mathbb{C}_x^{n-1} \, d\mathbb{C}_x, \qquad (5.2)$$

$$I_n^{(\pm)}(\hat{x}, \hat{x}') = \int_0^{\pm\infty} \exp\{-[\delta(\hat{x}, \hat{x}')/\mathbb{C}_x] - [\mathbb{C}_x - \bar{\mathfrak{U}}(\hat{x}')]^2\}$$

$$\times M_2(\mathbb{C}_x, \hat{x}, \hat{x}')\mathbb{C}_x^{n-1} \, d\mathbb{C}_x, \qquad (5.3)$$

and

$$M_1(\mathbb{C}_x, \hat{x}, \hat{x}') = \pi^{-1} \iint_{-\infty}^{+\infty} \exp(-\mathbb{C}_y^2 - \mathbb{C}_z^2)P(\mathbb{C}, \hat{x}')$$

$$\times \{1 - [\varepsilon(\mathbb{C}, \hat{x}, \hat{x}')/\mathbb{C}_x]\} \, d\mathbb{C}_y \, d\mathbb{C}_z, \qquad (5.4)$$

$$M_2(\mathbb{C}_x, \hat{x}, \hat{x}') = \pi^{-1} \iint_{-\infty}^{+\infty} (\mathbb{C}_y^2 + \mathbb{C}_z^2) \exp(-\mathbb{C}_y^2 - \mathbb{C}_z^2)P(\mathbb{C}, \hat{x}')$$

$$\times \{1 - [\varepsilon(\mathbb{C}, \hat{x}, \hat{x}')/\mathbb{C}_x]\} \, d\mathbb{C}_y \, d\mathbb{C}_z, \qquad (5.5)$$

$$\delta(\hat{x}, \hat{x}') = \int_{\hat{x}'}^{\hat{x}} [\beta(\hat{x}')/\beta(x)]^{1/2}[D(1, x)/\lambda(x)] \, dx, \qquad (5.6)$$

$$\varepsilon(\mathbb{C}, \hat{x}, \hat{x}') = \int_{\hat{x}'}^{\hat{x}} [\beta(\hat{x}')/\beta(x)]^{1/2}[\lambda(x)]^{-1}[D(\mathbb{C}, x) - D(1, x)] \, dx. \qquad (5.7)$$

At this level, the present equations can be compared again with the BGK model results (Darrozès, 1963) for which, we find, that $M_1 = M_2 = D = 1$ and consequently $I_0 = J_0$.

With the functions D and P known from Eqs. (4.3) and (4.5), M_1 and M_2 can be determined. On integrating the part which involves ε, it is assumed that U, the random speed in the flow direction, is equal to zero, which is an acceptable assumption, particularly as the contribution of the corresponding integral is basically small. Carrying out the integrations in M_1 and M_2 yields

$$M_i(\mathfrak{C}_x, \hat{x}, \hat{x}') = (2\pi)^{-1/2}\left[\exp(-\mathfrak{U}^2)\sum_{v/2=0}^{3} a_{iv}\mathfrak{U}^v + \tfrac{1}{2}\pi^{1/2}\,\mathrm{erf}(\mathfrak{U})\sum_{(v+1)/2=0}^{4} b_{iv}\mathfrak{U}^v\right.$$

$$+ \exp(\mathfrak{U}^2)\tfrac{1}{4}\pi\{1 - (\mathrm{erf}\,\mathfrak{U})^2\}\sum_{v/2=0}^{1} c_{iv}\mathfrak{U}^v$$

$$+ (d_i/\mathfrak{U}^2)(\exp(-\mathfrak{U}^2) - \mathfrak{U}^{-1}\,\mathrm{erf}\,\mathfrak{U})$$

$$\left. + [\varepsilon_i(\hat{x}, \hat{x}')/\mathfrak{C}_x]\right]; \qquad i = 1, 2, \tag{5.8}$$

where the coefficients a_{iv}, b_{iv}, c_{iv}, and d_i are functions of $\hat{x}'$ only and are given together with ε_i in Appendix B. It is worth noting that if we put in these coefficients $U = \theta = \lambda = \varepsilon_1 = \varepsilon_2 = 0$, we find that for this continuum flow case $M_1 = 1.026$ and $M_2 = 1.225$; in addition we find $D = 1.041$, where as we have seen, according to the BGK model these coefficients are equal to one.

The functions M_1 and M_2 can be introduced now in Eqs. (5.2) and (5.3) for the determination of J_n and I_n. However, the integrations involved in these functions cannot be performed analytically, though a considerable reduction in their number is possible. It is now convenient to express $J_2 + I_0$ by the symbol J_2 only, the resulting functions J_n have the form

$$J_n^{(\pm)}(\hat{x}, \hat{x}') = (2\pi)^{-1/2}\int_0^{\pm\infty} \exp(-\delta/\mathfrak{C}_x)\left[\exp(-2\{\mathfrak{C}_x - \overline{\mathfrak{U}}\}^2)\right.$$

$$\times [(D_n/\mathfrak{C}_x) + E_n + F_n\mathfrak{C}_x] + \exp(-\{\mathfrak{C}_x - \overline{\mathfrak{U}}\}^2)\tfrac{1}{2}\pi^{1/2}\,\mathrm{erf}(\mathfrak{C}_x - \overline{\mathfrak{U}})$$

$$\times \left\{\frac{A_n}{\mathfrak{C}_x - \overline{\mathfrak{U}}} + \frac{W_n}{\mathfrak{C}_x} + V_n + T_n\mathfrak{C}_x\right\}\tfrac{1}{4}\pi(1 - [\mathrm{erf}(\mathfrak{C}_x - \overline{\mathfrak{U}})]^2)B_n\right]d\mathfrak{C}_x. \tag{5.9}$$

The determination of the twenty four coefficients appearing in Eq. (5.9) is tedious and their final form is lengthy. However, ultimately they are all functions of $\overline{\mathfrak{U}}$, δ, θ/t_x, θ/t_{xx} and their products. In order to keep the size of this paper within limits, it was decided to omit these coefficients.

The number of integrals in the expression J_n can be reduced further by allowing the use of an operator which involves differentiations with respect to

δ, Eq. (5.6), or effectively with respect to $\hat{x}$. Carrying out this operation, we obtain

$$J_n^{(\pm)}(\hat{x}, \hat{x}') = (2\pi)^{-1/2}\left[A_n\int_0^{\pm\infty} \exp(-(\delta/\mathbb{C}_x) - (\mathbb{C}_x - \overline{\mathfrak{U}})^2)\tfrac{1}{2}\pi^{1/2}\frac{\mathrm{erf}(\mathbb{C}_x - \overline{\mathfrak{U}})}{\mathbb{C}_x - \overline{\mathfrak{U}}}\right.$$

$$\left. \times\, d\mathbb{C}_x + \mathfrak{D}_n\cdot\int_0^{\pm\infty} \exp(-\delta/\mathbb{C}_x)\tfrac{1}{4}\pi(1 - \{\mathrm{erf}(\mathbb{C}_x - \overline{\mathfrak{U}})\}^2)\right]d\mathbb{C}_x$$

$$\tag{5.10}$$

where the operator $\mathfrak{D}_n(\hat{x}, \hat{x}')$ is given by

$$\mathfrak{D}_n(\hat{x}, \hat{x}') = -2F_n\int_\infty^\delta d\delta' + (E_n + (\delta - \overline{\mathfrak{U}})F_n + \tfrac{1}{2}T_n + B_n)$$

$$+ (-E_n\delta + \overline{\mathfrak{U}}\delta F_n - T_n\tfrac{1}{2}\delta)\frac{\delta}{d\delta}$$

$$+ (D_n(\overline{\mathfrak{U}} + \delta) - \overline{\mathfrak{U}}\delta E_n - \tfrac{1}{2}W_n + V_n\tfrac{1}{2}\delta)\frac{d^2}{d\delta^2}$$

$$+ (D_n(1 + \overline{\mathfrak{U}}\delta) - E_n\delta - W_n\tfrac{1}{2}\delta + F_n\tfrac{1}{2}\delta^2)\frac{d^3}{d\delta^3}$$

$$+ (2\delta D_n - E_n\tfrac{1}{2}\delta^2)\frac{d^4}{d\delta^4} + D_n\tfrac{1}{2}\delta^2\frac{d^5}{d\delta^5},$$

$$\tag{5.11}$$

and it should be noted differentiation with respect to δ is made at constant $\hat{x}'$. Finally, Eq. (5.1), defining the flow parameters, can be expressed in the following form

$$\mathfrak{F}_n^{(1)}(\hat{x}) = \int_{-\infty}^{\hat{x}} \frac{n(\hat{x}')}{\pi^{1/2}\lambda(\hat{x}')}\frac{J_n^{(+)}(\hat{x}, \hat{x}')}{\beta^{n/2}(\hat{x}')}\,d\hat{x}' + \int_{\hat{x}}^\infty \frac{n(\hat{x}')}{\pi^{1/2}\lambda(\hat{x}')}\frac{J_n^{(-)}(\hat{x}, \hat{x}')}{\beta^{n/2}(\hat{x}')}\,d\hat{x}' \tag{5.12}$$

in which $n = 1, 2, 3$ and superscipt (1) refers to the first approximation, and the functions under the integral signs are the NS solutions. The integrals in Eqs. (5.9) and (5.10) do not appear to be solvable analytically. However, expansions for some limiting values of $\overline{\mathfrak{U}}$ should be possible. (Chahine and Narasimha, 1963). It is noted that some of these integrals are singular for certain values of δ, but the form of Eq. (5.12) is such that these singularities cancel out and $\mathfrak{F}_n^{(1)}(\hat{x})$ is always finite.

With the knowledge of the NS solutions, the present equations are in a form basically suitable for programming on a computing machine.

B. The Simplified Equations

An analytic solution of $J_n(\hat{x}, \hat{x}')$, Eq. (5.10), does not appear to be possible and even a numerical solution would be lengthy and involved. However, before attempting such a task, an insight into the basic factors affecting the problem can be gained by introducing a simplification in the form of the functions M_i [Eq. (5.8)]. It is noted, that most of the contribution of M_i comes from the neighborhood of the region where $\mathfrak{U}$ is equal to zero. To obtain the dominant terms, we put in M_i that $\mathfrak{U} = \varepsilon_i = 0$, and get

$$
M_1(x) = (2\pi)^{-1/2}[a_{10} + b_{-11} + (\pi/4)c_{10}]
$$
$$
= (2\pi)^{-1/2}\left[1 + \frac{\pi}{2} + \frac{\theta}{3t_{xx}} - \frac{\theta^2}{4}\left(\frac{7}{15}\frac{1}{t_x^2} + \frac{359}{2160}\frac{1}{t_{xx}^2}\right)\right], \quad (5.13a)
$$

$$
M_2(x) = (2\pi)^{-1/2}[a_{20} + b_{-21} + (\pi/4)c_{20}]
$$
$$
= (2\pi)^{-1/2}\left[\frac{3}{2} + \frac{2\pi}{4} + \left(\frac{1}{3} + \frac{\pi}{6}\right)\frac{\theta}{t_{xx}} + \frac{\theta^2}{4}\left(\frac{1}{15}\frac{1}{t_x^2} + \frac{41}{135}\frac{1}{t_{xx}^2}\right)\right], \quad (5.13b)
$$

and

$$
D(1, x) = (2\pi)^{-1/2}\left[\exp(-1)\left\{1 - \frac{\theta}{4t_{xx}}\right\} + \left\{3 + \frac{1}{12}\frac{\theta}{t_{xx}}\right\}\tfrac{1}{2}\pi^{1/2}\,\mathrm{erf}(1)\right], \quad (5.13c)
$$

where M_i is now a function of the displacement only, and the coefficients appearing in Eq. (5.13) are given in Appendix B.

By using θ, t_x, and t_{xx} from Eq. (4.2), and the expression relating the mean free path with the viscosity coefficient for the hard sphere molecules, at the NS approximation level, the dimensional form of the flow parameters, (5.1) becomes

$$
n^{(1)}(x) = \int_{-\infty}^{x} \frac{\beta^{1/2}(x')n(x')}{\pi^{1/2}}\frac{5\pi^{1/2}}{8}\frac{p(x')}{\mu(x')}M_1(x')j_0^{(+)}(x, x')\,dx'
$$
$$
+ \int_{x}^{\infty} \frac{\beta^{1/2}(x')n(x')}{\pi^{1/2}}\frac{5\pi^{1/2}}{8}\frac{p(x')}{\mu(x')}M_1(x')j_0^{(-)}(x, x')\,dx', \quad (5.14a)
$$

$$
n^{(1)}(x)\bar{u}^{(1)}(x) = \int_{-\infty}^{x} \frac{n(x')}{\pi^{1/2}}\frac{5\pi^{1/2}}{8}\frac{p(x')}{\mu(x')}M_1(x')j_1^{(+)}(x, x')\,dx'
$$
$$
+ \int_{x}^{\infty} \frac{n(x')}{\pi^{1/2}}\frac{5\pi^{1/2}}{8}\frac{p(x')}{\mu(x')}M_1(x')j_1^{(-)}(x, x')\,dx', \quad (5.14b)
$$

$$
(3k/m)n^{(1)}(x)T^{(1)}(x) + n^{(1)}(x)(\bar{u}^{(1)})^2(x)
$$
$$
= \int_{-\infty}^{x} \frac{n(x')}{\beta^{1/2}(x')\pi^{1/2}}\frac{5\pi^{1/2}}{8}\frac{p(x')}{\mu(x')}[M_1(x')j_2^{(+)}(x, x')
$$
$$
+ M_2(x')j_0^{(+)}(x, x')]\,dx' + \int_{x}^{\infty} \frac{n(x')}{\beta^{1/2}(x')\pi^{1/2}}\frac{5\pi^{1/2}}{8}\frac{p(x')}{\mu(x')}
$$
$$
\times [M_1(x')j_2^{(-)}(x, x') + M_2(x')j_0^{(-)}(x, x')]\,dx', \quad (5.14c)
$$

in which the functions under the integral sign refer to the NS solutions, and

$$j_n^{(\pm)}(x, x') = \beta^{n/2}(x') \int_0^{\pm\infty} \exp\{-[\delta(x, x')/u] - \beta(u - \bar{u})^2\}u^{n-1}\, du \quad (5.15)$$

where $\delta(x, x')$ is given now by

$$\delta(x, x') = \int_{x'}^x \frac{5\pi}{8} \frac{p(y)}{\mu(y)} D(1, y)\, dy. \quad (5.16)$$

Further, with

$$\frac{\theta}{t_{xx}} = \frac{2\mu}{p}\frac{d\bar{u}}{dx}, \qquad \frac{\theta}{t_x} = \frac{3\mu}{p}\frac{d(2RT)^{1/2}}{dx},$$

Eq. (5.13) becomes

$$M_1(x) = 1.0255 + 0.2659\frac{\mu}{p}\frac{d\bar{u}}{dx} - \frac{\mu^2}{p^2}\{0.0663(d\bar{u}/dx)^2$$

$$+ 0.4188[d(2RT)^{1/2}/dx]^2\}, \quad (5.17a)$$

$$M_2(x) = 1.2249 + 0.6837\frac{\mu}{p}\frac{d\bar{u}}{dx} + \frac{\mu^2}{p^2}\{0.1211(d\bar{u}/dx)^2$$

$$+ 0.0598[d(2RT)^{1/2}/dx]^2\}, \quad (5.17b)$$

and from Eq. (13c)

$$D(1, x) = 1.0404 - 0.0242\frac{\mu}{p}\frac{d\bar{u}}{dx}. \quad (5.17c)$$

Equations (5.14), for the flow parameters, together with Eqs. (5.15)–(5.17) make the system complete for the determination of the first approximations $n^{(1)}(x)$, $\bar{u}^{(1)}(x)$, and $T^{(1)}(x)$, provided, of course, that the NS solutions are known. Once these data are available, the equations can be programmed on a computing machine, and the normal shock profiles obtained. Regarding the NS profiles themselves, these can be determined for example by the saddle-point singularity method proposed by Gilbarg and Paolucci (1953) and used by Chahine (1963). With the knowledge of the functions D and P, Eqs. (4.3) and (4.5), the first approximation to the distribution function $f^{(1)}$, Eqs. (3.1) and (3.2), is known as well, and so the flow parameters to the same degree of approximation. The second approximation can then be attempted, first by finding $\varphi^{(1)}$ from Eq. (2.2), and then $D^{(1)}$ and $P^{(1)}$ from Eqs. (2.16) and (2.17), where the coefficients K_0, K_1, and K_2 remain unaltered as they are independent of the distribution function. From this information the second approximation $f^{(2)}$ is then found from Eqs. (3.1) and (3.2), and consequently the corresponding flow parameters are known.

IV. Discussion and Conclusions

The problem of normal shock wave structure has been studied by Liepmann *et al.* (1962) and Chahine (1963) using the BGK model. From Section II, it is seen that this model can actually be derived from the B.E. itself, by regarding f', f_1, f_1', to be local Maxwellian, and equating the collision operator K_0, Eq. (2.18a), to unity. Liepmann *et al.* and Chahine approached the shock problem by solving by iteration the resulting equations of the flow parameters, considering the NS approximation as the initial solution. In the present work the problem is tackled by using the B.E. itself, and a solution by iteration is proposed for f. The process is initiated by choosing as the first solution, the distribution function leading to the Navier-Stokes equations and substituting this for f', f_1, and f_1'. The resulting B.E. is then formally applied to the shock problem.

Equations (2.15)–(2.17) express the integral form of B.E. in terms of D and P, which are functions associated with the gain and loss of a certain type of molecule due to collisions. When D and P are considered unity, the BGK model is obtained as a special case of the B.E. Furthermore, with θ or μ/p being simply related to the Knudsen number, the integrated form of D and P, Eqs. (4.3) and (4.5), based on the distribution function of the NS equations, shows that when the continuum case is dealt with these coefficients are very nearly equal to unity (1.02 and 1.04, respectively), see also Eq. (5.17). This result implies that the BGK model is valid in the continuum case only.[1]

In the present study the iteration is basically performed on the distribution function, the knowledge of which determines the flow parameters, whereas in Liepmann *et al.* and Chahine's treatment the iteration is carried out on the flow parameters themselves. In fact, this latter way of iteration is a special one of the former, special in the sense that the distribution function remains unaltered in form throughout the whole iteration process. This type of iteration can be used, for example, on the simplified equations of the flow parameters (5.14), without further recourse being made to the distribution function, indeed for a constant form of f, and in the continuum regime the higher iterations will be identical to the BGK model results. However, it should be noted that in the present study no restriction was imposed on the Mach number or the Knudsen number, and the accuracy and range of validity of the results depend only on the number of iterations performed, assuming of course that the process is convergent. On the other hand, as the BGK model is found to be restricted to continuum media,[1] the higher iterations on the flow parameters themselves are suitable for stronger shocks only.

[1]The model is, of course, also valid in free molecule flow where the distribution function is uniformly Maxwellian.

An important aspect of the present study is the choice of the distribution function of NS equations as the starting step for the iteration scheme. This choice is, in fact, a natural one, owing to the relative simplicity of the distribution function, and the confidence in its validity. The use of the so-called higher continuum approximations is not necessary, and moreover, could prove to be unsatisfactory. As mentioned above, the present method basically seeks higher iterations of the distribution function, and in this sense it is similar to the Chapman-Enskog method. Liepmann *et al.* and Chahine noted that in their special case, their procedure was essentially different from the Chapman-Enskog sequence and their results converged more rapidly. From the present point of view this essential difference lies in the two different approaches to solve the same equation, namely the B.E. This question is indeed fundamental and requires further study. However, in the present equations there appears the term $\exp(-\delta/u)$, where δ and u vary independently between zero and infinity, and therefore its approximation by an expansion of finite terms may not be suitable, or permissible, in this case.

It is interesting to note in the equations the appearance of the coefficients

$$\frac{\mu}{p}\frac{d\bar{u}}{dx}; \quad \frac{\mu}{p}\frac{d(2RT)^{1/2}}{dx},$$

which can be interpreted as the local ratio of the mean free time to the time of variation of a parameter of the flow, or as a local Knudsen number based on an actual characteristic length. It is seen that two such ratios can be defined and associated with the local state of the flow. Now, as the flow becomes more rarefied μ/p increases but the gradients of $\bar{u}$ and the most probable speed $(2RT)^{1/2}$ decrease, and in the limit the above expressions will tend to a limit too. To obtain an idea of the order of magnitude of this limit, let us assume that

$$\left|\frac{d\bar{u}}{dx}\right| = \frac{d(2RT)^{1/2}}{dx},$$

and without recourse to higher iterations, consider Eq. (5.17a) when $M_1 = 0$, i.e., when the number density is actually zero. The solution of the resulting quadratic equation gives

$$\lim \frac{\mu}{p}\left|\frac{d\bar{u}}{dx}\right| = 1.2,$$

in which case there is no distinct shock which can be studied. More generally, with the assumption of constant total enthalpy across the shock, this limit will depend upon the Mach number and will vary between roughly 2 for $M = 1$ and zero for $M = \infty$. The result of Liepmann *et al.* in this respect is noteworthy here. They found, in a rather interesting manner, that the maximum value of this parameter is equal to 1.125 and occurs upstream of the point of maximum stress. This may mean, therefore, that the first iteration we have found could prove to be valid for a fairly pronounced degree of rarefaction and for stronger shocks also. The iteration could be continued on the flow parameters themselves, as in the work of Liepmann *et al.* and Chahine.

The problem of convergence of the iteration scheme is not dealt with here. However, Chahine's computed results indicate that the process converges quite rapidly, particularly for weak shocks. One would expect, therefore, that this should also hold for a "slight" degree of rarefaction.

The method used here, though applied to the shock structure, should also be useful for other problems of linear or nonlinear nature.

Appendix A. Coefficients in Connection with the First Approximation $f^{(1)}$ to the Distribution Function

The integrations involved in the expression $\overline{\varphi K_4}$, Eq. (2.17), yield

$$\overline{\varphi K_4} = (2\pi)^{-1/2}\tfrac{1}{4}\theta^2\left[\exp(-\mathbb{C}^2)\sum_{-2}^{3} N_{2n}\mathbb{C}^{2n} + \tfrac{1}{2}\pi^{1/2}\,\mathrm{erf}(\mathbb{C})\sum_{-3}^{3} N_{2n+1}\mathbb{C}^{2n+1}\right] \tag{A.1}$$

where

$$N_{-4} = -\frac{9}{64}\frac{1}{t_{xx}^2},$$

$$N_{-2} = \frac{1}{16}\frac{1}{t_x^2} - \frac{1}{6}\frac{1}{t_{xx}^2},$$

$$N_0 = -\frac{1}{3t_x^2} - \frac{67}{180}\frac{1}{t_{xx}^2},$$

$$N_2 = -\frac{19}{30}\frac{1}{t_x^2} + \frac{17}{270}\frac{1}{t_{xx}^2},$$

$$N_4 = \frac{8}{15t_x^2} + \frac{7}{540}\frac{1}{t_{xx}^2},$$

$$N_6 = -\frac{1}{15}\frac{1}{t_x^2},$$

$$N_{-5} = \frac{9}{64}\frac{1}{t_{xx}^2},$$

$$N_{-3} = -\frac{1}{16}\frac{1}{t_x^2} + \frac{7}{96}\frac{1}{t_{xx}^2},$$

$$N_{-1} = \frac{3}{8}\frac{1}{t_x^2} - \frac{5}{72}\frac{1}{t_{xx}^2},$$

$$N_1 = -\frac{2}{t_x^2} - \frac{1}{4t_{xx}^2},$$

$$N_3 = -\frac{2}{3}\frac{1}{t_x^2} + \frac{5}{36}\frac{1}{t_{xx}^2},$$

$$N_5 = \frac{1}{t_x^2} + \frac{7}{270}\frac{1}{t_{xx}^2},$$

$$N_7 = -\frac{2}{15}\frac{1}{t_x^2}.$$

Appendix B. Coefficients in Connection with the First Approximation to the Flow Parameters

The coefficients relating to Eq. (5.8) are:

For M_1

$$a_{10} = 1 + \frac{\theta}{12t_{xx}} - \frac{\theta^2}{4}\left(\frac{41}{120}\frac{1}{t_x^2} + \frac{269}{2160}\frac{1}{t_{xx}^2}\right),$$

$$a_{12} = \frac{\theta}{6t_{xx}} + \frac{\theta^2}{4}\left(\frac{3}{20}\frac{1}{t_x^2} + \frac{103}{1080}\frac{1}{t_{xx}^2}\right),$$

$$a_{14} = \frac{\theta^2}{4}\left(\frac{3}{10}\frac{1}{t_x^2} + \frac{7}{540}\frac{1}{t_{xx}^2}\right),$$

$$a_{16} = -\frac{\theta^2}{4}\frac{1}{15}\frac{1}{t_x^2};$$

$$b_{-11} = \frac{\theta}{4t_{xx}} - \frac{\theta^2}{4}\left(\frac{1}{8t_x^2} + \frac{1}{24}\frac{1}{t_{xx}^2}\right),$$

$$b_{11} = 2 + \frac{\theta}{3t_{xx}} - \frac{\theta^2}{4}\left(\frac{1}{t_x^2} - \frac{1}{18}\frac{1}{t_{xx}^2}\right),$$

$$b_{13} = \frac{\theta}{3t_{xx}} + \frac{\theta^2}{4}\left(\frac{2}{3}\frac{1}{t_x^2} + \frac{11}{54}\frac{1}{t_{xx}^2}\right),$$

$$b_{15} = \frac{\theta^2}{4}\left(\frac{8}{15t_x^2} + \frac{7}{270t_{xx}^2}\right),$$

$$b_{17} = -\frac{\theta^2}{4}\frac{2}{15}\frac{1}{t_x^2};$$

$$c_{10} = 2,$$

$$c_{12} = 0;$$

$$d_1 = -\frac{\theta^2}{4}\frac{3}{32}\frac{1}{t_{xx}^2};$$

$$\varepsilon_1 = \left(-0.1599 - 0.2499\frac{\theta}{t_{xx}} - \frac{\theta^2}{4}\left\{0.2916\frac{1}{t_x^2} + 0.1799\frac{1}{t_{xx}^2}\right\}\right.$$
$$\left. + \frac{\theta^3}{16t_{xx}}\left\{0.0307\frac{1}{t_x^2} + 0.0037\frac{1}{t_{xx}^2}\right\}\right)\frac{1}{2\pi}\int_{\hat{x}'}^{\hat{x}}\frac{dx}{\lambda(x)}.$$

For M_2

$$a_{20} = \frac{3}{2} + \frac{1}{3}\frac{\theta}{t_{xx}} + \frac{\theta^2}{4}\left(\frac{1}{15t_x^2} + \frac{251}{2160}\frac{1}{t_{xx}^2}\right),$$

$$a_{22} = \frac{\theta}{6t_{xx}} + \frac{\theta^2}{4}\left(\frac{7}{20}\frac{1}{t_x^2} + \frac{23}{180}\frac{1}{t_{xx}^2}\right),$$

$$a_{24} = \frac{\theta^2}{4}\left(\frac{1}{15}\frac{1}{t_x^2} + \frac{7}{540}\frac{1}{t_{xx}^2}\right),$$

$$a_{26} = -\frac{\theta^2}{4}\frac{1}{15}\frac{1}{t_x^2};$$

$$b_{-21} = \frac{\theta^2}{4}\frac{3}{16}\frac{1}{t_{xx}^2},$$

$$b_{21} = 4 + \frac{5}{6}\frac{\theta}{t_{xx}} + \frac{\theta^2}{4}\left(\frac{1}{4t_x^2} + \frac{11}{24}\frac{1}{t_{xx}^2}\right),$$

$$b_{23} = \frac{1}{3}\frac{\theta}{t_{xx}} + \frac{\theta^2}{4}\left(\frac{5}{6t_x^2} + \frac{29}{108}\frac{1}{t_{xx}^2}\right),$$

$$b_{25} = \frac{\theta^2}{4}\left(\frac{1}{15}\frac{1}{t_x^2} + \frac{7}{270}\frac{1}{t_{xx}^2}\right),$$

$$b_{27} = -\frac{\theta^2}{4}\frac{2}{15}\frac{1}{t_x^2};$$

$$c_{20} = 2 + \frac{2}{3} \frac{\theta}{t_{xx}},$$

$$c_{22} = -2;$$

$$d_2 = 0;$$

$$\varepsilon_2 = \left\{ -1.8284 - 0.9622 \frac{\theta}{t_{xx}} - \frac{\theta^2}{4} \left(\frac{0.2419}{t_x^{\,2}} + \frac{0.5993}{t_{xx}^2} \right) \right.$$

$$\left. + \frac{\theta^3}{16 t_{xx}} \left(\frac{0.0518}{t_x^{\,2}} + \frac{0.0273}{t_{xx}^2} \right) \right\} \frac{1}{2\pi} \int_{\hat{x}'}^{\hat{x}} \frac{dx}{\lambda(x)}.$$

ACKNOWLEDGMENT

The author wishes to express his thanks to Professor G. M. Lilley, of The College of Aeronautics, Cranfield, for proposing the problem, and for his close supervision and encouragement throughout the work.

REFERENCES

Chahine, M. T. (1963). In "Rarefied Gas Dynamics" (J. A. Laurmann, ed.), Vol. 1, pp. 260–273. Academic Press, New York.

Chahine, M. T., and Narasimha, R. (1963). Jet Propulsion Lab., Tech. Rept. No. 32–459.

Chapman, S., and Cowling, T. G. (1960). "The Mathematical Theory of Non-Uniform Gases," pp. 129–133 and Chapter 15. Cambridge Univ. Press, London and New York.

Darrozès, J. (1963). La Recherche Aerospatiale 95, 17–22.

Gilbarg, D., and Paolucci, D. (1953). J. Rat. Mech. Anal. 2, 4.

Liepmann, H. W., Narasimha, R., and Chahine, M. T. (1962). Phys. Fluids 5, 11.

Patterson, G. N. (1956). "Molecular Flow of Gases," Chapter 1. Wiley, New York.

Sherman, F. S. (1958), In "Transport Properties in Gases" (A. B. Cambel and J. B. Fenn, eds.), pp. 260–273. Academic Press, New York.

Waldmann, L. (1958). In "Handbuch der Physik" (S. Flügge, ed.), Vol. 12, pp. 364–366. Springer, Berlin.

Willis, D. R. (1961). In " Rarefied Gas Dynamics" (L. Talbot, ed.) p.432. Academic Press, New York.

Molecular-Beam Approximation for a Strong-Shock-Structure Problem

HAKURO OGUCHI

Institute of Space and Aeronautical Science, University of Tokyo, Tokyo, Japan

A simplified version of the Boltzmann equation in the BGK approximation is investigated. The simplification results from assuming the flow to be molecular-beam-like, and good results are therefore to be expected for high Mach number flows. To establish the suitability of the proposed procedure this paper is concerned with the structure of a plane normal shock in a free stream flow at large Mach numbers, so that comparisons can be made with available solutions obtained with the full BGK equation. Shock profiles for argon at Mach numbers of 5 and 10 are calculated and good agreement is obtained with the exact solutions. It is concluded that the present analysis is promising because of its simplicity, not only for shock structure problems, but also for extensive application to other problems in high-speed rarefied flow.

I. Introduction

An iteration technique has been developed by Liepmann *et al.* (1962) for the analysis of the structure of a plane normal shock. In the analysis, the simplified equation based on the BGK collision model has been treated (Bhatnagar *et al.*, 1954) instead of the full Boltzmann equation. Although a formal integration for the BGK equation can easily be obtained, the distribution function f contains unknowns, i.e., number density n, mean velocity $\mathbf{v}$ and temperature T. These unknowns must be determined to satisfy the integral equations which can be derived from the first three moments obtained by the use of the distribution function f. However, great difficulty is involved in the direct approach to the solution. In the iteration procedure by Liepmann *et al.* (1962), the integral equations for n (or u for the one-dimensional problem) and T have been solved using the Navier-Stokes values as the first step. The results of the computation for a plane shock structure appear to provide a convergent answer after a few iteration, though the convergence becomes slower for cases of higher free stream Mach number. In addition, the manipulation is complicated in that a multiple integral (quadruple for a plane shock) over unbounded domains must be dealt with in each step of the iteration procedure. Therefore the method does not seem promising for extensive application to cases with more complicated geometry.

As was discussed by Sherman and Talbot (1960), the Navier-Stokes equation provides a satisfactory description for the structure of a weak shock, while for strong shocks its validity is open to question. Indeed, the results by Liepmann *et al.* (1962) show that an appreciable deviation in flow quantities from the Navier-Stokes solution appears at the upstream side of a strong shock. Therefore, in the present paper, we are mainly concerned with the structure of a plane normal shock in a free stream of high Mach number. Although the BGK collision model is applied, the problem is reduced to the finding of a solution for the differential equations with respect to n (or u) and T under some further approximations. For simplicity a perfect, monatomic gas is considered throughout the paper, and the actual calculations have been performed for the structure of a plane normal shock in argon for the free stream Mach numbers 5 and 10. The method is remarkably simple, so that it may be promising for extensive application to other problems concerning high-speed rarefied flow.

II. Molecular-Beam Approximation

The Boltzmann equation for a steady motion of gas with no external forces can be written in the form

$$\mathbf{v} \cdot \frac{\partial}{\partial \mathbf{r}} f(\mathbf{r}, \mathbf{v}) = G(f) - f L(f)$$

where $G(f)$ and $L(f)$ are nonlinear integral operators on f. If the BGK collision model is assumed, the equation simply becomes

$$\mathbf{v} \cdot \frac{\partial}{\partial \mathbf{r}} f(\mathbf{r}, \mathbf{v}) = \alpha(f_0 - f) \tag{1}$$

with $\alpha = An$ where A is a free parameter to be determined so as to provide the best fit for some measured bulk property of the gas. f_0 is the equilibrium distribution.

For the one-dimensional feature such as a plane normal shock, Eq. (1) can be written as

$$v_x \frac{\partial f}{\partial x} = \alpha(f_0 - f). \tag{2}$$

Multiplying both sides of the equation by the operator $(v_x/\alpha)\, \partial/\partial x$, we have

$$\frac{v_x}{\alpha}\frac{\partial}{\partial x}\frac{v_x}{\alpha}\frac{\partial}{\partial x}f = f - \left[f_0 - \frac{v_x}{\alpha}\frac{\partial}{\partial x}f_0 \right]. \tag{3}$$

The function $[f_0 - (v_x/\alpha)\, \partial f_0/\partial x]$ is the distribution which results from the first trial in applying the Chapman-Enskog procedure to Eq. (1). The first trial from the Chapman-Enskog procedure for the Boltzmann equation gives the Navier-Stokes distribution. Therefore it should be expected that the function $[f_0 - (v_x/\alpha)\, \partial f_0/\partial x]$ has a form similar to the Navier-Stokes distribution. Indeed, this was indicated by Liepmann *et al.* (1962). Neglecting terms of higher order we find

$$f_0 - (v_x/\alpha)\partial f_0/\partial x$$
$$= f_0\left[1 + \frac{1}{\alpha}\left\{ \frac{C_x}{\beta}\frac{\partial \beta}{\partial x}(\beta C^2 - \tfrac{5}{2}) - 2\beta\frac{\partial u}{\partial x}(C_x{}^2 - \tfrac{1}{3}C^2) \right\} \right] \tag{4}$$

where C is the peculiar velocity of molecules and $\beta = 1/2RT$. The right-hand side of Eq. (4) becomes very similar to the well-known Navier-Stokes distribution function, when the parameter A or α is chosen as

$$A = \frac{m}{2\beta\mu}, \qquad \alpha = An = \frac{\rho}{2\beta\mu} \tag{5}$$

where μ is the viscosity coefficient and m the mass of a molecule. As can be easily shown, the pressure tensor and heat flux satisfy the Navier-Stokes relations, that is,

$$p_{xx} = \rho\overline{C_xC_x} = p - \tfrac{4}{3}\mu\frac{\partial u}{\partial x}, \qquad q_x = \rho\overline{C^2C_x/2} = -k\frac{\partial T}{\partial x} \tag{6}$$

where k is the thermal conductivity. Therefore we assume that the function $[f_0 - (v_x/\alpha)\, \partial f_0/\partial x]$ in Eq. (3) may be identified with the Navier-Stokes distribution function f_{NS}, which gives the following macroscopic equations with p_{xx} and q_x of Eqs. (6):

$$\rho u = \text{const}$$

$$\rho u^2 + p_{xx} = \text{const}$$

$$\tfrac{1}{2}\rho u^3 + \tfrac{3}{2}pu + p_{xx}u + q_x = \text{const}.$$

It should be noted that the distribution function in Eq. (4) with α chosen as in Eq. (5) leads to the wrong Prandtl number, that is,

$$\text{Pr} = \frac{\mu C_p}{k} = 1$$

where C_p is the specific heat, while the correct value for monatomic gases is very nearly $Pr = \frac{2}{3}$. However, as was indicated by Liepmann *et al.* (1962), the Navier-Stokes solutions are not appreciably affected by a slight variation in the Prandtl number. Therefore, within the present approximation, we shall ignore the slight deviation from the correct value in the Prandtl number.

We next rewrite the left-hand side of Eq. (3) as

$$\frac{v_x}{\alpha}\frac{\partial}{\partial x}\frac{v_x}{\alpha}\frac{\partial}{\partial x}f = \frac{u}{\alpha}\frac{\partial}{\partial x}\frac{u}{\alpha}\frac{\partial}{\partial x}f + \frac{u}{\alpha}\frac{\partial}{\partial x}\frac{C_x}{\alpha}\frac{\partial}{\partial x}f + \frac{C_x}{\alpha}\frac{\partial}{\partial x}\frac{u}{\alpha}\frac{\partial}{\partial x}f + \frac{C_x}{\alpha}\frac{\partial}{\partial x}\frac{C_x}{\alpha}\frac{\partial}{\partial x}f. \quad (7)$$

Using the characteristic dimension L and mean thermal velocity $\bar{C}$, the order of magnitude of each terms on the right-hand side may be represented, respectively, by

$$\frac{u_1^2}{\alpha^2 L^2}f, \qquad \frac{u_1 \bar{C}}{\alpha^2 L^2}f, \qquad \frac{u_1 \bar{C}}{\alpha^2 L^2}f, \qquad \frac{\bar{C}^2}{\alpha^2 L^2}f$$

where u_1 is the free stream velocity. By the use of Eq. (5) and the relation $\mu \sim l\rho\bar{C}$ where l is the mean free path, we obtain

$$\frac{u_1^2}{\alpha^2 L^2}f \sim \frac{T_1}{T}M_1^2\frac{l^2}{L^2}f, \qquad \frac{u_1 \bar{C}}{\alpha^2 L^2}f \sim \left(\frac{T_1}{T}\right)^{1/2}M_1\frac{l^2}{L^2}f, \qquad \frac{\bar{C}^2}{\alpha^2 L^2} \sim \frac{l^2}{L^2}f$$

where M_1 and T_1 are the free stream Mach number and temperature, respectively. On the upstream side the first term $(u/\alpha)\,\partial/\partial x(u/\alpha)\,\partial f/\partial x$ is predominant, while on the downstream side all of the terms reduce to the same order as $l^2 f/L^2$. Far downstream terms of $O(l^2 f/L^2)$ may be small enough to be neglected, so that the distribution f reduces to f_{NS} from Eq. (3). Therefore the first term, $(u/\alpha)\,\partial/\partial x(u/\alpha)\,\partial f/\partial x$, on the right-hand side of Eq. (7) should be retained, so far as terms of $O(l^2 f/L^2)$ are neglected.

With the foregoing approximations we have the following equation instead of Eq. (3):

$$\frac{u}{\alpha}\frac{\partial}{\partial x}\frac{u}{\alpha}\frac{\partial}{\partial x}f = f - f_{NS}. \quad (8)$$

As can be easily shown, the moments of the distribution f of Eq. (8) for the fluxes of the collisional invariants, i.e., mv_x, mv_x^2, $mv_x v^2$ give the true macroscopic equations of motion for a monatomic gas, that is,

$$\rho u = (\rho u)_{NS} = \text{const,}$$

$$\rho u^2 + p_{xx} = (\rho u^2 + p_{xx})_{NS} = \text{const,} \quad (9)$$

$$\tfrac{1}{2}\rho u^3 + \tfrac{3}{2}pu + p_{xx}u + q_x = (\tfrac{1}{2}\rho u^3 + \tfrac{3}{2}pu + p_{xx}u + q_x)_{NS} = \text{const}$$

where $(\ )_{NS}$ signifies the Navier-Stokes value.

The integration of Eq. (8) over velocity space leads to

$$2\beta\mu \frac{u}{\rho}\frac{d}{dx} 2\beta\mu \frac{u}{\rho}\frac{d}{dx} \rho = \rho - \rho_{\text{NS}}. \tag{10}$$

Dimensionless quantities are conveniently introduced as follows:

$$\xi = x/l_1, \qquad V = u/u_1 = \rho_1/\rho, \qquad \Theta = T/T_1 \tag{11}$$

where l_1 is the mean free path at upstream infinity. From kinetic theory the viscosity is expressed as

$$\mu = \delta\rho\bar{C}l \tag{12}$$

where δ is a constant. The mean thermal velocity $\bar{C}$ is related to the temperature of gas as follows:

$$\bar{C} = \sqrt{\frac{8RT}{\pi}} \tag{13}$$

where R is the gas constant.

By the use of Eqs. (11)–(13), Eq. (10) is rewritten as

$$\frac{K}{\Theta}\frac{\mu}{\mu_1} V^2 \frac{d}{d\xi} \frac{\mu}{\Theta\mu_1} \frac{d}{d\xi} V = \frac{1}{V_{\text{NS}}} - \frac{1}{V} \tag{14}$$

where, with γ denoting the specific heats ratio,

$$K = \frac{8\gamma\delta^2 M_1{}^2}{\pi}.$$

If the viscosity-temperature relation is assumed in the form

$$\mu \propto T^n, \tag{15}$$

then Eq. (14) simply becomes

$$K\Theta^{n-1}V^2 \frac{d}{d\xi} \Theta^{n-1} \frac{d}{d\xi} V = \frac{1}{V_{\text{NS}}} - \frac{1}{V}. \tag{16}$$

In a similar way we obtain the following equation for Θ by taking the moment of mv^2 for Eq. (8):

$$3K\Theta^{n-1}V^2 \frac{d}{d\xi} \Theta^{n-1}V^2 \frac{d}{d\xi} \frac{\Theta}{V} = 3\left(\frac{\Theta}{V} - \frac{\Theta_{\text{NS}}}{V_{\text{NS}}}\right)$$

$$- K\gamma M_1{}^2\Theta^{n-1}V^2 \frac{d}{d\xi} \Theta^{n-1}V^2 \frac{d}{d\xi} V + \gamma M_1{}^2(V - V_{\text{NS}}). \tag{17}$$

Since V_{NS} and Θ_{NS} are known from the Navier-Stokes equations, the dimensionless velocity V and temperature Θ can be determined by solving Eqs. (16)

and (17) to satisfy the following boundary conditions:

$$\xi \to -\infty \qquad V \to 1, \quad \Theta \to 1,$$

$$\xi \to +\infty \qquad V \to V_\infty = (V_{NS})_\infty, \tag{18}$$

$$\Theta \to \Theta_\infty = (\Theta_{NS})_\infty.$$

Since $p_{xx} - p$ and q_x must vanish both at upstream and downstream infinity, it follows from Eqs. (9) that the Rankine-Hugoniot relations are valid. Therefore we have

$$V_\infty = (V_{NS})_\infty = \frac{\gamma - 1}{\gamma + 1} + \frac{2}{\gamma + 1} \frac{1}{M_1^2} \equiv \alpha$$

$$\Theta_\infty = (\Theta_{NS})_\infty = 1 + \frac{\gamma - 1}{2} M_1^2 (1 - \alpha^2) \tag{19}$$

After the solutions for V and Θ (and hence u, ρ, and T) are obtained, the remaining unknowns such as p, p_{xx}, and q_x can be obtained by the use of Eqs. (9) with the equation of state.

III. Approximate Approach to the Solution

For simplicity we shall use the Navier-Stokes solutions for $Pr = \frac{3}{4}$, in which case V_{NS} and Θ_{NS} can be determined from the following equations (Morduchow and Libby, 1949):

$$\Theta_{NS}^n V_{NS} \frac{dV_{NS}}{d\xi} = \chi M_1 (V_{NS} - 1)(V_{NS} - \alpha), \tag{20}$$

$$\Theta_{NS} = 1 + \frac{\gamma - 1}{2} M_1^2 (1 - V_{NS}^2) \tag{21}$$

where

$$\chi = const = \frac{3}{8\delta} (\gamma + 1) \sqrt{\frac{\pi}{8\gamma}}$$

$$\alpha = \frac{\gamma - 1}{\gamma + 1} + \frac{2}{\gamma + 1} \frac{1}{M_1^2}.$$

For Maxwell molecules the viscosity-temperature relation is $\mu \propto T$ (and hence $n = 1$). For this case Eqs. (16) and (20) reduce, respectively, to

$$KV^2 \frac{d^2}{d\xi^2} V = \frac{1}{V_{NS}} - \frac{1}{V}, \tag{22}$$

$$\Theta_{\text{NS}} V_{\text{NS}} \frac{d}{d\xi} V_{\text{NS}} = \chi M_1 (V_{\text{NS}} - 1)(V_{\text{NS}} - \alpha). \tag{23}$$

The boundary conditions for V_{NS} are exactly the same as those for V given by Eq. (18).

Equation (21) implies that for the Navier-Stokes solution the total enthalpy is conserved across the shock wave, so that $[(p_{xx} - p)u + q_x]_{\text{NS}} = 0$. The term $(p_{xx} - p)u + q_x$ must vanish both at upstream and downstream infinity and its deviation from the Navier-Stokes value (i.e., 0) is considered small throughout the region of interest. Therefore, in the last of Eqs. (9) the term $(p_{xx} - p)u + q_x$ may be neglected compared with $\frac{1}{2}\rho u^3 + \frac{5}{2} pu$. We thus have

$$\rho u^3 + 5pu = \text{const}$$

which gives, with $\gamma = \frac{5}{3}$ for monatomic gases,

$$\Theta = 1 + \frac{\gamma - 1}{2} M^2 (1 - V^2) \tag{24}$$

or

$$\frac{T - T_1}{T_2 - T_1} = \frac{1 - V^2}{1 - \alpha^2}. \tag{25}$$

Consequently the problem for the case when $n = 1$ has been reduced to finding a solution for V from Eq. (22). This has been done for the cases of $M = 5$ and 10 with $\gamma = \frac{5}{3}$. The value of K in Eq. (22) was taken from Eq. (15) with $\delta = \frac{1}{3}$. The distribution of velocity and temperature are plotted against $\pi x / 4l_1$ in Figs. 1 and 2, respectively.

For the case of an arbitrary n we attempt to approximately evaluate V and Θ from the results already obtained for $n = 1$, without any straightforward attack to Eqs. (16) and (17). We introduce the coordinate $\bar{\xi}$, instead of ξ, by

$$\bar{\xi} = \int^\xi \Theta^{1-n} \, d\xi. \tag{26}$$

Equations (16) and (20) are rewritten in terms of $\bar{\xi}$, and become

$$KV^2 \frac{d^2}{d\bar{\xi}^2} V = \frac{1}{V_{\text{NS}}} - \frac{1}{V}, \tag{27}$$

$$\left(\frac{\Theta}{\Theta_{\text{NS}}}\right)^{1-n} \Theta_{\text{NS}} V_{\text{NS}} \frac{d}{d\bar{\xi}} V_{\text{NS}} = \chi M_1 (V_{\text{NS}} - 1)(V_{\text{NS}} - \alpha) \tag{28}$$

The value of V_{NS} approaches unity more rapidly than V does toward the upstream side. Therefore, for the upstream region where V_{NS} is identified with

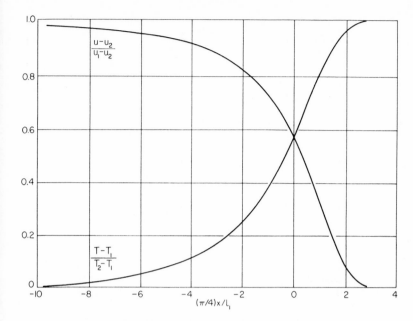

FIG. 1. Velocity and temperature profiles of a shock at $M_1 = 5$ ($\mu \propto T$).

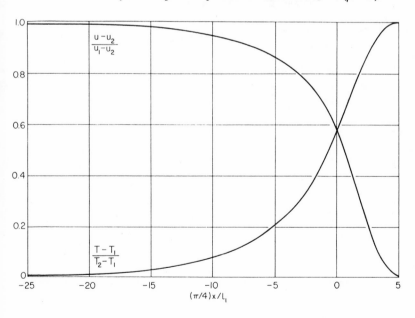

FIG. 2. Velocity and temperature profiles of a shock at $M_1 = 10$ ($\mu \propto T$).

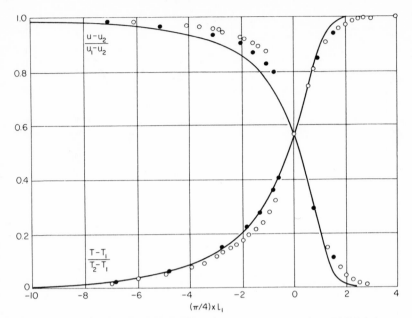

FIG. 3. Velocity and temperature profiles of a shock at $M_1 = 5$ ($\mu \propto T^{0.816}$) (Liepmann et al., 1962). O, First iteration; ●, second iteration.

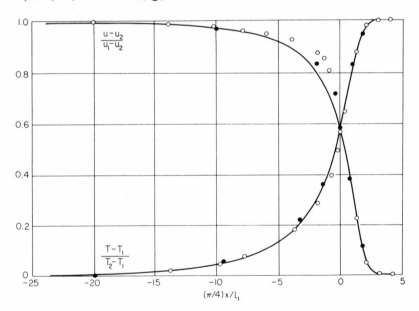

FIG. 4. Velocity and temperature profiles of a shock at $M_1 = 10$ ($\mu \propto T^{0.816}$) (Liepmann et al., 1962). O, First iteration; ●, second iteration.

unity, Eq. (27) reduces to the equation,

$$KV^2 \frac{d^2}{d\bar{\xi}^2} V \approx 1 - \frac{1}{V}$$

whose solution is not essentially relevant to V_{NS} and hence to Eq. (28). On the downstream side the solutions for V and Θ rapidly approach the Navier-Stokes values so that the factor $(\Theta/\Theta_{NS})^{1-n}$ is close to one. Therefore, Eq. (28) reduces approximately to the form of Eq. (25). Naturally this is further assured when n is close to one. From these arguments it follows that an approximate solution of Eq. (16) for arbitrary n can be obtained from that for $n = 1$ simply by the coordinate transformation given by Eq. (26).

IV. Results and Discussion

The viscosity-temperature relation for argon at low temperature is known to be $\mu \propto T^{0.816}$. Following the method prescribed in Section III, approximate solutions for V and Θ when $n = 0.816$ have been evaluated for $M = 5$ and 10, using the results for the case when $n = 1$. The distributions of velocity and temperature are shown in Figs. 3 and 4, respectively. For comparison, the results by the iteration method which has been applied to the case of argon with the Sutherland viscosity law and Pr = 1 (Liepmann et al., 1962) have been plotted in these figures.[1] These results by the iteration method must be exact, within the validity of the BGK collision model, if the iterations were repeated often enough to converge to an accurate answer. The present analysis is remarkably simple owing to some special approximations. Nevertheless, the results concerning velocity (and hence density) and temperature seem to be in good agreement with the results of the more precise method. It can be seen from the comparison of the results shown in Figs. 3 and 4 that the present approximation appears to provide results closer to the exact one for higher Mach numbers. In conclusion, we may expect that owing to its simplicity the present analysis is promising not only for further investigation of the structure of strong shocks, but also for extensive application to other problems concerning high-speed rarefied flow.

---

[1] The origin of the abscissa is chosen such that the results by Liepmann et al. fit the present results on the downstream side, because both the results should approach the Navier-Stokes values toward downstream infinity.

REFERENCES

Bhatnagar, P. L., Gross, E. P., and Krook, M. (1954). *Phys. Rev.* **94**, 511.
Liepmann, H. W., Narasimha, R., and Chahine, M. T. (1962). *Phys. Fluids* **5**, 1313.
Morduchow, M., and Libby, P. A. (1949). *J. Aeronaut. Sci.* **16**, 674.
Sherman, F. S., and Talbot, L. (1960). *In* " Rarefied Gas Dynamics" (F. M. Devienne, ed.), pp. 161–191. Macmillan (Pergamon), New York.

Kinetic Theory of Shock Structure
Using an Ellipsoidal Distribution Function

LOWELL H. HOLWAY JR.

Raytheon Research Division, Waltham, Massachusetts

The structure of a plane shock is calculated from kinetic theory using an ellipsoidal approximating function. The method satisfies two transport equations in addition to the three conservation equations, gives agreement with the Navier-Stokes equations near Mach one and provides a correction to the Mott-Smith solution near Mach infinity. In contrast to the Mott-Smith solution, this solution predicts a temperature overshoot for large Mach numbers even for a monatomic gas. An analytical form for the shock structure is obtained in the second approximation. The results are compared with other theoretical calculations and with experimental measurements.

I. Introduction

Although a number of methods for obtaining approximate solutions to the Boltzmann equation for a one-dimensional wave have been devised, few of these methods are accurate over the entire range of Mach numbers (Sherman and Talbot, 1961; Ziering *et al.*, 1961). In particular, both theoretical arguments and experimental results indicate that the Chapman-Enskog method is inadequate for strong shock waves, although it provides a solution which becomes exact in the limit of very weak shock waves. On the other hand, the Mott-Smith solution (1951) is inaccurate for weak shocks, but provides a good approximation for strong shocks and has received experimental verification for Mach numbers between 2 and 5 (Hansen *et al.*, 1963). In this paper, we shall present a new approximation procedure based on the use of ellipsoidal velocity distributions. The shock structures obtained by this method are in close agreement with the Chapman-Enskog solutions for low Mach numbers and provide a correction to the Mott-Smith solutions at high Mach numbers.

An interesting feature of these shock structure calculations is that the temperature in the interior of the shock overshoots the downstream temperature by approximately two per cent for large Mach numbers. Although small in magnitude, the temperature overshoot appears to be a real effect and not a result of the approximations involved in our calculations. Our result, for both the temperature overshoot and the shock thickness, agrees closely with some recent work by Salwen et al. (1964).

In this paper, the shock structure calculations are carried through in detail for Maxwell molecules, and numerical results are obtained. In addition, a first approximation to the shock structure is obtained in a form which can be immediately evaluated for any molecular law of force for which the Mott-Smith solutions are known.

II. The Approximating Form for the Distribution Function

The approximation procedure in this paper is based on an expansion of the distribution function in the form

$$f(\mathbf{c}, x) = n_1(x)\varphi_1 + \varphi_2 \sum a_{nm}(x)c^{2n}c_1{}^m \tag{1}$$

where

$$\varphi_1 = (2\pi R T_a)^{-3/2} \exp - \frac{1}{2RT_a}((c_1 - u_a)^2 + c_2{}^2 + c_3{}^2) \tag{2}$$

and

$$\varphi_2 = (2\pi)^{-3/2}\lambda_{22}^{-1}\lambda_{11}^{-1/2} \exp - \frac{1}{2}\left(\frac{(c_1 - Q)^2}{\lambda_{11}} + \frac{c_2{}^2 + c_3{}^2}{\lambda_{22}}\right). \tag{3}$$

Here, $\mathbf{c}$ is the molecular velocity in a reference frame in which the shock is stationary, the parameters T_a and u_a are the temperature and flow velocity in the supersonic region in front of the shock ($x \to -\infty$), and $R (=k/m)$ is the gas constant. The parameters $n_1(x)$, $\lambda_{11}(x)$, $\lambda_{22}(x)$, $Q(x)$, and $a_{nm}(x)$ are all functions of position and are determined by requiring the distribution function to satisfy an appropriate number of independent transport equations.

The term φ_1 appearing in Eq. (1) will be recognized as the supersonic stream appearing in the Mott-Smith method. The function φ_2 would have corresponded to Mott-Smith's subsonic stream, if we had required Q to be the constant flow velocity u_b and λ_{11} and λ_{22} to be the constant temperature T_b associated with the subsonic stream. However, in our formulation, φ_2 is an ellipsoidal distribution in velocity space.

It is worth listing several reasons for choosing the approximating form for the distribution function given by Eq. (1). This approximating form was deliberately chosen to represent a lack of symmetry between the roles of the upstream and downstream Maxwellians. First, we note that the majority of the particles in the supersonic stream φ_1 move from left to right. (For example, at Mach 1, 90.5% of the φ_1 particles are moving to the right; at Mach 2, 99.5%, etc.) Thus, especially at high Mach numbers, we can argue that the overwhelming majority of particles in the φ_1 distribution had their last collision at some point upsteam, and therefore retain the characteristics of the upstream equilibrium condition. In contrast, the majority of particles in Mott-Smith's subsonic Maxwellian distribution are moving from left to right so that this distribution cannot effectively penetrate from the downstream region into the center of the shock zone.

A second distinction between the upstream and downstream Maxwellians is that the supersonic Maxwellian, φ_1, is a sharply peaked function of velocity for large Mach numbers. In fact, in the limit as $M \to \infty$ with u_a fixed, the function φ_1 is a well-known representation of the Dirac delta function. Such a strongly peaked function cannot be adequately represented by the first few terms in an expansion in velocity polynomials. Thus it is important to introduce the function $n_1\varphi_1$ explicitly into the approximating form for the distribution function where it plays an important role in speeding the convergence of the expansion. On the other hand, the subsonic Maxwellian is well behaved in comparison to the sharply peaked supersonic Maxwellian, and can be adequately represented by a few terms in the polynomial expansion.

The approximating form of Eq. (1) may now be considered as an expansion of the function $f(\mathbf{c}, x) - n_1(x)\varphi_1$ in a series of velocity polynomials[1] multiplied by the weight function φ_2. A necessary condition for such an expansion to converge in the mean square sense is that $f - n_1\varphi_1$ must approach zero as $c \to \infty$ more rapidly than the square root of the weight function. For the shock wave problem, this requires that the weight function approach zero more slowly than $\exp(-c^2/RT_b)$ as $c \to \infty$, and the weight function φ_2 has been chosen to satisfy this condition.[2] It should be noted that φ_1 would not satisfy the necessary criterion for a weight function when the Mach number is greater than 1.851.

Finally, we note that the weight function φ_2 allows the longitudinal "temperature" λ_{11} to differ from the transverse "temperature" λ_{22}. This flexibility has been included in the distribution function to allow for the fact that the particles which are moving parallel to the x-axis suffered their last collision at points with a different average temperature than did the particles moving transverse to this axis.

---

[1] The term $\sum a_{nm}(x)c^{2n}c_1{}^m$ may be conveniently re-expressed in the form of a set of three-dimensional (ellipsoidal) velocity polynomials which are orthogonal with respect to the weight function φ_2. These polynomials possess a generating function and recurrence relations which have properties entirely analogous to Grad's three-dimensional Hermite polynomials (Holway, 1963).

[2] This point has been discussed more thoroughly elsewhere (Holway, 1964). In that paper, we argue that Grad's Hermite polynomial expansion will not converge for Mach numbers greater than 1.851.

In this paper, we concern ourselves with the simplest case of the approximating form given by Eq. (1) in which the expansion coefficients a_{nm} are all taken to be zero except for a_{00} ($=n_2$). The approximating form for the distribution function then becomes

$$f(\mathbf{c}, x) = n_1(x)\varphi_1 + n_2(x)\varphi_2. \tag{4}$$

The five parameters $n_1(x)$, $n_2(x)$, $\lambda_{11}(x)$, $\lambda_{22}(x)$, and $Q(x)$ which appear in Eq. (4) are determined by requiring the distribution function to satisfy five independent transport equations.

III. The Transport Equations

The Boltzmann equation for a one-dimensional shock wave can be written in the form

$$c_1 \frac{\partial}{\partial x} f(\mathbf{c}, x) = \left(\frac{df}{dt}\right)_{\text{coll}} \tag{5}$$

where the right-hand side of Eq. (5) is the Boltzmann collision term.

The transport equation for an arbitrary function of velocity $\psi(\mathbf{c})$ is obtained in the usual way by multiplying Eq. (5) by ψ and integrating over velocity space. We thereby obtain

$$\frac{d}{dx} N[c_1\psi] = J[\psi] \tag{6}$$

where

$$N[\psi] = \int f(\mathbf{c}, x)\psi(\mathbf{c})\, d\mathbf{c} \tag{7}$$

is a moment of the distribution function and

$$J[\psi] = \int \left(\frac{df}{dt}\right)_{\text{coll}} \psi(\mathbf{c})\, d\mathbf{c} \tag{8}$$

is an interaction moment.

A. Conservation Equations

In particular, if ψ is any one of the collisional invariants 1, c_1, or c^2, the interaction moments $J[\psi]$ vanish, and we obtain the three conservation equations

$$N\left[\begin{Bmatrix} c_1 \\ c_1{}^2 \\ c_1 c^2 \end{Bmatrix}\right] = \text{const.} \tag{9}$$

At this point, it is convenient to replace $n_1(x)$ and $n_2(x)$ by new variables defined as

$$\theta = \frac{n(x) - n_a}{n_b - n_a} \tag{10}$$

and

$$Y = \frac{n_a - n_1(x)}{n_2(x)} \tag{11}$$

where n_a and n_b are the constant number densities upstream and downstream of the shock, and the local number density is

$$n(x) = n_1(x) + n_2(x). \tag{12}$$

Next we substitute the distribution function in Eq. (4) into the three conservation relations given by Eq. (9), to obtain Q, λ_{11}, and λ_{22}. It turns out that these parameters are functions of Y alone, and are given by the formulas

$$Q = u_a Y, \tag{13}$$

$$\lambda_{11} = u_a{}^2 Y \left(\frac{5M^2 + 3}{5M^2} - Y \right), \tag{14}$$

and

$$\lambda_{22} = \tfrac{1}{2} u_a{}^2 \left(\frac{M^2 + 3}{M^2} - \frac{3(5M^2 + 3)Y}{5M^2} + 2Y^2 \right) \tag{15}$$

where the Mach number is defined by $M^2 = 3u_a{}^2 / 5RT_a$.

Far downstream, as $x \to \infty$, the boundary conditions require the fluid to be in equilibrium so that $\lambda_{11} = \lambda_{22}$. It follows from Eqs. (14) and (15) that the boundary conditions at $x = +\infty$ are

$$Y(\infty) = (M^2 + 3)/4M^2 \tag{16}$$

and

$$\theta(\infty) = 1. \tag{17}$$

The Rankine-Hugoniot relations can be obtained in their customary from by substituting Eq. (16) into Eqs. (13) and (14) to obtain

$$Q(\infty)/u_a = u_b/u_a = (M^2 + 3)/4M^2 = n_a/n_b, \tag{18}$$

and

$$\lambda_{11}(\infty)/RT_a = T_b/T_a = (M^2 + 3)(5M^2 - 1)/16M^2. \tag{19}$$

We note that our distribution function would reduce to Mott-Smith's distribution function, if we had taken $Y(x)$ to be the constant given by Eq. (16).

B. Additional Transport Equations

In order to determine the remaining unknowns, θ and Y, we make use of two additional transport equations with nonvanishing interaction moments. The first of these transport equations will be the c_1^2 transport equation, which is the only remaining nontrivial second-order moment. The c_1^3 and $c_1 c^2$ transport equations are the only nontrivial third-order moments. Because of the symmetry of the $c_1 c^2$ moment, it is somewhat simpler to choose this equation to complete the solution. Moreover the collision moment $J[c_1 c^2]$ has a direct physical significance since it describes the rate at which the collision operator destroys the energy flux in a nonequilibrium situation. However we shall also set up the equation for the c_1^3 transport equation, because, as we shall see, this will allow us to take advantage of certain numerical work which has been done by previous investigators for the Mott-Smith c_1^2 and c_1^3 methods.

For conciseness of notation, it is convenient to define the following non-dimensional quantities:

$$c_0(\theta, Y) = -\frac{5M^2(M^2 + 3)}{3(M^2 - 1)} \frac{\lambda_a}{u_a^3 n_a \theta} J[c_1^2], \tag{20}$$

$$c_1(\theta, Y) = -\frac{5M^2(M^2 + 3)}{6(M^2 - 1)} \frac{\lambda_a}{u_a^4 n_a \theta} J[c_1 c^2]. \tag{21}$$

and

$$c_2(\theta, Y) = -\frac{25M^4(M^2 + 3)}{3(M^2 - 1)} \frac{\lambda_a}{u_a^4 n_a \theta} J[c_1^3], \tag{22}$$

where λ_a is the mean free path in front of the shock, defined by

$$\frac{1}{\lambda_a} = \sqrt{\frac{\pi}{2}} \frac{n_a}{\sqrt{RT_a}} \Omega^2(2) \tag{23}$$

and $\Omega^2(2)$ is a quantity defined by Chapman and Cowling (1952).[3]

Next we substitute the distribution function of Eq. (4) into the transport equations [Eq. (6)] for c_1^2, c_1^3, and $c_1 c^2$, and carry out the integrations. After some algebraic manipulation, we obtain the following system of two

---

[3] For rigid spheres, $\Omega^2(2) = 2\sigma^2 \sqrt{\pi R T_a}$ where σ is the molecular diameter. For inverse power force laws of the form $F = K/r^s$, $\Omega^2(2) = \sqrt{\pi/2m} A_2(s) K^{2/s-1} (2kT)^{(s-5)/2(s-1)} \Gamma(4 - 2/(s-1))$ where $A_2(s)$ is a number of order unity which depends on the force law and equals 0.436 for Maxwell molecules. $\Omega^2(2)$ is related to Chapman and Cowling's first approximation to the coefficient of viscosity by $\Omega^2(2) = 5kT_a/8\mu$.

coupled ordinary differential equations for θ and Y:

$$a_0(Y)\frac{d\theta}{dx} + \theta b_0(Y)\frac{dY}{dx} = \theta c_0(\theta,\,Y), \tag{24}$$

and

$$a_j(Y)\frac{d\theta}{dx} + \theta b_j(Y)\frac{dY}{dx} = \theta c_j(\theta,\,Y). \tag{25}$$

Here Eq. (24) is the $c_1{}^2$ transport equation and Eq. (25) represents the $c_1 c^2$ transport equation if $j = 1$ and the $c_1{}^3$ transport equation if $j = 2$. The nondimensional distance $x' = x/\lambda_a$ has been introduced; hereafter we omit the primes. The coefficients $a_j(Y)$ and $b_j(Y)$ are independent of θ and are given by the formulas

$$a_0 = Y(5M^2 + 9 - 10M^2 Y), \tag{26}$$

$$a_1 = Y(3 + 3Y - 5M^2 Y^2), \tag{27}$$

$$a_2 = Y(27 + 90M^2 + 25M^4 - 50M^4 Y(1 + Y)), \tag{28}$$

$$b_0 = (5M^2 + 9 - 20M^2 Y), \tag{29}$$

$$b_1 = 3(1 + 2Y - 5M^2 Y^2), \tag{30}$$

$$b_2 = 27 + 90M^2 + 25M^4 - 50M^4 Y(2 + 3Y). \tag{31}$$

The coefficients $c_j(\theta,\,Y)$, given by Eqs. (20)–(22) depend upon the molecular law of force, and will be evaluated for Maxwell molecules.

It will prove convenient to replace Y by a new variable

$$\delta = Y - \frac{M^2 + 3}{4M^2}. \tag{32}$$

Equations (24) and (25) can be formally solved to obtain

$$\frac{d\theta}{dx} = \frac{c_0 b_j - c_j b_0}{a_0 b_j - a_j b_0}, \tag{33}$$

and

$$\frac{d\delta}{d\theta} = -\frac{1}{\theta}\frac{c_0 a_j - c_j a_0}{c_0 b_j - c_j b_0}. \tag{34}$$

C. Expansion in a Small Parameter

From Eq. (16), we see that $\delta \to 0$ as $x \to \infty$, so that the system point in the θ-δ phase plane will approach the point $(1, 0)$ as $x \to \infty$. Moreover, we recall that, if we take δ to be identically zero, our distribution function will become identical with that of Mott-Smith. This suggests that δ may be considered a small parameter, and later results will confirm this supposition. Therefore, it is appropriate to expand the coefficients in Eqs. (26)–(31) in a power series in δ, having the form

$$a_j(\delta) = a_j{}^0 + a_j{}^1\delta + a_j{}^2\delta^2 + \cdots, \tag{35}$$

$$b_j(\delta) = b_j{}^0 + b_j{}^1\delta + b_j{}^2\delta^2 + \cdots, \tag{36}$$

and

$$c_j(\theta, \delta) = c_j{}^0(\theta) + c_j{}^1(\theta)\delta + c_j{}^2(\theta)\delta^2 + \cdots. \tag{37}$$

The first few terms in Eqs. (35)–(37), which are obtained from Eqs. (26)–(31), are given by the formulas

$$a_0{}^0 = \frac{M^2 + 3}{8M^2}(5M^2 + 3), \tag{38}$$

$$a_0{}^1 = -6, \tag{39}$$

$$a_1{}^0 = -\frac{M^2 + 3}{64M^4}(5M^4 - 30M^2 + 9), \tag{40}$$

$$a_1{}^1 = -\frac{3}{16M^2}(5M^4 - 6M^2 - 15), \tag{41}$$

$$a_2{}^0 = \frac{3(M^2 + 3)}{32M^2}(25M^4 + 90M^2 - 3), \tag{42}$$

$$a_2{}^1 = -\tfrac{3}{8}(25M^4 + 110M^2 + 153), \tag{43}$$

$$b_0{}^0 = -6, \tag{44}$$

$$b_0{}^1 = -20M^2, \tag{45}$$

$$b_1{}^0 = -\frac{3}{16M^2}(5M^4 + 6M^2 + 21), \tag{46}$$

$$b_1{}^1 = -\tfrac{3}{2}(5M^2 + 11), \tag{47}$$

$$b_2{}^0 = -\tfrac{3}{8}(25M^4 + 110M^2 + 153), \tag{48}$$

$$b_2{}^1 = -25M^2(7M^2 + 9). \tag{49}$$

IV. The First Approximation

To obtain a first approximation to the shock structure, we keep only the lowest order term in the expansions of the coefficients of the transport equations given by Eqs. (24) and (25). A typical transport equation then has the form

$$a_j{}^0 \frac{d\theta}{dx} + \theta b_j{}^0 \frac{d\delta}{dx} = \theta c_j{}^0(\theta).$$ (50)

On the other hand, in the Mott-Smith method, the jth transport equation has the form

$$\frac{d\theta}{dx} = B_j \theta (1 - \theta)$$ (51)

where B_j is a constant which has been evaluated in the literature for the $c_1{}^2$ and $c_1{}^3$ transport equations for several intermolecular force laws.

Since Eq. (50) must be identical with the Mott-Smith transport equation when δ is identically zero, it follows that

$$c_j{}^0(\theta) = a_j{}^0 B_j(1 - \theta).$$ (52)

Since the $a_j{}^0$ are given by Eqs. (38)–(42), we can immediately evaluate the $c_j{}^0$ for any law of molecular force for which the Mott-Smith results are known. Next we substitute Eq. (52) into Eq. (33) and take $j = 2$ (corresponding to the $c_1{}^2$ and $c_1{}^3$ transport equations) and obtain

$$\frac{d\theta}{dx} = B^* \theta (1 - \theta),$$ (53)

where Eq. (53) has the same form as Mott-Smith's Eq. (51) but

$$B^* = B_0 + \frac{12}{5} \frac{25M^4 + 90M^2 - 3}{25M^6 + 65M^4 + 3M^2 + 99} (B_0 - B_2)$$ (54)

where B_0 is the result obtained by the Mott-Smith $c_1{}^2$ method and B_2 is the result obtained from the Mott-Smith $c_1{}^3$ method.[4] At this point, we shall not pause to justify this approximation except to say that, since the Mott-Smith method assumes that δ is identically zero, our results should be very good whenever the Mott-Smith method is accurate. Hereafter we refer to the result given by Eqs. (53) and (54) as the *first ellipsoidal approximation*.

The solution of Eq. (53) is

$$\theta = (1 + e^{-x/B^*})^{-1}.$$ (55)

The shock thickness, X, defined in the usual way by the maximum density

---

[4] An equation which is similar to Eq. (54) but uses the $c_1{}^2$ and $c_1 c^2$ transport equations instead of the $c_1{}^2$ and $c_1{}^3$ transport equations can easily be derived. However this equation is not equally useful since the results for the Mott-Smith $c_1 c^2$ transport equation are generally not available in the literature.

202 LOWELL H. HOLWAY, JR.

gradient, is given by

$$\lambda_a/X = \left(\frac{dn}{dx'}\right)_{max} \bigg/ (n_b - n_a) = \left(\frac{d\theta}{dx'}\right)_{max}, \tag{56}$$

so that, from Eq. (55), we obtain

$$\lambda_a/X = \tfrac{1}{4}B^*. \tag{57}$$

The shock thicknesses for a monatomic rigid sphere gas, as calculated from Eq. (54) and Eq. (57), are given in Table I where B_0 and B_2 have been

TABLE I

INVERSE SHOCK THICKNESSES FOR MONATOMIC RIGID SPHERES (λ_a/X)

M	Ellipsoidal method [Eq. (54)]	Navier-Stokes (Gilbarg and Paolucci)	Mott-Smith $c_1{}^2$ method	Two-fluid (Glansdorff)
1.1	0.0353	—	0.0301	0.0443
1.2	0.0688	0.070	0.0597	0.0783
1.4	0.1293	0.136	0.1160	0.1284
1.6	0.1734	—	0.1641	0.1644
2.0	0.2370	0.292	0.2396	0.2140
2.5	0.2919	0.381	0.3036	0.2528
3.0	0.3278	0.437	0.3456	0.2777
5.0	0.4082	—	0.4190	0.3212
10.0	0.4520	—	0.4555	0.3433
∞	0.4685	—	0.4685	0.368

evaluated from Mott-Smith's original calculations.[5] These results are compared with Navier-Stokes shock thicknesses (Gilbarg and Paolucci, 1953), with the Mott-Smith results and with Glansdorf's (1962) "two fluid" results.[6]

Similarly, the results for Maxwell molecules are plotted in Fig. 1, and compared with the Navier-Stokes results, Mott-Smith results, and with the "two fluid" results of Ziering et al. (1961).

These numerical results show that the first ellipsoidal approximation agrees quite closely with the Navier-Stokes results near Mach one and

[5] For $M = 1.1$, B_2 has been corrected to the value 0.1056 by Ziering and Ek (1961).

[6] The Gilbarg and Paolucci shock thicknesses are based on the velocity gradient. For the Navier-Stokes solution, Schwartz and Hornig (1963) show that the velocity thicknesses are significantly larger than the density thicknesses for Mach numbers greater than about two. Since density thicknesses are the experimentally measured quantities, the Navier-Stokes thicknesses are an even poorer approximation for large Mach numbers than would be indicated by Table I and Fig. 1.

approaches the Mott-Smith c_1^2 results for large Mach numbers. The numerical results from the first approximation give shock thicknesses which are about 4 per cent smaller than the Navier-Stokes shock thicknesses near Mach 1. For comparison, the Mott-Smith c_1^2 shock thicknesses are about 13 per cent larger and the "two fluid" shock thicknesses about 24 per cent smaller than the Navier-Stokes thicknesses near Mach 1.

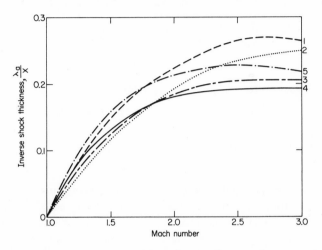

FIG. 1. Inverse shock thicknesses for Maxwell molecules according to several theories; the Navier-Stokes thicknesses are velocity thicknesses; the remainder are density thicknesses.

KEY: 1, Navier-Stokes solution (Gilbarg and Paolucci); 2, Mott-Smith c_1^3 method; 3, Mott-Smith c_1^2 method; 4, ellipsoidal expansion (1st approximation); 5, two-fluid method (Ziering *et al.*).

As can be seen directly from Eq. (54), the shock thicknesses calculated from the first ellipsoidal approximation approach the Mott-Smith c_1^2 thicknesses in the limit as $M \to \infty$. Later we shall show that an accurate numerical solution of the ellipsoidal approximation for Maxwell molecules gives shock thicknesses which are 14 per cent larger than the Mott-Smith result. The "two fluid" results by Ziering *et al.* (1961) predict shock thicknesses which are 13 per cent *smaller* than the Mott-Smith results.

V. Collision Moments for Maxwell Molecules

In order to proceed further, it is necessary to calculate explicitly the interaction moments of the Boltzmann collision integral. In the remainder of the paper, the ellipsoidal expansion will be carried out in detail for Maxwell molecules, and we confine ourselves to the method which satisfies the $c_1 c^2$ and the c_1^2 transport equations.

The method of evaluating interaction moments for Maxwell molecules is given in the Appendix. For the distribution function given by Eq. (4), the collision moments are

$$J[c_1^2] = q n_1 n_2 \{\lambda_{22} - \lambda_{11} - (Q - u_a)^2\} + q n_2^2 (\lambda_{22} - \lambda_{11}), \tag{58}$$

$$J[c_1 c^2] = q n_1 n_2 [(Q + u_a)(\lambda_{22} - \lambda_{11}) + (Q - u_a)$$
$$(u_a^2 + 5RT_a - Q^2 - 2\lambda_{11} - 3\lambda_{22})\} + 2 q n_2^2 Q(\lambda_{22} - \lambda_{11}), \tag{59}$$

and

$$J[c_1^3] = \tfrac{3}{2} q n_1 n_2 \{(Q + u_a)(\lambda_{22} - \lambda_{11}) + (Q - u_a)$$
$$(u_a^2 - Q^2 + 2(RT_a - \lambda_{11}))\} + 3 q n_2^2 Q(\lambda_{22} - \lambda_{11}), \tag{60}$$

where

$$q = \frac{16}{15} \sqrt{\frac{6}{5\pi}} \frac{u_a}{M n_a \lambda_a}. \tag{61}$$

The interaction moments for the Mott-Smith distribution function are obtained by setting λ_{11} and λ_{22} equal to RT_b and Q equal to u_b in Eqs. (58)–(60). In this case, the terms proportional to n_2^2, which represent collisions of particles in the ellipsoidal distribution with themselves, become zero. The rather surprising result that the Mott-Smith $c_1 c^2$ interaction moment vanishes is obtained by using the Rankine-Hugoniot relationship

$$u_a^2 + 5RT_a = u_b^2 + 5RT_b \tag{62}$$

in Eq. (59).

Later we shall need the expansions of the $c_j(\theta, \delta)$ in powers of δ. It follows from Eqs. (13)–(15), (20)–(22), (38), and (58)–(60) that these expansions are

$$c_0^0 = \sqrt{\frac{6}{5\pi}} \frac{4}{M} (M^2 - 1)(1 - \theta), \tag{63}$$

$$c_0^1 = \sqrt{\frac{6}{5\pi}} \frac{16M}{3} \left(1 + \frac{3(M^2 - 1)}{M^2 + 3} \theta\right), \tag{64}$$

$$c_1^0 = 0, \tag{65}$$

$$c_1^1 = \sqrt{\frac{6}{5\pi}} \frac{8}{3M} (4M^2 + \theta), \tag{66}$$

$$c_2^0 = \sqrt{\frac{6}{5\pi}} \frac{9}{2M} (M^2 - 1)(5M^2 + 3)(1 - \theta), \tag{67}$$

and

$$c_2{}^1 = \sqrt{\frac{6}{5\pi}}\, 8M(5M^2 + 9)\left(1 + \frac{4(8M^2 - 3)}{(M^2 + 3)(5M^2 + 9)}\,\theta\right). \qquad (68)$$

VI. A Numerical Solution for Infinite Mach Number

In this section we obtain an accurate numerical solution to the ellipsoidal expansion equations for infinite Mach number without making any *a priori* assumptions about the magnitude of δ. These results provide a standard of comparison for the first approximation which was discussed in Section IV and will also motivate a more accurate second approximation which will be discussed in the next section.

Equation (34) describes the solution curve for the shock wave problem in the θ-δ plane. For Maxwell molecules and infinite Mach number, it follows from Eqs. (13)–(15), (26)–(27), (29)–(30), and (58)–(60) that this equation is given by

$$\frac{d\delta}{d\theta} = -\frac{1}{\theta}\,\frac{(\frac{1}{4} + \delta)^3\{3(1 - \theta) + 4\delta(1 + 3\theta)\} + \delta(1 - 16\delta^2)}{3(\frac{1}{4} + \delta)^2\{3(1 - \theta) + 4\delta(1 + 3\theta)\} - 32\delta^2} \qquad (69)$$

where no approximations have been made about the magnitude of δ.

Equation (69) describes a direction field in the θ-δ plane which is drawn in Fig. 2 with the δ scale stretched by a factor of eight. The dotted curve AA is the locus of points where the slope is zero; the solid curve BB and the line $\theta = 0$ are the loci of points of infinite slope. The system point moves from the critical point $P_a(0, a_0)$ to the critical point $P_b(1, 0)$ as x changes from $-\infty$ to

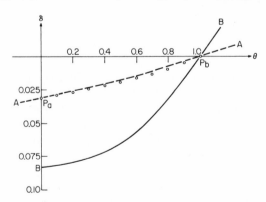

FIG. 2. Direction field for $M = \infty$ in the θ-δ plane.

KEY: ---, locus of zero slope; —, locus of infinite slope; ○, solution curve; P_a, "upstream" saddle point; P_b, "downstream" stable node.

$+\infty$. P_a is a saddle point and P_b is a stable node for all values of Mach number.

As already shown in Eqs. (16) and (17), the boundary conditions at $x = +\infty$ require the system point to lie at P_b. However, when $\theta = 0$, the physical properties of the system are independent of δ, so that the only a priori boundary condition at $x = -\infty$ is that $\theta = 0$. However, the line $\theta = 0$ is the stable eigenvector of the saddle point at P_a so that, if the system point is initially placed on the line $\theta = 0$ anywhere near P_a, it will tend to fall into P_a. It follows that the physical consequences are not changed by starting the system point from different positions on the line $\theta = 0$ near P_a. We are therefore free to choose the point P_a as the initial condition when $x = -\infty$, and integrate Eq. (69) out of the saddle point in the usual way. The saddle point P_a, whose position is determined from Eq. (69), is at the point (0, 0.0307764). The solution obtained in this way satisfies the 5 transport equations for all x, and the physical boundary conditions at $+\infty$ and $-\infty$.

Since the direction field has a positive slope between the curves AA and BB, it is obvious that a solution exists, and that the solution curve lies between AA and BB. Moreover, since the direction field has a zero slope along the curve AA and the slope of the curve AA is itself very small, the solution curve must lie close to AA. In fact, the numerically calculated solution curve in Fig. 2 is exceedingly close to the curve AA. This suggests that the curve AA can be taken as a good approximation to the solution curve. Hereafter we shall refer to this approximation as the second approximation and shall discuss its application for arbitrary Mach numbers in the following section.

Equation (33) which determines the density gradient can be evaluated with the help of Eqs. (13)–(15), (26)–(27), (29)–(30), and (58)–(59). For infinite Mach number we obtain

$$\frac{d\theta}{dx} = \sqrt{\frac{6}{5\pi}} \frac{2}{5M} \theta \frac{(\frac{1}{4} + \delta)^2 \{3(1 - \theta) + 4\delta(1 + 3\theta)\} - 32\delta^2/3}{(\frac{1}{4} + \delta)^3(\frac{3}{4} - \delta)}. \tag{70}$$

The numerical solution for δ and for the density gradient is listed in Table II, as computed by using a mesh thickness $\Delta\theta = 0.05$. Numerical checks with different mesh thicknesses indicate that the error is confined to the final digit in each entry. For comparison, the quantities are listed as computed by the second approximation method. The origin of x, which is arbitrary, was chosen to lie at the point where $\theta = \frac{1}{2}$.

The inverse shock thickness defined by the maximum density gradient is $0.8647/M$ and occurs at $\theta = 0.4663$. The inverse shock thickness defined by the maximum flow velocity gradient is $0.9170/M$ and occurs at $\theta = 0.1692$. The inverse shock thickness defined by the density gradient is $0.895/M$ for the second ellipsoidal approximation and $0.988/M$ for the Mott-Smith c_1^2

method. Thus the second approximation has an error of about three per cent compared with an error of more than fourteen per cent in the Mott-Smith method.

TABLE II

NUMERICAL SOLUTIONS FOR MAXWELL MOLECULES AT $M = \infty$

	Results of numerical integration			Results according to the second approximation	
θ	x/M	δ	$M\,d\theta/dx$	δ	$M\,d\theta/dx$
0	$-\infty$	-0.0307764	0	-0.02885	0
0.05	-0.7994	-0.02979	0.1813		
0.10	-0.6056	-0.02871	0.3346	-0.02657	0.3470
0.15	-0.4824	-0.02771	0.4769		
0.20	-0.3870	-0.02657	0.5711	-0.02419	0.6064
0.25	-0.3095	-0.02540	0.6870		
0.30	-0.2404	-0.02427	0.7603	-0.02212	0.7978
0.35	-0.1771	-0.02305	0.8196		
0.40	-0.1171	-0.02185	0.8480	-0.01907	0.8765
0.45	-0.0580	-0.02048	0.8637		
0.50	0	-0.01909	0.8604	-0.01630	0.8942
0.55	0.0588	-0.01764	0.8396		
0.60	0.1197	-0.01613	0.8017	-0.01339	0.8403
0.65	0.1842	-0.01454	0.7478		
0.70	0.2543	-0.01287	0.6781	-0.01032	0.7185
0.75	0.3329	-0.01110	0.5942		
0.80	0.4251	-0.00922	0.4904	-0.00708	0.5347
0.85	0.5398	-0.00720	0.3814		
0.90	0.6941	-0.00499	0.2667	-0.00364	0.2927
0.95	0.9426	-0.00268	0.1357		
1.00	$+\infty$	0	0	0	0

The density, flow velocity and temperature profiles for infinite Mach number are plotted in Fig. 3 for the numerical claculation and the Mott-Smith method.[7] The most outstanding difference in these profiles is the temperature maximum predicted by the ellipsoidal method. A temperature overshoot occurs whenever $dT/d\theta$ is negative near $\theta = 1$ and, for the Mott-Smith method, this derivative approaches zero as $M \to \infty$. This derivative will be

[7] Recent experimental measurements of the density profile at Mach five by Schultz-Grunow and Frohn (1965) show excellent agreement with the density profile in Fig. 3 (see their article in this Symposium).

negative as $M \to \infty$ for the ellipsoidal distribution whenever δ is negative. Since the solution curve for δ must lie below the curve AA in Fig. 2, the temperature overshoot cannot be due to errors in the numerical analysis of Eq. (69). Although the overshoot may conceivably be a result of approximations inherent in the ellipsoidal expansion, there seems to be no convincing reason for doubting its existence.

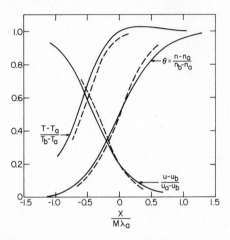

FIG. 3. Shock structure for Mach infinity. Solid lines are numerical solutions for the ellipsoidal expansion; dash lines are Mott-Smith results.

Quantities like $dT/d\theta$, which are independent of the molecular force law in the Mott-Smith method, depend upon the force law for the ellipsoidal method and other methods which satisfy more than one transport equation with nonvanishing collision moments. Thus the magnitude of the temperature overshoot or even its existence may depend on the force law. In the present calculations, the maximum temperature, which is 2.17 per cent greater than T_b, occurs at $\theta = 0.716$. As $x \to -\infty$, the longitudinal "temperature," λ_{11}, decreases by 8.7 per cent from its subsonic value RT_b while λ_{22} increases by 16.9 per cent.

VII. The Second Approximation for the Ellipsoidal Method

The second approximation for the ellipsoidal method is obtained by taking the locus of points in the θ-δ phase plane for which the slope of the direction field is zero to be the solution curve. As discussed in the previous section, the second approximation gives shock thicknesses which differ from the exact numerical solution by about three per cent for Mach infinity. The second approximation is accurate provided the solution curve lies close to the line $\delta = 0$, and we shall show that this condition is better satisfied for smaller Mach numbers than it is for Mach infinity.

Since δ is small, it is sufficient to keep the first two terms in the expansion of the coefficients of the transport equations in powers of δ. Making use of Eqs. (33)–(35), (38)–(41), (44)–(47), and (63)–(66), we obtain a solution in the form

$$\delta = g_1 \frac{(1 - \theta)}{1 + g_2\theta} \tag{71}$$

and

$$\frac{d\theta}{dx} = B\theta(1 - \theta)\left\{1 + \frac{g_3 + g_4\theta}{1 + g_2\theta} + \frac{g_5[1 + (\theta/4M^2)](1 - \theta)}{(1 + g_2\theta)^2}\right\}, \tag{72}$$

where

$$B = \sqrt{\frac{6}{5\pi}} \frac{32M(M^2 - 1)(5M^4 + 6M^2 + 21)}{(M^2 + 3)(25M^6 + 65M^4 + 3M^2 + 99)}, \tag{73}$$

$$g_1 = -\frac{3}{8} \frac{(M^2 - 1)(M^2 + 3)(5M^4 - 30M^2 + 9)}{65M^6 + 87M^4 - 9M^2 + 81}, \tag{74}$$

$$g_2 = -\frac{15M^6 - 7M^4 - 135M^2 + 63}{65M^6 + 87M^4 - 9M^2 + 8}, \tag{75}$$

$$g_3 = \frac{32g_1}{3(M^2 - 1)(M^2 + 3)}\left\{\frac{(M^2 + 3)(35M^4 - 22M^2 - 45)}{8(5M^4 + 6M^2 + 21)}\right.$$
$$\left. - \frac{(M^2 - 1)(25M^6 + 45M^4 + 81M^2 + 81)}{25M^6 + 65M^4 + 3M^2 + 99}\right\}, \tag{76}$$

$$g_4 = \frac{-32g_1}{3(M^2 - 1)(M^2 + 3)}\left\{\frac{15M^6 + 123M^4 + 13M^2 - 87}{8(5M^4 + 6M^2 + 21)}\right.$$
$$\left. - \frac{(M^2 - 1)(25M^6 + 45M^4 + 81M^2 + 81)}{25M^6 + 65M^4 + 3M^2 + 99}\right\}, \tag{77}$$

and

$$g_5 = \frac{-40(M^2 - 1)(M^2 + 3)^2(5M^4 - 30M^2 + 9)^2M^2}{(5M^4 + 6M^2 + 21)(65M^6 + 87M^4 - 9M^2 + 81)^2}. \tag{78}$$

In Table III, the shock thicknesses calculated from the second approximation are compared with Mott-Smith's $c_1{}^2$ calculation, with the third-order Chapman-Enskog results due to Wang Chang (1948) and with recent results due to Salwen et al. (1964).

TABLE III

λ_a/X for Maxwell Molecules, According to Different Theories

M	Ellipsoidal 2nd approx. c_1^2, $c_1 c^2$	Salwen *et al.* c_1^2, $c_1 c^2$	Mott-Smith c_1^2	Wang Chang (3rd-order Chapman-Enskog)	Navier-Stokes
1.05	0.0172	0.0174	0.0152	0.0173	0.0174
1.10	0.0335	0.0342	0.0300	0.0340	0.0343
1.15	0.0493	0.0502	0.0441	0.0495	0.0506
1.20	0.0642	0.0653	0.0577	0.0635	0.0661
1.50	0.1353	0.136	0.124	—	—
2.00	0.1922	0.192	0.184	—	—
5.00	0.1510	0.146	0.165	—	—
∞	$\frac{1}{M}(0.895)^a$	$\frac{1}{M}(0.828)$	$\frac{1}{M}(0.988)$	—	—

[a] The more exact numerical solution for the ellipsoidal method at $M = \infty$ is $1/M \, (0.8647)$.

In Table IV, the values of the constants B and g_i are tabulated for various Mach numbers for convenience in calculating the shock structure as given by Eqs. (71) and (72). Macroscopic properties such as temperature are easily expressed in terms of θ and δ from their kinetic theory definitions. Since the magnitude of δ is never greater than g_i, Table IV verifies that δ is small and has its largest magnitudes near $M = 1.5$ and $M = \infty$. Although terms proportional to δ^2 are neglected in Eq. (72), we have kept the term involving g_5 which, though small, includes the major effect of the δ^2 terms.

TABLE IV

Constants for Calculating Shock Structure According to Eqs. (74) and (75)

Mach no.	B	g_1	g_2	g_3	g_4	g_5
1.05	0.0814	0.00975	0.281	−0.145	−0.0646	−0.0040
1.10	0.1595	0.0175	0.269	−0.141	−0.0575	−0.0207
1.15	0.2330	0.0233	0.250	−0.133	−0.0508	−0.0294
1.20	0.3009	0.0274	0.229	−0.123	−0.0450	−0.0365
1.50	0.5871	0.0309	0.089	−0.0417	−0.0214	−0.0414
2.00	0.7703	0.0109	− 0.066	0.0004	0.00174	−0.00578
5.00	0.6475	−0.0225	−0.212	0.0070	−0.103	−0.0284
∞	$(1/M)0.9859$	−0.0289	−0.230	0.0385	−0.193	−0.0473

VIII. Shock Thicknesses as $M \to 1$

In this section, we obtain the solution for the ellipsoidal method in the limit as $M \to 1$, and compare the results with the Navier-Stokes shock thicknesses through terms of order $M - 1$.

It can be shown that the error in the second approximation approaches zero as $(M - 1)^2$ in the limit as $M \to 1$. In this limit, Eqs. (71) and (72) become

$$\delta = \tfrac{3}{2}(M - 1) \frac{1 - \theta}{7 + 2\theta} \tag{79}$$

and

$$\frac{d\theta}{dx} = \sqrt{\frac{6}{5\pi}} \frac{4}{3} (M - 1) \frac{12 + 3\theta}{7 + 2\theta} \theta(1 - \theta) \tag{80}$$

with an error of order $(M - 1)^2$. From Eq. (80), the inverse shock thickness normalized by the mean free path is found to be

$$\frac{\lambda_a}{X} = 0.5625 \sqrt{\frac{6}{5\pi}} (M - 1). \tag{81}$$

The comparable Navier-Stokes result, which was first obtained by Taylor (1910), is

$$\frac{\lambda_a}{X} = 0.5714 \sqrt{\frac{6}{5\pi}} (M - 1). \tag{82}$$

Thus the ellipsoidal method, which satisfies the c_1^2 and $c_1 c^2$ transport equations, agrees within 1.5 per cent with the Navier-Stokes result.

IX. Discussion

A. Comparison with Experiment

For low Mach numbers, say less than 1.8, Talbot and Sherman (1959) have found experimental shock thicknesses which are thinner than those predicted by Grad's thirteen moment method and which fall between the Navier-Stokes and Burnett curves. The shock thicknesses calculated from the ellipsoidal method also fall between these two curves, as can be seen from Table III. As shown in the previous section, the ellipsoidal shock thicknesses agree with Navier-Stokes results within 1.5 per cent in the limit as $M \to 1$.

Near Mach 2, the Mott-Smith shock thicknesses agree well with experiment, as has been pointed out by Muckenfuss (1960), and Table III shows that the ellipsoidal results are extremely close to the Mott-Smith results between Mach 2 and Mach 3.

To compare our theoretical results for Maxwell molecules with experiment, we observe that shock thicknesses normalized by the mean free path in the center of the shock are nearly independent of the force law (Ziering *et al.*, 1961). Using this fact and assuming that the argon force law is inversely proportional to the 7.329 power of distance, we have renormalized both our results and the Mott-Smith results and compared them with experimental results in Fig. 4. The renormalization procedure is expected to be quite accurate since the force law does not differ greatly from the Maxwell force law. As shown by Fig. 4, the agreement between theory and experimental results is well within the experimental error.

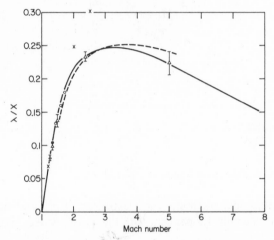

FIG. 4. Experimental and theoretical inverse shock thicknesses in argon, normalized by the mean free path in front of the shock. The Navier-Stokes thicknesses are Gilbarg and Paolucci's velocity thicknesses; the remainder are density thicknesses.

KEY: O, Talbot and Sherman; △, Hansen *et al.*; ×, Navier-Stokes calculation; ---, Mott-Smith calculation; —, ellipsoidal calculation.

B. Comparison with the Mott-Smith Theory

In general, the ellipsoidal approximation should be more accurate than the Mott-Smith approximation since it satisfies the $c_1 c^2$ transport equation in addition to the transport equations satisfied by the Mott-Smith c_1^2 method. Moreover the ellipsoidal approximating function includes five variables which are functions of position, rather than two, and therefore is able to take full advantage of the three collisional invariant transport equations, while two of these equations are redundant in the Mott-Smith method.

The most striking improvement of the ellipsoidal approximation over the Mott-Smith approximation is the agreement with the Navier-Stokes solution for low Mach numbers. In the limit of large Mach numbers, the ellipsoidal method predicts shock thicknesses about 14 per cent larger than the Mott-Smith thicknesses.

It is worth mentioning that, for Maxwell molecules, the Mott-Smith c_1^2 method should be especially good near Mach two because, in addition to the c_1^2 transport equation, it satisfied the $c_1 c^2$ equation at Mach 2.38 and the c_1^3 equation at Mach 1.84. The situation is similar for rigid sphere molecules.[8] The accuracy of the Mott-Smith method near Mach two is confirmed by comparison with experimental measurements and with the ellipsoidal results in Table III.

ACKNOWLEDGMENT

The author wishes to thank Professor Max Krook for many helpful discussions during the course of this research. The paper was adapted from Chapter VI of a thesis presented to Harvard University (1963), and I am grateful to the Raytheon Graduate Program for support of that work.

Appendix

In the usual manner (Chapman and Cowling, 1952), the interaction moments can be written as the eightfold integral

$$J[\mathbf{c}^n] = \tfrac{1}{2} \int f(c)f(w)[\mathbf{c}^n]gb\, db\, d\varepsilon\, d\mathbf{c}\, d\mathbf{w} \qquad (A.1)$$

where

$$[\mathbf{c}^n] = \mathbf{c}'^n + \mathbf{w}'^n - \mathbf{c}^n - \mathbf{w}^n \qquad (A.2)$$

and primes indicate velocities after collision and we are using the symmetric tensor notation such that

$$(\mathbf{c}^n)_{i_1 \cdots i_n} = c_{i_1} \cdots c_{i_n}. \qquad (A.3)$$

In terms of the relative velocity $\mathbf{g} = \mathbf{c} - \mathbf{w}$ and center of mass velocity $\mathbf{G} = \tfrac{1}{2}(\mathbf{c} + \mathbf{w})$, the collision laws are $\mathbf{G} = \mathbf{G}'$ and $g = g'$.

Following Grad (1949), the symmetric tensor $\mathbf{g}^m\mathbf{G}^n$ is defined by

$$(\mathbf{g}^m\mathbf{G}^n)_{i_1 \cdots i_{m+n}} = \frac{1}{m!n!} \sum_{P\{i\}} g_{i_1} \cdots g_{i_m} G_{i_{m+1}} \cdots G_{i_{m+n}} \qquad (A.4)$$

---

[8] If the Bhatnagar-Gross-Krook collision model is used, the Mott-Smith c_1^2 method will satisfy the c_1^3 transport equation at $M = \infty$ rather than $M = 1.84$. Thus one would expect that the Mott-Smith solution would be a much more accurate solution for the model equation at Mach infinity than it is for the Boltzmann equation at Mach infinity.

where the sum is over all permutations of the indices i_j, and the factor in front of the summation sign is chosen to eliminate redundant permutations. In this notation, after making use of the collision laws, Eq. (A.2) becomes

$$[\mathbf{c}^n] = \sum_{s=1}^{n/2} 2^{1-2s} \mathbf{G}^{n-2s}(\mathbf{g}'^{2s} - \mathbf{g}^{2s}). \tag{A.5}$$

We now specialize to the case where $n = 2$ or 3, so that s takes on only the value 1 in Eq. (A.5). For a given value of $\mathbf{c}$ and $\mathbf{w}$, we define a new coordinate system $\mathbf{x}^*$, so that the x_3^*-axis points in the same direction as $\mathbf{g}$, and $x_i = a_{ik}x_k^*$. [The orientation of the x_1^*- and x_2^*-axes in arbitrary with respect to rotation about the x_3^*-axis. In the x^* system $g'^* = g(\cos \varepsilon \sin \chi, \sin \varepsilon \sin \chi, \cos \chi)$.] Defining the vectors $\mathbf{a}_{.k} = (a_{1k}, a_{2k}, a_{3k})$, we get

$$\int_0^{2\pi} [\mathbf{c}^n]\, d\varepsilon = \frac{\pi}{2}(1 - \cos^2 \chi)g^2\mathbf{G}^{n-2}\{\mathbf{a}_{.1}^2 + \mathbf{a}_{.2}^2 - 2\mathbf{a}_{.3}^2\} \tag{A.6}$$

where χ is the angle of deflection of the relative velocity. By using the relations $a_{ik}a_{jk} = \delta_{ij}$ and $\mathbf{g} = g\mathbf{a}_{.3}$, Eq. (A.6) can be simplified and we obtain

$$\iint [\mathbf{c}^n]gb\, db\, d\varepsilon = \frac{\pi}{2}\varphi^{(2)}(g)\mathbf{G}^{n-2}(g^2\boldsymbol{\delta} - 3\mathbf{g}^2) \tag{A.7}$$

where $\varphi^{(2)}(g)$ is defined by Chapman and Cowling (1952) as

$$\varphi^{(2)}(g) = \int_0^\infty (1 - \cos^2 \chi)gb\, db. \tag{A.8}$$

The c_1^2, c_1^3, and c_1c^2 interaction moments, which follow immediately from Eq. (A.7) are

$$J[c_1^2] = \frac{\pi}{4}\int f(\mathbf{c})f(\mathbf{w})\varphi^{(2)}(g)(g^2 - 3g_1^2)\, d\mathbf{c}\, d\mathbf{w}, \tag{A.9}$$

$$J[c_1c^2] = \frac{\pi}{2}\int f(\mathbf{c})f(\mathbf{w})\varphi^{(2)}(g)(G_1g^2 - 3g_1\mathbf{g}\cdot\mathbf{G})\, d\mathbf{c}\, d\mathbf{w}, \tag{A.10}$$

and

$$J[c_1^3] = \frac{3\pi}{4}\int f(\mathbf{c})f(\mathbf{w})\varphi^{(2)}(g)G_1(g^2 - 3g_1^2)\, d\mathbf{c}\, d\mathbf{w}. \tag{A.11}$$

In the case of Maxwell molecules, $\varphi^{(2)}(g)$ is a constant and the integrations in Eqs. (A.9)–(A.11) are especially simple. Carrying out these integrations for the distribution function in Eq. (4), and noting that $\varphi^{(2)}(g) = q/\pi$ where q is defined by Eq. (61), we obtain Eqs. (58)–(60).

REFERENCES

Chapman, S., and Cowling, T. G. (1952). "The Mathematical Theory of Non-Uniform Gases," Cambridge Univ. Press, London and New York.

Glansdorf, P. (1962). *Phys. Fluids* **5**, 371.

Gilbarg, D., and Paolucci, D. (1953). *J. Rat. Mech. Anal.* **4**, 617.

Grad, H. (1949). *Communs. Pure Appl. Math.* **2**, 325.

Holway, L. H. (1963). "Approximation Procedures for Kinetic Theory," Ph.D. Thesis, Harvard Univ.

Holway, L. H. (1964). *Phys. Fluids* **7**, 911.

Hansen, K., Hornig, D. F., Levitt, B., Linzer, M., and Myers, B. F. (1961). *In* "Rarefied Gas Dynamics" (L. Talbot, ed.), p. 593. Academic Press, New York.

Mott-Smith, H. M. (1951). *Phys. Rev.* **82**, 885

Muckenfuss, C. (1960). *Phys. Fluids* **3**, 320.

Salwen, H., Grosch, C. E., and Ziering, S. (1964). *Phys. Fluids* **7**, 180.

Schultz-Grunow, F., and Frohn A. (1965). This volume, p. 250.

Schwartz, L. M., and Hornig, D. F. (1963) *Phys. Fluids* **6**, 1669.

Sherman, F. S., and Talbot, L. (1961). *In* "Rarefied Gas Dynamics" (F. M. Devienne, ed.), p. 161. Macmillan (Pergamon), New York.

Talbot, L., and Sherman, F. S. (1959). NASA Memo. 12–14–58W.

Taylor, G. I. (1910). *Proc. Roy. Soc.* **A84**, 371.

Wang Chang, C. S. (1948). Univ. Michigan Eng. Rept. APL/JHU CM–503 UMH–3–F.

Ziering, S., Ek, F., and Koch, P. (1961). *Phys. Fluids* **4**, 975.

Ziering, S., and Ek, F. (1961). *Phys. Fluids* **4**, 765.

Shock-Wave Structure in a Rigid Sphere Gas[1]

G. A. BIRD[2]

Department of Mechanics of Fluids, University of Manchester, Manchester, England

Consideration is given to a gas composed of rigid sphere molecules, initially in thermal equilibrium between two infinite, plane, parallel and specularly reflecting walls. A Monte Carlo approach is used to study the shock wave which is formed when one wall impulsively acquires a uniform velocity towards the other. The method essentially consists of carrying out a "numerical experiment" with a model gas on a very fast computer. Shock wave density profiles are presented for shock Mach numbers from 1.5 to 30. These are compared with the profiles predicted by various analytical methods.

I. Introduction

The difficulties associated with the analytical determination of the structure of strong shock waves have been widely discussed, for example by Talbot (1962). Solutions based on the continuum Navier-Stokes equations have been verified by experiment for weak shock waves, but are almost certainly in error for very strong shocks. A number of kinetic solutions have been put forward for strong shock waves. However, all the theories involve some degree of approximation and experiments with strong shocks have not been sufficiently precise to serve as a check.

This paper presents the results of a "numerical experiment" performed on a computer model of a gas composed of rigid sphere molecules. The gas is initially in equilibrium between two infinite, plane, parallel and specularly reflecting walls. A Monte Carlo approach is used to study the shock wave

[1] This research was supported by the Air Force Office of Scientific Research under Grant AF EOAR 64-65, with the European Office of Aerospace Research (OAR) U.S. Air Force.

[2] On leave from the University of Sydney where the study was initiated.

216

which is formed when one wall impulsively acquires a uniform velocity towards the other. Unlike the iterative Monte Carlo method developed by Haviland (1963), the shock structure is found directly and without recourse, at any stage, to the profile given by one of the analytical methods.

Shock wave density profiles are presented for shock Mach numbers between 1.5 and 30, and these are compared with the profiles given by the solution of the Navier-Stokes equations by Gilbarg and Paolucci (1953) and by the bimodal model of Mott-Smith (1951).

II. Description

A. Initial Data

The initial positions of the walls are fixed and a total of N_0 molecules are set up between them with the Maxwellian velocity distribution corresponding to a most probable molecular speed $1/\beta$. For a given wall spacing and molecular number density, the number of mean free paths between the walls is fixed by the molecular radius σ. This is chosen such that the wall spacing is large compared with the expected shock wave thickness. Since the flow is one-dimensional, the only position coordinate which need be stored for each molecule is that in the x direction normal to the walls. The three velocity components are also stored.

The time t is set to zero and one of the walls is impulsively given a velocity

$$U = \left(\frac{15}{2}\right)^{1/2} \frac{M_s^2 - 1}{4\beta M_s}$$

where M_s is the desired Mach number of the shock. β is conveniently put equal to unity.

B. General Procedure

The collision frequency for pairs of molecules having a relative velocity v_r in a gas of local number density N is

$$\pi\sigma^2 N v_r.$$

Therefore, each time such a collision takes place the time is advanced by an amount

$$\Delta t = (2/N_0)(\pi\sigma^2 N v_r)^{-1}$$

The ideal procedure would be to move the molecules and the wall simultaneously with the computation of collisions. However, there is a considerable saving of computer time if the locations of the molecules and wall are un-changed while a number of collisions appropriate to some time interval t_m (which is much less than the mean collision time) are calculated. All the molecules and the wall are then moved through the distances appropriate to t_m and their current velocities. Collisions between the walls and the molecules are computed when necessary.

At much larger time intervals, the velocity and density profiles between the walls are sampled.

C. Computation of Collisions

The computation of the collisions must allow for the fact that the probability of a pair of molecules suffering a collision is proportional to the local density and the relative velocity between them. The first step in the procedure which has been adopted is to select one molecule at random. The number density in the vicinity of this molecule is then sampled and the molecule is retained or rejected in such a way that the probability of retention is proportional to this local density. A second molecule is chosen at random, subject to the condition that its x coordinate must be within half a local mean free path of that of the first and on the "right" side of it for a collision to occur. The relative velocity between the two molecules is determined and the pair are retained or rejected in such a way that the probability of retention is directly proportional to the relative velocity.

The half mean free path condition arises because the molecules are moving in any direction in space, rather than along the x axis, and, while their relative velocity is such that they are approaching, their absolute velocity components in the x direction may be of the same or opposite signs. Rather than accept all pairs of molecules with a separation less than this average condition, it would be preferable to choose pairs with separations distributed about the mean condition. However, this was precluded by computing time considerations and tests showed that the results are insensitive to variations in this condition.

When a pair of molecules is retained, a line of impact is chosen at random (Jeans, 1921) and the new sets of velocity components for the molecules are computed (e.g., Patterson, 1956).

D. Operational Details

The calculations were carried out on the Atlas digital computer in the University of Manchester. This machine has a speed of the order of 500,000 instructions per second, and a run to obtain a shock wave density profile with a standard deviation varying from two to four per cent lasted approximately thirty minutes.

Between one and two thousand molecules were used in each calculation. Increased accuracy was obtained by averaging profiles sampled at intervals after the shock was fully formed. In doing this, it was assumed that the shock travels at the speed predicted by the Rankine-Hugoniot equations. The fact that there was no systematic variation in the profile over the successive samplings verified that the shock did, in fact, travel at the predicted speed.

III. Results and Discussion

In Figs. 1 to 4, the shock wave density profiles given by the computer "experiment" on the model gas are compared with those predicted by the Navier-Stokes equations with the appropriate viscosity coefficient and Prandtl number for a rigid sphere gas. The profiles given by Mott-Smith's solution (for rigid sphere molecules and with the u^2 transport equation) are also shown. Density and mean free path are denoted by ρ and λ, respectively, while the subscript 1 denotes the undisturbed value upstream of the shock wave.

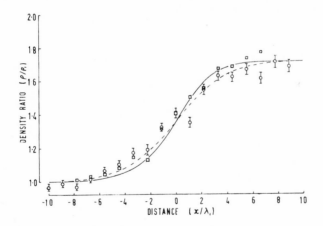

FIG. 1. Shock wave density profile for $M_s = 1.5$. Model gas, *run 1*, ○, $\updownarrow \pm$ one standard deviation; *run 2*, □; Navier-Stokes, — ; Mott-Smith, – – – .

Figure 1 shows the results from two separate runs for a shock Mach number of 1.5. The agreement with the theoretical profiles is quite good, that with the Mott-Smith profile being slightly the better. For a shock Mach number of 3, the "gas model" profile is rather thicker than the Mott-Smith profile and significantly thicker than the Navier-Stokes profile. The profiles predicted by

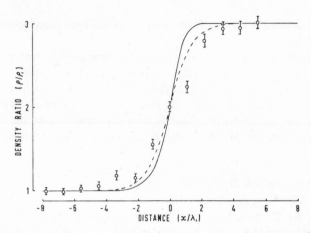

FIG. 2. Shock wave density profile for $M_s = 3$. Model gas, O; Navier-Stokes, —; Mott-Smith, – – – .

the theory of Ziering *et al.* (1961) are thinner than the Mott-Smith profiles and, for a rigid sphere gas up to a shock Mach number of three, thinner than the Navier-Stokes profile. These results do not, therefore, provide any support for the theory of Ziering as opposed to that of Mott-Smith.

Figures 3 and 4 indicate that there is no significant change in the density profile as the Mach number is increased to very large values. This is in agreement with the very simple two-fluid model of Rott and Whittenbury (1961).

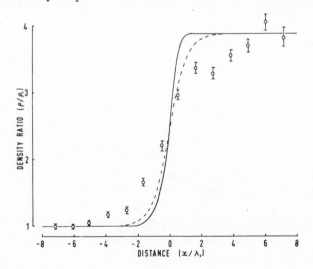

FIG. 3. Shock wave density profile for $M_s = 10$. Model gas, O; Navier Stokes, —; Mott-Smith, – – – .

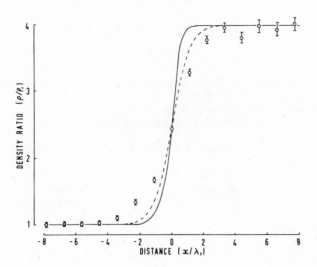

FIG. 4. Shock wave density profile for $M_s = 30$. Model gas, $\bigcirc$; Navier-Stokes, —; Mott-Smith, – – –.

In contrast to the results of Chahine (1963), there appears to be a significant departure from the continuum profile on the downstream as well as the upstream side of the shock wave.

IV. Concluding Remarks

It is possible to construct a computer model of a gas with which "numerical experiments" can be performed in the transition flow regime. However, even with the fastest contemporary computers, the restriction on the number of molecules which can be used is such that large random fluctuations must be expected in the results, and it is difficult to arrive at definitive conclusions. Any attempt to extend the solution into the continuum regime would be ruled out by considerations of computing time, the method being most suitable for high-speed problems in the transition regime. Since this is an area in which solutions which are completely independent of the corresponding solutions in the continuum and free-molecule regimes are required, it is proposed to extend the method to two-dimensional steady flow problems.

ACKNOWLEDGMENT

The author would like to acknowledge the assistance of Mr. P. A. Madden in writing the computer program for this work.

REFERENCES

Chahine, M. T. (1963). *In* "Rarefied Gas Dynamics" (J. A. Laurmann, ed.,)., Vol. I, p. 260. Academic Press, New York.

Gilbarg, D., and Paolucci, D. (1953). *J. Rat. Mech. Anal.* **2**, 617.

Haviland, J. K. (1963). *In* "Rarefied Gas Dynamics" (J. A. Laurmann, ed.)., Vol. I, p. 274. Academic Press, New York.

Jeans, J. (1921). "The Dynamical Theory of Gases," p. 261. Cambridge Univ. Press, London and New York.

Mott-Smith, H. M. (1951). *Phys. Rev.* **82**, 885.

Patterson, G. N. (1956). "Molecular Flow of Gases." Wiley, New York.

Rott, N., and Whittenbury, C. G. (1961). "A Flow Model for Hypersonic Rarefied Gas Dynamics with Application to Shock Structure and Sphere Drag." Douglas Aircraft Co. Rept. SM-3824.

Talbot, L. (1962). *ARS (Am. Rocket Soc.) J.* **32**, 1009.

Ziering, S., Ek, F., and Koch, P. (1961). *Phys. Fluids* **4**, 975.

Shock-Wave Structure in Binary Gas Mixtures with No Chemical Reaction

TETSUO FUJIMOTO

Nagoya University, Nagoya, Japan

The shock-wave structure in binary gas mixtures is studied in terms of the Mott-Smith method. The molecules of the component gases are considered to be monatomic and chemically inert. Numerical results are obtained for the mixtures of xenon-129–xenon-132, argon-36–argon-40, neon-argon, and helium-argon.

I. Introduction

The shock-wave structure of a binary gas mixture has been studied from two points of view: the first is that of continuum theory of fluid mechanics and the second is that of kinetic theory. The approach in terms of continuum theory has been taken by Cowling (1942), Dyakov (1954) and Sherman (1960). They have shown that the broadening of the shock thickness is caused by diffusion, in addition to viscosity and thermal conductivity. As for the adequacy of the Navier-Stokes equation for the study of shock-wave structure, Sherman (1955) and Sherman and Talbot (1959) have shown its applicability for weak shock waves of a single species gas ($M < 2$). This may be true also for shock waves in gas mixtures. Moreover, as pointed out by Sherman (1960), when the masses of the constituent gas molecules are very different, it is necessary to consider separate temperatures for each species and employ a relaxation equation for the temperatures, since the large difference in mass makes energy transfer between the species difficult.

The kinetic theory approach is based upon the equation for the distribution function of molecular velocity. To obtain an approximate solution of the Boltzmann equation for the shock wave problem of a simple gas, Mott-Smith (1951) assumed a distribution function which is the sum of two Maxwellian

223

distribution functions corresponding to the conditions upstream and down-stream of the shock wave, respectively. The density distribution is solved by satisfying four moment equations of the Boltzmann equation, among which two equations are dependent. The generalized Rankine-Hugoniot relation is assumed to hold in the shock wave, and this determines the downstream conditions in terms of the upstream conditions. In spite of its mathematical simplicity, the Mott-Smith method gives good agreement with the experimental results for strong shock waves $(M > 2)$.

The Mott-Smith method has been applied to a fully ionized gas of hydrogen by Tidman (1958) and a partially ionized gas by Grewal (1962). Their procedure mainly consists of two steps: first, the computation of the shock-wave structure of a mixture of heavy particles as a single species gas, considering the heavy particles to be of the same mass and ignoring the presence of electrons; secondly, the computation of the motion of the electrons through the computed flow field of the heavy particles. This procedure is adequate because the mass of an electron can be neglected compared with that of an atom or ion. However, when the difference in the masses of the constituent gases is not very large, this procedure is not applicable.

In this paper the shock-wave structure in a binary gas mixture is studied by the direct application of the Mott-Smith method. The molecules of the component gases are considered to be monatomic and chemically inert. The distribution function for each species is assumed to be the sum of two Max-wellian distribution functions which correspond to the uniform states ahead of, and behind the shock wave. In the Mott-Smith treatment for a simple gas, a generalized Rankine-Hugoniot relation is derived from the dependency of the momentum and energy conservation equations on the equation of mass conservation. These equations and the derived Rankine-Hugoniot relation are satisfied in the shock wave. In the case of a binary gas mixture such a general relation cannot be obtained if we restrict the number of dependent variables to four. If distribution functions of the Mott-Smith type represent the physical phenomena realistically, then the Rankine-Hugoniot relation may be used to obtain rather qualitative results, since the parameters must satisfy the Rankine-Hugoniot relation in front of, and behind the shock wave regardless of the structure of the shock wave. In other words, the conservation equations of momentum and energy which hold at each point in the shock wave are replaced by equations which hold only between the upstream and downstream conditions of the shock wave. With the aid of the Rankine-Hugoniot relation, the number densities of each species are determined by using the continuity equations and ξ_{ix}^2-moment equations. Numerical results are obtained for mixtures of xenon-129–xenon-132, argon-36–argon-40, neon-argon, and helium-argon.

II. Distribution Functions and the Rankine-Hugoniot Relation

The gas mixture is assumed to be composed of molecules of mass m_1 and m_2 which are monatomic and chemically inert. The distribution functions for these two components $f^{(I)}$ and $f^{(II)}$ are assumed to be the sum of Maxwellian distribution functions as in the Mott-Smith treatment (1951) for a simple gas:

$$f^{(i)} = f_u^{(i)} + f_d^{(i)}, \qquad i = \text{I or II},$$

$$f_u^{(i)} = n_u^{(i)}(x)(m_i/2\pi k T_u)^{3/2} \exp\{-(m_i/2kT_u)(\xi_i - \mathbf{j}u_u)^2\},$$

$$f_d^{(i)} = n_d^{(i)}(x)(m_i/2\pi k T_d)^{3/2} \exp\{-(m_i/2kT_d)(\xi_i - \mathbf{j}u_d)^2\}, \tag{1}$$

where the suffix "u" denotes quantities ahead of the shock wave, the suffix "d" denotes quantities behind the shock wave, $\mathbf{j}$ is the unit vector along the x axis which is the direction of the flow, ξ_i is the molecular velocity of the i species, T is the temperature, and u is the velocity.

In Eq. (1), $n_u^{(i)}$ and $n_d^{(i)}$ are functions of x and subject to the following boundary conditions:

$$\left.\begin{array}{l} n_u^{(i)}(x) \to n_u^{(i)}(-\infty) = n_0^{(i)} \\ n_d^{(i)}(x) \to 0 \end{array}\right\} \quad \text{as} \quad x \to -\infty,$$

$$\left.\begin{array}{l} n_u^{(i)}(x) \to 0 \\ n_d^{(i)}(x) \to n_d^{(i)}(\infty) \end{array}\right\} \quad \text{as} \quad x \to \infty. \tag{2}$$

The number density of each species is obtained by integrating the distribution functions:

$$n^{(i)}(x) = n_u^{(i)}(x) + n_d^{(i)}(x). \tag{3}$$

Similarly, the macroscopic velocities of each species are given by the integration of the distribution functions multiplied by ξ_{ix}:

$$n^{(i)}u^{(i)} = n_u^{(i)}u_u + n_d^{(i)}u_d. \tag{4}$$

From the boundary conditions (2) and Eq. (4), it is seen that both species have the same velocity ahead of, and behind the shock wave. In the same way, the temperatures of the two species are the same on both sides of the shock wave. On the other hand, the velocity and temperature of each species in the shock wave are different.

The Boltzmann equations for $f^{(I)}$ and $f^{(II)}$ are

$$\xi_{1x}\, \partial f^{(I)}/\partial x = (\partial f^{(I)}/\partial t)_{\text{coll}}$$

$$\xi_{2x}\, \partial f^{(II)}/\partial x = (\partial f^{(II)}/\partial t)_{\text{coll}}, \tag{5}$$

where the collision terms are given by

$$(\partial f^{(I)}/\partial t)_{\text{coll}} = \iint_0^{2\pi} \int_0^\infty \{f^{(I)}(\xi_1')f^{(I)}(\xi_{10}') - f^{(I)}(\xi_1)f^{(I)}(\xi_{10})\}g_{11}b \; db \; d\varepsilon \; d\xi_{10}$$

$$+ \iint_0^{2\pi} \int_0^\infty \{f^{(I)}(\xi_1')f^{(II)}(\xi_2') - f^{(I)}(\xi_1)f^{(II)}(\xi_2)\}g_{12}b \; db \; d\varepsilon \; d\xi_2,$$

$$(\partial f^{(II)}/\partial t)_{\text{coll}} = \iint_0^{2\pi} \int_0^\infty \{f^{(II)}(\xi_2')f^{(II)}(\xi_{20}') - f^{(II)}(\xi_2)f^{(II)}(\xi_{20})\}g_{22}b \; db \; d\varepsilon \; d\xi_{20}$$

$$+ \iint_0^{2\pi} \int_0^\infty \{f^{(II)}(\xi_2')f^{(I)}(\xi_1') - f^{(II)}(\xi_2)f^{(I)}(\xi_1)\}g_{21}b \; db \; d\varepsilon \; d\xi_1,$$

and the vector ξ_{i0} denotes the velocity of a molecule colliding with another of the same kind, the relative velocities are defined by

$$g_{11} = |\xi_{10} - \xi_1|, \qquad g_{21} = |\xi_2 - \xi_1| = g_{12}, \qquad g_{22} = |\xi_{20} - \xi_2|.$$

The collision parameters b and ε have the usual meaning (Chapman and Cowling, 1939). The $\varphi(\xi_i)$-moment equation of the Boltzmann equation is defined as follows:

$$\int \varphi(\xi_i)\xi_{ix} \; \partial f^{(i)}/\partial x \; d\xi_i = \int \varphi(\xi_i)(\partial f^{(i)}/\partial t)_{\text{coll}} \; d\xi_i.$$

As mentioned above, the parameters T_u, u_u, T_d, and u_d which appear in the assumed distribution functions are quantities representing the conditions upstream and downstream of the shock wave. In the Mott-Smith treatment for a simple gas, the generalized Rankine-Hugoniot relation is derived from the equations of mass, momentum and energy conservation which are satisfied in the interior as well as the outside of the shock wave. That is, the equations of momentum and energy conservation (ξ_x- and ξ^2-moment equations) are assumed to be dependent on the equation of mass conservation. Then the generalized Rankine-Hugoniot relation is obtained as the relation among the coefficients of these equations, and two unknown functions (n_u and n_d) are found by the use of the continuity equation and the ξ_x^2- or ξ_x^3-moment equation, thereby satisfying the momentum and energy conservation equations simultaneously.

For a binary gas mixture, the equations of mass, momentum, and energy conservation for each component gas, can be obtained from Eq. (5) as 1-, ξ_{ix}- and ξ_i^2-moment equations:

$$n_u^{(I)}u_u + n_d^{(I)}u_d = \text{const}$$

$$n_u^{(II)}u_u + n_d^{(II)}u_d = \text{const}$$

$$\frac{d}{dx}\left\{n_u^{(I)}\left(u_u^2 + \frac{kT_u}{m_1}\right) + n_d^{(I)}\left(u_d^2 + \frac{kT_d}{m_1}\right)\right\} = \int \xi_{1x}\left(\frac{\partial f^{(I)}}{\partial t}\right)_{coll} d\xi_1,$$

$$\frac{d}{dx}\left\{n_u^{(II)}\left(u_u^2 + \frac{kT_u}{m_2}\right) + n_d^{(II)}\left(u_d^2 + \frac{kT_d}{m_2}\right)\right\} = \int \xi_{2x}\left(\frac{\partial f^{(II)}}{\partial t}\right)_{coll} d\xi_2,$$

$$\frac{d}{dx}\left\{n_u^{(I)}u_u\left(u_u^2 + \frac{5kT_u}{m_1}\right) + n_d^{(I)}u_d\left(u_d^2 + \frac{5kT_d}{m_1}\right)\right\} = \int \xi_1^2\left(\frac{\partial f^{(I)}}{\partial t}\right)_{coll} d\xi_1,$$

$$\frac{d}{dx}\left\{n_u^{(II)}u_u\left(u_u^2 + \frac{5kT_u}{m_2}\right) + n_d^{(II)}u_d\left(u_d^2 + \frac{5kT_d}{m_2}\right)\right\} = \int \xi_2^2\left(\frac{\partial f^{(II)}}{\partial t}\right)_{coll} d\xi_2.$$

(6)

The conservation equations for the mixture as a whole can be obtained by the addition of each component equation multiplied by m_i:

$$m_1 u_u n_u^{(I)} + m_1 u_d n_d^{(I)} + m_2 u_u n_u^{(II)} + m_2 u_d n_d^{(II)} = \text{const},$$

$$m_1(u_u^2 + kT_u/m_1(n_u^{(I)} + m_1(u_d^2 + kT_d/m_1)n_d^{(I)}$$
$$+ m_2(u_u^2 + kT_u/m_2)n_u^{(II)} + m_2(u_d^{(2)} + kT_d/m_2)n_d^{(II)} = \text{const}, \quad (7)$$

$$m_1 u_u(u_u^2 + 5kT_u/m_1)n_u^{(I)} + m_1 u_d(u_d^{(2)} + 5kT_d/m_1)n_d^{(I)}$$
$$+ m_2 u_u(u_u^2 + 5kT_u/m_2)n_u^{(II)} + m_2 u_d(u_d^2 + 5kT_d/m_2)n_d^{(II)} = \text{const}.$$

If we assume a dependency of the momentum and energy equations on the continuity equation in order to solve for the four unknown functions $n_u^{(i)}$ and $n_d^{(i)}$ by the use of the continuity equation and ξ_{ix}^2-moment equation, the relation among the coefficients of Eq. (7) ends up with $m_1 = m_2$. Therefore, we cannot expect the generalized Rankine-Hugoniot relation to hold for binary gas mixtures, as far as we restrict the number of dependent variables to four.

Here we shall assume the usual Rankine-Hugoniot relation without consulting the equations of momentum and energy conservation in the shock wave. If distribution functions of the Mott-Smith type represent the physical phenomena realistically, this assumption may be used to obtain rather qualitative results, since the parameters which appear in the distribution functions must satisfy the usual Rankine-Hugoniot relation across the shock wave regardless of the shock wave structure.

The Rankine-Hugoniot relation for gas mixtures is derived from the conservation of mass, momentum and energy across the shock wave:

$$\rho_u u_u = \rho_d u_d,$$

$$\rho_u u_u^2 + p_u = \rho_d u_d^2 + p_d,$$

$$\tfrac{1}{2}u_u^2 + h_u = \tfrac{1}{2}u_d^2 + h_d,$$

(8)

where ρ, p, and h are the density, pressure, and enthalpy, respectively, of the mixture. If we assume that the mixture is thermally and calorically perfect, we have

$$p_u/\rho_u = R_u T_u, \qquad p_d/\rho_d = R_d T_d,$$
$$h_u = c_{p_u} T_u, \qquad h_d = c_{p_d} T_d, \tag{9}$$

where R_u, R_d, c_{p_u} and c_{p_d} are gas constants and specific heat at constant pressure ahead of, and behind the shock wave, respectively. These constants for the mixture are given by

$$R_u = \frac{\rho_u^{(I)} R^{(I)} + \rho_u^{(II)} R^{(II)}}{\rho_u^{(I)} + \rho_u^{(II)}}, \qquad R_d = \frac{\rho_d^{(I)} R^{(I)} + \rho_d^{(II)} R^{(II)}}{\rho_d^{(I)} + \rho_d^{(II)}},$$

$$R^{(I)} = k/m_1, \qquad\qquad R^{(II)} = k/m_2, \tag{10}$$

$$c_{p_u} = \frac{\rho_u^{(I)} c_p^{(I)} + \rho_u^{(II)} c_p^{(II)}}{\rho_u^{(I)} + \rho_u^{(II)}}, \qquad c_{p_d} = \frac{\rho_d^{(I)} c_p^{(I)} + \rho_d^{(II)} c_p^{(II)}}{\rho_d^{(I)} + \rho_d^{(II)}},$$

Under the assumption of a chemically inert gas mixture, the equations of continuity should be satisfied for each component gas:

$$\rho_u^{(I)} u_u = \rho_d^{(I)} u_d, \qquad \rho_u^{(II)} u_u = \rho_d^{(II)} u_d, \tag{11}$$

or

$$\rho_u^{(II)}/\rho_u^{(I)} = \rho_d^{(II)}/\rho_d^{(I)}$$

where

$$\rho_u^{(I)} = m_1 n_0^{(I)}, \qquad \rho_d^{(I)} = m_1 n_{(\infty)}^{(I)},$$
$$\rho_u^{(II)} = m_2 n_0^{(II)}, \qquad \rho_d^{(II)} = m_2 n_{(\infty)}^{(II)}.$$

Equations (10) and (11) show that the gas constants and specific heats of the mixture ahead of, and behind the shock wave, are the same:

$$R_u = R_d = R, \qquad c_{p_u} = c_{p_d} = c_p.$$

Solving Eq. (8) with the aid of the above relations, the downstream velocity and temperature of the mixture may be expressed in terms of the upstream conditions:

$$u_d = \left(\frac{\gamma - 1}{\gamma + 1}\right)\sqrt{\gamma R T_u}\left(\frac{2}{(\gamma - 1)M} + M\right),$$

$$T_d = T_u \frac{2\gamma(\gamma - 1)}{(\gamma + 1)^2}\left\{M^2 + \left(\frac{2}{\gamma - 1}\right)\right\}\left\{M^2 - \left(\frac{\gamma - 1}{2\gamma}\right)\right\}\frac{1}{M^2}, \tag{12}$$

where $\gamma = c_p/c_v$ and M is the Mach number ahead of the shock wave defined by

$$M^2 = u_u{}^2/\gamma R T_u.$$

III. The ξ_{ix}^2-Moment Equations

In order to solve for the functions $n_u^{(i)}$ and $n_d^{(i)}$, the continuity equations and ξ_{ix}^2-moment equations are employed. The continuity equations for each species are

$$n_u^{(I)}u_u + n_d^{(I)}u_d = n_0^{(I)}u_u,$$

$$n_u^{(II)}u_u + n_d^{(II)}u_d = n_0^{(II)}u_u. \tag{13}$$

The ξ_{ix}^2-moment equations are

$$u_u\left(u_u^2 + \frac{3kT_u}{m_1}\right)\frac{dn_u^{(I)}}{dx} + u_d\left(u_d^2 + \frac{3kT_d}{m_1}\right)\frac{dn_d^{(I)}}{dx} = \int \xi_{1x}^2\left(\frac{\partial f^{(I)}}{\partial t}\right)_{coll} d\xi_1 = J_1,$$

$$u_u\left(u_u^2 + \frac{3kT_u}{m_2}\right)\frac{dn_u^{(II)}}{dx} + u_d\left(u_d^2 + \frac{3kT_d}{m_2}\right)\frac{dn_d^{(II)}}{dx} = \int \xi_{2x}^2\left(\frac{\partial f^{(II)}}{\partial t}\right)_{coll} d\xi_2 = J_2, \tag{14}$$

where the collision terms can be represented as

$$J_1 = \Delta_{Id}\varphi_u^{(I)} + \Delta_{Iu}\varphi_d^{(I)} + \Delta_{IId}\varphi_u^{(I)} + \Delta_{IIu}\varphi_d^{(I)},$$

$$J_2 = \Delta_{IId}\varphi_u^{(II)} + \Delta_{IIu}\varphi_d^{(II)} + \Delta_{Id}\varphi_u^{(II)} + \Delta_{Iu}\varphi_d^{(II)}, \tag{15}$$

with

$$\Delta_{j\beta}\varphi_\alpha^{(i)} = \iiint_0^{2\pi}\int_0^\infty (\xi_{ix}'^2 - \xi_{ix}^2)f_\alpha^{(i)}(\xi_i)f_\beta^{(j)}(\xi_j)g_{ij}b \, db \, d\varepsilon \, d\xi_j \, d\xi_i.$$

Other collision terms vanish because the assumed distribution functions are Maxwellian:

$$\Delta_{Iu}\varphi_u^{(I)} = \Delta_{Id}\varphi_d^{(I)} = \Delta_{IIu}\varphi_u^{(II)} = \Delta_{IId}\varphi_d^{(II)} = 0,$$

$$\Delta_{IIu}\varphi_u^{(I)} = \Delta_{IId}\varphi_d^{(I)} = \Delta_{Iu}\varphi_u^{(II)} = \Delta_{Id}\varphi_d^{(II)} = 0.$$

The first two terms of collision integrals in Eq. (15) represent collisions between the same kind of molecules. Mott-Smith's results for a simple gas show that

$$\Delta_{Id}\varphi_u^{(I)} + \Delta_{Iu}\varphi_d^{(I)} = -\tfrac{1}{3}\sqrt{\pi}\sigma_1^2 n_u^{(I)}n_d^{(I)}\Theta(s_1)$$

$$\Delta_{IId}\varphi_u^{(II)} + \Delta_{IIu}\varphi_d^{(II)} = -\tfrac{1}{3}\sqrt{\pi}\sigma_2^2 n_u^{(II)}n_d^{(II)}\Theta(s_2) \tag{16}$$

where hard sphere molecules of diameter σ_1 and σ_2 are assumed, and

$$\Theta(s) = (s^2 + 1 - \tfrac{3}{4}s^{-2})\exp(-s^2) + (2s^3 + 3s - \tfrac{3}{2}s^{-1} + \tfrac{3}{4}s^{-3})\tfrac{1}{2}\sqrt{\pi} \text{ erf } s,$$

$$s_1 = (u_u - u_d)[m_1/2k(T_u + T_d)]^{1/2},$$

$$s_2 = (u_u - u_d)[m_2/2k(T_u + T_d)]^{1/2}.$$

The other collision terms in Eq. (15) which represent the collisions between molecules of different kinds can be calculated in a similar way. The results are

$$\Delta_{IId}\varphi_u^{(I)} = -n_u^{(I)}n_d^{(II)}\left\{2k\left(\frac{T_u}{m_1} + \frac{T_d}{m_2}\right)\right\}^{3/2}\sqrt{\pi}M_2{}^2\sigma_{12}^2\Phi(s_{ud_1}, \omega_1, \eta_1),$$

$$\Delta_{IIu}\varphi_d^{(I)} = -n_d^{(I)}n_u^{(II)}\left\{2k\left(\frac{T_d}{m_1} + \frac{T_u}{m_2}\right)\right\}^{3/2}\sqrt{\pi}M_2{}^2\sigma_{12}^2\Phi(s_{ud_2}, \omega_2, -\eta_2),$$

$$\Delta_{Id}\varphi_u^{(II)} = -n_d^{(I)}n_u^{(II)}\left\{2k\left(\frac{T_d}{m_1} + \frac{T_u}{m_2}\right)\right\}^{3/2}\sqrt{\pi}M_1{}^2\sigma_{12}^2\Phi(s_{ud_2}, \omega_3, \eta_3),$$

$$\Delta_{Iu}\varphi_d^{(II)} = -n_u^{(I)}n_d^{(II)}\left\{2k\left(\frac{T_u}{m_1} + \frac{T_d}{m_2}\right)\right\}^{3/2}\sqrt{\pi}M_1{}^2\sigma_{12}^2\Phi(s_{ud_1}, \omega_4, -\eta_4),$$

(17)

where $M_1 = m_1/(m_1 + m_2)$, $M_2 = m_2/(m_1 + m_2)$, $\sigma_{12} = (\sigma_1 + \sigma_2)/2$,

$$\Phi(s, \omega, \eta) = \{(\eta - \tfrac{4}{3})s^2 + (2\omega + \tfrac{1}{2}\eta - (7/3)) + (\tfrac{1}{2} - \omega)s^{-2}\}\exp(-s^2)$$
$$+ \{(\omega - \tfrac{1}{2})s^{-3} - (\eta/2s) + (4\omega - 6 + 2\eta)s$$
$$+ 2(\eta - \tfrac{4}{3})s^3\}\tfrac{1}{2}\sqrt{\pi}\,\text{erf}\,s,$$

and

$$\omega_1 = \frac{T_u}{m_1 M_2(T_u/m_1 + T_d/m_2)}, \qquad \omega_2 = \frac{T_d}{m_1 M_2(T_d/m_1 + T_u/m_2)},$$

$$\omega_3 = \frac{T_u}{m_2 M_1(T_d/m_1 + T_u/m_2)}, \qquad \omega_4 = \frac{T_d}{m_2 M_1(T_u/m_1 + T_d/m_2)},$$

$$\eta_1 = \frac{2u_u}{M_2(u_u - u_d)}, \qquad \eta_2 = \frac{2u_d}{M_2(u_u - u_d)},$$

$$\eta_3 = \frac{2u_u}{M_1(u_u - u_d)}, \qquad \eta_4 = \frac{2u_d}{M_1(u_u - u_d)},$$

$$s_{ud_1} = (u_u - u_d) \qquad\qquad s_{ud_2} = (u_u - u_d)$$
$$\times\sqrt{\frac{1}{2k(T_u/m_1 + T_d/m_2)}}, \qquad \times\sqrt{\frac{1}{2k(T_u/m_2 + T_d/m_1)}}.$$

The mean free paths of each species in the mixtures are given by

$$\lambda_1 = \frac{1}{\pi\{n_0^{(I)}\sigma_1{}^2\sqrt{2} + n_0^{(II)}\sigma_{12}^2\sqrt{m_0/m_2}\}},$$

$$\lambda_2 = \frac{1}{\pi\{n_0^{(II)}\sigma_2{}^2\sqrt{2} + n_0^{(I)}\sigma_{12}^2\sqrt{m_0/m_1}\}},$$

where $m_0 = m_1 + m_2$. We may define another length λ as follows:

$$\lambda = \frac{n_0^{(I)}\lambda_1 + n_0^{(II)}\lambda_2}{n_0^{(I)} + n_0^{(II)}} = \frac{K}{2\pi n_0^{(I)}\sigma^2},$$

where

$$K = \frac{\sqrt{M_1} + 2\sqrt{2M_1M_2} + \sqrt{M_2}}{(\sqrt{2M_1} + 1)(\sqrt{2M_2} + 1)}.$$

We may now introduce dimensionless variables $v_1 = n_u^{(I)}/n_0^{(I)}$, $v_2 = n_u^{(II)}/n_0^{(II)}$ and $x' = x/\lambda$. In order to simplify the calculations, we assume the following:
(1) The number density of each species ahead of the shock wave is the same:

$$n_0^{(I)} = n_0^{(II)};$$

(2) The diameters of the two component molecules are the same:

$$\sigma_1 = \sigma_2 = \sigma_{12};$$

(3) Both component molecules have no internal degrees of freedom: $\gamma = 5/3$.
Eliminating $n_d^{(I)}$ and $n_d^{(II)}$ by the use of Eq. (13), and employing the results of Eq. (17) Eq. (14) ends up as

$$\frac{dv_1}{dx'} + A_1v_1(1 - v_1) + B_1v_1(1 - v_2) + C_1v_2(1 - v_1) = 0,$$

$$\frac{dv_2}{dx'} + A_2v_2(1 - v_2) + B_2v_2(1 - v_1) + C_2v_1(1 - v_2) = 0,$$

$$(18)$$

where the coefficients are expressed in terms of Eq. (12) as follows:

$$A_1 = \frac{\sqrt{3}K}{\sqrt{5\pi}M_1^{3/2}(10 - (3/M_1))} \frac{(5M^4 + 30M^2 - 3)^{3/2}}{(3 + M^2)(M^2 - 1)(5M^2 + 3)} \Theta(s_1),$$

$$B_1 = \frac{\sqrt{3M_2}K}{\sqrt{5\pi}(10 - (3/M_1))} \frac{\{5M^4 + (14 + 16\,m_2/m_1)M^2 - 3\}^{3/2}}{(3 + M^2)(M^2 - 1)(5M^2 + 3)} \Phi(s_{ud_1}, \omega_1, \eta_1),$$

$$C_1 = \frac{\sqrt{3}M_2{}^2K}{\sqrt{5\pi}M_1^{3/2}(10 - (3/M_1))} \frac{\{5M^4 + (14 + 16\,m_1/m_2)M^2 - 3\}^{3/2}}{(3 + M^2)(M^2 - 1)(5M^2 + 3)}$$

$$\times \Phi(s_{ud_2}, \omega_2, -\eta_2),$$

$$A_2 = \frac{\sqrt{3}K}{\sqrt{5\pi}M_2^{3/2}(10 - (3/M_2))} \frac{(5M^4 + 30M^2 - 3)^{3/2}}{(3 + M^2)(M^2 - 1)(5M^2 + 3)} \Theta(s_2),$$

$$B_2 = \frac{\sqrt{3M_1}K}{\sqrt{5\pi}(10 - (3/M_2))} \frac{\{5M^4 + (14 + 16\,m_1/m_2)M^2 - 3\}^{3/2}}{(3 + M^2)(M^2 - 1)(5M^2 + 3)} \Phi(s_{ud_2}, \omega_3, \eta_3),$$

$$C_2 = \frac{\sqrt{3}M_1{}^2 K}{\sqrt{5\pi}M_2^{3/2}(10-(3/M_2))} \frac{\{5M^4+(14+16\,m_2/m_1)M^2-3\}^{3/2}}{(3+M^2)(M^2-1)(5M^2+3)}$$
$$\times \, \Phi(s_{ud_1}, \omega_4, -\eta_4),$$

$$s_1 = \sqrt{15M_1}\,\frac{M^2-1}{\sqrt{5M^4+30M^2-3}}, \qquad s_2 = \sqrt{15M_2}\,\frac{M^2-1}{\sqrt{5M^4+30M^2-3}},$$

$$s_{ud_1} = (M^2-1)\,\frac{15M_2}{5M^4+(14+16\,m_2/m_1)M^2-3},$$

$$s_{ud_2} = (M^2-1)\,\frac{15M_1}{5M^4+(14+16\,m_1/m_2)M^2-3},$$

$$\omega_1 = \frac{16M^2}{M_1\{5M^4+(14+16\,m_2/m_1)M^2-3\}},$$

$$\omega_2 = \frac{(3+M^2)(5M^2-1)}{M_2\{5M^4+(14+16\,m_1/m_2)M^2-3\}},$$

$$\omega_3 = \frac{16M^2}{M_2\{5M^4+(14+16\,m_1/m_2)M^2-3\}},$$

$$\omega_4 = \frac{(3+M^2)(5M^2-1)}{M_1\{5M^4+(14+16\,m_2/m_1)M^2-3\}},$$

$$\eta_1 = \frac{8}{3M_2}\left(\frac{M^2}{M^2-1}\right), \qquad\qquad \eta_2 = \frac{2}{3M_2}\left(\frac{3+M^2}{M^2-1}\right),$$

$$\eta_3 = \frac{8}{3M_1}\left(\frac{M^2}{M^2-1}\right), \qquad\qquad \eta_4 = \frac{2}{3M_1}\left(\frac{3+M^2}{M^2-1}\right).$$

The boundary conditions (2) becomes

$$v_1, v_2 \to 1 \quad\text{as}\quad x' \to -\infty,$$
$$v_1, v_2 \to 0 \quad\text{as}\quad x' \to \infty. \tag{19}$$

The point $x' = 0$ may be chosen arbitrarily. We shall choose it at $v_1 = \frac{1}{2}$.

IV. Results

The independent variable x' may be eliminated by dividing the second equation in Eq. (18) by the first:

$$\frac{dv_2}{dv_1} = \frac{A_2 v_2(1-v_2)+B_2 v_2(1-v_1)+C_2 v_1(1-v_2)}{A_1 v_1(1-v_1)+B_1 v_1(1-v_2)+C_1 v_2(1-v_1)}. \tag{20}$$

Equation (20) has singular points at $(v_1 = 0, v_2 = 0)$ and $(v_1 = 1, v_2 = 1)$, which correspond to the conditions upstream and downstream of the shock wave, respectively.

Numerical calculations were carried out for mixtures of xenon-129–xenon-132 $(m_1/m_2 = 0.9772)$, argon-36–argon-40 $(m_1/m_2 = 0.9000)$, neon-argon $(m_1/m_2 = 0.5053)$, and helium-argon $(m_1/m_2 = 0.1002)$.

TABLE I

Coefficients of Eq. (18)

			M		
	2	4	6	8	10
		(a) For Xe^{129}-Xe^{132}			
A_1	0.49019	0.80548	0.88592	0.91635	0.93089
B_1	1.48346	1.84164	1.91984	1.96108	1.97650
C_1	−1.00364	−1.05534	−1.06459	−1.06770	−1.06905
A_2	0.46862	0.77122	0.84867	0.87799	0.89202
B_2	1.41412	1.76460	1.85057	1.88279	1.89802
C_2	−0.93572	−0.97536	−0.97607	−0.98327	−0.98408
		(b) For Ar^{36}-Ar^{40}			
A_1	0.53555	0.87754	0.96431	0.99704	1.01268
B_1	1.62756	2.00125	2.09000	2.12295	2.13861
C_1	−1.14563	−1.22269	−1.23869	−1.24441	−1.24708
A_2	0.43529	0.71820	0.79105	0.81868	0.83192
B_2	1.30556	1.64335	1.72752	1.75927	1.77444
C_2	−0.83015	−0.85141	−0.85250	−0.85254	−0.85238
		(c) For Ne-Ar			
A_1	2.13777	3.43712	3.75177	3.86840	3.92357
B_1	6.51404	7.38326	7.51684	7.55568	7.57174
C_1	−5.96477	−6.90604	−7.14909	−7.24222	−7.28703
A_2	0.30328	0.50898	0.56374	0.58477	0.59488
B_2	0.84071	1.10957	1.18058	1.20783	1.22093
C_2	−0.40737	−0.36396	−0.34812	−0.34151	−0.33823
		(d) For He-Ar			
A_1	−0.16088	−0.25491	−0.27430	−0.28102	−0.28420
B_1	−0.45913	−0.39524	−0.35141	−0.32947	−0.31776
C_1	0.67376	0.84686	0.89349	0.91129	0.92005
A_2	0.15210	0.33112	0.36986	0.38494	0.39229
B_2	0.31767	0.43929	0.47211	0.48464	0.49060
C_2	−0.09320	−0.05371	−0.04077	−0.03522	−0.03253

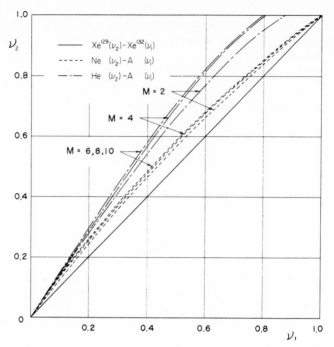

FIG. 1. Solutions of Eq. (20). KEY: —, Xe^{129} (v_2)-$Xe^{132}(v_1)$; - - -, $Ne(v_2)$-$Ar(v_1)$; – – –, $He(v_2)$-$Ar(v_1)$.

The coefficients of Eq. (18) or Eq. (20) for these mixtures are given in Table I. The solutions of Eq. (20) are shown in Fig. 1. For the first three mixtures, the point $(v_1 = 0, v_2 = 0)$ is a nodal point and the point $(v_1 = 1, v_2 = 1)$ is a saddle point. The solution for the mixture of xenon-129–xenon-132 is a straight line, with a slope of approximately 45°. In other words, this mixture does not separate; it behaves like a simple gas. The other mixtures show some separation. The effect of the Mach number on the separation decreases for Mach numbers higher than four.

After the solution to Eq. (20) is obtained, Eq. (18) can be solved with the boundary condition $v_1 = \frac{1}{2}$ at $x' = 0$. The boundary condition for v_2 at $x' = 0$ is obtained from the results of Eq. (20).

The results are shown in Fig. 2 (xenon-129–xenon-132), Fig. 3 (argon-36–argon-40), Fig. 4 (neon-argon), and Fig. 5 (helium-argon). From these results, the number density profiles in the shock wave are calculated with the aid of Eqs. (3) and (4) (Figs. 6–9).

The shock thickness based upon the maximum slope is defined by

$$\frac{\delta}{\lambda} = \frac{n_{max} - n_{min}}{(dn/dx')_{max}} = \frac{(n^{(I)} + n^{(II)})_{max} - (n^{(I)} + n^{(II)})_{min}}{(d(n^{(I)} + n^{(II)})/dx')_{max}}.$$

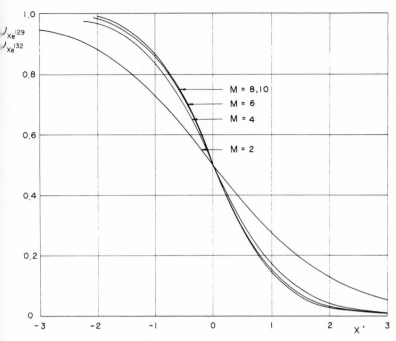

FIG. 2. Solution of Eq. (18) for Xe^{129}-Xe^{132}.

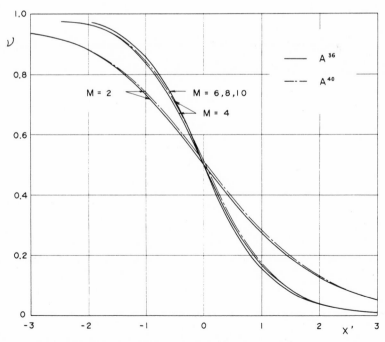

FIG. 3. Solution of Eq. (18) for Ar^{36}-Ar^{40}. KEY: —, Ar^{36}; — – —, Ar^{40}.

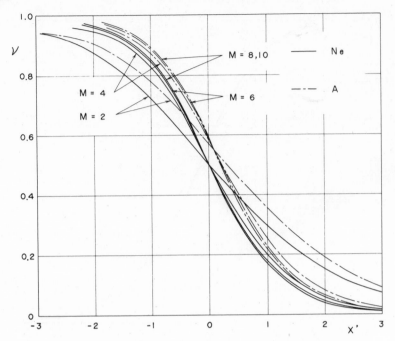

FIG. 4. Solution of Eq. (18) for Ne-Ar. KEY: —, Ne; — – —, Ar.

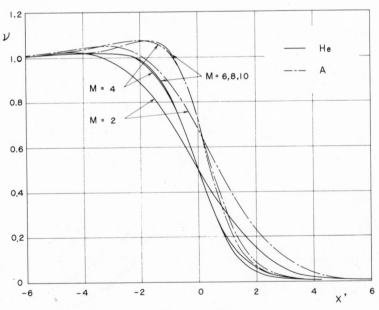

FIG. 5. Solution of Eq. (18) for He-Ar. KEY: —, He; — – —, Ar.

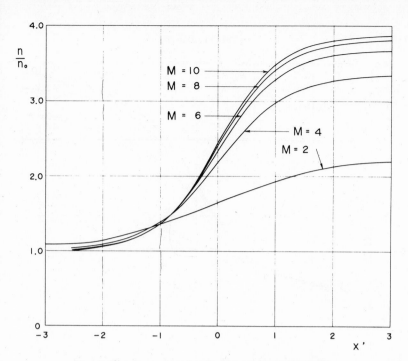

FIG. 6. Density profile of a shock wave for Xe^{129}-Xe^{132}.

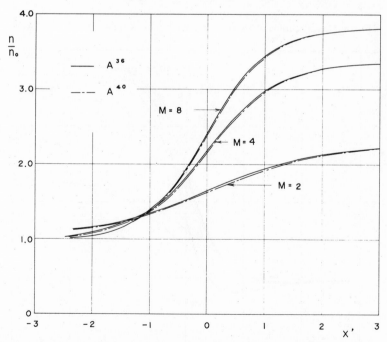

FIG. 7. Density profile of a shock wave for Ar^{36}-Ar^{40}. KEY: ——, Ar^{36}; —— ——, Ar^{40}.

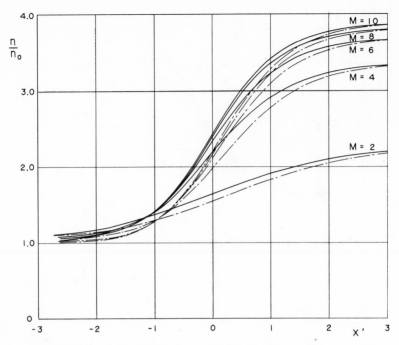

FIG. 8. Density profile of a shock wave for Ne-Ar. KEY: —, Ne; — — —, Ar.

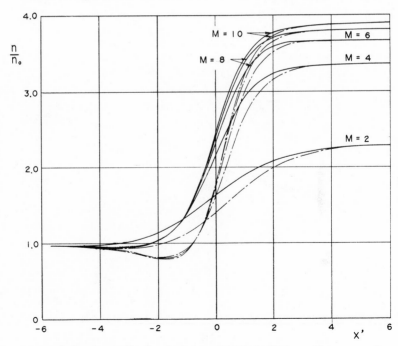

FIG. 9. Density profile of a shock wave for He-Ar. Key: —, He; — — —, Ar.

As seen from the figures which show the density distributions at each Mach number, the maximum slopes of the density profile for each component in a mixture are almost equal. Furthermore, the limiting values at infinity converge to the same values as those for a simple gas. Consequently large broadening of the shock thickness cannot be expected.

As shown in Fig. 9, the density profile of the helium-argon mixture has valleys; this causes the acceleration of both particles somewhere in the shock wave. [See Eq. (13).] If only the light particles pile up by collisions with heavy particles, the density profile for the lighter particles should exhibit hills. The strange feature in Fig. 9 may be caused by the fact that application of the Rankine-Hugoniot relation is inadequate. In other words, when the mass ratio of the constituent molecules differs largely from unity, more variables than just $n_u^{(i)}$ and $n_d^{(i)}$ may be necessary. The technique used in this paper should be valid in the case of nearly equal masses because the usual Rankine-Hugoniot relation is satisfied in the shock wave when the masses of constituent molecules are the same.

ACKNOWLEDGMENT

The author wishes to acknowledge his thanks to Dr. K. Takao for many valuable discussions and continuous encouragement. He is also indebted to the Mitsubishi Heavy Industry Company for use of their analog computer.

REFERENCES

Chapman, S., and Cowling, T. G. (1939). "The Mathematical Theory of Non-Uniform Gases." Cambridge Univ. Press, London and New York.
Cowling, T. G. (1942). *Phil. Mag.* **33**, 61.
Dyakov, S. P. (1954). *Zh. Eksp. i Teoret. Fiz.* **27**, 728.
Grewal, M. S. (1962). "Shock Wave Structure in Partially Ionized Gases." Univ. of California, Tech. Rept. HE-150-198.
Mott-Smith, H. M. (1951). *Phys. Rev.* **82**, 885.
Sherman, F. S. (1955). "A Low-Density Wind-Tunnel Study of Shock Wave Structure and Relaxation Phenomena in Gases." NACA TN 3298.
Sherman, F. S., and Talbot, L. (1959). "Structure of Weak Shock Wave in a Monatomic Gas." NASA Memo 12-14-58 W.
Sherman, F. S. (1960). *J. Fluid Mech.* **8**, 465.
Tidman, D. A. (1958). *Phys. Rev.* **111**, 1439.

Argon Shock Structure

MORTON CAMAC

Avco-Everett Research Laboratory, Everett, Massachusetts

The density variation during translational adjustment in argon shock waves was measured in the shock velocity range from 1.5 to 3.2 km/sec, corresponding to Mach 5 to 10. The major equipment used consisted of a 24-in. diameter shock tube and an electron gun. The density variation was determined by the single (Rutherford) scattering intensity of a well-collimated ($\frac{1}{2}$ mm diameter) 100 keV electron beam. Shock curvature effects were minimized by making measurements over less than one-inch height of the shock front at the shock tube center. The density variation through the shock front and the downstream density was compared directly to the upstream density. The scattered beam intensity is proportional to gas density. Thus, each oscillogram gives a direct display of a self-calibrated density variation with time. The shock density thicknesses based on the maximum slope vary from 4 to 5 times the upstream mean free path. The experimental shock density thicknesses are in excellent agreement with the Mott-Smith bimodal theory and over 1.5 thicker than the Navier-Stokes predictions.

I. Introduction

There are an increasing number of theoretical papers on shock wave structure. Shock structure predictions using the Navier-Stokes equations have been evaluated for various assumptions of the interatomic force laws (Becker, 1922; Gilbarg and Paolucci, 1953). The Boltzmann transport equation was used by Mott-Smith (1951) to investigate the shock structure. He introduced the bimodal distribution function in the shock wave; the gas was a two-component mixture, one at the downstream and the other at the upstream temperature. The bimodal model has been solved for a variety of interparticle force laws (Muckenfuss, 1962), and for more complicated distribution functions (Ziering *et al.*, 1961; Weitzsch, 1961). Shock structure for argon was determined with the BGK approximation to the Boltzmann equation (Liepmann *et al.*, 1962; Chahine and Narasimha, 1965; Anderson and Macomber,

240

1965). Other solutions of the Boltzmann equation were obtained with the thirteen-moment approximation (Grad, 1952), and the Monte-Carlo method (Haviland, 1963; Hicks, 1963).

Measurements of the argon shock thickness by various techniques have been reported in the literature. At low shock velocities, Sherman (1954) determined shock thickness in argon with the hot wire technique. The optical reflectivity method (Cowan and Hornig, 1950; Greene et al., 1951) was used to investigate shock thickness in argon up to Mach 4.85 (Linzer and Hornig, 1963). Ballard and Venable (1958) and Duff and Webster (1959) reported use of an electron beam to investigate shock structure; the beam transmission through the shock tube was measured. In the present experiment, essentially the same electron beam technique is employed except the large angle scattering of the electron beam was measured. Such differential scattering measurements permit (1) operation at lower gas densities, and (2) use of only a portion of the electron beam path in the shock tube.

Our previous work (Camac, 1963, 1964) consisted of preliminary measurements. Only the gross features of the density profile were obtained, since there were several important sources of error inherent in the system. In this work, these sources of error were minimized, thereby permitting description of the density profile. Section II discusses the theory of the experiment and the experimental measurements. In Section III, our results are compared with the work of others.

II. Theory of Experiment

A. Electron Beam Technique

The experimental arrangement employed is illustrated schematically in Fig. 1. The electron beam with approximately 10^5 eV kinetic energy traverses the shock tube perpendicular to the axis of the tube. The beam attenuation is small at low ($< 100 \mu$ Hg) densities. Only a small fraction, less than 1%, of the beam is scattered through a large angle. A portion of the scattered beam is detected by a scintillation photomultiplier system. This system is placed downstream of the beam and consequently does not affect the gas density at the scattering position. This detection system has great sensitivity because it produces a measurable signal for each electron scattered into the detector. Thus, the observed signal noise is due to the statistical fluctuations (Poisson distribution) in the number of electrons entering the detector.

The effects of shock curvature were minimized by using only the central portion of the shock tube. A 3.5-in. diameter electron gun extended 7.5-in. into the shock tube. A " drift " tube (0.125-in. outside diameter, 3.75-in. long)

passed the beam from the gun to the shock tube causing only a small disturbance to the flow. A $\frac{1}{32}$-in. diameter aperture, placed at the end of the tube,
served two purposes. It defined the beam size and also restricted the flow of
gas from the shock tube to the gun, maintaining a pressure ratio of 10^{-3}.

The scattered beam detection system was placed symmetrically downstream
of the primary electron beam. The detector consisted of a liquid scintillator

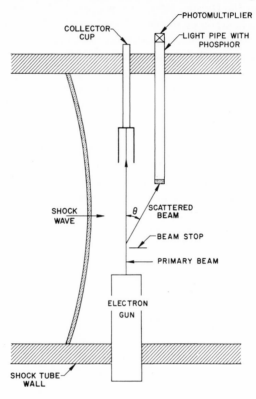

FIG. 1. Schematic arrangement for electron beam scattering measurements.

covered with a 0.8-mil thick aluminium foil, which also shielded against
visible light from the shock tube. A 0.375-in. diameter "collector cup" was
used to measure the primary beam. The electron beam striking the inner wall
of the drift tube was also measured, and was from 2 to 5 times the current
to the collector cup.

A 10 mil thick razor blade was used for a beam stop to define the region
from which the detector could observe scattering. The edge of the drift tube
was a strong source of scattered electrons, but this beam was masked by the
beam stop. The distance from the beam stop to the drift tube was 0.75- in.,

and from the beam stop to the detector ranged from 2 to 3 in. The electron beam scattered from the gas all along its path in the shock tube, but only the region between the beam stop and the detector could scatter into the detector. Because of the strong angular dependence of the scattering, most of the detected electrons came from the vicinity of the beam stop.

Flat plates with knife edges were placed on the detector assembly and the electron gun to isolate the flow around them from the region where beam scattering to the detector occurred. The gun required a 1-in. high plate in order to delay the aerodynamic disturbances from the gun for 100 microseconds.

B. Experimental Measurements

The shock tube was operated with pressure breaks and the driver gas consisted of hydrogen gas diluted with nitrogen. Measurements were obtained with initial argon pressures of 0.030, 0.045 and 0.060 Torr. Oscillograms illustrating the experimental measurements are shown in Fig. 2. The operation

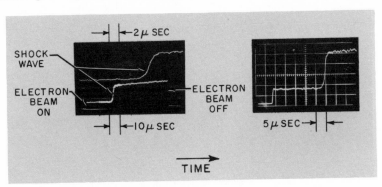

FIG. 2. Oscillograms illustrating the variation of the scattered electron beam with time. The electron beam is turned on and off during the 10 μsec per division sweep. The 2 μsec per division sweep shows an enlargement of the shock wave. Shock velocity $= 1.54$ mm/ μsec; initial argon pressure $= 0.060$ Torr.

of the system is shown on the 10 microsecond per division sweep. The electron beam was turned on several microseconds after the start of the trace but before shock passage. The initial voltage deflection, say V_1, occurred before shock passage while the gas still had the upstream density ρ_1. During shock passage and subsequently, the gas density changed and the scattered electron beam followed proportionally. The ratio of the density to the initial density ρ/ρ_1 is equal to the ratio of the scope deflection V/V_1. Thus, each experimental run is self-calibrating giving the density variation in terms of the initial density. For each run, three traces at different sweep speeds were taken of the same photomultiplier output. We thus were able to obtain several features of the density variation.

The gross density variation was given by the 10 microsecond per division sweep. Note that the beam was turned off before the end of the sweep and that the signal drops to zero. This indicates that there were no light leaks into the detection system from the luminous gases. This also gave a direct measure of the response time of the entire phosphor electron beam system, which was 0.15 μsec. The 5 μsec per division sweep was used to measure the density ratio across the shock, as well as to follow the density variation downstream of the shock. The 2 μsec per division sweep was used to determine the shock profile and the maximum density slope.

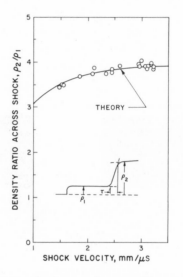

Fig. 3. Density ratio across shock waves in argon. The points are the electron beam measurements. The theory curve is for argon with $\gamma = 5/3$. The insert illustrates how the density ratio and the shock transit time were determined.

The observed density ratio across the shock is compared to the theoretical predictions for argon in Fig. 3. Because of the linearity of the system, the ratio of the upstream and downstream conditions, V_2/V_1 is equal to ρ_2/ρ_1. The value of V_2 just after shock passage was used before the variation of the downstream density became significant. Note that the agreement between experiment and theory is within the accuracy of the measurements, of the order of 5%.

The maximum slope thickness is obtained from the time interval τ between the intersection of the maximum slope with the upstream and downstream voltages, i.e.,

$$\tau = \frac{V_2 - V_1}{(dV/dt)_{max}}. \tag{1}$$

Figure 4 presents the measured shock transit times τ (i.e., the time for the shock to cross the electron beam) defined by Eq. (1) as a function of the shock velocity.

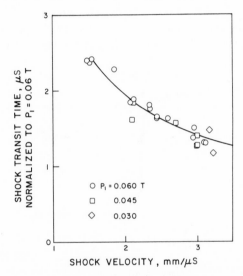

FIG. 4. The measured shock transit time τ based on the maximum density slope, see Fig. 3. The time is normalized by the scaling factor ($P_1/0.06$ Torr.).

Several important measurements are required in order to evaluate the accuracy of the shock transit time τ. These are (1) electronic rise time, (2) size of the primary beam, (3) beam blowup due to the multiple scattering, (4) beam attenuation due to absorption and scattering; (5) gas disturbances produced by the beam stop and the knife edged plates on the gun and detector; and (6) the effects of the shock tube side wall boundary layer.

The detection system response time was 0.15 μsec, and the shock transit time was over 1.2 μsec; the correction to the maximum density slope due to response time was less than 5%. The correction due to the primary beam width was less than 1%; the beam width was $\frac{1}{2}$ mm, while the shock thickness was over 3.5 mm.

Beam blowup due to multiple scattering was estimated in our previous report (Camac, 1963), using the multiple scattering theory for high-energy electrons (Rossi and Greisen, 1941). Experimental measurements of the beam width were made at 4 inches from the drift tube and at 1 Torr argon pressure. The theory predicted a multiple scattering full width of 14 mm, while we find 1 mm. The effects of screening by orbital electrons becomes more important for 100 kV electrons than this theory predicts. The small amount of multiple scattering is very fortunate for this experiment, as the directionality of the primary beam remains constant and is determined only by the electron optics.

It can be shown that disturbances from the beam stop and from the knife edged plates on the electron gun and detector do not affect the gas density along the primary beam path where scattering to the detector occurs. The downstream gas is choked by the insertion of the electron gun and detector

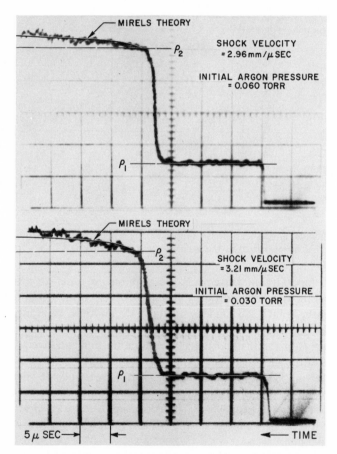

FIG. 5. Comparison of the measured downstream density variation with the predictions of Mirels. The ρ_2 line is the theoretical value. Mirels' curves were adjusted in time for the best fit.

assemblies in the shock tube, and a standing shock starts to develop across the shock tube. However, the plates separate the flow around these parts from the central region for over 100 μsec. The choking occurs along the outer regions immediately, but the central region remains unaffected until after the experimental measurements have been completed.

The variation of the density in the downstream region, see Fig. 2, is mainly due to the effects of the side wall boundary layer. The downstream gas was cooled by the wall, causing the density to increase. Mirels (1963) evaluated the effects of the side wall boundary layer on the free stream. Figure 5 shows a comparison of our data taken at initial pressures of 0.03 and 0.06 Torr with the predictions of Mirels (1963), and there is substantial agreement. At pressures above 0.06 Torr the effect of the side wall boundary layer on the shock profile is small.

We now summarize the discussions of the correction to the data. The primary beam is limited by the electron optics of the system. Beam attenuation and beam blowup by multiple scattering is negligible even up to pressures of 1 Torr. The shock thickness is at least 7 times larger than the width of the primary beam, and the corrections for the beam width is negligible. The correction due to the response time of the photomultiplier system is never larger than 5%. The major uncertainty introduced into the density profiles is due to the side wall boundary layer. The observed density profiles are in substantial agreement with the theory of Mirels (1963).

III. Data Analysis

Experimental measurements of the maximum slope thickness are usually compared to the upstream mean free path, λ_1, which is given by the relation

$$\lambda_1 = \frac{16}{5} \frac{\mu}{n\sqrt{2\pi mkT}}. \tag{2}$$

μ is the viscosity; n the number density; m, the mass; k, Boltzmann constant, and T, the temperature. $\mu = 2.27 \times 10^{-4}$ poise for argon at 300°K. The mean free path ahead of the shock λ_1 becomes $(54.0/P_1)$ mm, where the temperature is as taken at 300°K, and P_1 is the initial pressure in microns Hg. Figure 6 shows the reciprocal shock density thickness Λ in terms of the mean free path ahead of the shock: $\lambda_1/\Lambda = (54.0/u_s\tau P_1)$. Also shown are the experimental results of Linzer and Hornig (1963). The theoretical curves shown are for the Mott-Smith bimodal distribution (Muckenfuss, 1962), the Navier-Stokes theory (Liepmann et al., 1962; Chahine and Narasimha, 1965), and the BGK approximation to the Boltzmann equation (Anderson, 1963; Anderson and

Macomber, 1965). Experimental measurements of the thermal conductivity of argon can be fit with the power law T^v temperature dependence. Up to 4000°K, the temperature dependence is $v = 0.81 \pm 0.02$ (Sturtevant, 1964). Amdur and Mason's work from 1500°K to 15,000°K can be fit with $v = 0.75$.

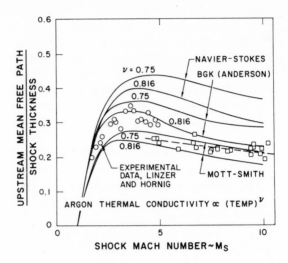

FIG. 6. The reciprocal shock density thickness for argon based on the mean free path ahead of the shock. □, this experiment; O, data of Linzer and Hornig.

Between 20,000°K and 75,000°K, Camac and Feinberg (1963) measure $v = 0.76 \pm 0.03$. Theoretical calculations based on values of $v = 0.75$ and 0.816, and Prandtl numbers of $\frac{2}{3}$ for Mott-Smith (Muckenfuss, 1962) and Navier-Stokes (Liepmann *et al.*, 1962; Chahine and Narasimha, 1965) and unity for BGK (Anderson, 1963) are shown in Fig. 6. The experimental data are in good agreement with the Mott-Smith bimodal theory. Argon shock waves are about 50% thicker than the Navier-Stokes prediction, and 20% thicker than the predictions of Anderson (1963). There is a 30% discrepancy between the results of this experiment and that of Linzer and Hornig.

The electron beam technique has sufficient resolution to make detailed measurements of the density profile through the shock. Preliminary comparisons show that the experimental density profiles agree with the Mott-Smith bimodal predictions, and do match the Navier-Stokes profiles.

Acknowledgment

This work was supported jointly by Headquarters, Ballistic Systems Division, Air Force Systems Command, U.S. Air Force under Contract No. AF 04(694)-414, and Advanced Research Projects Agency monitored by the Army Missile Command, U.S. Army under Contract No. DA-19-020-AMC-0210 (part of Project DEFENDER).

REFERENCES

Anderson, D. G. (1963). Ph.D. Thesis, Harvard University, Cambridge, Mass.

Anderson, D. G., and Macomber, H. K. (1965). This volume, p. 96.

Ballard, H. N., and Venable, D. (1958). *Phys. Fluids* **1**, 225.

Becker, R. (1922). *Z. Physik* **8**, 321.

Camac, M. (1963). AIAA Aerospace Sciences Meeting, New York, January 20-22. Preprint No. 64-35.

Camac, M. (1964). *Phys. Fluids* **7**, 1076.

Camac, M., and Feinberg, R. M. (1963). Avco-Everett Research Laboratory Research Rept. 168 [(1965) *J. Fluid Mech.* **20** (to be published)].

Chahine, M. T., and Narasimha, R. (1965). This volume, p. 140.

Cowan, G. R., and Hornig, D. F. (1950). *J. Chem. Phys.* **18**, 1008.

Duff, R. E., and Webster, W. M. (1959). *Bull. Am. Phys. Soc.* **4**, 283.

Gilbarg, D., and Paolucci, D. (1953). *J. Rat. Mech. Anal* **2**, 617.

Grad, H. (1952). *Communs. Pure Appl. Meth* **5**, 257.

Greene, E. F., Cowan, G. R., and Hornig, D. F. (1951). *J. Chem. Phys.* **19**, 427.

Haviland, J. K. (1963). *In* " Rarefied Gas Dynamics " (J. A. Laurmann, ed.), Vol. 1, p. 274, Academic Press, New York.

Hicks, B. L. (1963). Univ. of Illinois, Coordinated Sci. Lab. Rep. I-122.

Liepmann, H. W., Narasimha, R., and Chahine, M. T. (1962). *Phys. Fluids* **5**, 1313.

Linzer, M., and Hornig, D. F. (1963). *Phys. Fluids* **6**, 1661.

Mirels, H. (1963). *Bull. Am. Phys. Soc.* **8**, 437.

Mott-Smith, H. M. (1951). *Phys. Rev.* **82**, 885.

Muckenfuss, C. (1962). *Phys. Fluids* **5**, 1325.

Rossi, B., and Greisen, K. (1941). *Revs. Mod. Phys.* **13**, 240.

Sherman, F. S. (1954). Univ. of California, Inst. of Eng. Research Rep. No. HE-150-122.

Sturtevant, B. (1964). *Bull. Am. Phys. Soc.* **9**, 583.

Weitzsch, F. (1961). *Ann. Physik* **7**, 403.

Ziering, S., Ek, F., and Koch, P. (1961). *Phys. Fluids* **4**, 975.

Density Distribution in Shock Waves Traveling in Rarefied Monatomic Gases

F. SCHULTZ-GRUNOW AND A. FROHN
Technische Hochschule Aachen, Germany

The density distributions within shock fronts in argon and helium are determined in a 4.9 × 4.9 cm. shock tube using the attenuation of an electron beam. Shock Mach numbers are produced over a range from 1.65 to 9.5. The initial pressures are chosen at about 5×10^{-2} Torr in Ar and at 2×10^{-1} Torr in He to yield the same mean free path in both gases. The curvature of the shock wave is determined by an array of resistance thermometers mounted on a glass plate spanning the shock tube. The effects of shock curvature and finite width of the electron beam are considered theoretically and shown to be acceptably small. Comparison of the experimental results with various available theories shows best agreement for Mach numbers above 2 with the Mott-Smith theory.

I. Introduction

Considerable theoretical and experimental work has been devoted to the structure of shock waves. The theoretical results relying on continuum mechanics or molecular kinetics are showing remarkable discrepancies. On the other hand the experimental work utilizing thermocouples or the reflection of light beams by the shock do not yield absolute quantities or have to assume special density profiles.

The measurements of the density distribution, which will be described here, were performed in a shock tube. In such a facility the shock Mach number can be easily varied by using different driver gases, but the test times are so short that special experimental equipment has to be developed. To achieve sufficiently thick shock layers low pressures have to be utilized with an upper limit of 10^{-1} mm Hg in the low-pressure section of the shock tube. This low pressure emphasizes the effects of the boundary layer and a serious reduction of the length of the uniform flow adjacent to the shock results. Earlier shock-wave measurements may be mentioned here (Venable and Kaplan, 1955; Ballard and Venable, 1958). In these experiments the curvature of the shock was not regarded. The experimental equipment which was used in the investigations to be presented here, will be described in the following sections.

II. Shock Tube

Density profiles of shock waves in argon and helium have been measured in a conventional shock tube with a high-pressure tube length of 1 meter and a low-pressure tube length of 4 meters. The cross section of both tubes was 49 mm × 49 mm. The volume of the low-pressure tube was increased by a dump tank. Thus the pressure in the shock tube after having performed an experiment did not exceed 140 mm Hg. Prior to a run the low-pressure section was

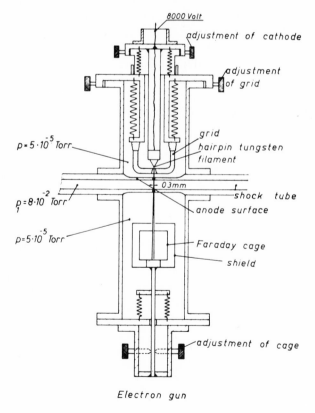

FIG. 1. Electron gun and detector.

pumped down to about $4 \cdot 10^{-4}$ mm Hg by means of a two-stage Roots pump and flushed with argon at 30 mm Hg. The leak rate after shutting off the Roots pump was less than 10^{-3} mm Hg/min. The pressure in the low-pressure section was measured by an Alphatron vacuum gauge that was calibrated against a McLeod gauge. The shock-wave velocity was measured by means of glow discharge probes (Lundquist, 1952; Grönig, 1960).

III. Electron Beam Densitometer

The present work utilizes the attenuation of an electron beam by molecules. An electron gun consisting of a hair pin cathode, a Wehnelt cylinder and an anode with an aperture of 0.3 mm was built providing an electron beam of 0.3 mm diameter and an electron energy of 2000 to 9000 eV (Fig. 1). The shock tube wall was used as the anode. The entrance aperture and the exit aperture which had the same diameter have to be regarded as leaks as the pressure in the electron gun and the detector had to be lower than 10^{-4} mm Hg in order to avoid the burning up of the cathode and additional scattering of the electrons respectively. This requirement was met by evacuating the electron gun and the detector housing continuously by means of two oil diffusion pumps, each having a pumping rate of 100 liters/sec. This resulted in a pressure, lower than 5×10^{-5} mm Hg.

The error due to the finite diameter of the electron beam was determined

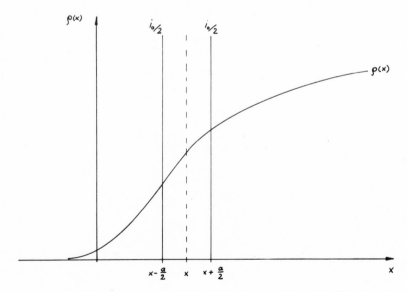

FIG. 2. Electron beam of diameter a replaced by two lines with distance a.

for an assumed Mott-Smith shock profile. For this calculation the electron beam of finite diameter a was replaced by two straight lines at a distance a in the plane through the beam center and the flow direction. An average of the expected signals along these two lines gives an upper estimate for the lack of definition (Fig. 2). In the equation for the difference, δi, between the (measured) average current $\bar{i}$ and the ideal current $i(x)$ for an infinitely thin beam,

$$\delta i = \bar{i} - i(x),$$

for $i(x)$ the current corresponding to the Mott-Smith profile is introduced

$$i = \frac{i_{00}}{1 + \exp(-4x/L)}.$$

In this equation L is the maximum slope shock thickness and i_{00} the current change across the shock. Then the errors of the measurements are obtained which are plotted in Fig. 3. In our case with an electron beam diameter of 0.3 mm and a shock wave thickness of 3 mm one finds that the maximum error is a fraction of 1 %.

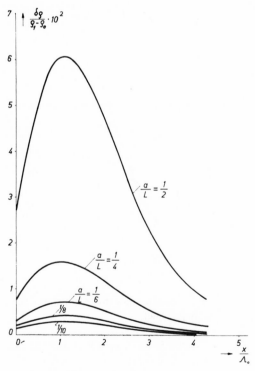

FIG. 3. Maximum error of measurement for the density due to the finite beam diameter a.

IV. Detector and Electronic Equipment

After crossing the shock tube the nondeflected electrons pass through a hole of 0.3 mm diameter situated exactly on the axis of the electron gun. The transmitted electron beam current was measured by a shielded Faraday cage that was grounded by a 5000-ohm resistor R. In order to suppress secondary

FIG. 4. Detector circuit with detector capacity C and resistor R.

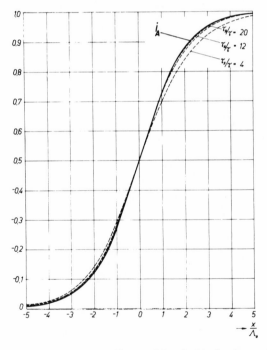

FIG. 5. Detector current i_A corresponding to Mott-Smith density profile (solid line). Influence of response time (dotted line).

electrons a voltage of -200 V was applied to the shield. The voltage drop across the 5000-ohm resistor is fed to a dc-coupled amplifier equipped with a cathode follower output located within 15 cm of the Faraday cage. The input capacity of this amplifier is 6 pF, and the effective capacity of the Faraday cage was $C = 26$ pF. This yielded a time constant of 1.3×10^{-7} sec. The applied electron beam currents ranged from 2×10^{-6} A to 20×10^{-6} A. Assuming that the current of the transmitted electron beam, i_A, has a time dependence corresponding to the Mott-Smith shock-wave profile, the current i_R flowing through the resistor R has been calculated for the equivalent circuit shown in Fig. 4. For the present working conditions the distortion of the signal is less than 0.5% as may be seen in Fig. 5. In this figure, the parameter τ_s represents the time needed by the shock-wave thickness to pass an electron

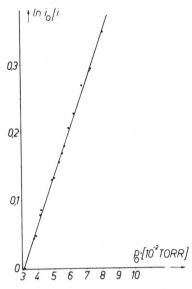

FIG. 6. Calibration of Electron gun for argon.

beam of infinitely small cross section, τ is the time constant $\tau = RC$, and i_R is indicated by the dashed curves. The calibration of the electron gun is shown in Fig. 6. The linear dependence is in agreement with the exponential absorption law.

V. Determination of the Shock-Wave Curvature

Previous measurements of the shape of the shock-wave indicate that shock waves traveling in shock tubes at low densities are curved (Duff and Young, 1961; Lin and Fyfe, 1961; Johnson, 1962). If this curvature is too large the electron densitometer will spuriously indicate a thicker shock and a distorted density profile.

This effect has been estimated by assuming parallel parabolic lines of constant density ρ. The average density, $\bar{\rho}$, which is measured by the electron beam densitometer along a straight path perpendicular to the shock tube axis, can be calculated for this model. In the calculation it has again been assumed that the shock profile has the form predicted by the Mott-Smith theory.

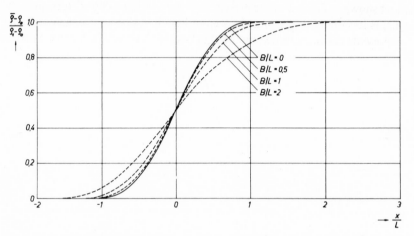

FIG. 7. Mott-Smith density profile approximated by two parabolas (solid line). Deviations caused by different shock curvatures (dotted lines). Present measurements $B/L \leq 1$.

A further approximation was made by fitting the Mott-Smith profile by two parabolas which is possible with a maximum error of only 2%. Profiles of $\bar{\rho}$ have been calculated for three values of B/L, where B is the axial extent of the shock wave due to its curvature (see Fig. 10). The results in Fig. 7 and Table I indicate that the error in the measurement of the density is not larger than 6% if $B/L \leqslant 1$.

TABLE I

DENSITY THICKNESS $\bar{L}$ OF CURVED SHOCK AND MAXIMUM
ERROR IN DENSITY MEASUREMENTS

B/L:	0	0.5	1	2
$\bar{L}$:	L	$1.14L$	$1.33L$	$1.78L$
$\lvert\bar{\rho}-\rho\rvert_{\max}$ (%):	0	1.5	6	16

The axial extent, B, of the shock was determined by resistance thermometers situated on a glass plate which was mounted perpendicular to the tube axis and covered half of the height and one third of the width of the shock tube cross section (Fig. 8). Reference thermometers were attached to the rear of the glass plate to compensate for line ripple. Oscillograms clearly showed the time

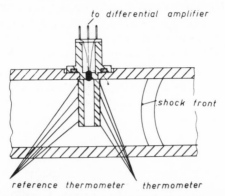

FIG. 8. Thin film resistor thermometers for the measurement of the shock-wave bulge.

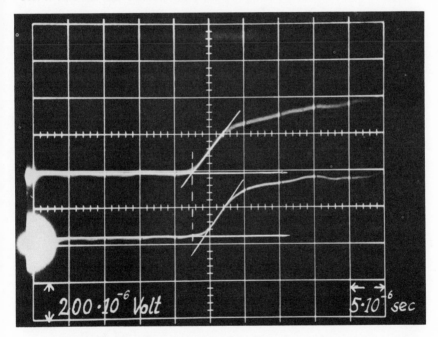

FIG. 9. Signals of the resistance thermometers. *Upper beam*: thermometer at center. *Lower beam*: thermometer near the wall.

delay between shock impingement at the center of the tube and that at a point 1.5 mm from the wall. (Fig. 9). The arrival time of the shock wave was defined as the intersection of the tangent at the inflection point and the zero line. The axial extent, B, was calculated from records like this and based on the assumption of a parabolic shape of the shock front. It may be mentioned that the geometric interpretation is simple, because the angle of incidence of the curved part of the shock on the plate is too small for a Mach reflection to develop (Schultz-Grunow, 1948).

Duff and Young (1961) and Johnson (1962) reported similar measurements performed with piezoelectric pressure gauges in circular tubes and they established empirical relations for the axial extent as a function of the mean free path and the Reynolds number respectively. Our results confirm Duff

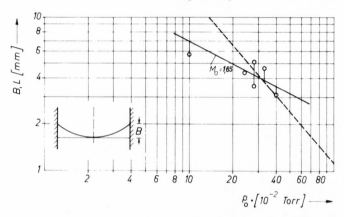

FIG. 10. Bulge B for $M_0 = 1.65$ and helium (solid line). Shock-wave thickness (dotted line).

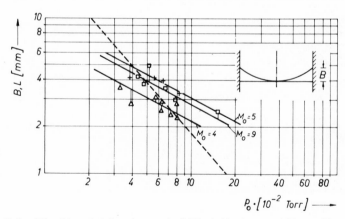

FIG. 11. Bulge B for $M_0 = 4, 5, 9$ and argon (solid line). Shock-wave thickness (dotted line).

and Young's expression, but a small additional Mach number dependence was found. The average values of B determined in our experiments are indicated as the solid straight lines in Fig. 10 for helium and Fig. 11 for argon.

Duff expressed B as follows:

$$B = b\sqrt{\Lambda_0 R}$$

where Λ_0 is the mean free path and R is the tube radius. From his experiments he deduced a value $b = 0.84$. For comparison purposes we list the values for b obtained in our experiments in Table II. Since our tube had a rectangular cross section we used the hydraulic radius for R.

TABLE II

VALUES OF CONSTANT b

	b	
M_0	Ar	He
1.65	—	1.22
4.0	0.65	—
5.0	0.88	—
9.5	0.82	—

The maximum slope shock thickness, L, is plotted in Figs. 10 and 11 as a dashed line. From the results of Fig. 7 we required $B/L \leqslant 1$ to ensure a small error due to shock curvature. The operating conditions of the shock tube to satisfy this condition can be found immediately from Figs. 10 and 11.

VI. Measurements

The shock-wave structure has been measured over the range $1.65 \leqslant M \leqslant 9.5$. Table III presents the experimental working conditions. Two examples of the oscillograms which were obtained with the attenuation experiment are shown

TABLE III

EXPERIMENTAL CONDITIONS

M_0	Driver gas	Driven gas	p_3 (atm)	$p_0/10^{-2}$ (mm Hg)
1.65	Ar	He	3	18–43
4.0	Ar	Ar	3	5
5.0	N_2	Ar	3	4.5–5.9
9.5	He	Ar	3	5.1–6.3

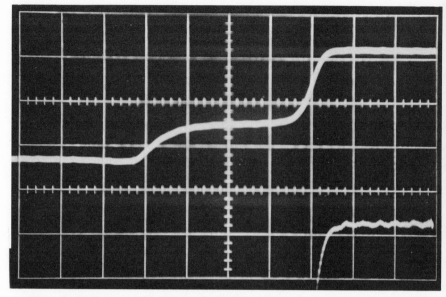

Fig. 12. Oscillogram with density distribution. Upper beam sensitivity is twice that of lower beam.

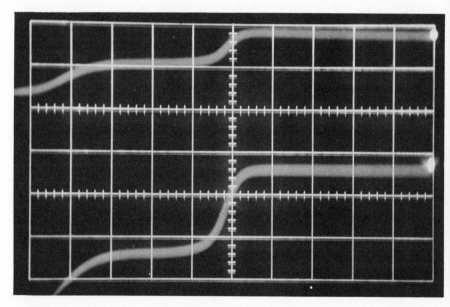

Fig. 13. Oscillogram of density distribution. Upper beam sensitivity is five times that of lower beam.

in Figs. 12 and 13. One unit along the abscissa corresponds to 5×10^{-6} sec. The time runs from left to right; the first deflection of the beam is caused by the density change in the shock, the second deflection by the contact surface. In Fig. 12 the upper beam has a twofold sensitivity compared with the lower beam. Special attention is paid to the low density region of the shock in Fig. 13, where the upper trace is five times more sensitive than the lower trace. Recent shock profile calculations based on the Krook model (Liepmann *et al.*, 1962) predicted a slow density increase in this region. However, it is clear from Fig. 13 that such a slow rise was not observed in our experiments.

The density profile was evaluated point by point from the oscillograms by means of the relation

$$\frac{\rho(x) - \rho_0}{\rho_1 - \rho_0} = \frac{\ln i(x) - \ln i_0}{\ln i_1 - \ln i_0}.$$

In this relation i_0 and i_1 are the transmitted current before and after passage of the shock, respectively. The results are plotted in Figs. 14 to 16 for three

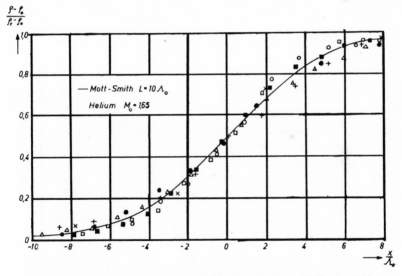

FIG. 14. Experimental results compared with Mott-Smith profile for $L = 10\Lambda_0$.

different Mach numbers. Fig. 14 corresponding to the lowest Mach number shows the thickest shock layer. A remarkably good fit to the Mott-Smith distribution is obtained if $L = 10\Lambda_0$ is used in this distribution. Here, Λ_0 is the mean free path ahead of the shock, which is 0.475 cm and 1.33 cm at 293°K and 10^{-2} mm Hg for argon and helium, respectively. In Figs. 15 and 16 the best fit to the Mott-Smith profiles was obtained for a thickness of $L = 4\Lambda_0$.

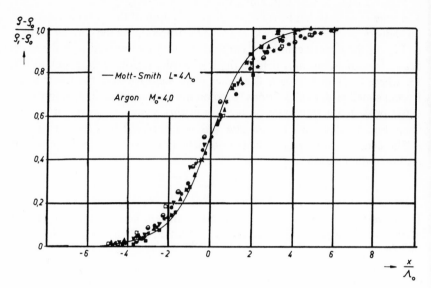

Fig. 15. Experimental results compared with Mott-Smith profile for $L = 4\Lambda_0$.

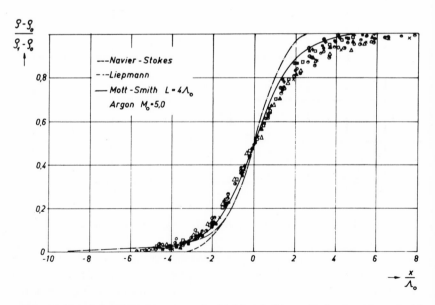

FIG. 16. Experimental results compared with Mott-Smith profile for $L = 4\Lambda_0$ and with Liepmann et al. (1962) (dotted line).

In Fig. 16, which corresponds to $M_0 = 5$ in argon, the Navier-Stokes solution and the calculation on the basis of the Krook Model (Liepmann *et al.*, 1962) are presented in addition to the Mott-Smith profile. The theoretical density profiles in this figure are deduced from the theoretical temperature and velocity distributions by means of the continuum equation. It is seen that the Mott-Smith profile provides the best fit to the experimental points. However, in Figs. 15 and 16 systematic deviations from the Mott-Smith profile do occur. They are similar to the deviations caused by the curvature of the shock layer. Also, the magnitude of the deviations agrees with the calculations for $0.5 \leqslant B/L \leqslant 1$.

TABLE IV

Times τ_1 Corresponding to Uniform Flow Region
and τ_s Corresponding to Shock Thickness

M_0	$p_0/10^{-2}$ (mm Hg)	$\tau_1/10^{-6}$ (sec)	τ_1/τ_s
1.65	18–43	35–50	10–20
4.0	4.9–5.1	15	5
5.0	4.5–5.9	8–15	2–6
9.5	5.1–6.3	6	0.5

Results for higher Mach numbers could not be obtained, because the length of the uniform region behind the shock was found to be too short. The maximum obtainable Mach number was $M_0 = 9.5$. Table IV shows the time τ_1,

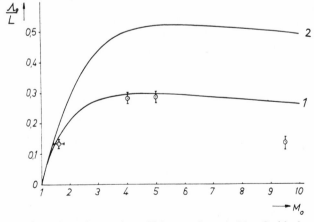

Fig. 17. Reciprocal maximum slope thickness. *Curve 1,* Mott-Smith theory; *Curve 2,* Navier-Stokes theory.

related to the length of the uniform flow, in terms of the time τ_s, related to the maximum slope shock thickness.

As was mentioned previously, the shock layer thickness was determined by the condition of the best fit to the Mott-Smith distribution. These values are plotted in Fig. 17 and compared with calculations on the basis of the Mott-Smith theory, and the continuum theory taking full account of the real temperature dependence of viscosity and the thermal conductivity (Schwartz and Hornig, 1963). The vertical bars at the points indicate the uncertainty due to the curvature and the horizontal bar indicates the maximum and minimum Mach number occurring on the curved shock layer. Our experimental results agree remarkably well with the calculations based on the Mott-Smith theory.

The results of this paper support the assumption of a Mott-Smith density distribution that was made by Linzer and Hornig (1963) in their determination of shock thickness by the light reflection method. Our measurements therefore confirms the previous measurements with this light reflection technique.

REFERENCES

Ballard, H. N., and Venable, D. (1958). *Phys. Fluids* 1, 225.

Duff, R. E. (1959). *Phys. Fluids* 2, 207.

Duff, R. E., and Young J. L. (1961). *Phys. Fluids* 4, 812.

Grönig, H. (1960). Thesis, Institut fur Mechanik, Rheinisch-Westfälische Technische Hochschule, Aachen.

Johnson, S. (1962). "Some Measurements of Curvature and Thickness of Reflecting Normal Shocks at Low Initial Pressures." California Inst. of Technol., Pasadena, California.

Liepmann, H. W., Narasimha, R., and Chahine, M. T. (1962). *Phys. Fluids* 5, 1313.

Lin, S. C., and Fyfe, W. I. (1961). *Phys. Fluids* 4, 238.

Linzer, M., and Hornig, D. F. (1963). *Phys. Fluids* 6, 1661.

Lundquist, G. A. (1952). U.S. Naval Ordnance Lab., Navard Rept. 2449.

Schultz-Grunow, F. (1948). *ZAMM* 28, 30.

Schwartz, L. M., and Hornig, D. F. (1963). *Phys. Fluids* 6, 1669.

Venable, D., and Kaplan, D. E. (1955). *J. Appl. Phys.* 26, 639.

Electron-Beam Measurements
of Shock-Wave Thickness

DAVID A. RUSSELL
Jet Propulsion Laboratory, California Institute of Technology, Pasadena, California

Shock-wave density profiles have been measured in the GALCIT 17-in. shock tube in argon and helium at Mach numbers between 2 and 8. A 5–15 kV electron beam was injected into the shock tube through a needle and collected by a small Faraday cage. The change in cage current was monitored as the shock wave passed the measuring station, and this change was related to the density profile. Maximum-slope shock thicknesses were found to be consistently thinner than the mean of the experimental data of Camac (1964). The measurements are shown to deviate from the Navier-Stokes predictions and to fall between the bimodal model and the BGK model of Liepmann *et al.* (1962a).

I. Introduction

Measurements of the profile of a plane normal shock wave are expected to provide information about the limits of validity of the Navier-Stokes equations, and more particularly, to provide a test for the various approximate theories (i.e., Mott-Smith, 1951; Liepmann *et al.*, 1962a). Of the earlier experimental work on this problem, the low-density wind-tunnel studies of Sherman (1955) and Talbot and Sherman (1959) have been the most precise. This work, however, was limited to low Mach numbers where differences from the Navier-Stokes theory are expected to be small. Linzer and Hornig (1963) measured shock thicknesses to a Mach number of 4.85 in argon, utilizing an optical reflectivity technique in a shock tube. Their results showed substantial deviations from the Navier-Stokes predictions.

Recently, Camac (1964) has reported direct measurements of shock-wave thickness made with a 90 kV electron beam in a 24-in. shock tube at shock Mach numbers up to 10. The technique employed the measurement of large-angle scattering from an essentially unattenuated electron beam. The present set of measurements utilizes a highly-collimated electron beam of lower

265

energy (5–15 kV) which is shot through the gas into a small Faraday cage inserted into the flow. When the shock wave passes the measuring station, the increasing gas density causes a detectable fraction of electrons to be scattered out of the beam. The resulting drop in cage current is then related to the density history through the shock wave. This is an "absorption" measurement, and as such it is related to the work of Ballard and Venable (1958), Duff and Webster (1959), and Schultz-Grunow and Frohn (1965).

II. Equipment and Technique

A. Shock Tube

The measurements were performed in the GALCIT 17-in. diameter shock tube (see Liepmann *et al.*, 1962b). The shock tube is equipped with a simple pressure driver, which was operated with helium and/or nitrogen gas for the present experiments. The maximum useful shock Mach number was about 8 when driving into argon, and 3 into helium. The lower Mach number limits were set by the thin-film trigger-gage sensitivity. Two sets of film gages were used to monitor the shock speed at two different positions along the shock tube. The first set was centered at 37.8 shock-tube diameters from the diaphragm and the second at 46.6 diameters. The electron-beam instrumentation was located at 48.6 diameters from the diaphragm.

The initial pressure for which shock profiles were taken was varied between 10 and 30 μ Hg in argon, and 30 to 90 μ Hg in helium. The lower limit was set by the necessity of keeping the expected over-all shock thickness to less than $\frac{1}{10}$ of the shock-tube diameter, in order to ensure reasonable one-dimensionality. The upper limit was determined by the geometric resolution of the beam, and to a lesser extent, by the time response. The observed test-gas length was never less than $\frac{1}{2}$ of a shock-tube diameter for all of the measurements.

The shock tube was flushed and pumped to below 0.05 μ Hg before each shot. For this purpose it was necessary to add a liquid-nitrogen cold trap to the low-pressure Roots pump. The leak rate was measured and the time taken to fire the shock tube was recorded, allowing an estimate to be made of the purity of the test gas. The impurity levels were kept to less than 1 % in the argon gas samples, and below 0.1 % in the helium samples. It should be noted that the pressures and leak rates were measured with an ionization gage—a McLeod gage generally indicated an order-of-magnitude lower leak rate. This suggests that the "leak" rate is largely provided by degassing of condensable substances. The initial pressure was set with the use of a calibrated volume (1000 to 1) and a 0–50 mm Wallace and Tiernan gage. It was frequently checked with a McLeod gage.

B. Electron-Beam Instrumentation

The electron beam was provided by a television gun (type 21CE). The gun was mounted on a base which could be adjusted in such a way that the beam passed through the injection needle (see Fig. 1). Both the Faraday cage and the needle were mounted to a rigid frame which was connected to the shock tube by two diametrically opposed isolation bellows.

Two different needles and two different cages were used. The cages were constructed of two pieces of stainless-steel tubing separated by quartz or glass insulating rings. The cages had external diameters of $\frac{1}{8}$ and $\frac{3}{8}$ in., and internal diameters of 0.063 and 0.201 in., respectively. Measured capacitance was always below 50 pF. One of the needles was $\frac{1}{2}$-in. in diameter with a 0.040-in. orifice. The other consisted of a $\frac{1}{8}$-in. outside-diameter stainless tube which had been swaged shut and then drilled through to provide a 0.040-in. orifice. For the final results, the $\frac{1}{2}$-in. needle and the $\frac{3}{8}$-in. cage were used on a 6-in. spacing (large probe configuration), and the $\frac{1}{8}$-in. needle and cage on a 3-in. spacing (small probe configuration). The spacings were centered on the shock-tube axis. Beam collimation was better than $5(10)^{-3}$ rad.

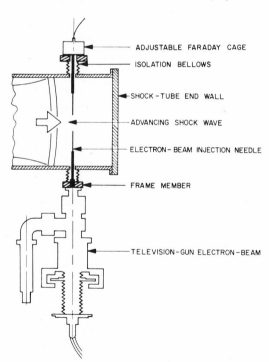

FIG. 1. Schematic of the experiment.

A load resistor of 1000 ohms was placed across the cage output, and the voltage transmitted through 6 inches of cable to a Tektronix Type L pre-amplifier in a Type 132 power supply, thence to an array of oscilloscopes. This arrangement resulted in measured rise times of no more than 0.16 μsec. Beam currents were varied between 10 and 100 μA. The accelerating potential was fixed at 15 kV for the argon runs, but it was necessary to drop to 5 kV in order to provide sufficient sensitivity when helium was used.

C. Measurement Details

Oscilloscope traces from typical runs are reproduced in Fig. 2. Time proceeds from left to right on each trace, and decreasing current is in the upward direction. The upper trace of each set is on a relatively long sweep speed. The

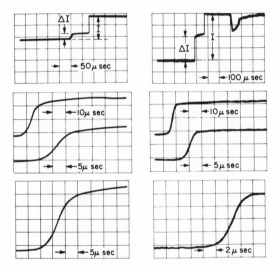

FIG. 2. Sample Faraday-cage traces obtained in argon with the large probe configuration. Traces on the left are for a Mach number of 7.85 into 10 μ Hg initial pressure. Those on the right are for Mach number 5.4 into 30 μ Hg.

current is fixed at some value I before the arrival of the shock wave, after which it decreases by an amount ΔI. There is a slight climb in density (decrease in current) as time progresses, due to the effects of the shock-tube boundary layer. The beam is then electrostatically deflected to provide a zero current level on the trace. The lower traces show the details of the shock jumps on expanded scales. For these measurements the cage-current traces were taken as directly representing the actual density profiles. A discussion of the errors involved in this procedure is presented in Section III, B.

The principal measurement for this study was the maximum-slope density thickness. A line of maximum slope is drawn on the shock density trace to meet the horizontal projections of the upstream and downstream densities. The maximum-slope thickness is then defined as the horizontal distance between the interception points. A time interval is actually measured in the experiment, but this is readily converted to a distance by multiplying by the measured shock speed. The process of measuring the time interval is complicated by the fact that the indicated density behind the shock wave is not constant, but generally rises with time (see Fig. 2). This is particularly noticeable at lower initial pressures where the boundary-layer effects are more severe. The method used for determining the Rankine-Hugoniot density level behind the

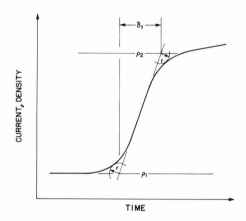

FIG. 3. Determination of the Rankine-Hugoniot density level behind the shock wave.

shock wave is depicted in Fig. 3. The line of maximum slope is drawn to meet the projection of the upstream density, ρ_1. An arc is then struck with a radius equal to the shortest distance between the density trace and the intersection point. The point on the line of maximum slope on the high-density side of the shock wave is then located from where an arc with the same radius is just tangent to the high-density profile. A horizontal line through this latter point is taken to be the Rankine-Hugoniot density level ρ_2. The time interval δ_t is measured as shown in the figure.

Each measured time interval was multiplied by the shock speed and then normalized by division into the upstream mean-free path, resulting in the shock-thickness parameter

$$\frac{\lambda_1}{\delta_s} = \left(\frac{5\pi}{6}\right)^{1/2} \frac{v_1}{a_1} \frac{1}{\delta_t u_s}. \tag{1}$$

Here λ is the mean-free path, v the kinematic coefficient of viscosity, a the speed of sound, and u_s the measured shock speed. The subscript 1 refers to the properties of the gas on the low-density side of the shock wave. λ_1 has the value of 5.38 cm for argon at a pressure of 1 μ Hg and temperature of 300°K.

The quantities I and ΔI were also measured in order to check the density-current relationship. The simple absorption law

$$\frac{I}{I_0} = \exp[-(\rho/\rho_{STP})\mu L] \tag{2}$$

is assumed to hold for this experiment, where I_0 is the current entering the gas sample, L is the length of the gas sample, and ρ is the sample density. μ is defined as the "absorption" coefficient, and it is a function of the beam voltage and collimation, the angle subtended by the collector, and the properties of the test gas. It can easily be shown that

$$\frac{\Delta I}{I} = \frac{I_1 - I_2}{I_1} = 1 - \exp[-(\rho/\rho_{STP})(\rho_2/\rho_1 - 1)\mu L]. \tag{3}$$

$\Delta I/I$ is measured for each run, and ρ_2/ρ_1 is known from the measured shock Mach number and the Rankine-Hugoniot relations. Figure 4 shows the results plotted in the form of $\ln(1 - \Delta I/I)$ versus the density parameter in Eq. (3). The slope of this plot should be constant if μL is independent of density and Eq. (2) is appropriate for these experiments.

III. Accuracy and Limitations of the Experiment

A. Shock Tube

Since both the initial pressure and the shock Mach number are involved in the normalized data, inaccuracies in these quantities must be kept to a minimum. The absolute value of the pressure was believed to be known to better than 5%, while the individual shock Mach numbers were accurate to better than 2%. The two shock speed measurements (see Section II, A) usually agreed with each other to within 2%, indicating little attenuation or acceleration of the shock wave.

It was found that an indicated test-gas contamination of less than 1% produced no measurable change in the argon data, whereas an order-of-magnitude higher purity level was necessary in helium. This is to be expected since helium has a much smaller collision cross-section with the beam electrons than does any shock-tube contaminant.

Shock curvature and skewness could directly influence the data, causing thicker shock waves to be observed. End-wall thin-film measurements by

Bowman (1965) show virtually no skewness at low pressures, but they indicate that the shock displacement at the wall amounts to roughly one shock thickness. Graphical integrations of the individual effects of curvature and skewness on the theoretical profiles indicate that, if the shock displacement over the sampling distance does not exceed $\frac{1}{3}$ of a maximum-slope thickness, the modification of the experimental maximum slope should not exceed a few per cent. This insensitivity to curvature effects is due to the wide region within the shock wave where the density grows nearly linearly with distance. Bowman's measurements for a shock Mach number of 8 into argon at 10 μ Hg show a curvature of only 8 % of the shock thickness over the center 6 in. of the shock tube, contrasting with the allowable 33 %. The conclusion that curvature is not important for these measurements is further supported by the fact that the runs made with the 3-in. probe spacing show no significant difference from the runs with the 6-in. spacing.

The amount of artificial skewness introduced by the possibility of the beam axis not being perpendicular to the shock tube was checked occasionally by measuring the distance from the probe tips to the end wall. This skewness was kept to within $\frac{1}{6}$ of the maximum-slope thickness for the thinnest shockwaves, and was thus not expected to have influenced the measurements.

B. Electron Beam

It is convenient to take the measured current trace as directly representing the density profile. If it is assumed that the simple absorption law [Eq. (2)] is valid, $\Delta I/I$ from Eq. (3) must be kept small in order to keep the error small. With $\Delta I/I = 10\%$, the maximum difference between the current and density shock profiles would be slightly greater than 1 % of the jump value, and would be indiscernible on the oscilloscope traces. However, some values of $\Delta I/I$ as high as 50 % were used in these experiments, and a noticeable profile distortion (9 %) would be expected. This effect would have to be corrected for if the actual profile were being studied, but by plotting out the corrected profile for a typical case it is found that the change in the maximum-slope thickness is negligible.

The above argument is based on the assumption that the single-scattering absorption law [Eq. (2)] is valid. If this were not the case, the correction would have to be modified accordingly. As mentioned in Section II, C, a plot of $(1 - \Delta I/I)$ versus the density parameter of Eq. (3) should show a straight line on semilog paper if Eq. (2) is correct. Figure 4 shows the data plotted in this fashion, and there can be little doubt that Eq. (2) is valid for each configuration. An occasional run at higher initial pressures than those used for the actual profiles provided a further check on the conclusion that a multiple scattering law was not appropriate for these experiments.

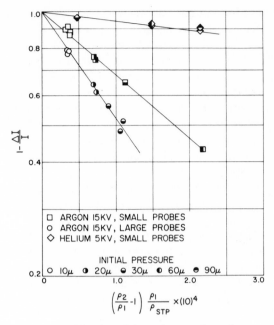

FIG. 4. Calibration of the various configurations.

The scatter in the points of Fig. 4 is thought to represent a limitation of this method of checking the data. Each point represents a different run, for which it is possible that a slightly different beam geometry and needle-cage alignment existed. The error in reading the oscilloscope traces also contributed to the scatter. It is probable that more care with both alignment and reading accuracy would reduce the scatter, but it is felt that effort might be better spent in developing a procedure that makes each shot self-calibrating (as was done by Camac, 1964).

C. Experiment

Time response is of vital importance to the accuracy of the over-all experiment. A simple analytic study has shown that if the characteristic time for the cage circuit is kept under $\frac{1}{10}$ of the time for the shock passage, less than 1 % error is introduced in the actual profile. This result was verified experimentally by deliberately raising the value of the load resistor. The measured rise time for a data run never exceeded 0.16 μsec. Since the thinnest shock wave was over 2 μsec thick, adequate time response was not a problem.

The geometric resolution of the probe must also be considered, since too large a beam would smear out the shock profile. For a 0.040-in. diameter beam, a graphical analysis determined that no detectable error in the shock profile would occur if the shock-wave total thickness is greater than 0.4 in. This limit was observed even though maximum thickness measurements require considerably less stringent conditions.

The test-gas sample could have been heated by the beam and/or the hot needle tip, which would result in an underestimate of λ_1 and λ_1/δ_s. To check for this effect, the beam current was varied by an order-of-magnitude for identical runs. No difference in the traces was observed.

No effects of aerodynamic probe disturbances or mass flow in the beam needle could be isolated. A time-dependent mass flow down the needle would be expected to contribute to the indicated density rise behind the shock wave, since the beam scattering would increase with time. However, the observed density rise between the shock and the contact surface was usually consistent with predictions based on the analysis of Mirels (1963). Two traces actually showed a slight density decrease after the shock wave, but the rest of the runs were much like those shown in Fig. 2. Some difficulty was experienced with the small probes at high initial pressures, where the density trace would often show a severe climb or fall during or after the shock wave. This was thought to be due to aerodynamic loading on the probes, and traces that exhibited this effect were discarded.

The best oscilloscope trace from each run was photographically enlarged before the maximum-slope thickness was read. The average reading accuracy in the determination of this quantity was thought to be 3%. No traces were used for which there was not a reasonable assurance of 4% accuracy. The oscilloscope sweep speeds were checked and were accurate to within a few per cent.

The definition of maximum-slope thickness shown on Fig. 3 would be expected to over-emphasize the thickness if the shock-wave profile has an asymmetry of the type predicted by the Navier-Stokes and BGK models. The error for the Navier-Stokes profile is 3% at a Mach number of 10, while it is less than $\frac{1}{2}$ of this value for the BGK model. Since the asymmetry increases with Mach number, the error for the actual experiments would be reduced from these values.

IV. Results and Discussion

The maximum-slope thickness measurements are presented on Fig. 5, where they are compared with the mean data of Camac (1964) and Linzer and Hornig (1963). The scatter bands from these previous studies are indicated by the vertical bars. The present data are seen to substantially agree with Camac's measurements; however, they indicate consistently thinner shock-waves than

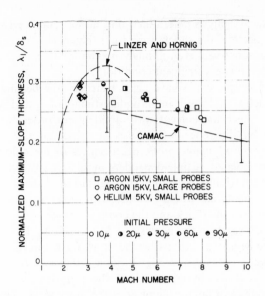

FIG. 5. Comparison of the maximum-slope data with the results of previous experiments.

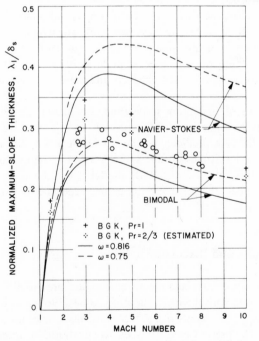

FIG. 6. Comparison of the maximum-slope data with theory.

the mean line of those results. The difference is 10% or greater. No systematic trends with pressure or probe configuration are evident in the data.

The mean value of the results is thought to be accurate to within 5%, this limit arising from uncertainty in the absolute value of the pressure measurement. The scatter in the results generally agrees with the estimated average reading accuracy of 3%. There is some excessive scatter at low Mach numbers, the source of which is not understood.

The results are compared with the various theories on Fig. 6. Here ω is the exponent in the viscosity power law. The BGK model points have been taken from Chahine and Narasimha (1965). These points are for $\omega = 0.816$ and a Prandtl number of unity. A correction to $\text{Pr} = \frac{2}{3}$ has been made by multiplying by the ratio of the equivalent Navier-Stokes results. It is seen that the data points deviate from the Navier-Stokes model as the Mach number increases, falling between the bimodal and BGK models. The importance of the correct viscosity law is obvious, as is the need for more precise data.

It should be noted that complete density profiles could be accurately obtained by the method discussed in this paper by restricting the measurements to small values of $\Delta I/I$ and short needle-to-cage distances. However, Chahine and Narasimha (1965) have shown that when the various theoretical profiles are normalized to the same maximum-slope thickness, the maximum difference in the density at any point is only a few per cent at a Mach number of 10. Liepmann et al. (1964) further pointed out that the low density tail of the BGK model is probably exaggerated. It is therefore suggested that, if density profiles are to be used for comparison with the theories, the maximum-slope measurement will be the most useful.

ACKNOWLEDGMENT

This paper presents the results of one phase of research carried out at the Jet Propulsion Laboratory, California Institute of Technology, under Contract No. NAS7–100, sponsored by the National Aeronautics and Space Administration. The author would like to thank Professor H. W. Liepmann and his associates at the Graduate Aeronautical Laboratories of· the California Institute of Technology for the use of the GALCIT 17-in. shock tube. Thanks are also due to Professor Rex Nelson of Occidental College for developing the first electron beam, and to D. Sidwell and W. Simms for assistance in that and subsequent developments. However, the author is most deeply indebted to A. Bouck, who provided capable and enthusiastic assistance for the measurements reported herein.

REFERENCES

Ballard, H. N., and Venable, D. (1958). *Phys. Fluids* **1**, 3.

Bowman, R. M. (1965). Ph.D. Thesis (to be published), California Institute of Technology.

Camac, M. (1964). *AIAA* Aerospace Sciences Meeting, New York, Preprint No. 64–35. (Also see this volume, p. 240.)

Chahine, M. T., and Narasimha, R. (1965). This volume, p. 140.

Duff, R. E., and Webster, W. M. (1959). *Bull. Am. Phys. Soc.* **4**, 283.

Liepmann, H. W., Narasimha, R., and Chahine, M. T. (1962a). *Phys. Fluids* **5**, 11.

Liepmann, H. W., Roshko, A., Coles, D., and Sturtevant, B. (1962b). *Rev. Sci. Instr.* **33**, 6.

Liepmann, H. W., Narasimha, R., and Chahine, M. T. (1965). In *Proc. 11th Inter. Congr. Appl. Mech., Munich* (to be published).

Linzer, M., and Hornig, D. F. (1963). *Phys. Fluids* **6**, 12.

Mirels, H. (1963). *Phys. Fluids* **6**, 9.

Mott-Smith, H. M. (1951). *Phys. Rev.* **82**, 885.

Schultz-Grunow, F., and Frohn, A. (1965). This volume, p. 250.

Sherman, F. S. (1955). NACA TN 3298.

Talbot, L., and Sherman, F. S. (1959). NASA Memo. 12–14–58W.

TRANSITION FLOW—THEORY

Near Free Molecule Behavior of Gases with Infinite Collision Cross Section[1]

J. J. SMOLDEREN

von Kármán Institute for Fluid Dynamics, Rhode-St-Genese, Belgium

The paper deals with the behavior, at large Knudsen numbers, of solutions of the Boltzmann equation in the realistic case of molecular interactions with infinite range. So far, most of the applications of the Boltzmann equation to the treatment of transitional or near free molecule flow problems have been based on simple molecular models with finite range of interaction, such as the rigid sphere model, or the BGK model, which can be treated as a finite range interaction.

The present paper deals essentially with one-dimensional problems such as Couette flow and heat conduction between parallel plates, and power law type interactions are considered, although the results could be extended to arbitrary laws, at the cost of considerable mathematical complications.

The full Boltzmann equation is replaced by a reduced linear integro-differential equation exhibiting the same singular behavior, caused essentially, by the divergence of the collision integral if the distribution function becomes discontinuous. It is then shown that the gas-kinetic boundary value problem for this linear integro-differential equation may be reduced to the solution of an integral equation of a rather complicated and singular type.

The essential practical result from these mathematical developments is the nature of the Knudsen number dependence of the dominant term of the near free molecule corrections, which turns out to be $K^{-(s-1)/(s+1)}$, s being the exponent in the interaction force law. Numerical treatment is briefly outlined for the case of hyperthermal Couette flow, assuming a rather rough estimate for the solution of the integral equation.

I. Introduction

The difficulties arising in the treatment of gas dynamic problems at Knudsen numbers of the order of unity, the transitional problems, are well known.

[1] The present investigation was sponsored by the Air Force European Office of Aerospace Research, under Grant AF EOAR 63–38.

Continuum description breaks down and the full Boltzmann equation has to be used, but the situation greatly simplifies if the Knudsen number is large enough for free molecule conditions to exist.

It is therefore natural to try and extrapolate these comparatively simple free molecule results into the transitional regime by computing corrections or establishing iterative methods of solution. This has been attempted by several authors, using either the Boltzmann equation or simple first collision models. A typical mathematical phenomenon has been encountered in some of these treatments, consisting in an unexpected Knudsen number dependence of the correction terms, as well as in the occurrence of infinite gradients at boundaries. The phenomenon is most marked in the case of one-dimensional, or parallel plane geometries, and yields a Knudsen number dependence of $K^{-1} \ln(K)$, in contrast with all results derived from approximations based on a finite number of moment equations. The most detailed analysis of this phenomenon was carried out by Willis (1961), who considered several molecular models with finite range. The physical explanation of the phenomenon can be given as follows: for large Knudsen numbers, molecular collisions become very infrequent except, in the case of plane parallel geometries, for a class of "hesitant molecules" which do not definitely head for one or the other plane boundary, and therefore travel large distances before hitting a boundary. There are thus always some molecules which will not be subjected to free molecule conditions, whatever the Knudsen number, if their velocity perpendicular to the plane boundaries is sufficiently small, and these molecules are responsible for the abnormal behavior described. Mathematically, the phenomenon results from the singular nature of the Boltzmann equation considered as a differential equation with respect to the space coordinates, when the molecular velocity component perpendicular to the boundaries tends to zero.

It might also be mentioned that the singular behavior described is alleviated in the case of two- or three-dimensional geometries, arising for instance in the study of gas flows around infinite cylindrical or finite obstacles, except in the case of an infinitely long cylinder immersed in a flow also of infinite extent in directions perpendicular to the generators of the cylinder. In this case, the Knudsen number dependence of the near free molecule correction is again $K^{-1} \ln K$, but the occurrence of this term is intimately connected with the infinite lateral extent of the flow.

Willis (1961) stresses the fact that the $K^{-1} \ln K$ dependence of the correction term for plane parallel geometries cannot be valid for molecular interaction laws with infinite range, because the total cross section selected to represent the finite interaction appears as a factor in the correction term.

The present paper attempts to elucidate the situation created by the infinite extent of the range of the actual, physical molecular interactions. This situation is characterized by an entirely different kind of singularity, originating in the collision term of the Boltzmann equation. The singularity of this equation when considered as a differential equation with respect to the space coordinates is still present, of course, but it merely adds to the pathological character of the collision term.

Let us first analyze the behavior of this Boltzmann collision term, namely,

$$\iiiint [f^*f'^* - ff']g\sigma \sin\theta \; d\theta \; d\varepsilon \; d\xi'$$

The notation is more or less standard and is defined in the list of symbols. The convergence of this integral with respect to the scattering angle, which is obvious for interactions with finite range, must be carefully analyzed in the general case, for the differential cross section exhibits a nonintegrable singularity for vanishing scattering angle. The difficulty lies of course in the fact that account is taken of very weak, or grazing, collisions, the frequency of which is extremely large compared with the frequency of strong collisions. The contribution of these grazing collisions to the collision term may be finite because of near cancellation between the effect of direct and inverse grazing collisions, resulting in vanishing values for the factor $(f^*f'^* - ff')$ because the velocities after collision differ very little from the velocities before collision. It is of fundamental importance for what follows to observe that the above considerations are valid only if the distribution function is continuous, otherwise the factor in question would not tend to zero when the final velocities tend to the initial velocities, as is the case for grazing collisions.

It may be shown that the collision term converges if the distribution function is differentiable and if the interaction force dies out sufficiently rapidly at large distance. The Coulomb type interaction is a notable exception, but the binary collision description obviously breaks down altogether in this case. The essential conclusion to be drawn from these considerations is that the convergence of the collision integral requires the continuity of the distribution function if the range of molecular interaction is considered infinite. This means that the collision term will resist any tendency for such a discontinuity to occur, a situation somewhat reminiscent of the influence of viscosity and thermal conduction in resisting the development of discontinuities such as shock waves and vortex sheets in continuum aerodynamics. Mathematically, however, there is a great difference between these phenomena: the case of a nearly inviscid and nonconducting gas leads to a singular perturbation problem for a partial differential system, while the present gas kinetic problem leads to a singular perturbation problem for an integro-differential equation.

The singular perturbation problem to be treated here is thus dominated by the behavior of the integral term which will diverge at the free molecule limit, because of the discontinuous nature of the free molecule distribution function. This type of singular perturbation problem does not seem to appear in any other applications and is not mentioned in the classical literature on integral and integro-differential equations.

In the present paper, the one-dimensional case will be treated under the assumption of a power law type interaction. The analytical treatment is in fact considerably simpler for such interactions, which also appear to be the most important for practical application. Results for various exponential type interactions are quoted by Smolderen (1963), but the considerable analytical difficulties encountered in their treatment are not in proportion to their only academic interest.

II. The Reduced Integro-Differential Equation

Let x_1 represent the coordinate perpendicular to the planes of the solid boundaries. The Boltzmann equation for the one-dimensional situation to be studied will be written as follows:

$$\xi_1 \, \partial f/\partial x_1 = K^{-1} \iiiint [f^* f'^* - ff']g\sigma \sin \theta \, d\theta \, d\varepsilon \, d\xi'. \tag{1}$$

K represents a Knudsen number which can be introduced by assuming that x_1 is a reduced coordinate, referred to a standard length, say L, and f a reduced distribution function taken as the ratio of the actual distribution function to a reference number density, say N. If the differential cross section σ is also considered as the ratio of the actual differential cross section to a reference cross section, say Σ (not the total cross section, which is infinite in the present case), then

$$K = (N\Sigma)^{-1}/L$$

which agrees with the usual definition, because $(N\Sigma)^{-1}$ defines a scale for the mean free path.

The first step in the treatment of our problem consists in identifying and isolating the terms responsible for the singular behavior that we wish to analyze. In all terms which do not exhibit a divergent character for discontinuous distribution functions, we will ultimately replace the actual f by its free molecule limit f_m, and this procedure will be taken as the first step of an iteration. It is then to be expected that the following steps will yield terms of smaller order of magnitude for large values of K, and this can easily be proved *a posteriori*. Rigorous proofs of convergence will, of course, have to be replaced by plausibility arguments.

It is essential to keep in mind that the phenomenon to be analyzed, being caused by the discontinuity appearing in f_m for $\xi_1 = 0$, will result in large gradients for f in the vicinity of this value of ξ_1. For values of ξ_1 which are not small, f will differ from f_m by terms of order K^{-1}, which are smaller than the dominant terms, as will become clear. The main terms will therefore arise from contributions in the vicinity of $\xi_1 = 0$.

First consider the factor

$$D(f) = f^*f'^* - ff'$$

in the collision term, which will be split as follows:

$$D[f] = [f\xi_1^*, \xi_2, \xi_3) - f(\xi_1, \xi_2, \xi_3)]f' + (f'^* - f')f^*$$
$$+ [f\xi_1^*, \xi_2^*, \xi_3^*) - f(\xi_1^*, \xi_2, \xi_3)]f'.$$

It is clear that the last term at the right cannot lead to a divergence at the free molecule limit, for f_m is a continuous function of ξ_2 and ξ_3.

In the second term, however, the discontinuity of f_m would cause trouble, but we must keep in mind that $D(f)$ is going to be integrated with respect to ξ_1'. Considering the critical grazing collisions, which correspond to small values of the scattering angle θ, we see that the term in question will be small of order θ unless ξ_1' itself is small of this order, so that $\xi_1'^*$ and ξ_1' can be of opposite sign, as required for the discontinuity to intervene. The integration with respect to ξ_1' will therefore yield a quantity of order θ for small θ, and its contribution to the collision term will therefore converge, if the integral

$$\int \theta\sigma \sin\theta \, d\theta$$

exists for $\theta = 0$. This can easily be shown to be true for power law interactions with force exponent larger than 3.

The first term in the decomposition of $D(f)$ is therefore the only one which will cause the collision integral to diverge at the free molecule limit. It may still be significantly simplified. We may write

$$\xi_1^* = \xi_1 + a(\xi, \xi', \theta, \varepsilon).$$

The function a evidently vanishes with θ, but its dependence on ξ_1 would prove extremely troublesome for the mathematical treatment of our problem. Remembering that we have to deal with a phenomenon localized in the vicinity of $\xi_1 = 0$, we write

$$\xi_1^* = \tilde{\xi}_1^* + [a(\xi, \xi', \theta, \varepsilon) - a_{\xi_1 = 0}],$$

with

$$\tilde{\xi}_1^* = \xi_1 + a_{\xi_1 = 0}$$

and split the critical term in $D(f)$ further as follows:

$$[f(\xi_1{}^*, \xi_2, \xi_3) - f]f' = [f(\tilde{\xi}_1{}^*, \xi_2, \xi_3) - f]f'$$
$$+ [f(\xi_1{}^*, \xi_2, \xi_3) - f(\tilde{\xi}_1{}^*, \xi_2, \xi_3)]f'.$$

By considering in detail the contributions of grazing collisions, it is again possible to show that the second term on the right cannot cause a divergence, if first integrated with respect to ξ_1', but the demonstration is rather lengthy and will be omitted here. Similar arguments also indicate that $\tilde{\xi}_1{}^*$ may be replaced by the following, simpler expression, valid for grazing collisions:

$$\tilde{\xi}_1{}^* = \xi_1 + (1/2)\sqrt{g_2{}^2 + g_3{}^2} \cos \varepsilon \cdot \theta \qquad (2)$$

for a suitable choice of the reference plane defining the origin for the angle ε.

We must now turn our attention to the factor $g\sigma(g, \theta)$ in the collision integral. Its dependence on ξ_1 would also considerably complicate the analysis, so that we write

$$g\sigma = (g\sigma)_{\xi_1 = 0} + [g\sigma - (g\sigma)_{\xi_1 = 0}].$$

It can now be shown that the contribution of the second term will be convergent at the free molecule limit, by virtue of the fact that it vanishes at the critical $\xi_1 = 0$. The demonstration is not straightforward, because of the fact that the differential cross section is singular for $g = 0$, and will be omitted because of its length. It consists essentially of the proof that the integral, with respect of the components of ξ', of the quantity

$$[g\sigma - (g\sigma)_{\xi_1 = 0}]/\xi_1$$

is bounded, however small ξ_1, although the derivative $(\partial g\sigma/\partial \xi_1)_{\xi_1 = 0}$ is not integrable with respect to the components mentioned. We may also write

$$(g\sigma)_{\xi_1 = 0} \sin \theta = (g\sigma_P)_{\xi_1 = 0}\theta + (g\sigma_F)_{\xi_1 = 0} \sin \theta,$$

σ_F being any function of θ for which the integral

$$\int_0^\pi \sigma_F \sin \theta \, d\theta$$

converges, so that the essential singular contributions to σ for grazing collisions may be grouped under σ_P.

Finally, the collision term may be written as follows:

$$\mathscr{C}(f) = \iiiint [f(\tilde{\xi}_1{}^*, \xi_2, \xi_3) - f]f'(g\sigma_P)_{\xi_1 = 0}\theta \, d\theta \, d\varepsilon \, d\xi' + \mathscr{C}_R(f)$$

where

$$\mathscr{C}_R(f) = \iiiint \{f'[f(\tilde{\xi}_1{}^*, \xi_2, \xi_3) - f][(g\sigma_F)_{\xi_1 = 0} + g\sigma - (g\sigma)_{\xi_1 = 0}]$$
$$+ [f^*f'^* - f(\tilde{\xi}_1{}^*, \xi_2, \xi_3)f']g\sigma\} \sin \theta \, d\theta \, d\varepsilon \, d\xi'$$

represents a regular contribution to $\mathscr{C}(f)$, in the sense that it converges also for a distribution function discontinuous at $\xi_1 = 0$. It is therefore natural, now, to attempt an iterative procedure, the first step of which consists in replacing f by f_m in $\mathscr{C}_R(f)$. One should notice, however, the occurrence, in $\mathscr{C}_R(f)$, of terms containing the nonintegrated f as a factor, and remember that the Willis iteration is essentially based on the retention of the actual f in this case, f_m being used only in integrated terms. For instance, one should make the following substitution:

$$f \iiiint f'(g\sigma_F)_{\xi_1=0} \sin\theta \, d\theta \, d\varepsilon \, d\xi' \rightarrow f \iiiint f_m'(g\sigma_F)_{\xi_1=0} \sin\theta \, d\theta \, d\varepsilon \, d\xi',$$

but it will appear that this is finally irrelevant for the computation of the dominant term in the present case. The above procedure is clearly not applicable to the expression

$$\iiiint [f(\tilde{\xi}_1{}^*, \xi_2, \xi_3) - f][g\sigma - (g\sigma)_{\xi_1=0}] \sin\theta \, d\theta \, d\varepsilon \, d\xi',$$

which we cannot split because the parts would be divergent integrals. The behavior of this expression is, however, different because the factor $g\sigma - (g\sigma)_{\xi_1=0}$ vanishes at the critical point $\xi_1 = 0$, and this affords a reduction in the influence of the singularity. The first step in our iteration therefore leads to an inhomogeneous linear integro-differential equation for the dominant part of f:

$$\xi_1(\partial f/\partial x_1) = K^{-1}\left\{ \iiiint [f(\tilde{\xi}_1{}^*, \xi_2, \xi_3) - f]f_m'(g\sigma)_P \theta \, d\theta \, d\varepsilon \, d\xi' \right.$$

$$\left. - fQ_m(\xi_2, \xi_3) + R_m(\xi_1, \xi_2, \xi_3) \right\} \tag{3}$$

where

$$Q_m = \iiiint f_m' (g\sigma_F)_{\xi_1=0} \sin\theta \, d\theta \, d\varepsilon \, d\xi'$$

$$R_m = \iiiint \{f_m(\tilde{\xi}_1{}^*, \xi_2, \xi_3)f_m'(g\sigma_F)_{\xi_1=0}$$

$$+ [f_m(\tilde{\xi}_1{}^*, \xi_2, \xi_3) - f_m]f_m'[g\sigma - (g\sigma)_{\xi_1=0}]$$

$$+ [f_m{}^* f_m'{}^* - f_m(\tilde{\xi}_1{}^*, \xi_2, \xi_3)f_m']g\sigma\} \sin\theta \, d\theta \, d\varepsilon \, d\xi'.$$

Equation (3) will be called the reduced equation, and the dominant term of its solution at the free molecule limit will be equivalent to the dominant term of the solution of the full Boltzmann equation.

In most practical applications leading to discontinuous free molecule solutions, such as Couette flow, thermal conduction etc., the boundary conditions are given on two plane solid boundaries. The length scale L will be selected so as to represent the walls by the equations $x_1 = \pm\frac{1}{2}$. The corresponding gas kinetic boundary conditions would then be of the form

$$J_{\xi_1 > 0, x_1 = -\frac{1}{2}} = \mathscr{F}_- [f_{\xi_1 < 0, x_1 = -\frac{1}{2}}]; \qquad f_{\xi_1 < 0, x_1 = +\frac{1}{2}} = \mathscr{F}_+ [f_{\xi_1 > 0, x_1 = +\frac{1}{2}}].$$

The symbols $\mathscr{F}_\pm$ denote functionals of the distributions of incident molecules, and represent the nature of the molecular interaction with solid walls. They are normally expressed by integrals over the distribution of incident molecules. In the first iteration we will naturally replace f by its free molecule value f_m in these functionals, so that the boundary conditions for the reduced equation will be of the form

$$f_{\xi_1 > 0, x_1 = -\frac{1}{2}} = \mathscr{F}_m{}^-,$$

$$f_{\xi_1 < 0, x_1 = +\frac{1}{2}} = \mathscr{F}_m{}^+.$$

It is clear that the singular behavior to be analyzed will be caused by the fact that, in general,

$$(\mathscr{F}_m{}^-)_{\xi_1 = 0} - (\mathscr{F}_m{}^+)_{\xi_1 = 0} \neq 0.$$

This creates the discontinuity in the free molecule solution.

III. Reduction of the Integro-Differential Boundary Problem to an Integral Equation

The integral operator occurring in the reduced equation (3) may be put in a more familiar form:

$$\int_{-\infty}^{+\infty} \mathscr{K}(\xi_1, \xi_1{}') f(\xi_1{}') \, d\xi_1{}',$$

but this involves a kernel exhibiting awkward singularities, as should be expected in view of the nature of the problem. This form does not appear to be very useful.

A Fourier integral transformation with respect to the variable ξ_1,

$$\Phi(\omega, \xi_2, \xi_3, x_1) = \int_{-\infty}^{+\infty} e^{i\omega\xi_1} f(\xi_1, \xi_2, \xi_3, x_1) \, d\xi_1, \tag{4}$$

however, leads to a considerable simplification, for Eq. (3) transforms into a hyperbolic partial differential equation

$$i(\partial^2 \varphi / \partial \omega \, \partial x_1) = K^{-1}\{\varphi(\omega, \xi_2, \xi_3)\Phi + \psi(\omega, \xi_2, \xi_3)\} \tag{5}$$

where

$$\varphi(\omega, \xi_2, \xi_3) = \iiiint \{\exp[i\omega\tfrac{1}{2}(g_2{}^2 + g_3{}^2)^{1/2} \cos \varepsilon\cdot\theta]$$
$$- 1\}(g\sigma_P)_{\xi_1 = 0}\theta \; d\theta \; d\varepsilon f_m{}' \; d\xi' - Q_m(\xi_2, \xi_3)$$

and

$$\psi(\omega, \xi_2, \xi_3) = \int_{-\infty}^{+\infty} e^{i\omega\xi_1} R_m(\xi_1, \xi_2, \xi_3) \; d\xi_1.$$

The functions φ and ψ may be computed for given law of intermolecular forces and given free molecule solutions. If a power law type interaction is considered, the intermolecular force being

$$F = Ar^{-s},$$

the principal contribution to the differential cross section for grazing collision is readily obtained as

$$\sigma_P = (s - 1)^{-1}\left[(4A/m)\int_0^{r/2} (\sin v)^{s-1} \; dv\right]^{2/(s-1)} g^{-4/(s-1)}\theta^{-2s/(s-1)}$$
$$= (s - 1)^{-1}[(2A\pi^{1/2}/m,\Gamma(\tfrac{1}{2}s)/\Gamma(\tfrac{1}{2}(s + 1)))]^{2/(s-1)}g^{-4/(s-1)}\theta^{-2s/(s-1)}$$

by perturbation of the rectilinear undisturbed molecular trajectories. Here, v is the angle between the line connecting the molecules and their parallel undisturbed trajectories in the center of mass system.

The computation of the integral the expression for φ is rather lengthy, but the essential point is clearly its dependence on the Fourier variable ω. The following remark is essential in this respect: We are investigating a phenomenon occurring in the neighborhood of $\xi_1 = 0$, and it will thus depend on the behavior of the Fourier transforms for large values of ω, according to a well known property of the transformation. It is also seen, from the formula defining φ, that the asymptotic behavior of this function for large ω is controlled by the properties of the grazing collisions, and not at all by the strong collisions for which θ is not small. This is of course to be expected from our previous considerations. Extension of the integration over θ to $+\infty$ rather than to π leads to a convergent result which will have the same asymptotic behavior for large ω. Introducing a new variable $\theta' = \theta\cdot\omega$ in this integration then shows the integral in φ to be proportional to

$$\omega^{2/(s-1)}.$$

Note now that the remaining term Q_m is of smaller order of magnitude for large ω and dropping it will therefore have the same effect as some modification of the law of interaction at close range which controls the strong collisions. Detailed analysis shows that the presence of such a term can contribute only terms of the order $K^{-1} \ln K$, as encountered in the treatment of finite range interactions.

In what follows, we will therefore keep only the leading term in φ, which may actually be put in the form

$$\varphi = |\omega|^{2/(s-1)} \pi^{(s+1)/2(s-1)} \sin\left(\frac{\pi}{2} \frac{s+1}{s-1}\right) \left[\frac{\Gamma\left(\frac{s}{2}\right)}{\Gamma\left(\frac{s+1}{2}\right)}\right]^{2/(s-1)}$$

$$\times \frac{\Gamma\left(\frac{s-3}{s-1}\right)\Gamma\left(\frac{s+1}{2(s-1)}\right)}{\Gamma\left(\frac{s}{s-1}\right)} \left(\frac{A}{m}\right)^{2/(s-1)}$$

$$\times \iiint g_{\xi_1=0}^{(s-5)/(s-1)}(g_2{}^2 + g_3{}^2)_{\xi_1=0}^{1/(s-1)} f_m{}' \, d\xi'.$$

It is interesting to note that the treatment of the asymptotic behavior of the Fokker-Planck equation for small coupling parameter, would lead to an entirely similar transformed equation, formally equivalent to the case $s = 2$, which would correspond to the (unacceptable) Coulomb interactions. Most of the results obtained below may therefore be applied to the Fokker-Planck equation, but a direct treatment of the corresponding reduced equation is possible. This equation turns out to be a partial differential equation of singular parabolic type, as treated by Gevrey (1914).

The transformed equation (5) may be put in a more standard form (telegraph equation) using the substitution

$$\Omega = \int_0^\omega \varphi(\omega) \, d\omega \sim \omega^{(s+1)/(s-1)},$$

which yields

$$i(\partial^2 \Phi / \partial x_1 \, \partial\Omega) = K^{-1}\Phi + (\psi/\varphi). \tag{6}$$

The important fact which appears here, is that this equation is now independent of the law of interaction, which occurs only implicitly through the dependence of Ω on ω. This remark immediately suggests to apply an inverse Fourier transformation with respect to Ω,

$$g(\eta, \xi_2, \xi_3, x_1) = \pi^{-1} \int_{-\infty}^{+\infty} e^{i\eta\Omega}\Phi(\Omega, \xi_2, \xi_3, x_1) \, d\Omega,$$

which yields a very simple first order differential equation:

$$\eta \, \partial g / \partial x_1 = -K^{-1}g + K^{-1}\pi^{-1}\int_{-\infty}^{+\infty} e^{i\eta\Omega}\psi(\omega) \, d\omega = -K^{-1}g + P.$$

This equation, similar to those encountered in the linearized treatment of the BGK model, may be immediately solved for suitable gas-kinetic type boundary conditions, such as

$$g_{\eta>0,x_1=-\frac{1}{2}} = G_+(\eta),$$

$$g_{\eta<0,x_1=+\frac{1}{2}} = G_-(\eta).$$

It must, however, be realized that we have only been shifting the problem, because it is impossible to compute the pertinent boundary values. In fact, we must first construct the solution

$$g(\eta, x_1) = +G_\pm(\eta) \exp\left[-K^{-1}\frac{x_1 \pm \frac{1}{2}}{\eta}\right]$$

$$+ P\left(1 - \exp\left[-K^{-1}\frac{x_1 \pm \frac{1}{2}}{\eta}\right]\right) \quad \text{for} \quad \pm\eta > 0$$

and then transform it by two inverse Fourier transformations (with different arguments), introduce it in the original boundary conditions, and an integral equation of the first kind will result for G.

The product of the two inverse Fourier transformations is equivalent to a single integral transformation with the kernel

$$K(\xi_1, \eta) = \pi^{-1}\int_0^\infty \cos[\omega\xi_1 - \Omega(\omega)\eta]\, d\omega.$$

It is easy to show that the integral converges. For power law interactions, this kernel has the special form

$$\xi_1\mathscr{K}(\eta\xi_1^{-(s+1)/(s-1)}), \qquad \mathscr{K}(u) = \pi^{-1}\int_0^\infty \cos[\omega - \text{const } u\omega^{(s+1)/(s-1)}]\, d\omega.$$

It does not appear possible to express the function $\mathscr{K}$ in terms of classical transcendentals, except for $s = 3$ (complex error function), and $s = 2$ (Bessel functions of order $\frac{1}{3}$, Airy integral). The integral equations for the functions $G_\pm$ may thus be written as follows:

$$\int_0^{+\infty} K(\xi_1, \eta)G_+(\eta)\, d\eta + \int_{-\infty}^0 K(\xi_1, \eta)[G_-(\eta)\exp(K^{-1}/\eta)]\, d\eta$$

$$= \mathscr{F}_+(\xi_1) - \int_{-\infty}^0 K(\xi_1, \eta)P(\eta)[1 - \exp(K^{-1}/\eta)]\, d\eta \qquad (\xi_1 > 0),$$

$$\int_0^{+\infty} K(\xi_1, \eta)G_+(\eta)\exp(-K^{-1}/\eta)\, d\eta + \int_{-\infty}^0 K(\xi_1, \eta)G_-(\eta)\, d\eta$$

$$= \mathscr{F}_-(\xi_1) - \int_0^\infty K(\xi_1, \eta)P(\eta)[1 - \exp(-K^{-1}/\eta)]\, d\eta \qquad (\xi_1 < 0).$$

First of all, attention should be drawn to the right-hand members of the equation which involve both the boundary conditions and the contribution of the inhomogeneous term of the reduced equation. In view of the nature of the singularity under study, it is clear that the discontinuity characterized by the difference between the limits of these second members for $\xi_1 \to \pm 0$ will dominate the behavior of f at the free molecule limit. It is possible to show that this discontinuity is small of order $K^{-2/(s+1)}$ for the inhomogeneous term, because of the fact that the term R_m in Eq. (3) is a continuous function of ξ_1. We may therefore limit ourselves in an analysis of the dominant term to the finite discontinuity introduced by the boundary conditions. The problem may then be significantly simplified by symmetry considerations, based on the splitting of the boundary problem into an antisymmetrical, discontinuous part

$$f_{(\xi_1 > 0, x_1 = -\frac{1}{2})} = \frac{\mathscr{F}_+(|\xi_1|) - \mathscr{F}_-(-|\xi_1|)}{2},$$

$$f_{(\xi_1 < 0, x_1 = +\frac{1}{2})} = -\frac{\mathscr{F}_+(|\xi_1|) - \mathscr{F}_-(-|\xi_1|)}{2},$$

responsible for the principal singularity, and a continuous symmetrical part which will be dropped, as it does not contribute to a leading term. In the antisymmetrical problem, the two branches of the unknown function G are equal and opposite and we need only consider one branch, satisfying the following integral equation:

$$\int_0^{+\infty} [K(\xi_1, \eta) - K(\xi_1, -\eta) \exp(-(K\eta)^{-1})] G_+(\eta)\, d\eta$$
$$= \frac{\mathscr{F}_+(|\xi_1|) - \mathscr{F}_-(-|\xi_1|)}{2}. \quad (7)$$

The numerical treatment of this integral equation is by no means easy, as it does not appear to belong to any standard form. It is natural to attempt an iteration starting from its "free molecule" solution ($K^{-1} = 0$), which is found to be

$$G_m(\eta) = \left[\sin\{(\pi/2)(s-1)/(s+1)\} \Gamma\left(\frac{s-1}{s+1}\right) \right]^{-1} \left[\frac{\mathscr{F}_+(0) - \mathscr{F}_-(0)}{2} \right] \eta^{-2/(s+1)},$$

but it must be realized that the successive iterations introduce logarithmic factors increasing the singularity at $\eta = 0$. The rapidity of convergence and this convergence itself are therefore doubtful. It has been found possible to transform the equation into an integral equation of the second kind, by means of a Fourier sine transformation:

$$\chi(\Omega) + \int_0^{+\infty} \mathscr{L}(\Omega, \Omega^*) \chi(\Omega^*)\, d\Omega^* = \mu(\omega)$$

where

$$\chi(\Omega) = (2/\pi) \int_0^{+\infty} G(\eta) \sin(\Omega\eta)\, d\eta,$$

$$\mu(\omega) = \int_0^{+\infty} \sin \omega\xi_1 \frac{\mathscr{F}_+(\xi_1) - \mathscr{F}_-(-\xi_1)}{2}\, d\xi_1,$$

$\mathscr{L}(\Omega, \Omega^*)$

$$= \pi^{-2}K^{-1} \operatorname{Im}\left\{ \int_0^{\infty e^{i\alpha}} [dW/(1 - W^2)][\mathscr{I}[K^{-1}(\Omega W^{(s+1)/(s-1)} + \Omega^*)]\right.$$

$$\left. - \mathscr{I}[K^{-1}(\Omega W^{(s+1)/(s-1)} - \Omega^*)]\right\} \qquad (0 < \alpha < \pi(s-1)/s+1).$$

$$\mathscr{I}(z) = iz^{-1} - 2e^{i\pi/4}z^{-1/2}K_1(2e^{-i\pi/4}z^{1/2}).$$

The "free molecule" solution corresponds here to the first step of the Neumann iteration, but the equation is singular in that the integral

$$\iint \mathscr{L}^2(\Omega, \Omega^*)\, d\Omega\, d\Omega^*$$

diverges. A possible approach seems to consist in isolating the critical parts of the kernel in order to obtain an equation with symmetrical difference kernels amenable to a Wiener-Hopf procedure. This work is in progress.

Most of the qualitative features of the solution may however be derived without detailed numerical solution of the integral equation. The introduction of reduced variables

$$\tilde{\xi} = K^{(s-1)/(s+1)}\xi, \qquad \tilde{\eta} = K\eta$$

is useful for this purpose. Equation (7) reads, after introduction of these variables,

$$\tilde{\xi}^{-1} \int_0^{+\infty} [\mathscr{K}(\tilde{\eta}\tilde{\xi}^{-(s+1)/(s-1)}) - \mathscr{K}(-\tilde{\eta}\tilde{\xi}^{-(s+1)/(s-1)}) \exp(-\tilde{\eta}^{-1})]G(\tilde{\eta})\, d\tilde{\eta}$$

$$= K^{2/(s+1)} \frac{\mathscr{F}_+(0) - \mathscr{F}_-(0)}{2},$$

and the solution is therefore expected to be of the form

$$G(\eta) = K^{2/(s+1)}\mathscr{G}(K\eta).$$

The dominant part of the near free molecule correction to the distribution function and its moments representing the physical observables, are easily computed from this solution.

IV. Nature of the Near Free Molecule Terms for Power Laws of Interaction

The dominant part of the near free molecule correction to the distribution function may be written as follows:

$$\bar{\xi}^{-1} \int_0^{+\infty} \{\mathscr{K}[\tilde{\eta}\bar{\xi}^{-(s+1)/(s-1)}]e^{-(x_1+\frac{1}{2})/\tilde{\eta}}$$
$$- \mathscr{K}[-\tilde{\eta}\bar{\xi}^{-(s+1)/(s-1)}]e^{-(\frac{1}{2}-x_1)/\eta}\}G(\tilde{\eta})\,d\tilde{\eta},$$

using the reduced variables. This expression may also be put in the following form:

$$\int_0^{+\infty} \{\mathscr{K}(\lambda) \exp[-(x_1 + \tfrac{1}{2})\lambda^{-1}\bar{\xi}^{-(s+1)/(s-1)}]$$
$$- \mathscr{K}(-\lambda) \exp[-(\tfrac{1}{2} - x_1)\lambda^{-1}\bar{\xi}^{-(s+1)/(s-1)}]\}\bar{\xi}^{2/(s-1)}\mathscr{G}(\lambda\bar{\xi}^{(s+1)/(s-1)})d\lambda,$$

which shows terms of the form $\exp(-\text{const }\bar{\xi}^{-(s+1)/(s-1)})$, and indicates the fact that these terms are the only ones to depend on ξ_1 in the case where G is replaced by its "free molecule" form $G_m \sim \eta^{2/(s+1)}$. Practical results, however, are derived from the computation of moments of f, and these moments are immediately obtained from the consideration of the Fourier transform, Φ, according to the well known formula

$$\int_{-\infty}^{+\infty} \xi_1^l f(\xi_1)\,d\xi_1 = i^{-l}\{\partial^l\Phi/\partial\omega^l\}_{\omega=0} \qquad (l = 1, 2, \ldots).$$

It is clear, also, that all moments involving the component ξ_1 as a factor will only present attenuated singularities, so that we will concern ourselves with the other, critical moments, which are all proportional to

$$\int_{-\infty}^{+\infty} f(\xi_1)\,d\xi_1 = \Phi(0)$$
$$= \int_0^{+\infty} G(\eta)\{\exp[-(x_1 + \tfrac{1}{2})K^{-1}\eta^{-1}] - \exp[-(\tfrac{1}{2} - x_1)K^{-1}\eta^{-1}]\}\,d\eta.$$

This would be the case, for instance, for the bulk velocity parallel to the plates, in Couette flow, and for the temperature in the thermal conduction problem.

The use of our reduced variables now immediately leads to the announced result, namely, that the corrections to the free molecule data are dominated by terms proportional to $K^{-(s-1)/(s+1)}$ for large Knudsen numbers.

It appears from experimental and theoretical data that the far field of interaction between neutral molecules is well represented by an attractive force field proportional to r^{-7}. This would thus yield near free molecule corrections proportional to $K^{-3/4}$, which will clearly dominate all finite cross section effects in $K^{-1} \ln K$ for sufficiently large K.

The results also apply to the interaction between ions and neutrals, the far field now corresponding to an attractive force field proportional to r^{-5}. The near free molecule terms would then be of an even higher order of magnitude, as they are proportional to $K^{-2/3}$ in this case.

It should be noted also, that the limiting case of small coupling coefficient in the Fokker-Planck equation, which corresponds formally to taking s equal to 2 in the present treatment, yields terms in $K^{-1/3}$, where K now represents a quantity inversely proportional to the coupling coefficient. This represents the most spectacular near free molecule corrections met in practice.

V. Hyperthermal Couette Flow

In order to illustrate the theory, we will briefly outline the treatment of the plane Couette flow problem.

In order to simplify the integrations occurring in the expression for φ introduced in Section III, we consider a hyperthermal condition by assuming the relative velocity W between the plates to be much larger than the thermal velocities $(2RT)^{1/2}$. The free molecule velocity distributions may then be expressed in terms of Dirac functions so that the integrations may be carried out without any difficulty. Complete accommodation at the walls is also assumed.

It must be stressed that the numerical treatment which follows is based on the " free molecule " value G_m of the function G. As mentioned in Section III, it is not likely that this represents a valid approximation to the actual solution of the integral equation (7). The numerical coefficients occurring in the expressions to be derived should not, therefore, be taken too strictly. The dependence on the significant parameters is correct, however.

The free molecule solution for the present Couette flow problem can immediately be written as follows:

$$f_m = (2\pi RT)^{-1/2} \exp[\xi_1^2/2RT]\delta(\xi_2 \pm \tfrac{1}{2}W)\delta(\xi_3) \quad \text{for} \quad \pm\xi_1 > 0,$$

δ being the Dirac function, which has not been used here to represent the ξ_1-dependence because it would introduce difficulties at the critical point. The δ representation may, however, be used in computing the integral occurring in the expression for φ. Note that the distribution function corresponds to a unit number density, as required for introducing the Knudsen number explicitly in the Boltzmann equation (1). The integral in the expression for φ is readily obtained, using the properties of the Dirac functions:

$$\iiint g^{(s-5)/(s-1)}(g_2{}^2 + g_3{}^2)^{1/(s-1)}f_m{}' \, d\xi'$$
$$= \tfrac{1}{2}\{[(\xi_2 - \tfrac{1}{2}W)^2 + \xi_3{}^2]^{(s-3)/2(s-1)} + [(\xi_2 + \tfrac{1}{2}W)^2 + \xi_3{}^2]^{(s-3)/2(s-1)}\}.$$

We have, furthermore,

$$\mathscr{F}_+(0) - \mathscr{F}_-(0) = \delta(\xi_3)[\delta(\xi_2 - \tfrac{1}{2}W) - \delta(\xi_2 + \tfrac{1}{2}W)](2\pi RT)^{-1/2},$$

using the Gaussian representation of the ξ_1 dependence. The "free molecule" G_m now becomes

$$G_m = \tfrac{1}{2}\delta(\xi_3)[\delta(\xi_2 - \tfrac{1}{2}W) - \delta(\xi_2 + \tfrac{1}{2}W)](2\pi RT)^{-1/2}C\eta^{-2/(s+1)}$$

where

$$C = \{\sin[(\tfrac{1}{2}\pi)(s-1)/(s+1)]\Gamma[(s-1)/(s+1)]\}^{-1}.$$

Using G_m as a representation for G, we get

$$\int_{-\infty}^{+\infty} f \, d\xi_1 = \tfrac{1}{2}\delta(\xi_3)[\delta(\xi_2 - \tfrac{1}{2}W) - \delta(\xi_2 + \tfrac{1}{2}W)](2\pi RT)^{-1/2}CK^{-(s-1)/(s+1)}$$
$$\times \int_0^{\infty} \tilde{\eta}^{-2/(s+1)}\{\exp[-\tilde{\eta}^{-1}(x_1 + \tfrac{1}{2})] - \exp[\tilde{\eta}^{-1}(x_1 - \tfrac{1}{2})]\} \, d\tilde{\eta}.$$

The integral may be expressed in terms of the Gamma function:

$$\int_0^{\infty} \tilde{\eta}^{-2/(s+1)}\{\exp[-\tilde{\eta}^{-1}(x_1 + \tfrac{1}{2})] - \exp[\tilde{\eta}^{-1}(x_1 - \tfrac{1}{2})]\} \, d\tilde{\eta}$$
$$= \frac{s+1}{s-1}\Gamma\left(\frac{2}{s+1}\right)\{(\tfrac{1}{2} - x_1)^{(s-1)/(s+1)} - (\tfrac{1}{2} + x_1)^{(s-1)/(s+1)}\}.$$

We must now replace K^{-1} by its product with

$$\tfrac{1}{2}C'\{[(\xi_2 - \tfrac{1}{2}W)^2 + \xi_3{}^2]^{(s-3)/2(s-1)} + [(\xi_2 + \tfrac{1}{2}W)^2 + \xi_3{}^2]^{(s-3)/2(s-1)}\}$$

where

$$C' = \pi^{(s+1)/2(s-1)} \sin\left[(\tfrac{1}{2}\pi)\frac{s+1}{s-1}\right]\left\{\frac{\Gamma(s/2)}{\Gamma[(s+1)/2]}\right\}^{2/(s-1)}$$
$$\times \left(\frac{A}{m}\right)^{2/(s-1)} \frac{\Gamma[(s-3)/(s-1)]\Gamma[(s+1)/2(s-1)]}{\Gamma[s/(s-1)]},$$

according to the expression for φ given in Section III. The velocity distribution between the walls may now be computed. We have

$$u_2 = \iint_{-\infty}^{+\infty} \xi_2 \, d\xi_2 \, d\xi_3 \int_{-\infty}^{+\infty} f \, d\xi_1 = \tfrac{1}{2}C(\tfrac{1}{2}C')^{(s-1)/(s+1)}$$
$$\times [(s+1)/(s-1)]\Gamma[2/(s+1)](2\pi RT)^{-1/2}K^{-(s-1)/(s+1)}$$
$$\times \{(\tfrac{1}{2} - x_1)^{(s-1)/(s+1)} - (\tfrac{1}{2} + x_1)^{(s-1)/(s+1)}\}2W^{2(s-1)/(s+1)}$$

In the case of neutral nonpolar molecules, the far field is best represented by taking $s = 7$, which also results from quantum theory. This yields, for the dominant term describing the velocity distribution,

$$u_2/(2RT)^{1/2} = 2.9(W/(2RT)^{1/2})^{3/2}(K')^{-3/4}\{(\tfrac{1}{2} - x_1)^{3/4} - (\tfrac{1}{2} + x_1)^{3/4}\},$$

K' being an effective Knudsen number based on the mean free path for the far field, and given by

$$K' = \{n(A/2mRT)^{1/3}\}^{-1}/L.$$

Comparison with finite cross-section contributions is not significant because these depend on the complete law of force while the present leading term is conditioned by the far field, and there is no general connection between interactions at large distance and at short distance.

VI. Conclusions. Generalizations

A marked qualitative dependence of the leading term of the near free molecule corrections on the molecular interaction law has been shown to exist, at least for one-dimensional problems.

The study of two- and three-dimensional problems is considerably more complicated because the integral operator of the reduced equation will depend explicitly on the space coordinates as the free molecule solution is no longer uniform in space.

A simple order of magnitude argument, however, leads one to expect that the contribution of the effect analyzed in the present paper would be of order $K^{-2(s-1)/(s+1)}$ and $K^{-3(s-1)/(s+1)}$ in cylindrical and full three dimensional cases, respectively. This contribution would therefore be smaller than the leading terms ($K^{-1} \ln K$ and K^{-1}, respectively) except for the Fokker-Planck equation. The influence of an infinite range of interaction would thus generally be felt only in approximations higher than the first.

List of Symbols

$a(\xi, \xi', \theta, \varepsilon)$	$= \xi_1^* - \xi_1$	$D(f)$	$= f^*f'^* - ff'$
A	Coefficient in intermolecular force law: $F = Ar^{-s}$	f	$= f(\xi_1, \xi_2, \xi_3, x_1)$ velocity distribution function.
$\mathscr{C}(f)$	Collision term in the Boltzmann equation	f'	$= f(\xi_1', \xi_2', \xi_3', x_1)$
		f^*	$= f(\xi_1^*, \xi_2^*, \xi_3^*, x_1)$
C, C'	Constants	f'^*	$= f(\xi_1'^*, \xi_2'^*, \xi_3'^*, x_1)$

f_m	Distribution function for the free molecule solution	$\mathbf{u}$	Bulk velocity of gas
F	Intermolecular force	W	Relative velocity between walls in Couette flow problem
$\mathscr{F}_\pm(f)$	Functionals representing interactions with solid boundaries	x_1	Space coordinate perpendicular to solid boundaries
$\mathbf{g} = \boldsymbol{\xi} - \boldsymbol{\xi}'$	Relative velocity of colliding molecules	*Greek letters*	
g_1, g_2, g_3	Components of $\mathbf{g}$	α	Angle $(0 < \alpha < (s-1)/(s+1))$
$g(\eta, \xi_2, \xi_3, x_1)$	Fourier transform of Φ with respect to Ω	Γ	Gamma function
$G_\pm(\eta)$	Boundary values for g, $G_\pm(\eta) = g(x_1 = \pm \frac{1}{2})$	δ	Dirac function
$\mathscr{G}(\tilde{\eta})$	Solution of the integral equation in reduced variables	ε	Angle defining the position of the plane of relative trajectories of colliding molecules
$\mathscr{I}(z)$	$= iz^{-1} - 2[\exp(i\pi/4)z^{1/2} \times K_1[2z^{1/2}\exp(-i\pi/4)]$	η	Fourier variable in transformation of Φ with respect to Ω
K	Knudsen number	$\tilde{\eta}$	$= K\eta$
$\mathscr{K}(\xi_1, \xi_1')$	Kernel of reduced integro - differential equation	θ	Angle of scattering in molecular collision
$K(\xi_1, \eta)$	$= \pi^{-1} \int_0^\infty \cos[\omega\xi_1 - \eta\Omega(\omega)] \, d\omega$	$\mu(\omega)$	$= \int_0^\infty \sin \omega\xi_1 [\mathscr{F}_+(\xi_1) - \mathscr{F}_-(-\xi_1)] \, d\xi_1/2$
$\mathscr{K}(u)$	$= \pi^{-1} \int_0^\infty \cos[\omega - \text{const } u\omega^{(s+1)/(s-1)}] \, d\omega$	ν	Angle between line connecting colliding molecules and the direction of their relative undisturbed trajectories
L	Length scale		
$\mathscr{L}(\Omega, \Omega^*)$	Kernel of an integral equation of the second kind	$\boldsymbol{\xi}$	Molecular velocity vector
m	Mass of a molecule	$\boldsymbol{\xi}'$	Velocity of partner in a collision
N	Reference number density	$\boldsymbol{\xi}^*$	Velocity after collision
P	$= (\pi K)^{-1} \int_0^\infty \psi(\omega) \exp(i\eta\Omega) \, d\omega$, nonhomogeneous term in integral equation for $g(\eta)$	$\boldsymbol{\xi}'^*$	Velocity of partner after collision
		ξ_1^*	$= \xi_1 + (\theta/2)\cos\varepsilon(g_2^2 + g_3^2)^{1/2}$
		$\tilde{\xi}$	$= K^{(s-1/(/)s+1)}\xi_1$
Q_m	See Eq. (3)	$\sigma(g, \theta)$	Differential cross section
r	Distance between colliding molecules		
R	Gas constant per unit mass	Σ	Reference cross section
R_m	See Eq. (3)	$\varphi(\omega, \xi_2, \xi_3)$	$= \int\int\int\int\int \{\exp[i\omega(g_2^2 + g_3^2)^{1/2}\cos\varepsilon \cdot\theta/2] - 1\} (g\sigma_P)_{\xi_1=0}\theta \, d\theta \, d\varepsilon f_m'$ $d\boldsymbol{\xi} - Q_m(\xi_2, \xi_3)$
s	Exponent in intermolecular force		
T	Absolute temperature of wall in Couette problem	Φ	Fourier transform of f with respect to ξ_1
		$\chi(\Omega)$	Fourier transform of G with respect to η

| ψ | Fourier transform of R_m with respect to ξ_1 | | formation with respect to ξ_1 |
| ω | Fourier variable in trans- | Ω | $= \int_0^\omega \varphi(\omega)\, d\omega$ |

REFERENCES

Gevrey, M. (1914). *J. Math.* [6] **10**, 105.

Smolderen, J. J. (1963). *Phys. Fluids* **6**, 1356.

Willis, D. R. (1961). *In* "Rarefied Gas Dynamics" (L. Talbot, ed.), p. 429. Academic Press, New York.

A Uniformly Valid Asymptotic Theory of Rarefied Gas Flows under Nearly Free Molecular Conditions, II[1]

YOUNG-PING PAO

Gas Dynamics Laboratory, Princeton University, Princeton, New Jersey

For a rarefied gas flow of infinite extent over a submerged body, at very large Knudsen number, the free molecular solution is not a uniformly valid approximation throughout the flow field. This nonuniform validity will necessarily invalidate the collisional corrections obtained (even in the vicinity of the submerged body) by any iteration procedure based on the free molecular solution as the order of correction becomes higher. In the present study, a uniformly valid asymptotic theory is developed, based on the BGKW model equation, for the simple nearly free molecular flow problem of a two-dimensional cylinder rotating in an infinite gas otherwise at rest. The asymptotic solutions given by this theory will be uniformly valid approximate solutions.

I. Introduction

For a gas flow of infinite extent over a submerged body, when the characteristic dimension L of the body is very small in comparison with the mean free path λ of the gas, i.e., when $\alpha = L/\lambda \ll 1$, one method of constructing an approximate solution to the flow problem is to neglect the interaction between the molecules re-emitted from the body and the incident stream, cf. Epstein (1924) and Tsien (1946). The solution so obtained is called the free molecular solution. The simplifying feature of such problems is that most of the molecules re-emitted from the body do not collide with the molecules of the incident stream until far away from the body. This justifies the separate

---

[1] This work was supported by the U.S. Air Force under Contract AF 49(638)-1271.

consideration of the re-emitted molecules and the incident stream. A number of improvements over the free molecular solution have been suggested in order to take into account the collisional effects, e.g., by Baker and Charwat (1958), and Willis (1958). Willis has transformed the Boltzmann equation into an integral equation somewhat similar to the Volterra type and the method of solution he has proposed is an iteration procedure for this integral equation using the free molecular solution as the zeroth iterate. Taking the Boltzmann equation as the basic framework, Willis has been able to obtain the collisional correction to higher orders and to eliminate unnecessary assumptions and restrictions in the previous works. Solutions that take into account the collisional effects for $\alpha \ll 1$ are called the nearly free molecular solutions.

However, it should be noted that the description of the flow field by the free molecular solution is only valid in the inner region, a region within a distance much larger than the body dimension L but much smaller than the mean free path λ from the body. Outside of this region the collisional effects cannot be neglected even in the lowest order approximation and as a result, the free molecular solution is not a uniformly valid approximation throughout the flow field. It is then clear that a systematic method of obtaining higher order collisional corrections cannot be achieved based on the free molecular solution only. To secure such a method, it would be necessary to be able to treat adequately the outer region, i.e., the part of the physical space complementary to the inner region. For this purpose an asymptotic theory for obtaining nearly free molecular solutions which are uniformly valid throughout the flow field has been proposed by Pao (1964) for the linearized Boltzmann equation for the case of hard-sphere molecules. Power-law molecules may be treated in a like manner. In the present study, this theory will be carried out in considerable detail for the simple problem of a two-dimensional circular cylinder rotating in an infinite gas, otherwise at rest, using a model equation. This specific problem not only demonstrates the techniques and principles of carrying out the asymptotic theory to arbitrarily high orders but also is simple enough that the asymptotic solutions so obtained can be rigorously proved to be uniformly valid approximate solutions throughout the flow field and thus helps to illustrate the mathematical nature of the asymptotic theory. The mathematical formulation of the cylinder problem is given in Section II. In Section III, the asymptotic theory is carried out for this problem to yield the asymptotic solutions. These solutions are proved in Section IV to be uniformly valid approximate solutions throughout the flow field. The model equation to be used is the one proposed independently by Bhatnagar *et al.* (1954) and by Welander (1954) and may be called the BGKW equation. A brief discussion of the reasonableness of this model equation may be found in Liepmann *et al.* (1962).

II. Formulation of the Problem

Let n_∞ and T_∞ be the number density and temperature of the gas at infinity and c the molecular velocity divided by $(2RT_\infty)^{1/2}$. The perturbation distribution function $f(c; r)$ may be introduced through the relation

$$F = n_\infty \left(\frac{1}{2\pi R T_\infty} \right)^{3/2} \exp(-c^2)[1 + f]$$

where F is the distribution function.

For the simple problem of a rotating cylinder, it can be easily seen that the variations in the density and temperature fields are second order quantities in the angular speed of the cylinder and may, therefore, be neglected. Also, the radial component of the macroscopic velocity vanishes identically because of the conservation of molecules and the boundary conditions at the cylinder surface and at infinity. If a cylindrical (r, θ, z) coordinate system is chosen with its origin at a cross-sectional center of the two-dimensional cylinder, the linearized BGKW equation may be written as

$$c_r \frac{\partial f}{\partial r} + \frac{c_\theta^2}{r} \frac{\partial f}{\partial c_r} - \frac{c_r c_\theta}{r} \frac{\partial f}{\partial c_\theta} = \alpha\{2\pi^{-3/2} r\omega(r)c_\theta - f\}, \tag{1}$$

the condition at infinity requires

$$f \to 0 \quad \text{as} \quad r \to \infty, \quad \text{for} \quad c_r < 0, \tag{2}$$

and the boundary condition at the cylinder surface is

$$f = 2\pi^{-3/2} c_\theta \quad \text{at} \quad r = 1, \quad \text{for} \quad c_r > 0 \tag{2a}$$

where the angular speed of the cylinder is 1, the radius of the cylinder is 1, α is a constant inversely proportional to the mean free path of the gas and $\omega(r)$ is the mean angular speed of the gas defined by

$$\omega(r) = r^{-1} \iiint \exp(-c^2) f c_\theta \, d^3c. \tag{3}$$

The characteristic equations for Eq. (1) are

$$dr/c_r = -r \, dc_\theta/c_r c_\theta = r \, dc_r/c_\theta^2. \tag{4}$$

Along a characteristic curve defined by Eq. (4), f may be integrated in terms of $\omega(r)$ using Eq. (1). The results are:

For $\pi/2 < |\varphi| < \pi$,

$$f = 2\pi^{-3/2}\alpha r \sin \varphi \int_r^\infty \frac{\eta\omega(\eta)}{(\eta^2 - r^2 \sin^2 \varphi)^{1/2}}$$
$$\times \exp\left[-\frac{\alpha}{s}[(\eta^2 - r^2 \sin^2 \varphi)^{1/2} - r \cos \varphi]\right] d\eta; \quad (5a)$$

for $|\varphi| < \sin^{-1}(1/r)$,

$$f = 2\pi^{-3/2}sr \sin \varphi \exp\left[-\frac{\alpha}{s}[r \cos \varphi - (1 - r^2 \sin^2 \phi)^{1/2}]\right]$$
$$+ 2\pi^{-3/2}\alpha r \sin \varphi \int_1^r \frac{\eta\omega(\eta)}{(\eta^2 - r^2 \sin^2 \varphi)^{1/2}}$$
$$\times \exp\left[-\frac{\alpha}{s}[r \cos \varphi - (\eta^2 - r^2 \sin^2 \varphi)^{1/2}]\right] d\eta, \quad (5b)$$

and for $\sin^{-1}(1/r) < |\varphi| < \pi/2$,

$$f = 2\pi^{-3/2}\alpha r \sin \varphi \int_{r \sin \varphi}^\infty \frac{\eta\omega(\eta)}{(\eta^2 - r^2 \sin^2 \varphi)^{1/2}}$$
$$\times \exp\left[-\frac{\alpha}{s}[(\eta^2 - r^2 \sin^2 \varphi)^{1/2} + r \cos \varphi]\right] d\eta$$
$$+ 2\pi^{-3/2}\alpha r \sin \varphi \int_{r \sin \phi}^r \frac{\eta\omega(\eta)}{\eta^2 - r^2 \sin^2 \varphi)^{1/2}}$$
$$\times \exp\left[-\frac{\alpha}{s}[r \cos \varphi - (\eta^2 - r^2 \sin^2 \varphi)^{1/2}]\right] d\eta, \quad (5c)$$

where $\qquad s = (c_r^2 + c_\theta^2)^{1/2} \qquad$ and $\qquad \varphi = \tan^{-1}(c_\theta/c_r)$.

Substituting Eq. (5) into Eq. (1) gives a linear integral equation for $\omega(r)$. From physical considerations the unknown function $\omega(r)$ will be restricted to be uniformly bounded in r. For such functions, the order of integrations over s, φ, and η in the linear integral equation for $\omega(r)$ may be interchanged according to the Fubini theorem and the result may be written as

$$\omega(r, \alpha) = \Omega(r, \alpha) + \int_1^\infty K(r, \eta; \alpha)\omega(\eta, \alpha) d\eta \qquad (6)$$

where the dependence of $\omega(r)$ on α has been brought out explicitly and the functions $\Omega(r, \alpha)$ and $k(r, \eta; \alpha)$ are defined by

$$\Omega(r, \alpha) = 4\pi^{-1} \int_0^{\sin^{-1}(1/r)} \int_0^\infty \exp\left[-s^2 - \frac{\alpha}{s}[r \cos \varphi - (1 - r^2 \sin^2 \varphi)^{1/2}]\right]$$
$$\times s^3 \sin^2 \varphi \, ds \, d\varphi,$$

$$K(r, \eta; \alpha) = \frac{4\alpha\eta}{\pi} \left\{ \int_0^b \int_0^\infty \frac{s^2 \sin^2 \varphi}{(\eta^2 - r^2 \sin^2 \varphi)^{1/2}} \right.$$

$$\times \exp\left[-s^2 - \frac{\alpha}{s} [|r \cos \varphi - (\eta^2 - r^2 \sin^2 \varphi)^{1/2}|] \right] ds \, d\varphi$$

$$+ \int_{\sin^{-1}(1/r)}^b \int_0^\infty \frac{s^2 \sin^2 \varphi}{(\eta^2 - r^2 \sin^2 \varphi)^{1/2}}$$

$$\times \exp\left[-s^2 - \frac{\alpha}{s} [r \cos \varphi + (\eta^2 - r^2 \sin^2 \varphi)^{1/2}] \right] ds \, d\varphi \right\},$$

where

$$b = \sin^{-1}(\eta/r) \qquad \text{for} \quad \eta < r,$$

$$= \pi/2 \qquad\qquad \text{for} \quad \eta > r.$$

The condition at infinity requires that

$$\lim_{r \to \infty} \omega(r, \alpha) = 0. \tag{7}$$

An analytic solution to Eqs. (6) and (7) can not be found. In the next section, a method of constructing asymptotic solutions to Eqs. (6) and (7) will be given for small α. In Section IV, it will be proved that the asymptotic solutions so obtained are indeed uniformly valid approximate solutions to the problem.

III. Asymptotic Solutions for $\alpha \ll 1$

For the purpose of constructing asymptotic solutions, the physical space is divided into two regions: an inner region for $1 < r < \tau$ and an outer region for $\tau < r < \infty$, where τ is a function of α having the property that $\tau \to \infty$ and $\alpha\tau \to 0$ as $\alpha \to 0$. The explicit form of $\tau(\alpha)$ is yet to be determined. Before going into the details of how the asymptotic solutions can be obtained, it is found most clarifying to point out two basic ideas which underlie the entire asymptotic theory. First, at a point in the inner region, the distance from the body is very small compared with the mean free path which is proportional to $1/\alpha$ as is evidenced by the property of τ that $\alpha\tau \to 0$ as $\alpha \to 0$. Consequently, the effects due to the collisions among the molecules coming to this point from the body and from their last collision in the inner region are only secondary, at least for molecules of moderate speeds. Secondly, inasmuch as the effects of the body is felt in the outer region, the size of the body shrinks to zero in the limit $\alpha \to 0$, if the mean free path is taken as the length scale. Consequently the flow field in the outer region is independent of the Knudsen number in a sense that will be made precise later. These observations seem to suggest that in the limit $\alpha \to 0$, the function $\omega(r, \alpha)$ will have different behaviors in the two regions, i.e., $\omega(r, \alpha)$ will have different asymptotic representations in the two regions.

In the inner region r and η are used as the independent variable and the variable of integration, while in the outer region $\rho = \alpha r$ and $\xi = \alpha \eta$ are used. Also, for the sake of distinction, the dependent variable $\omega(r, \alpha)$ is denoted as $\hat{\omega}(r, \alpha)$ in the inner region and $\omega(r, \alpha) = \omega(\rho/\alpha, \alpha)$ is denoted as $\tilde{\omega}(\rho, \alpha)$ in the outer region. In terms of these new functions, Eqs. (6) and (7) become, in the outer region for $\alpha\tau < \rho < \infty$,

$$\tilde{\omega}(\rho, \alpha) = \Omega(\rho/\alpha, \alpha) + \int_1^\tau K(\rho/\alpha, \eta; \alpha)\hat{\omega}(\eta, \alpha)\, d\eta$$

$$+ \alpha^{-1} \int_{\alpha\tau}^\infty K(\rho/\alpha, \xi/\alpha; \alpha)\tilde{\omega}(\xi, \alpha)\, d\xi \tag{8}$$

and $\qquad\qquad \tilde{\omega}(\rho, \alpha) \to 0 \qquad$ as $\quad \rho \to \infty.$ $\qquad\qquad$ (9)

Also, similarly in the inner region $1 < r < \tau$, Eq. (6) becomes

$$\hat{\omega}(r, \alpha) = \Omega(r, \alpha) + \int_1^\tau K(r, \eta; \alpha)\hat{\omega}(\eta, \alpha)\, d\eta + \alpha^{-1} \int_{\alpha\tau}^\infty K(r, \xi/\alpha; \alpha)\tilde{\omega}(\xi, \alpha)\, d\xi. \tag{10}$$

Since $\hat{\omega}(r, \alpha)$ and $\tilde{\omega}(\rho, \alpha)$ are assumed to possess different asymptotic representations, they will have to be treated as if they were different functions. The asymptotic representations for $\hat{\omega}(r, \alpha)$ and $\tilde{\omega}(\rho, \alpha)$ are assumed to be of the type $\sum_n \hat{\sigma}_n(\alpha)\hat{\omega}_n(r)$ and $\sum_n \tilde{\sigma}_n(\alpha)\tilde{\omega}_n(\rho)$, respectively, and will be derived from Eqs. (8)–(10) in what follows.

A. The Outer Solutions

In the outer region $\rho > \alpha\tau$, the inhomogeneous term $\Omega(\rho/\alpha, \alpha)$ of Eq. (8) may be expanded asymptotically as

$$\Omega(\rho/\alpha, \alpha) = 4\pi^{-1}(\alpha^3/3\rho^3)[J_3(\rho) + O(\alpha)J_2(\rho)] \tag{11}$$

where the order symbol capital O has been used (Erdélyi, 1956, p. 5) and the functions $J_n(x)$ are defined by

$$J_n(x) = \int_0^\infty s^n \exp[-s^2 - (x/s)]\, ds.$$

The kernel $\alpha^{-1}K(\rho/\alpha, \xi/\alpha; \alpha)$ has the following asymptotic expansion:

$$\alpha^{-1} K\left(\frac{\rho}{\alpha}, \frac{\xi}{\alpha}; \alpha\right) = \tilde{K}(\rho, \xi)[1 + O(\tau^{-3})] \tag{12}$$

where

$$\tilde{K}(\rho, \xi) = \frac{4\xi}{\pi} \left\{ \int_0^b \int_0^\infty \frac{s^2 \sin^2 \varphi}{(\eta^2 - r^2 \sin^2 \varphi)^{1/2}} \right.$$

$$\times \exp\left[-s^2 - \frac{1}{s} [\rho \cos \varphi + (\xi^2 - \rho^2 \sin^2 \varphi)^{1/2}] \right] ds \, d\varphi$$

$$+ \int_0^b \int_0^\infty \frac{s^2 \sin^2 \varphi}{(\eta^2 - r^2 \sin^2 \varphi)^{1/2}}$$

$$\left. \times \exp\left[-s^2 - \frac{1}{s} [|\rho \cos \varphi - (\xi^2 - \rho^2 \sin^2 \varphi)^{1/2}|] \right] ds \, d\varphi \right\},$$

and

$$b = \sin^{-1} \frac{\xi}{\rho} \qquad \text{for} \quad \xi < \rho,$$

$$= \pi/2 \qquad \text{for} \quad \xi > \rho.$$

For the kernel $K(\rho/\alpha, \eta; \alpha)$ it will be assumed that $\rho \gg \alpha \eta$ for $1 < \eta < \tau$. The result is

$$K(\rho/\alpha, \eta; \alpha) = (O\alpha^4)(\eta^3/\rho^3)J_2(\rho). \tag{13}$$

It perhaps should be noted that the condition $\rho \gg \alpha \eta$ is not valid for $\rho \to \alpha \tau$. Therefore, to use Eq. (13), it is necessary to make the restriction that $\rho \geqslant \alpha \tau_1$ where $\tau_1(\alpha)$ has the property that $\tau_1 \to \infty$, $\alpha \tau_1 \to 0$ and $\tau_1/\tau \to \infty$ as $\alpha \to 0$. Since $\tilde{\omega}_n(\rho)$ does not depend on α, the validity of the asymptotic expansions $\sum \tilde{\sigma}_n(\alpha)\tilde{\omega}_n(\rho)$ for $\tilde{\omega}(\rho, \alpha)$ will be extended to cover the interval $(\alpha \tau, \alpha \tau_1)$.

Substituting Eqs. (11)–(13) into Eq. (8) and neglecting the higher order terms yield the following result:

$$\omega(\rho, \alpha) = 4\pi^{-1}(\alpha^3/3\rho^3)J_3(\rho) + O(\alpha^4)[J_2(\rho)/\rho^3] \int_1^\tau \eta^3 \hat{\omega}(\eta, \alpha) \, d\eta$$

$$+ \int_{\alpha\tau}^\infty \tilde{K}(\rho, \xi)\tilde{\omega}(\xi, \alpha) \, d\xi.$$

It is now clear from the above equation that $\tilde{\sigma}_0(\alpha) = \alpha^3$. Indeed, divided through by α^3, the above equation becomes, in the limit $\alpha \to 0$,

$$\tilde{\omega}_0(\rho) = 4\pi^{-1}[J_3(\rho)/3\rho^3] + \int_0^\infty \tilde{K}(\rho, \xi)\tilde{\omega}_0(\xi) \, d\xi. \tag{14}$$

In the derivation of Eq. (14) it has been assumed that $\hat{\omega}(\eta, \alpha)$ to the lowest order is the free molecular solution $\hat{\Omega}_0(\eta)$ where as $\eta \to \infty$

$$\Omega_0(\eta) \to 2/3\pi\eta^3.$$

In this connection it is also assumed that as $\xi \to 0$, $\tilde{\omega}_0(\xi) \to 2/3\pi\xi^3$, which may be justified by examining the singularity of $\tilde{\omega}_0(\rho)$ according to Eq. (14) as $\rho \to 0$.

For $\tilde{\omega}_0(\rho)$ the condition (9) at infinity becomes

$$\lim_{\rho \to \infty} \tilde{\omega}_0(\rho) = 0. \tag{15}$$

Equations (14) and (15) are free of α and determine the zeroth order outer solution $\tilde{\omega}_0(\rho)$. The next order outer solution $\tilde{\omega}_1(\rho)$ can then be computed based on $\tilde{\omega}_0(\rho)$, taking $\hat{\omega}(r, \alpha)$ to the lowest order to be the free molecular solution.

B. The Inner Solutions

Recall that in Eq. (10)

$$\Omega(r, \alpha) = 4\pi^{-1} \int_0^{\sin^{-1}(1/r)} J_3\{\alpha[r \cos \varphi - (1 - r^2 \sin^2 \varphi)^{1/2}]\} \sin^2 \varphi \, d\varphi,$$

and since in the inner region $\alpha r < \alpha \tau$ where $\alpha \tau \to 0$ as $\alpha \to 0$, the argument of J_3 in the last integral is very small. Using the asymptotic expansions of $J_3(x)$ for small x (Abramowitz, 1953) the following result is found:

$$\Omega(r, \alpha) = \hat{\Omega}_0(r) + \alpha\hat{\Omega}_1(r) + \alpha^2\hat{\Omega}_2(r) + O(\alpha^3)\hat{\Omega}_3(r) \tag{16}$$

where

$$\hat{\Omega}_0(r) = \pi^{-1}\{\sin^{-1}(1/r) - (1/2r)[1 - (1/r^2)]^{1/2}\},$$

$$\hat{\Omega}_1(r) = -\pi^{-1/2} \int_0^{\sin^{-1}(1/r)} [r \cos \varphi - (1 - r^2 \sin^2 \varphi)^{1/2}] \sin^2 \varphi \, d\varphi,$$

$$\hat{\Omega}_2(r) = \pi^{-1} \int_0^{\sin^{-1}(1/r)} [r \cos \varphi - (1 - r^2 \sin^2 \varphi)^{1/2}]^2 \sin^2 \varphi \, d\varphi,$$

and

$$\hat{\Omega}_3(r) = \int_0^{\sin^{-1}(1/r)} [r \cos \varphi - (1 - r^2 \sin^2 \varphi)^{1/2}]^3 \sin^2 \varphi \, d\varphi.$$

In a similar manner the asymptotic expansion for the kernel $K(r, \eta; \alpha)$ in Eq. (10) is found to be

$$K(r, \eta; \alpha) = \alpha\hat{K}_0(r, \eta) + \alpha^2\hat{K}_1(r, \eta) + O(\alpha^3)\hat{K}_2(r, \eta) \tag{17}$$

where

$$\hat{K}_0(r, \eta) = \frac{\eta}{\pi^{1/2}} \left\{ \int_0^b \frac{\sin^2 \varphi \, d\varphi}{(\eta^2 - r^2 \sin^2 \varphi)^{1/2}} + \int_{\sin^{-1}(1/r)}^b \frac{\sin^2 \varphi \, d\varphi}{(\eta^2 - r^2 \sin^2 \varphi)^{1/2}} \right\},$$

$$\hat{K}_1(r, \eta) = \frac{2\eta}{\pi^{1/2}} \left\{ \int_0^b \frac{|r \cos \varphi - (\eta^2 - r^2 \sin^2 \varphi)^{1/2}|}{(\eta^2 - r^2 \sin^2 \varphi)^{1/2}} \sin^2 \varphi \, d\varphi \right.$$

$$\left. + \int_{\sin^{-1}(1/r)}^b \frac{[r \cos \varphi + (\eta^2 - r^2 \sin^2 \varphi)^{1/2}]}{(\eta^2 - r^2 \sin^2 \varphi)^{1/2}} \sin^2 \varphi \, d\varphi \right\},$$

$$\hat{K}_2(r, \eta) = \frac{\eta}{\pi^{1/2}} \left\{ \int_0^b \frac{[r \cos \varphi - (\eta^2 - r^2 \sin^2 \varphi)^{1/2}]^2}{(\eta^2 - r^2 \sin^2 \varphi)^{1/2}} \sin^2 \varphi \, d\varphi \right.$$

$$\left. + \int_{\sin^{-1}(1/r)}^b \frac{[r \cos \varphi + (\eta^2 - r^2 \sin^2 \varphi)^{1/2}]^2}{(\eta^2 - r^2 \sin^2 \varphi)^{1/2}} \sin^2 \varphi \, d\varphi \right\},$$

and

$$b = \sin^{-1}(\eta/r) \quad \text{for} \quad \eta < r,$$
$$= \pi/2 \quad \text{for} \quad \eta > r.$$

For the kernel $K(r, \xi/\alpha; \alpha)$ it will again be assumed that $\xi \gg \alpha r$, and consequently

$$K(r, \xi/\alpha; \alpha) = 4\alpha\pi^{-1/2}[1 + O(\alpha)]J_2(\xi)\{\tfrac{1}{2}\pi - (1/4r)[1 - (1/r^2)]\}. \quad (18)$$

Substituting Eqs. (16)–(18) into Eq. (10) and replacing $\tilde{\omega}(\rho, \alpha)$ by $\alpha^3 \tilde{\omega}_0(\rho)$ shows that $\hat{\sigma}_0(\alpha)\hat{\omega}_0(r) = \hat{\Omega}_0(r)$ is a consistent lowest order solution to Eq. (10) and justifies the earlier estimate made for the lowest order behavior of $\hat{\omega}(r, \alpha)$ in the derivation of Eqs. (14) and (15).

For the next order inner solution $\hat{\omega}_1(r)$ Eq. (10) may be written in the form of

$$\lim_{\alpha \to 0} \left[\frac{\hat{\omega}(r, \alpha) - \hat{\Omega}_0(r)}{\alpha} \right] = \hat{\Omega}_1(r) + \lim_{\alpha \to 0} \int_1^\tau \hat{K}_0(r, \eta)\hat{\Omega}_0(\eta) \, d\eta$$

$$+ \left[\frac{\pi}{2} - \frac{1}{4r} \left(1 - \frac{1}{r^2} \right)^{1/2} \right]$$

$$\times \lim_{\alpha \to 0} \left\{ 4\alpha^3 \pi^{-1/2} \int_{\alpha\tau}^\infty J_2(\xi)\tilde{\omega}_0(\xi) \, d\xi \right\}. \quad (19)$$

The last two limits may be computed as follows. As $\eta \to \infty$ it is known that

$$\hat{\Omega}_0(\eta) \to 2/3\pi\eta^3$$

and

$$K_0(r, \eta) \to \frac{4}{\pi} \left[\frac{\pi}{2} - \frac{1}{4r} \left(1 - \frac{1}{r^2} \right)^{1/2} \right],$$

and on the other hand as $\xi \to 0$,

$$\tilde{\omega}_0(\xi) \to 2/3\pi\xi^3 \quad \text{and} \quad K(r, \xi/\alpha; \alpha) \to \frac{4}{\pi} \left[\frac{\pi}{2} - \frac{1}{4r} \left(1 - \frac{1}{r^2} \right)^{1/2} \right].$$

Therefore the limit

$$\lim_{\substack{\alpha \to 0 \\ (\tau \to \infty)}} \int_1^\tau \hat{K}_0(r, \eta)\hat{\Omega}_0(\eta)\, d\eta = \int_1^\infty \hat{K}_0(r, \eta)\hat{\Omega}_0(\eta)\, d\eta$$

is a finite quantity, and

$$\lim_{\substack{\alpha \to 0 \\ (\alpha\tau \to 0)}} \left\{ 4\alpha^3 \pi^{-1/2} \int_{\alpha\tau}^\infty K(r, \xi/\alpha; \alpha)\tilde{\omega}_0(\xi)\, d\xi \right\} = 0.$$

As a consequence, Eq. (19) yields the following results:

$$\hat{\sigma}_1(\alpha) = \alpha,$$

$$\hat{\omega}_1(r) = \hat{\Omega}_1(r) + \int_1^\infty \hat{K}_0(r, \eta)\hat{\Omega}_0(\eta)\, d\eta.$$

To obtain $\hat{\omega}_2(r)$, it is convenient to rewrite Eq. (10) in the following form:

$$\alpha^{-2}\left[\hat{\omega}(r, \alpha) - \hat{\Omega}_0(r) - \alpha\hat{\Omega}_1(r) - \alpha \int_1^\infty \hat{K}_0(r, \eta)\hat{\Omega}_0(\eta)\, d\eta \right]$$

$$= \hat{\Omega}_2(r) + \int_1^\tau \hat{K}_0(r, \eta)\hat{\omega}_1(\eta)\, d\eta + \int_1^\tau \hat{K}_1(r, \eta)\hat{\Omega}_0(\eta)\, d\eta$$

$$+ \alpha \int_{\alpha\tau}^\infty K(r, \xi/\alpha; \alpha)\tilde{\omega}_0(\xi)\, d\xi.$$

In the above equation, the behavior of the integrands has to be examined in the neighborhoods of τ and $\alpha\tau$ in order to carry out the limiting process $\alpha \to 0$. In such limit, the L.H.S. of the last equation is $\hat{\omega}_2(r)$ and the equation becomes

$$\hat{\omega}_2(r) = \hat{\Omega}_2(r) + \int_1^\infty \hat{K}_0(r, \eta)\hat{\omega}_1(\eta)\, d\eta + \int_1^\infty \hat{K}_1(r, \eta)\hat{\Omega}_0(\eta)\, d\eta,$$

and it is clear that

$$\hat{\sigma}_2(\alpha) = \alpha^2.$$

From the fact that $\tilde{\sigma}_0(\alpha) = \alpha^3$ it is evident that the lowest order outer solution $\tilde{\omega}_0(\rho)$ will contribute to the next order inner solution. Higher order analysis can be carried out straightforwardly making alternate use of Eq. (10) and Eqs. (8) and (9). However, this will not be done here. In the next section, a rigorous mathematical foundation will be furnished for the asymptotic theory for this cylinder problem.

In concluding, it may be emphasized that the outer region is not a region throughout which collisional effects dominate. In fact, in the part of this region, where $\rho \to \alpha\tau$ which is very small, the nature of the flow field is that of the free molecular flow. In the part of the outer region where $\rho \to \infty$, the flow field is presumably a collision-dominated one. In between, a full transition may be expected.

IV. Mathematical Foundation

The mathematical problem for the rotating cylinder in an infinite gas otherwise at rest, is to find a function $\omega(r, \alpha)$ uniformly bounded for $1 \leqslant r < \infty$ which satisfies Eqs. (6) and (7). The condition of uniform boundedness is probably the least restrictive one and yet is sufficient to give the desirable results. For example, if $\omega(r, \alpha)$ is uniformly bounded for $1 \leqslant r < \infty$, $\omega(r, \alpha)$ is continuous. In fact, a stronger result has been obtained and may be stated in the following theorem.

Theorem 1. *If $\omega(r, \alpha)$ is a function uniformly bounded for $1 \leqslant r < \infty$ and satisfies Eq. (6), then there exist $M(N)$ and $\delta(N)$ such that $|\omega(r_1, \alpha) - \omega(r_2, \alpha)| < M|r_1 - r_2|^{1/2}$ for $|r_1 - r_2| < \delta$, $r_1 \in [1, N]$, and $r_2 \in [1, N]$.*

The proof of this theorem which involves straightforward but lengthy computations may be found in Appendix V, Pao (1964). An immediate result of this theorem is that $\omega(r, \alpha)$ is continuous. Using this result the uniqueness theorem can be proved. In the sequel two properties of the kernel $K(r, \eta; \alpha)$ will be of frequent use. In this connection suffice it to note that $K(r, \eta; \alpha) > 0$ and

$$\int_1^N K(r, \eta; \alpha)\, d\eta = 1 - \Omega(r, \alpha) - \Gamma(r, \alpha; N) \tag{20}$$

where

$$\Gamma(r, \alpha; N) = 4\pi^{-1} \int_0^{\pi/2} J_3\{\alpha[(N^2 - r^2 \sin^2 \varphi)^{1/2} - r \cos \varphi]\} \sin^2 \varphi\, d\varphi$$

$$+ 4\pi^{-1} \int_{\sin^{-1}(1/r)}^{\pi/2} J_3\{\alpha[(N^2 - r^2 \sin^2 \varphi)^{1/2}$$

$$+ r \cos \varphi]\} \sin^2 \varphi\, d\varphi,$$

and consequently for any finite r_0

$$\max_{1 \leqslant r \leqslant r_0} \int_1^N K(r, \eta; \alpha)\, d\eta < \max_{1 \leqslant r \leqslant r_0} \int_1^\infty K(r, \eta; \alpha)\, d\eta = k(r_0, \alpha) < 1.$$

Theorem 2. (Uniqueness). *If both $v_1(r, \alpha)$ and $v_2(r, \alpha)$ are uniformly bounded for $1 \leqslant r < \infty$ and satisfy Eqs. (6) and (7) then $v_1(r, \alpha) \equiv V_2(r, \alpha)$.*

Proof. Suppose the function $v(r, \alpha) = v_1(r, \alpha) - v_2(r, \alpha)$ does not vanish identically. Then $\|v\| = \sup_{[1,\infty)} |v(r, \alpha)| > 0$. Equation (7) requires that $|v(r, \alpha)| \to 0$ as $r \to \infty$, and consequently there must exist a finite r_0 such that $\|v\| = \max_{1 \leqslant r \leqslant r_0} |v(r(r, \alpha)|$. From Eq. (6),

$$v(r, \alpha) = \int_1^{\infty} K(r, \eta; \alpha) v(\eta, \alpha)\, d\eta$$

and henceforth

$$|v(r, \alpha)| \leqslant \|v\| \int_1^{\infty} K(r, \eta; \alpha)\, d\eta.$$

The last inequality holds for all r in $[1, \infty)$ and in particular, for r in $[1, r_0]$. Therefore,

$$\|v\| \leqslant \|v\| \left[\max_{1 \leqslant r \leqslant r_0} \int_1^{\infty} K(r, \eta; \alpha)\, d\eta \right]$$

or

$$\|v\| [1 - k(r_0, \alpha)] \leqslant 0$$

which implies $\|v\| = 0$ or $v(r, \alpha) \equiv 0$ for $1 \leqslant r < \infty$ and completes the proof.

In order to construct a solution to Eqs. (6) and (7), a sequence of functions $\omega(r, \alpha; N)$ is introduced as follows:

$$\omega(r, \alpha; N) = \Omega(r, \alpha) + \int_1^N K(r, \eta; \alpha) \omega(\eta, \alpha; N)\, d\eta. \tag{21}$$

Equation (21) in fact, defines a two-cylinder problem in which an inner cylinder of radius 1 is rotating at unit angular speed and an outer cylinder of radius N is at rest. This sequence $\omega(r, \alpha; N)$ with increasing N will be used to approximate $\omega(r, \alpha)$. The physical meaning of this approximation is self-evident.

The uniqueness of the solution of Eq. (21) for a given N can be proved in an almost identical manner as Theorem 2. The existence of a solution $\omega(r, \alpha; N)$ of Eq. (21) follows from the convergence of the Neumann series. In fact,

$$\omega(r, \alpha; N) = \sum_{n=0}^{\infty} \int_1^N K^{(n)}(r, \eta; \alpha) \Omega(\eta, \alpha)\, d\eta \quad + \Omega(r, \alpha) \tag{22}$$

is a solution to Eq. (21) where

$$K^{(0)}(r, \eta; \alpha) = K(r, \eta; \alpha),$$

and

$$K^{(n)}(r, \eta; \alpha) = \int_1^N K(r, t; \alpha) K^{(n-1)}(t, \eta; \alpha)\, dt.$$

The convergence of the series in Eq. (22) is an immediate result of the convergence of the series $\sum_{n=1}^{\infty} [\max_{1 \leqslant r \leqslant N} \int_1^N K(r, \eta; \alpha)\, d\eta]^n$. A number of the properties of $\omega(r, \alpha; N)$ should be noted. It is clear from Eq. (22) that $\omega(r, \alpha; N) > 0$, since $K(r, \eta; \alpha) > 0$ and $\Omega(r, \alpha) > 0$. The fact that $\omega(r, \alpha; N) \leqslant 1$ follows from the observation that

$$[1 - \omega(r, \alpha; N)] = \Gamma(r, \alpha; N) + \int_1^N K(r, \eta; \alpha)[1 - \omega(\eta, \alpha; N)]\, d\eta \qquad (23)$$

where $\Gamma(r, \alpha; N)$ is defined in Eq. (20) and $\Gamma(r, \alpha; N) > 0$ for all $r \in [1, N]$, because then the unique solution $[1 - \omega(r, \alpha; N)]$ to Eq. (23) can be constructed from the Neumann series and is positive and hence the desired result follows. This result says that $\omega(r, \alpha; N)$ forms an equibounded sequence of functions. Finally it should be noted that $\omega(r, \alpha; N)$ is a monotone sequence i.e., $\omega(r, \alpha; N_2) > \omega(r, \alpha; N_1)$ for $1 \leqslant r \leqslant N_1$, if $N_2 > N_1$. This follows from the following equation defined for $r \in [1, N_1]$ for the function $v(r, \alpha) = \omega(r, \alpha; N_2) - \omega(r, \alpha; N_1)$:

$$v(r, \alpha) = \int_{N_1}^{N_2} K(r, \eta; \alpha)\omega(\eta, \alpha; N_2)\, d\eta + \int_1^{N_1} K(r, \eta; \alpha)v(\eta, \alpha)\, d\eta$$

which implies $v(r, \alpha) > 0$ for $r \in [1, N_1]$ and hence the result.

An immediate consequence of the fact that $\omega(r, \alpha; N)$ is an equibounded monotone sequence is that the limit function

$$\omega_{\lim}(r, \alpha) = \lim_{N \to \infty} \omega(r, \alpha; N)$$

exists and is positive and uniformly bounded by 1. It can be shown that $\omega_{\lim}(r, \alpha)$ satisfies Eq. (6).

Lemma 1. *The function $\omega_{\lim}(r, \alpha)$ satisfies the equation*

$$\omega_{\lim}(r, \alpha) = \Omega(r, \alpha) + \int_1^{\infty} K(r, \eta; \alpha)\omega_{\lim}(\eta, \alpha)\, d\eta.$$

Proof. A limiting process $N \to \infty$ is taken for Eq. (21):

$$\lim_{N \to \infty} \omega(r, \alpha; N) = \Omega(r, \alpha) + \lim_{N \to \infty} \int_1^N K(r, \eta; \alpha)\omega(\eta, \alpha; N)\, d\eta$$

or

$$\omega_{\lim}(r, \alpha) = \Omega(r, \alpha) + \lim_{N \to \infty} \int_1^{\infty} K(r, \eta; \alpha)\omega^*(\eta, \alpha; N)\, d\eta$$

where

$$\omega^*(r, \alpha; N) = \omega(r, \alpha; N) \qquad \text{for} \quad 1 \leqslant r \leqslant N,$$
$$= 0 \qquad\qquad \text{for} \qquad r > N.$$

Since $K(r, \eta; \alpha)\omega^*(\eta, \alpha; N)$ is dominated by the integrable function $K(r, \eta; \alpha)$, it then follows from the Lebesque dominated convergence theorem that

$$\lim_{N \to \infty} \int_1^\infty K(r, \eta; \alpha)\omega^*(\eta, \alpha; N) \, d\eta = \int_1^\infty K(r, \eta; \alpha)\omega_{\lim}(\eta, \alpha) \, d\eta.$$

This concludes the proof.

For the existence theorem it remains to prove that $\lim_{r \to \infty} \omega_{\lim}(r, \alpha) = 0$. To prove this is a rather complicated task. For this purpose, it is useful to develop a lemma for obtaining more refined upper bounds for $\omega(r, \alpha; N)$. For a function $f(r)$, a particular iterate of f is defined as

$$I\{f\} = \Omega(r, \alpha) + \int_1^b K(r, \eta; \alpha)\omega(\eta, \alpha; N) \, d\eta + \int_b^N K(r, \eta; \alpha)f(\eta) \, d\eta$$

where $1 \leqslant b \leqslant N$. This lemma may be stated as follows:

Lemma 2. *If, for some $\varepsilon > 0$, $I\{f\} > f(r)$ for $b + \varepsilon \leqslant r \leqslant N$ and $f(r) \geqslant \omega(r, \alpha; N)$ for $b \leqslant r \leqslant b + \varepsilon$, then $f(r) \geqslant \omega(r, \alpha; N)$ for $b \leqslant r \leqslant N$.*

Using this lemma it may be shown that $f = C/r^2$ for some constant C is an upper bound for $\omega(r, \alpha; N)$ for all N and α and consequently $\omega_{\lim}(r, \alpha) \to 0$ as $r \to \infty$. The proof of the above statements as well as of Lemma 2 may be found in Pao (1964). Summarizing the results leads to the following theorem.

Theorem 3. (Existence). *There exists a function $\omega_{\lim}(r, \alpha)$ defined by*

$$\omega_{\lim}(r, \alpha) = \lim_{N \to \infty} \sum_{n=0}^\infty \int_1^N K^{(n)}(r, \eta; \alpha)\Omega(\eta, \alpha) \, d\eta \quad + \Omega(r, \alpha)$$

which satisfies Eqs. (6) and (7).

It is clear from the uniqueness theorem that $\omega_{\lim}(r, \alpha) = \omega(r, \alpha)$.

Having obtained the uniqueness and existence theorems, it becomes a simple matter to show that the solution $\omega(r, \alpha)$ depends continuously on the boundary term $\Omega(r, \alpha)$. A more precise statement can be given as follows:

Theorem 4. (Continuous dependence). *If the function $g(r, \alpha)$ satisfies*

$$g(r, \alpha) = G(r, \alpha) + \int_1^\infty K(r, \eta; \alpha)g(\eta, \alpha) \, d\eta,$$

and

$$g(r, \alpha) \to 0 \qquad as \quad r \to \infty,$$

where

$$|G(r, \alpha) - \Omega(r, \alpha)| < \varepsilon\Omega(r, \alpha), \qquad 0 < \varepsilon < 1,$$

then

$$|g(r, \alpha) - \omega(r, \alpha)| < \varepsilon\omega(r, \alpha).$$

Proof. Let the functions $e(r, \alpha)$ and $E(r, \alpha)$ be defined as $e(r, \alpha) = g(r, \alpha) - \omega(r, \alpha)$ and $E(r, \alpha) = G(r, \alpha) - \Omega(r, \alpha)$. Then

$$e(r, \alpha) = E(r, \alpha) + \int_1^\infty K(r, \eta; \alpha)e(\eta, \alpha)\, d\eta, \tag{24}$$

$$e(r, \alpha) \to 0 \qquad \text{as} \quad r \to \infty. \tag{25}$$

According to Theorems 2 and 3, there exists a unique solution to Eqs. (24) and (25) defined by

$$e(r, \alpha) = \lim_{N \to \infty} \sum_{n=0}^\infty \int_1^N K^{(n)}(r, \eta; \alpha)E(\eta, \alpha)\, d\eta \qquad + \mathbf{E}(r, \alpha)$$

or

$$|e(r, \alpha)| \leqslant \lim_{N \to \infty} \sum_{n=0}^\infty \int_1^N K^{(n)}(r, \eta; \alpha)|E(\eta, \alpha)|\, d\eta \qquad + |E(r, \alpha)|$$

$$\leqslant \varepsilon \lim_{N \to \infty} \sum_{n=0}^\infty \int_1^N K^{(n)}(r, \eta; \alpha)\Omega(\eta, \alpha)\, d\eta \qquad + \Omega(r, \alpha)$$

$$\leqslant \varepsilon\omega(r, \alpha),$$

and hence the theorem is proved.

Now this powerful theorem will be used to prove that the asymptotic solutions obtained in Section III, indeed are uniformly valid approximate solutions. In this connection, consider the function $g(r, \alpha)$ defined by

$$\begin{aligned} g(r, \alpha) &= \sum_{n=0}^2 \tilde{\sigma}_n(\alpha)\tilde{\omega}_n(\rho) \qquad \text{for} \quad r > \tau, \\ &= \sum_{n=0}^2 \hat{\sigma}_n(\alpha)\hat{\omega}_n(r) \qquad \text{for} \quad r < \tau. \end{aligned} \tag{26}$$

To prove that $g(r, \alpha)$ is a uniformly valid approximation solution to Eqs. (6) and (7), it is sufficient to show that

$$|g(r, \alpha) - \omega(r, \alpha)| < o(\alpha^2)\omega(r, \alpha) \tag{27}$$

where the order symbol has been used. According to Theorem 4, to prove inequality (27) it is only necessary to compute the function $G(r, \alpha)$ defined by

$$G(r, \alpha) = g(r, \alpha) - \int_1^\infty K(r, \eta; \alpha)g(\eta, \alpha)\, d\eta$$

and show that

$$|G(r, \alpha) - \Omega(r, \alpha)| < o(\alpha^2)\Omega(r, \alpha). \tag{28}$$

For this purpose, detailed calculations have been carried out in the Appendices of Pao (1964). It has been found that inequality (28) is valid, or, in other words, the asymptotic solutions $\sum_{n=0}^{2} \tilde{\sigma}_n \tilde{\omega}_n$ and $\sum_{n=0}^{2} \hat{\sigma}_n \hat{\omega}_n$ form a uniformly valid approximate solution to the cylinder problem for $\alpha \ll 1$. For higher order asymptotic solutions, the proof can be carried out in a similar manner.

The form of function τ is dictated by the minimization of $E(r, \alpha)$ and is taken, in the above calculation, to be $\alpha^{-1/2}$.

ACKNOWLEDGEMENTS

The author wishes to express his gratitude to Professor M. D. Kruskal for many stimulating suggestions and discussions. The author is grateful to Professor D. R. Willis not only for the suggestion of this problem and discussions in the initial stage of this work, but also for his encouragement throughout the preparation of this work.

REFERENCES

Abramowitz, M. (1953). *J. Math. and Phys.* **32**, 188.
Baker, R. M. L., Jr., and Charwat, A. G. (1958). *Phys. Fluids* **1**, 73.
Bhatnagar, P. L., Gross, E. P., and Krook, M. (1954). *Phys. Rev.* **94**, 511.
Epstein, P. S. (1924). *Phys. Rev.* **23**, 710.
Erdelyi, A. (1956). "Asymptotic Expansions," Dover, New York.
Liepmann, H. W., Narasimha, R., and Chahine, M. T. (1962). *Phys. Fluids* **5**, 1313.
Pao, Y. P. (1964). Ph.D. Thesis, Princeton Univ.; also Rept. MF-43, Courant Inst. Sci., New York Univ.
Tsien, H. S. (1946). *J. Aeronaut. Sci.* **13**, 653.
Welander, P. (1954). *Arkiv fysik* **7**, 44.
Willis, D. R. (1958). Princeton Univ. Aeronaut. Eng. Rep. 440.

The Transitional Drag on a Cylinder at Hypersonic Mach Numbers[1]

MARIAN H. ROSE

Courant Institute of Mathematical Sciences, New York University, New York

The drag on a cylinder traversing a neutral, rarefied gas is computed in the hypersonic range. Although intermolecular collisions are assumed rare they are not entirely negligible and, therefore, will give rise to a small departure from free-flow conditions. The mathematical procedure is similar to that previously applied to the case of a sphere. Using the identical boundary conditions for both geometries, it is then possible to gain some insight into the effect of shape upon drag. Comparisons are also made with the theoretical results obtained for an infinite, two-dimensional strip. Finally, an attempt is made to relate our theoretical predictions for the cylinder with the presently available experimental results.

I. Introduction

A. Review of Previous Work

This study is concerned with determining the drag on an object traversing a rarefied gas at high, constant speed. The gas is assumed to be in nearly free flow, i.e., the Knudsen number K_n is large but finite with the result that intermolecular collisions, although rare, are not negligible. It is the effect of these collisions on the drag or, more precisely, the departure from the free-flow value of the drag that is to be determined here.

Several theoretical investigations in this field have been previously carried out. They may be divided into two main groups, namely the "first collision" (Lubonski and Lunc, 1956; Lubonski and Lunc, 1957; Baker and Charwat, 1958) and "integral iteration" (Willis, 1958) methods. In a general way, these theories predict the correct experimental trends; for example, the agreement between Willis' (1958) results for the two-dimensional, infinite

[1] Work carried out under Grant No. AF-AFOSR-62-266 with the Air Force Office of Scientific Research.

strip and Maslach and Schaaf's (1963) experimental results for the cylinder is significant. On the other hand, they all suffer from fairly serious draw-backs.

In the "first collision" method, numerous assumptions of a physical nature have to be introduced in order to make the mathematical computations tractable. Principal among these is that the main contribution to the correction to the drag over its free-flow value is provided by those particles which, after having been reflected by the object, collide once in the gas with an unreflected particle. Furthermore, the results are restricted to the cold wall, hypersonic case. In a searching analysis Willis (1960) has shown that extrapolation of the theory to reflected molecules with higher emergent energies is restricted to certain types of molecules. With the foregoing in mind, it need scarcely be stressed that, in cases where extremely small corrections are involved, physical intuition may often be misleading. Another drawback is that there is no clearcut way for improving upon the first approximation. Finally, this method is remarkably sensitive to the choice of numerical procedures used in the computations. For example, the results of Hammerling and Kivel (1958) for the drag on a sphere differ significantly from those obtained by Baker and Charwat (1958) even though both groups of investigators use the same physical picture.

The "integral iteration" method is of more general applicability. First of all, it is capable of handling collisions other than, merely, "first collisions." Furthermore, the results are valid at finite Mach numbers and wall temperatures and are not restricted to the "cold wall, hypersonic" case. This method also has the advantage that, in principle at least, higher approximations may be derived in a mathematically straightforward way although, in practice, the computations are formidable. A drawback is that the iteration has not been proved convergent except in the case of linearized Couette flow. However, a factor weighing heavily in its favor is that it has always led to physically reasonable results.[2]

B. Proposed Method

The theory to be described here circumvents, to some extent, the drawbacks and difficulties of the two previous methods. For example, it is an exact first order solution in the sense that it takes into account all collisions and not merely "first collisions." Furthermore, there exists a clearcut procedure for improving upon this solution. Finally, it is possible to obtain results in the hypersonic range without recourse to numerical work. This, however, is not true in the intermediate range. A disadvantage that should be mentioned is

---

[2] *Note added in proof.* A comparison between the domains of validity of the "integral iteration" method and the method described here has been made recently by Pao (see p. 296 of this volume).

that this theory postulates a mean free path independent of velocity: this assumption is not needed in Willis' scheme but is used in the "first collision" approach.

The method has already been applied to the sphere (Rose, 1964); therefore, wherever possible, repetitious computations will be omitted. In spite of the similarities between the two cases, it was felt that results for the cylinder would be of value. First, it enables one to gain further insight into the effect of shape upon drag by adding yet another result to the existing body of knowledge obtained for the sphere, plate and two-dimensional infinite strip. Secondly, the theory may be compared with the experimental results of Maslach and Schaaf (1963).

The aim of the proposed method is to determine the distribution function in a region D, many object diameters away from the origin (the coordinate system is assumed to be fixed in the body) but yet well within the distance of a mean free path λ. This is possible if the mean free path is large compared with the object diameter a; in brief, we assume that $a \ll D \ll \lambda$. In this region, intermolecular collisions exert a small but significant effect on the distribution function. On the other hand, the effect of the object on the distribution function may be ascribed to a point source. More specifically, for $K_n(=\lambda/a)$ $\rightarrow \infty$, the source term will simply be the radial flow from the origin of the free-molecular perturbation function; obviously, it must be related in the appropriate manner to the shape of the object and to the boundary conditions both at its surface and at infinity. The drag associated with this source will simply be the free-molecular drag. Collisions will give rise to a slight modification in the source flow and it is precisely this modification which is responsible for the change in the drag over its free-flow value.

The analysis is simplified by use of the Krook equation with the addition of a point source term, rather than the full Boltzmann equation. We shall show (Section III) that it is permissible to linearize this equation about values at infinity. The Fourier transformation of the linearized equation is then performed resulting in an expression for the transform of the perturbed distribution function. It follows that the transforms of the first three moments may also be found. The inversion of these moments is of no special difficulty and their knowledge leads to that of the perturbed distribution function itself. Applying the appropriate boundary conditions at the surface of the body, the expression for the drag is derived in the usual way by calculating the rate of transfer of momentum to the object in the direction of the free stream velocity.

This result may be improved upon, i.e., its range of validity extended further into the region of transitional flow. A possible approach has been outlined by Grad (1959) and the significance of the following comments will be more apparent if his arguments are kept in mind. Assume that the perturbed distribution function has been determined in the region D ($a \ll D$

$\ll \lambda$) using the free-flow perturbation function in the source term. An improvement on this solution would be to include the perturbed distribution function due to collisions in the source term and then to continue this procedure by iteration. Thus, the range of validity of the solution would be extended from a region fairly close to the source where departures from free-flow are small further into the region of transitional flow where these departures become more marked.

We note, finally, that the evaluation of the drag coefficient will be restricted to the hypersonic range. The practical applications to satellite and meteor flight need scarcely be stressed.

C. Results

The cylinder is assumed to reflect the particles diffusely with an accommodation coefficient equal to unity. Thus, $T_r = T_w$ where T_r is the temperature of the reflected stream, and T_w the wall temperature. On the other hand, it is not necessary to assume that $T_r \approx T_0$ where T_0 is the temperature of the undisturbed gas.

Taking the distribution function at infinity to be Maxwellian and the axis of the cylinder perpendicular to the direction of flow at infinity, the resulting drag coefficient c_D is

$$c_D = c_{D_{FM}} - (0.50/K_n)\tau^{1/2} \log_e[(l/a) + (1 + l^2/a^2)^{1/2}] \tag{1}$$

where

$c_{D_{FM}}$ = free-molecular value of the drag coefficient
K_n = (Knudsen number) = λ/a
λ = mean free path
a = radius of cylinder
$\tau = T_0/T_r$
l = length of the axis of the cylinder.

In deriving Eq. (1), both l and a are required to be small compared with λ. Therefore, Eq. (1) is not only restricted to the hypersonic range but also by the condition $l/a \ll K_n$.

II. Basic Equations

For the sake of simplifying the analysis, the distribution function for the gas will be described by the "single relaxation time" Boltzmann equation or "Krook" equation (Bhatnagar *et al.*, 1954) with the addition of a point source term:

$$\xi \cdot \partial f / \partial x = v(f_0 - f) + \sigma(\xi)\delta(x) \tag{2}$$

Here, $f(x, \xi)$ is the distribution function, $f_0(x, \xi)$ is the local Maxwellian and v is the collision frequency assumed independent of velocity; x and ξ refer to the position and velocity vectors. Equation (2) is time-independent since the coordinate system is fixed in the object which is assumed to move at constant speed through a gas at rest. The function $\sigma(\xi)\delta(x)$ [$\delta(x)$ is the Dirac delta function] represents the point source which will be described subsequently in greater detail.

In order to determine the drag, a prior knowledge of the distribution function in the neighborhood of the body is necessary. More precisely, if λ is the mean free path and a is a typical dimension of the body (e.g., the radius of the cylinder), then a main purpose of the following analysis is to determine $f(x, \xi)$ at a distance D from the object such that $a \ll D \ll \lambda$. This has two immediate consequences; first, in this region, collisions between particles, although few, are not negligible and secondly, the object may be viewed as a point source. We note that the function $\sigma(\xi)$ may be identified with the net mass radial flow from the origin.

III. Linearization Procedure

Equation (2) is linear in f except for the nonlinearities introduced by the local Maxwellian f_0 whose moments are

$$\bar{\rho}(x) = \int f \, d\xi,$$

$$\overline{\rho(x)u(x)} = \int \xi f \, d\xi, \tag{3}$$

$$\overline{p(x)} = \bar{\rho}R\bar{T} = \int \tfrac{1}{3}(\xi - \bar{u})^2 f \, d\xi.$$

These moments, as will be shown, decay inversely as the square of the distance from the origin and hence, for $D \gg a$, these nonlinearities are small.

The function $f(x, \xi)$ is linearized about its value $f^{(0)}(\xi)$ in the undisturbed gas at infinity; $f^{(0)}(\xi)$ is assumed Maxwellian although this assumption may not necessarily be valid in the regions of space where satellite and meteor flights occur. The moments of $f^{(0)}(\xi)$ are denoted by ρ_0, u_0, T_0 where u_0 is the velocity of the body through the undisturbed gas. Subsequently, the direction of u_0 will be assumed perpendicular to the axis of the cylinder.

The mechanics of the linearization procedure have been described in great detail by Grad (1959) and others and only the barest outline is needed here. We have

$$f = f^{(0)} + g, \qquad \bar{\rho} = \rho_0 + \rho,$$
$$\bar{u} = u_0 + u, \qquad \bar{T} = T_0 + T.$$

The function $f_0(x, \xi)$ is also linearized about $f^{(0)}(\xi)$. These expansions substituted into Eq. (2) yield

$$\xi \cdot \frac{\tilde{g}}{x} + \frac{1}{L}\tilde{g} = \frac{\omega}{L}\{\tilde{\rho}(x) + (\tfrac{1}{2}\tilde{c}^2 - \tfrac{3}{2})\tilde{T}(x) + \tilde{c} \cdot \tilde{u}(x)\} + \tilde{\sigma}(\xi)\delta(x) \qquad (4)$$

where the tilde symbol ($\sim$) denotes dimensionless quantities and

$$\omega = (2\pi)^{-3/2} \exp(-\tfrac{1}{2}\tilde{c}^2) \qquad (\tilde{c} = \tilde{\xi} - \tilde{u}_0).$$

The only remaining dimensional quantities are the length variable x, the source term and a length parameter $L = v/(RT_0)^{1/2}$ which is related to the mean free path λ by the expression (Kennard, 1938) $L = \tfrac{1}{2}(\pi/2)^{1/2}\lambda$. The dimensionless quantity $\tilde{u}_0 = u_0/(RT_0)^{1/2}$ is related to the Mach number M by $\tilde{u}_0 = \gamma^{1/2}M$ where $\gamma = c_p/c_v$, the ratio of specific heats.

In keeping with the linearization, the source term in Eq. (4) is simply the net mass flow of the free-flow perturbation function. Following Sirovich (1961) we have

$$\sigma(\xi) \sim \int_\Sigma g\xi \, dS + O(a^3/D^3) \qquad (5)$$

to be taken over the surface Σ of the body, the outward drawn normal to a surface element being positive. To lowest order and assuming diffuse reflection, expression (5) for the cylinder is (see Fig. 1)

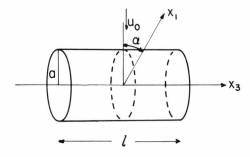

FIG. 1. Coordinate system for the cylinder.

$$(2\pi)^{3/2}\tilde{\sigma}(\tilde{\xi})$$

$$\approx \int dS|\tilde{\xi}_1|H(\tilde{\xi}_1)N_f^{(0)}\exp(-\tfrac{1}{2}\tau\tilde{\xi}^2)$$

$$-\int dS|\tilde{\xi}_1|H(-\tilde{\xi}_1)\exp\{-\tfrac{1}{2}[(\tilde{\xi}_1 + \tilde{u}_0\cos\alpha)^2 + (\tilde{\xi}_2 + \tilde{u}_0\sin\alpha)^2 + \tilde{\xi}_3{}^2]\}$$

$$+\int dS|\tilde{\xi}_1|H(-\tilde{\xi}_1)N_b^{(0)}\exp(-\tfrac{1}{2}\tau\tilde{\xi}^2)$$

$$-\int dS|\tilde{\xi}_1|H(\tilde{\xi}_1)\exp\{-\tfrac{1}{2}[(\tilde{\xi}_1 + \tilde{u}_0\cos\alpha)^2 + (\tilde{\xi}_2 + \tilde{u}_0\sin\alpha)^2 + \tilde{\xi}_3{}^2]\},$$

$$(6)$$

with $dS = a\,d\alpha\,dx_3$, the x_1 axis being perpendicular to dS. Here, $\tau = T_0/T_r$, the ratio of the temperatures of the impinging and reflected streams. The assumption that $T_r = T_w = $ constant will be made although, in cases where the material is a poor conductor, T_w may vary with position.

The functions $N_f^{(0)}\exp(-\tfrac{1}{2}\tau\tilde{\xi}^2)$ and $N_b^{(0)}\exp(-\tfrac{1}{2}\tau\tilde{\xi}^2)$ represent the distribution functions of the streams reflected diffusely from front and back, respectively. The coefficients $N_f^{(0)}$ and $N_b^{(0)}$ are found from the condition specifying conservation of number at each surface element. The results, in the hypersonic range, are

$$N_b^{(0)} \approx 0, \qquad N_f^{(0)} \approx (\tau^2/2\pi)\cos\alpha. \qquad (7)$$

In this range, furthermore, the end contributions may be neglected (see Section V).

In order to calculate the drag, the expression for $\tilde{g}(x, \tilde{\xi})$ evaluated for $D \gg a$ must be extrapolated to the close neighborhood of the source, i.e., to $D \approx a$; the error, however, is negligible because collisions near the body are rare and will not alter $\tilde{g}(x, \tilde{\xi})$ appreciably. The linearization of the Krook equation is still valid for $D \approx a$ since the collision term may be disregarded here and the convection term is already linear in f.

IV. Solution of Equation (4)

A. Fourier Transformation of Equation (4)

The Fourier transformation of Eq. (4) has already been fully discussed by Grad (1959) and Sirovich (1961), hence only a brief outline will be presented here.

The transformed functions are denoted by $\bar{\varphi}(k, \xi) = \int e^{-ik\cdot x}\,\bar{\varphi}(x, \xi)\,dx$.

Taking the first three moments of $\tilde{g}(x, \xi)$, i.e., multiplying $\tilde{g}(x, \xi)$ by 1, $\tilde{c}$, and $(\frac{1}{3}\tilde{c}^2 - 1)$ and integrating over velocity space leads to

$$\frac{\tilde{\bar{\rho}}(k)}{L} = \int \frac{\tilde{\sigma}(\tilde{\xi}) \, d\tilde{\xi}}{1 + iL\tilde{\xi}\cdot k} + \cdots ,$$

$$\frac{\tilde{\bar{T}}(k)}{L} = \int \frac{(\frac{1}{3}\tilde{c}^2 - 1)\tilde{\sigma}(\tilde{\xi}) \, d\tilde{\xi}}{1 + iL\tilde{\xi}\cdot k} + \cdots , \tag{8}$$

$$\frac{\tilde{\bar{u}}^{(s)}(k)}{L} = \int \frac{\tilde{c}_s\tilde{\sigma}(\tilde{\xi}) \, d\tilde{\xi}}{1 + iL\tilde{\xi}\cdot k} + \cdots ,$$

where it is sufficient to take the first term in each of these expansions in order to obtain the desired accuracy for $\tilde{g}(x, \xi)$.

B. Evaluation of Expressions (8)

The evaluation of the transformed moments in Eq. (8) follows closely along the lines for the case of the sphere and the details of the calculations underlying the following results may be found in Rose (1964). At hypersonic Mach numbers these are

$$\tilde{\bar{\rho}}(k) = \frac{k_1}{4i|k|^2} [2(2\pi\tau)^{1/2}\tilde{u}_0 - \pi],$$

$$\tilde{\bar{T}}(k) = \frac{k_1}{4i|k|^2} \left\{ \frac{\pi}{6} \tilde{u}_0^2 \left[1 - \left(\frac{k_1^2 + k_2^2}{|k|^2} \right) \right] + 2(2\pi\tau)^{1/2}\tilde{u}_0\left(\frac{1}{3\tau} - 1 \right) \right\},$$

$$\tilde{\bar{u}}^{(1)}(k) = \frac{\tilde{u}_0 k_1}{2i|k|^2} \left\{ 1 - \frac{k_1^2}{|k|^2} \right\} + \tilde{u}_0\pi \frac{(k_2^2 + k_3^2)}{|k|^3}, \tag{9}$$

$$\tilde{\bar{u}}^{(2)}(k) = \frac{\tilde{u}_0 k_2}{2i|k|^3} \left\{ 1 - \frac{k_1^2}{|k|^2} \right\} - \tilde{u}_0\pi \frac{k_1 k_2}{|k|^3},$$

$$\tilde{\bar{u}}^{(3)}(k) = \frac{\tilde{u}_0 k_3}{2i|k|^3} \left\{ 1 - \frac{k_1^2}{|k|^2} \right\} - \tilde{u}_0\pi \frac{k_1 k_3}{|k|^3},$$

where $|k| = (k_1^2 + k_2^2 + k_3^2)^{1/2}$.

C. Inversion of Expressions (9)

In this section, the inversion of a typical term in Eq. (9) such as

$$I(x) = (2\pi)^{-3} \int (e^{ik\cdot x}k_1)/|k|^2 \, dk \tag{10}$$

will be discussed; the inversion of all others proceeds along similar lines.

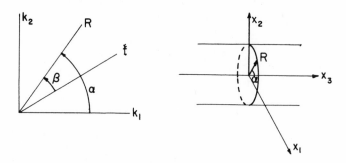

FIG. 2. Coordinate system used in the integration of Eq. (10).

Referring to Figs. 2(a) and 2(b) we have

$$e^{ik \cdot x} = e^{itR \cos \beta} e^{ik_3 x_3} \quad \text{with} \quad R = (x_1{}^2 + x_2{}^2)^{1/2},$$

$$dk = \mathfrak{k} \, d\mathfrak{k} \, dk_3 \, d\beta \quad \text{with} \quad \mathfrak{k} = (k_1{}^2 + k_2{}^2)^{1/2},$$

and

$$k_1 = \mathfrak{k} \cos(\alpha - \beta) = k[\cos \alpha \cos \beta + \sin \alpha \sin \beta],$$

of which only the first term will contribute to the integration over β (Magnus and Oberhettinger, 1954). Thus, Eq. (10) may be put in the form

$$I(\alpha, R, x_3) = \frac{\cos \alpha}{(2\pi)^3} \int \frac{\cos \beta \, e^{itR \cos \beta} e^{ik_3 x_3} \mathfrak{k}^2 \, d\mathfrak{k} \, dk_3 \, d\beta}{(\mathfrak{k}^2 + k_3{}^2)}, \tag{11}$$

with $0 \leqslant \beta \leqslant 2\pi$, $0 \leqslant k \leqslant \infty$, $-\infty \leqslant k_3 \leqslant \infty$. Integration over β yields (Magnus and Oberhettinger, 1954)

$$I(\alpha, R, x_3) = \frac{4\pi i \cos \alpha}{(2\pi)^3} \int \frac{J_1(\mathfrak{k}R) \cos k_3 x_3 \mathfrak{k}^2 \, d\mathfrak{k} \, dk_3}{(\mathfrak{k}_2 + k_3{}^2)}, \tag{12}$$

The two remaining integrations may be performed with the aid of the following expressions (Magnus et al., 1954):

$$\int_0^\infty \frac{\cos(xy) x^{2m}}{(a^2 + x^2)^{\nu + \frac{1}{2}}} \, dx = \frac{(-1)^{3m} \pi^{1/2}}{2^\nu \Gamma(\nu + \frac{1}{2})} y^\nu a^{2m - \nu} K_{\nu - 2m}(ay),$$

$$\text{Re } a > 0, \quad y > 0, \quad 0 \leqslant m \leqslant \text{Re } \nu + \tfrac{1}{2},$$

$$\int_0^\infty x^{-\lambda} J_\nu(xy) K_\mu(ax) \, dx = \frac{\Gamma[\frac{1}{2}(\nu - \lambda + \mu + 1)] \Gamma[\frac{1}{2}(\nu - \lambda - \mu + 1)]}{2^{\lambda + 1} a^{\nu - \lambda + 1} \Gamma(\nu + 1) y^{-\nu}}$$

$$\times F\left[\frac{\nu - \lambda + \mu + 1}{2}, \frac{\nu - \lambda - \mu + 1}{2}; \nu + 1; -\frac{y^2}{a^2} \right]$$

where $F(a,b; c; z)$ is a hypergeometric function (Magnus and Oberhettinger, 1954) and $K_\nu(z)$ is a modified Bessel function of the second kind (Watson, 1944). The result is

$$I(\alpha, R, x_3) = \frac{4\pi\pi^{1/2}i\Gamma(\frac{3}{2})}{(2\pi)^3} \cos\alpha \, \frac{R}{x_3^2} F(2, \tfrac{3}{2}; 2; -R^2/x_3^2). \tag{13}$$

This expression may be simplified by use of (Magnus and Oberhettinger, 1954)

$$F(a, b; c; z) = (1 - z)^{-a} F\left(z, c - b; c; \frac{z}{z-1}\right)$$

$$= (1 - z)^{-b} F\left(b, c - a; c; \frac{z}{z-1}\right),$$

which yields

$$F(2, \tfrac{3}{2}; 2; -R^2/x_3^2) = (1 + R^2/x_3^2)^{-3/2} F\left(\tfrac{3}{2}, 0; 2; \frac{R^2/x_3^2}{1 + R^2/x_3^2}\right).$$

The resulting hypergeometric function may be expanded in a hypergeometric series which converges absolutely on the entire unit circle including $R^2/(R^2 + x_3^2) = z = 1$; it follows that

$$F\left(\tfrac{3}{2}, 0; 2; \frac{R^2/x_3^2}{1 + R^2/x_3^2}\right) = 1,$$

and

$$I(\alpha, R, x_3) = \frac{4\pi\pi^{1/2}i\Gamma(\frac{3}{2})}{(2\pi)^3} \cos\alpha \, \frac{R}{(x_3^2 + R^2)^{3/2}}. \tag{14}$$

The resulting expressions for the moments are

$$\tilde{\rho}(x) = \frac{2\pi\pi^{1/2}}{(2\pi)^3} \Gamma\left(\frac{3}{2}\right) \frac{R}{r^3} \cos\alpha \left[(2\pi\tau)^{1/2}\tilde{u}_0 - \frac{\pi}{2}\right],$$

$$\tilde{u}^{(1)}(x) = \frac{2\pi\pi^{1/2}}{(2\pi)^3} \frac{\tilde{u}_0}{r^3} \left\{\Gamma\left(\frac{3}{2}\right) R \cos\alpha - \frac{1}{4}\left[3\Gamma(3)\Gamma\left(\frac{3}{2}\right)\left(1 - \frac{3}{4}\frac{R^2}{r^2}\right) R \cos\alpha\right.\right.$$

$$\left.\left. - \Gamma\left(\frac{5}{2}\right) \frac{R^3}{r^2} \cos 3\alpha\right] - \frac{\pi}{2\Gamma(\frac{3}{2})}\left[\frac{x_3^2}{r} + \frac{R^2}{r} \cos 2\alpha\right]\right\},$$

$$\tilde{u}^{(2)}(x) = \frac{2\pi\pi^{1/2}}{(2\pi)^3} \tilde{u}_0 \frac{R}{r^3} \sin\alpha \left\{\Gamma\left(\frac{3}{2}\right) - \pi^{1/2}\left[1 - \frac{3}{2}\frac{R^2}{r^2}\right] + \frac{\pi}{\Gamma(\frac{3}{2})} \cos\alpha \frac{R}{r}\right\},$$

$$\tilde{u}^{(3)}(x) = \frac{2\pi\pi^{1/2}\tilde{u}_0}{(2\pi)^3} \frac{x_3}{r^3} \left\{\Gamma\left(\frac{3}{2}\right) - \frac{1}{2}\left[1 - \frac{3}{2}\frac{R^2}{r^2} - \Gamma\left(\frac{5}{2}\right) \cos 2\alpha \frac{R^2}{r^2}\right]\right.$$

$$\left. + \frac{\pi}{\Gamma(\frac{3}{2})} \cos\alpha \frac{R}{r}\right\}, \tag{15}$$

$$\tilde{T}(x) = \frac{2\pi\pi^{1/2}}{(2\pi)^3} \frac{R}{r^3} \tilde{u}_0 \left\{ \frac{\pi\tilde{u}_0}{12} \Gamma\left(\frac{3}{2}\right) \cos\alpha - \frac{\pi\tilde{u}_0}{24} \left[3\Gamma\left(\frac{3}{2}\right)\Gamma(3) \right. \right.$$

$$\times \left(1 - \frac{3}{4}\frac{R^2}{r^2}\right) \cos\alpha - \Gamma\left(\frac{5}{2}\right) \frac{R^2}{r^2} \cos 3\alpha \right] - \frac{\pi\tilde{u}_0}{96} \left[\Gamma\left(\frac{3}{2}\right)\Gamma(3) \right.$$

$$\left. \cdot t_1(\alpha)\left(1 - \frac{3}{4}\frac{R^2}{r^2}\right) - t_2(\alpha)\Gamma\left(\frac{5}{2}\right)\frac{R^2}{r2} \right] + \sqrt{2\pi}\tau\left(\frac{1}{3\tau} - 1\right)\Gamma\left(\frac{3}{2}\right)\cos\alpha \right\},$$

where

$$t_1(\alpha) = \cos\alpha(3\cos 2\alpha - 1) + 3\sin 2\alpha,$$

$$t_2(\alpha) = \sin 2\alpha - \cos\alpha(3\cos 2\alpha - 1),$$

$$r^2 = x_3{}^2 + R^2,$$

and α is the angle between the directions of R and $\tilde{u}_0$.

D. Calculation of the Perturbed Distribution Function $\tilde{g}(x, \xi)$

The inhomogeneous term in Eq. (4) having been determined, it is now possible to find the appropriate solution satisfying $\lim_{R\to\infty} \tilde{g}(x, \tilde{\xi}) = 0$ by integrating along a ray.

The solution is

$$\tilde{g}(x, \tilde{\xi}) = \int_R^\infty \frac{dR}{\tilde{\chi}} \left\{ \frac{\tilde{\sigma}(\tilde{\xi})\delta(\alpha)\delta(R - a)\delta(x_3)}{R} + \frac{\omega}{L} G(R, x_3, \alpha) \right\} \qquad (16)$$

where $G(r, x_3, \alpha) = \tilde{\rho} + (\frac{1}{2}\tilde{c}^2 - \frac{3}{2})\tilde{T} + \tilde{c}\cdot\tilde{u}$ and $\tilde{\chi} = (\tilde{\xi}_1{}^2 + \tilde{\xi}_2{}^2)^{1/2}$.

With $\tilde{g} = g^{(0)} + g^{(1)}$, where $g^{(0)}$ represents the free-flow perturbation and $g^{(1)}$ the perturbation introduced by collisions, it is easily verified that

$$g^{(0)} = -\frac{\tilde{\sigma}(\tilde{\xi})\delta(\alpha)\delta(x_3)}{a\tilde{\chi}} H(a - R) \qquad (17)$$

which leads to the correct value for the free-molecular drag at hypersonic Mach numbers.

Rather than displaying the complete expression for $\tilde{g}^{(1)}$, we shall restrict ourselves to the component $\tilde{g}_\infty^{(1)}$ which provides the dominant contribution to the drag when $\tilde{u}_0 \to \infty$. This is easily shown to be

$$\tilde{g}_\infty^{(1)} = -\frac{1}{4(2\pi)^{1/2}} \frac{\omega}{L\tilde{\chi}} \frac{\tau^{1/2}\tilde{u}_0 \cos\alpha}{(R^2 + x_3{}^2)^{1/2}} \qquad (18)$$

V. Calculation of the Drag for $\tilde{u}_0 \to \infty$

The drag is found by evaluating the momentum per unit time imparted to the cylinder in the $\tilde{u}_0$ direction. For the impinging stream, the drag depends on the values of $\tilde{g}^{(0)}$ and $\tilde{g}^{(1)}$ at $R = a$. It is easy to show that these contributions are proportional to $u_0{}^2$ and $\tau^{1/2}\tilde{u}_0{}^2$, respectively. The force imparted by the reflected stream will, of course, depend upon the particular type of reflection occurring at the surface. For the diffuse case, the free-molecular contribution is of the order of $\tilde{u}_0/\tau^{1/2}$ and may give a sizable contribution even at high Mach numbers if $\tau^{1/2}$ is sufficiently small. On the other hand, the reflected contribution due to particles that have undergone collisions is proportional to $\tilde{u}_0$; since it is multiplied by an extremely small coefficient it will not be included here. By the same token, the end contributions to the drag may be disregarded.

Using Eq. (18), the leading correction to the drag arising from intermolecular collisions is (see Fig. 1)

$$
D^{(1)}_{\tilde{u}_0 \to \infty} \sim -\frac{1}{4(2\pi)^2}\frac{\tau^{1/2}\tilde{u}_0}{L}\int_{-\infty}^{0} d\tilde{\xi}_1 \int_{-\infty}^{\infty} d\tilde{\xi}_2 \int_{-\infty}^{\infty} d\tilde{\xi}_3
$$
$$
\cdot \int dS \frac{(-\tilde{\xi}_1)(\tilde{\xi}_1 \cos \alpha + \tilde{\xi}_2 \sin \alpha)}{(a^2 + x_3{}^2)^{1/2}\tilde{\chi}}
$$
$$
\cdot \exp\{-\tfrac{1}{2}[(\tilde{\xi}_1 + \tilde{u}_0 \cos \alpha)^2 + (\tilde{\xi}_2 + \tilde{u}_0 \sin \alpha)^2 + \tilde{\xi}_3{}^2]\}, \qquad (19)
$$

with $dS = a\, dx_3\, d\alpha$ and $0 \leqslant x_3 \leqslant l$, $-\pi/2 \leqslant \alpha \leqslant \pi/2$ (the x_1 axis is perpendicular to the surface element dS).

The integration is straightforward and the result, expressed in terms of the drag coefficients C_D, is

$$
C_D = C_{D_{FM}} - (0.50/K_n)\tau^{1/2} \log_e\{(l/a) + (1 + l^2/a^2)^{1/2}\}. \qquad (20)
$$

VI. Comparison with Theoretical and Experimental Results

The author is not aware of any other published theories regarding the transitional drag on a cylinder with which this one may be compared. However, comparisons can be made with results for other shapes.

For example, using entirely similar methods, the drag coefficient for a sphere has been found to be (Rose, 1964)

$$
C_D = C_{D_{FM}} - (0.66/K_n)\tau^{1/2} \qquad \text{(sphere)} \qquad (21)
$$

Setting $l = a$, the expression for the cylinder becomes

$$C_D = C_{D_{FM}} - (0.44/K_n)\tau^{1/2} \qquad \text{(cylinder)} \qquad (22)$$

where, in each case, the appropriate value of $C_{D_{FM}}$ must be used.

Maslach and Schaaf (1963) have reduced Willis' results for the two-dimensional, infinite strip to the form

$$C_D = C_{D_{FM}} - \{F[u_0/(2RT_0)^{1/2}, u_0/(2RT_w)^{1/2}] \log_e K_n\}/K_n \qquad (23)$$

For a Mach number of 5.92 and $\tau \sim 1$ they find that $F = 0.247$ (see Table I in their article). Assuming $K_n = 10$ which should be well within the range of validity of the various theories, then

$$C_D \quad \text{(2-dimensional, infinite strip)} = C_{D_{FM}} - 0.06$$

$$C_D \quad \text{(sphere)} \qquad\qquad = C_{D_{FM}} - 0.07\tau^{1/2}$$

$$C_D \quad \text{(cylinder)} \qquad\qquad = C_{D_{FM}} - 0.04\tau^{1/2}$$

Maslach and Schaaf conclude from their experiments that there is no discernible effect of l/a upon drag for values of l/a ranging from 40 to 200. Table I shows the dependence of C_D on l/a for various values of K_n, according

TABLE I

DEPENDENCE OF C_D ON K_n FOR $l/a = 40$ AND $l/a = 200$
($C_{D_{FM}} = 2.85$, $M = 5.96$, $\sqrt{\tau} = 0.33$)

C_D ($l/a = 40$)	C_D ($l/a = 200$)	K_n
2.83	2.83	40
2.82	2.80	20
2.78	2.75	10
2.73	2.69	6
2.68	2.61	4

to our theory. The values of M, $\tau^{1/2}$, and $C_{D_{FM}}$ used in calculating C_D are the same as in Fig. 5 of Maslach and Schaaf's article. Although we find a slight dependence of C_D upon l/a, the differences for $l/a = 40$ and $l/a = 200$, insofar as can be ascertained from the experimental curve for C_D versus K_n, lie well within the limits of experimental error. We recall that our theory is expected to hold for $l/a \ll K_n$ whereas the experiments were carried out on long, thin wires. Therefore, the foregoing comparison between theory and experiment should be viewed with caution.

ACKNOWLEDGMENTS

The author wishes to thank, in particular, Professor D. R. Willis whose comments were instrumental in leading to the correct expression for the drag.

REFERENCES

Baker, R. M. L., and Charwat, A. F. (1958). *Phys. Fluids* **1**, 73.

Bhatnagar, P. L., Gross, E. P., and Krook, M. (1954). *Phys. Rev.* **94**, 511.

Grad, H. (1959). *Proc. Symp. Aerodynamics Upper Atmosphere* (Project Rand).

Hammerling, P., and Kivel, P. (1958). *Phys. Fluids* **1**, 357.

Kennard, E. H. (1938). "Kinetic Theory of Gases." McGraw-Hill, New York.

Lubonski, J., and Lunc, M. (1956), *Arch. Mech. Stosowanaj (Warsaw)* **4**, 597.

Lubonski, J., and Lunc, M. (1957), *Bull. Acad. Polon. Sci. Cl. IV* **5**, 41.

Magnus, W., and Oberhettinger, F. (1954). "Formulas and Theorems for the Functions of Mathematical Physics." Chelsea, New York.

Magnus, W., Oberhettinger, F., and Tricomi, F. G. (1954). "Tables of Integral Transforms." McGraw-Hill, New York.

Maslach, G. J., and Schaaf, S. A. (1963). *Phys. Fluids* **6**, 315.

Rose, M. H. (1964). *Phys. Fluids*, **7**, 1262.

Sirovich, L. (1961). *In* "Rarefied Gas Dynamics" (L. Talbot, ed.), p. 283. Academic Press, New York.

Watson, G. N. (1944). "A Treatise on the Theory of Bessel Functions." Cambridge Univ. Press, London and New York.

Willis, D. R. (1958). Princeton Univ. Aeronaut. Eng. Lab. Rept. No. 440.

Willis, D. R. (1960). TIS Rept. R60SD399.

Improved "First-Collision" Model Theory

MICHAEL LUNC

University of Warsaw and Institute for Nuclear Research, Warsaw, Poland

A modification to the "first-collision" model theory is presented, which gives good agreement with experimental data for the drag coefficient of cylinders over a range of Knudsen numbers from about 1 to ∞ and over a Mach number range from about 4 to ∞.

Some experimental data concerning the drag of cylindrical bodies in a flow of rarefied gases for a large range of Knudsen numbers have been published in the last few years (Schaaf and Maslach, 1963; Maslach and Schaaf, 1963). It will be shown in this paper that the experimental results are consistent with a somewhat modified "first-collision" model theory over a range of Knudsen numbers from about 1 to ∞ and a range of Mach numbers from about 4 to ∞.

We take for the basis of the present paper a simplified "first-collision" theory used previously by Lunc and Lubonski (1956). In the previous paper the drag of an infinite plane strip in a flow with an infinite Mach number was calculated. An important simplification, resulting from the coolness of the strip as compared with the stagnation temperature of the gas, was that the molecules emitted by the strip could be considered to be at rest. The calculated drag comprised two parts:

1. The drag of molecules striking the strip and arriving in a "direct way" from infinity, i.e., without colliding with other molecules;

2. The drag of molecules which underwent one collision.

We shall use here the same "names" for different species of molecules as in the work by Lunc and Lubonski (1956). Thus we denote as "white" a molecule arriving from infinity without collision, as "red" a molecule emitted *diffusely* by the wall, and as "green" or "blue" a formerly white or red molecule after their mutual collision. Only three different species have to be considered: the blue and the green had, indeed, the same statistical properties.

Besides the partial drag with which each species acts on the strip there was another important property which was calculated by Lunc and Lubonski (1956): the frequency of collision of each species with the wall. All these calculations were performed using an expansion procedure. Since the time of the previous paper new mathematical tables were published (Karmazina and Chistova, 1958) in which the integrals of the Bessel functions of imaginary argument K_0 were tabulated. Using the new tables one can avoid the expansion in series used by Lunc and Lubonski (1956) and reduce the final results of the calculation of partial drags and partial frequency of impact to an algebraical expression containing the Bessel functions K_0 and K_1 and the integral of K_0.

The impact frequencies of the white and green-blue molecules v_w and v_q are then given by the equations

$$v_w = n_\infty v_w[1 - Q(\alpha)]/[1 + P(\alpha) - Q(\alpha)], \tag{1}$$

and

$$v_g = n_\infty v_w Q(\alpha)/[1 + P(\alpha) - Q(\alpha)], \tag{2}$$

where

n_∞ = the number density at infinity,
v_w = the velocity of the gas at infinity
   = mean velocity of the white molecules,
$\alpha = A/L_r$ the ratio of
A = half-width of the strip and
L_{rw} = mean free path of the red molecules versus white molecules of
   number density n_∞,
$P(\alpha)$ and $Q(\alpha)$ are functions of α given by

$$P(\alpha) = 1 - \tfrac{2}{3}\pi\alpha$$
$$+ (\tfrac{4}{3}\pi)\left[\alpha K_0(2\alpha) + (1 - 2\alpha^2)K_1(2\alpha) - (\tfrac{3}{2} - 2\alpha^2)\int_{2\alpha}^\infty K_0(x)\,dx\right], \tag{3}$$

and

$$Q(\alpha) = (2 - \tfrac{8}{3}\pi\alpha + \tfrac{1}{4}\alpha^2) + (\tfrac{2}{3}\pi)\left[(-\tfrac{3}{2}\alpha + 2\alpha)K_0(2\alpha)\right.$$
$$\left. + (5 - 4\alpha^2)K_1(2\alpha) - (\tfrac{3}{4}\alpha^2 + 6 - 4\alpha^2)\int_{2\alpha}^\infty K_0(x)\,dx\right], \tag{4}$$

in which $K_0(x)$ and $K_1(x)$ are Bessel functions of orders 0 and 1.

From Eqs. (1) and (2) the global impact frequency v can be deduced. It is given by

$$v = n_\infty v_w/[1 + P(\alpha) - Q(\alpha)]. \tag{5}$$

A relationship may be easily established between the Knudsen number of the flow, which is related to the free mean path at infinity and the parameter α used in this work and by Lunc and Lubonski (1956).

We denote by

$\Omega_\infty = \Omega_w =$ the thermal velocity at infinity,
$\quad\quad \Omega_r =$ the thermal velocity corresponding to the temperature of the strip (considered constant).

We introduce also, for future use,

$\quad\quad \Omega_g =$ the thermal velocity of the green-blue molecules.

We denote by

$$S_n = v_n/\Omega_n \tag{6}$$

the dimensionless velocity of the nth species. The Knudsen number for a flow with mean free path $L_\infty \equiv L_{ww}$ is defined by

$$K = L_{ww}/2A. \tag{7}$$

Between L_{ww} and L_{rw} there is the well-known relationship

$$L_{rw}/L_{ww} = (8/\pi)^{1/2}\Omega_r/v_w, \tag{8}$$

which, after taking in account Eqs. (6) and (7), gives

$$K = (\pi/32)^{1/2}S_r/\alpha. \tag{9}$$

Is it really possible to compare Knudsen numbers of different bodies? One could argue that what actually matters in a flow of rarefied gas is not the lateral dimension of a body but the area which is "wetted" by the flow. In such case a strip of width $2A$ is to be compared with a cylinder with a diameter of A/π, having the same wetted surface area. In such a case the Knudsen number K_c for a cylinder corresponding to the parameter α of the strip will be expressed by

$$K_c = (\pi/2)K = (\pi^3/128)^{1/2}S_r/\alpha. \tag{10}$$

In the present work we consider the flow as composed of three noninteracting *free-molecular* flows of white, green-blue, and red gases. The drag is then composed of three parts which can be calculated by the well-known equations for free-molecular flow. What we have to compute, first of all, are the characteristic parameters of these flows, i.e., the mean velocities, the thermal velocities, and the number densities. This can be done if we know the values of the impact frequencies v_w and v_g in the case where the Mach number is finite.

The emitted red molecules have now a finite velocity and the green and blue molecules will have a higher temperature and a lower mean velocity than in the case of infinite Mach number. The result of this is that a smaller number of green and blue molecules return to the wall. The reduction coefficient τ_g was computed and is given by an approximate equation

$$\tau_g \approx (S_r - \pi^{-1/2})/2(S_r + \pi^{-1/2}) + \arcsin[\alpha K_0(\alpha)]/\pi\alpha K_0(\alpha)$$
$$+ [(S_r - \pi^{-1/2})/2S_r]^2 \exp(-\alpha). \tag{11}$$

(The details of this calculation will be published elsewhere). Equations (1), (2), and (5) are then modified and we obtain new values for the impact frequencies, denoted by v_w', v_g', and v', and expressed by

$$v_w' = n_\infty v_w[1 - \tau_g Q(\alpha)]/[1 + P(\alpha) - \tau_g Q(\alpha)], \tag{12}$$

$$v_g' = v_g \tau_g = n_\infty v_w \tau_g Q(\alpha)/[1 + P(\alpha) - \tau_g Q(\alpha)], \tag{13}$$

$$v' = n_\infty v_w/[1 + P(\alpha) - \tau_g Q(\alpha)]. \tag{14}$$

There is a well-known equation relating the impact frequency, the number density, the velocity, and the thermal velocity for a free molecular flow. It is

$$v_k = n_k v_k\{[\exp(-S_k^2)]/\pi^{1/2} + S_k(1 + \operatorname{erf} S_k)\} \tag{15}$$

where $\operatorname{erf} x = (2/\pi^{1/2}) \int_0^x \exp(-u^2)\, du$ is the error function.

The white gas has then the velocity v_w which is known, the known thermal velocity Ω_w and the number density n_w which will be deduced from Eqs. (12) and (15). Thus

$$n_w = n_\infty[1 - \tau_g Q(\alpha)]/[1 + P(\alpha) - \tau_g Q(\alpha)][\exp(-S_w^2)/\pi^{1/2} + S_w(1 + \operatorname{erf} S_w)]. \tag{16}$$

The red gas is emitted diffusely by the wall. We assume it to be in thermal equilibrium with the strip and to have a half-Maxwellian distribution of velocity. Hence, the mean velocity of such a gas can be calculated. It is

$$v_r = \Omega_r/\pi^{1/2}. \tag{17}$$

The collision between a white and a red molecule produces two green-blue molecules. If the molecules are hard and smooth spheres then the distribution function of the green-blue gas is Maxwellian. The mean velocity and the thermal velocity of this gas in the vicinity of the wall can be deduced from the laws of momentum and energy conservation. After some very easy transformations we obtain

$$v_g = (v_w - v_r)/2 = (v_w - \Omega_r/\pi^{1/2})/2, \tag{18}$$

and

$$\Omega_g^2 = (\tfrac{1}{4} - \tfrac{1}{6}\pi)\Omega_r^2 + \Omega_r v_w/6\pi^{1/2} + \Omega_w^2/4 + v_w^2/6. \tag{19}$$

The next step is the computation of the dimensionless velocity $S_g = v_g/\Omega_g$ and then the substitution of S_g and v_g in Eq. (15). Finally, we solve the so-obtained equation and find the number density n_g of the green-blue gas.

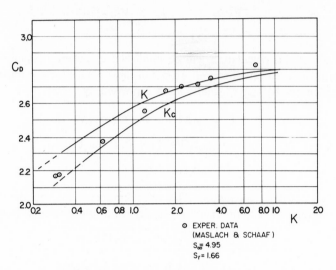

FIG. 1. Drag coefficient as a function of Knudsen number; $M = 5.92$. ⊙, Experimental data (Maslach and Schaaf); $S_\infty = 4.95$; $S_r = 1.66$.

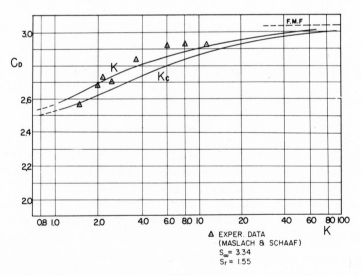

FIG. 2. Drag coefficient as a function of Knudsen number; $M = 4.00$. △, Experimental data (Maslach and Schaaf); $S_\infty = 3.34$; $S_r = 1.55$.

The drag of the white and of the green-blue gases is given by the well-known equation (flow normal to a plane)

$$p_k = m n_k v_k \Omega_k [\exp(-S_k^2)/\pi^{1/2} + (S_k + 1/2S_k) \operatorname{erf} S_k] \tag{20}$$

which was stated by Luntz (1949).

The drag of the red gas is given by a somewhat different equation, which can be written in the following way:

$$p_r = \tfrac{1}{2}\pi^{1/2} m v_r \Omega_r = \tfrac{1}{2} m n_\infty v_w^2 \frac{v_r}{n_\infty v_w} \frac{\pi^{1/2}}{v_w/\Omega_r}. \tag{21}$$

The total drag,

$$p_t = p_w + p_g + p_r, \tag{22}$$

can be represented as

$$p_t = C_D \tfrac{1}{2} m n v_w^2, \tag{23}$$

and the the drag coefficient C_D expressed with the aid of Eqs. (11) to (22).

The graphs shown in Figs. 1 and 2 show the value of the drag coefficient converted from a strip to a cylinder using the approximate equation

C_D (cylinder) = C_D (cylinder in free molecular flow)

$$\cdot \frac{C_D \text{ (plane)}}{C_D \text{ (plane in free molecular flow)}}. \tag{24}$$

REFERENCES

Karmazina, L. N., and Chistova, E. A. (1958). "Tables of Bessel Functions of Imaginary Argument and Their Integrals." Academy of Sciences, U.S.S.R., Moscow (in Russian).

Lunc, M., and Lubonski, J. (1956). *Arch. Mech. Stos.* **8**, 597–616.

Luntz, M. (1949). *Rech. Aeron.* **7**, 28, Eq. (11₁).

Maslach, G. J., and Schaaf, S. A. (1963). *Phys. Fluids* **6**, 3.

Schaaf; S. A., and Maslach, G. J. (1963). *In* "Rarefied Gas Dynamics" (J. Laurmann, ed.), Vol. II, p. 317. Academic Press, New York.

Rayleigh's Problem at Low Mach Numbers According to Kinetic Theory

CARLO CERCIGNANI AND FRANCO SERNAGIOTTO

A.R.S., Applicazioni e Ricerche Scientifiche and Università di Milan, Milano, Italy

In this paper Rayleigh's problem is solved analytically over the full range of Knudsen numbers. The BGK model is used. In particular, explicit results are given for the stress and velocity at the plate; also short-time and long-time behavior are investigated.

I. Introduction

Time-dependent problems for an arbitrary Knudsen number have been little investigated in rarefied gasdynamics. In fact, if exception is made for the rather special (though interesting) investigations on sound propagation by Wang Chang and Uhlenbeck (1952), Sirovich and Thurber (1963), Pekeris *et al.* (1962), only one spatially inhomogeneous problem appears to have been considered: Rayleigh's problem. Also, for this problem only approximate solutions have been given for the full range of Knudsen numbers by Yang and Lees (1956), and Gross and Jackson (1958). The former work is based on Grad's thirteen-moment equations, the latter on the half-range expansion method. Exact solutions have been given in the limiting cases of continuum theory (Rayleigh, 1911; also, with corrections for slip velocity, by Schaaf, 1950), and of free molecular flow (Yang and Lees, 1960).

The aim of the present paper is to give a complete analytical solution of Rayleigh's problem with the only restrictions of linearization and use of the BGK model (Bhatnagar *et al.*, 1954) to describe collisions.

II. Basic Equations

Let a half space be filled with a gas of density ρ_0 and temperature T_0 and bounded by an infinite plane wall; the gas is initially in equilibrium and the

332

wall is at rest; then the plate is set impulsively in motion in its plane with uniform velocity u_0. The propagation into the gas of the disturbance produced by the motion of the plate is to be studied.

Let

$$f_0(\mathbf{c}) = \rho_0 \pi^{-3/2} \exp(-c^2) \tag{1}$$

be the initial unperturbed Maxwellian state (here the molecular velocity $\mathbf{c}$ is measured in $(2RT_0)^{1/2}$ units, where R is the Boltzmann constant divided by the molecular mass). If the Mach number is small one can linearize the problem and write

$$f(x, t, \mathbf{c}) = f_0[1 + h(x, t, \mathbf{c})] \tag{2}$$

where f is the distribution of the molecules and $h(x, t, \mathbf{c})$ is treated as small with respect to 1; as usual, the Boltzmann equation takes the following form:

$$(\partial h/\partial t) + c_x \, \partial h/\partial x = L(h) \tag{3}$$

where $L(h)$ is the linearized collision operator.

The initial and boundary conditions are

$$h(x, 0, \mathbf{c}) = 0, \tag{4}$$

$$h(0, t, \mathbf{c}) = 2u_0 c_z \qquad \text{for} \quad c_x > 0. \tag{5}$$

Besides, when $x \to \infty$, $h(x, t, \mathbf{c})$ must be limited for every fixed t and $\mathbf{c}$.

Now if the BGK Ansatz is introduced to describe collisions, Eq. (3) becomes

$$\frac{\partial h}{\partial t} + c_x \frac{\partial h}{\partial x} = \frac{1}{\theta}\left(\frac{2c_z}{\pi^{1/2}}\int_{-\infty}^{+\infty} c_{z_1} h_1 \, exp(-c_1^2) \, d\mathbf{c}_1 - h\right) \tag{6}$$

where $h_1 \equiv h(x, t, c_1)$ and θ is the mean free time; in addition, use has been made of the constancy of density and temperature, which is a consequence of linearization.

It is easily seen that Eq. (6) under conditions (4) and (5) has a solution of the following form:

$$h(x, t, \mathbf{c}) = 2c_z Y(x, t, c_x) \tag{7}$$

where $Y(x, t, c_x)$ satisfies the following equation:

$$(\partial Y/\partial t) + c_x \, \partial Y/\partial x = \pi^{-1}\int_{-\infty}^{+\infty} \exp(-c_{x_1}^2) Y(x, t, c_{x_1}) \, dc_{x_1} - Y(x, t, c_x), \tag{8}$$

provided that x and t are measured in θ units.

The initial and boundary conditions on $Y(x, t, c_x)$ are

$$Y(x, 0, c_x) = 0, \tag{9}$$

$$Y(0, t, c_x) = u_0. \tag{10}$$

Introducing the Laplace transform of Y, $\overline{Y}(x, s, c_x)$, Eq. (8) is reduced to

$$(s + 1)\overline{Y} + c_x \, \partial\overline{Y}/\partial x = \pi^{-1/2} \int_{-\infty}^{+\infty} \exp(-c_{x_1}^2)\overline{Y}(x, s, c_{x_1}) \, dc_{x_1}, \qquad (11)$$

while the boundary condition becomes

$$\overline{Y}(0, s, c_x) = \frac{u_0}{s} \qquad (c_x > 0). \qquad (12)$$

Equation (11) can be reduced to an integral equation according to well-known procedures. However, we shall follow another way by using the method of elementary solutions. This method previously used for stationary problems (Cercignani, 1962, 1964a, b, c), was recently extended to time-dependent situations by the authors (Cercignani and Sernagiotto, 1964).

A brief summary of this method is given in the following section.

III. A Summary of the Method of Elementary Solutions

Briefly described, the method of elementary solutions consists of finding separate-variables solutions of Eq. (11) and then constructing the general solution by superposition. It is easily seen that separate-variables solutions can be written as follows:

$$\overline{Y}(x, s, c_x) = \exp[-(s + 1)x/v]f_v(c_x, s) \qquad (13)$$

where $f_v(c_x, s)$ satisfies

$$\left(1 - \frac{c_x}{v}\right)f_v(c_x, s) = \frac{1}{(s + 1)\pi^{1/2}} \int_{-\infty}^{+\infty} f_v(c_{x_1}, s) \exp(-c_{x_1}^2) \, dc_{x_1}. \qquad (14)$$

A careful discussion of this integral equation leads to the following results (Cercignani and Sernagiotto, 1964): (1) For every s there is a continuous spectrum of values of v covering the full real axis. The corresponding solution of Eq. (14) are not ordinary functions but generalized functions (or distributions):

$$f_v(c_x, s) = P \frac{v}{v - c_x} + p(v, s)\delta(v - c_x) \qquad (15)$$

where $p(v, s)$ is given by

$$p(v, s) = \pi^{1/2}\left[(s + 1) \exp(v^2) - 2v \int_0^v \exp(u^2) \, du\right], \qquad (16)$$

and the symbol P means Cauchy principal value when integrals involving

$f_v(c_x)$ are considered. (2) For complex values of s inside a curve γ having the following parametric representation

$$\text{Re } s = -1 + 2v \exp(-v^2) \int_0^v \exp(u^2) \, du,$$

$$\text{Im } s = -\pi^{1/2} v \exp(-v^2),$$

(17)

there are two complex values of v, opposite to each other, $\pm v_0(s)$, such that Eq. (14) is satisfied by

$$f_v(c_x, s) = \frac{\pm v_0(s)}{\pm v_0(s) - c_x},$$

(18)

$v_0(s)$ is fixed by the following relation:

$$\frac{1}{(s+1)\pi^{1/2}} \int_{-\infty}^{+\infty} \frac{v_0 \exp(-u^2)}{v_0 - u} \, du = 1.$$

(19)

The γ-curve is sketched in Fig. 1. It is an easy matter to prove that the set of

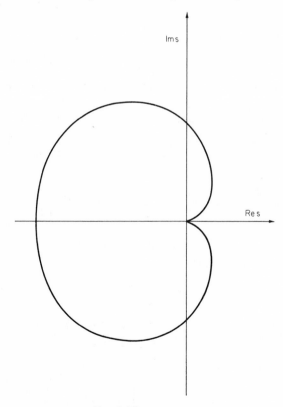

FIG. 1. The γ-curve

solutions of Eq. (14) has the properties of full and partial range complete-ness.

Particular emphasis is to be given to the half-range completeness since it is well known that boundary conditions for the Boltzmann equation are given only for molecules leaving a physical wall which bounds the gas.

Owing to this half-range property, if s is outside the γ curve, a function $Y(c_x)$, given for $c_x < 0$, can be represented as follows:

$$Y(c_x) = \int_0^\infty A(v, s) f_v(c_x, s)\, dv \tag{20}$$

where

$$A(v, s) = \frac{p(v, s)}{[p(v, s)]^2 + \pi^2 v^2} Y(v)$$
$$- \frac{e^{v^2} X_A(-v, s)}{[p(v, s)]^2 + \pi^2 v^2} P \int_0^\infty \frac{u e^{-u^2} Y(u)}{X_A(-u, s)} \frac{du}{u - v}. \tag{21}$$

Here $X_A(-v, s)$ is given by

$$X_A(-v, s) = \exp\left\{\frac{1}{\pi} \int_0^\infty \tan^{-1}\left[\frac{\pi}{p(t, s)}\right] \frac{dt}{t + v}\right\}, \tag{22}$$

and the determination of $\tan^{-1}[\pi t/p(c, s)]$ is such that this function goes to zero when $t \to \infty$.

Analogously, when s is inside the γ-curve, we have

$$Y(c_x) = B_0(s\, f_{v_0}(c_x, s) + \int_0^\infty B(v, s) f_v(c_x, s)\, dv \tag{23}$$

where

$$B_0 = \int_0^\infty \frac{u e^{-u^2} Y(u)\, du}{(v_0{}^2 - u^2) X_B(-u, s)} \Big/ \int_0^\infty \frac{u f_{v_0}(u) e^{-u^2}\, du}{(v_0{}^2 - u^2) X_B(-u, s)},$$

and

$$B(v, s) = \frac{p(v, s)}{[p(v, s)]^2 + \pi^2 v^2} f(v)$$
$$- \frac{(v_0 + v) e^{v^2} X_B(-v, s)}{[p(v, s)]^2 + \pi^2 v^2}$$
$$\times P \int_0^\infty \frac{u e^{-u^2} f(u)\, du}{X_B(-u, s)(v_0 + u)(u - v)}. \tag{25}$$

Here $X_B(-v, s)$ is given by

$$X_B(-v, s) = -\frac{1}{v} \exp\left\{\frac{1}{\pi} \int_0^\infty \tan^{-1}\left[\frac{\pi t}{p(t, s)}\right] \frac{dt}{t + v}\right\}. \tag{26}$$

IV. Analytical Expression of the Laplace Transform of the Solution

According to the method previously described, Eq. (11) has the general solution

$$\bar{Y}(x, s, c_x) = \int_{-\infty}^{+\infty} A(v, s) \exp[-(s+1)x/v]f_v(c_x, s)\, dv \qquad (27)$$

when s is outside the γ-curve, and

$$\bar{Y}(x, s, c_x) = B_0^{+}(s)f_{v_0}(c_x, s) + B_0^{-}(s)f_{-v_0}(c_x, s)$$

$$+ \int_{-\infty}^{+\infty} B(v, s)f_v(c_x, s)\exp[-(s+1)x/v]\, dv \qquad (28)$$

when s is inside the γ-curve. Here $A(v, s)$, $B_0^{\pm}(s)$, $B(v, s)$ are arbitrary functions of their arguments. These functions are fixed by the boundary conditions. Using boundedness at space infinity and boundary condition (12) together with the half-range completeness, we find

$$\bar{Y}(x, s, c_x) = u_0\pi^{1/2}\int_0^{\infty} \frac{f_v(c_x, s)X_A(-v, s)\exp[-(s+1)(x/v) + v^2]}{[p(v, s)]^2 + \pi^2 v^2}\, dv \qquad (29)$$

when s is outside the γ-curve and at the right of the straight line Re $s = -1$.

Analogously, when s is inside the γ-curve, we find

$$\bar{Y}(x, s, c_x) = \frac{u_0\exp[-(s+1)x/v_0(s)]}{s(v_0 - c_x)X_B(v_0, s)}$$

$$- u_0\pi^{1/2}\int_0^{\infty} \frac{(v_0 + v)X_B(-v, s)f_v\exp[-(s+1)(x/v) + v^2]}{[p(v, s)]^2 + \pi^2 v^2}\, dv \qquad (30)$$

where $v_0(s)$ is selected between the two possible values in such a manner that

$$\mathrm{Re}\left[\frac{s+1}{v_0(s)}\right] > 0. \qquad (31)$$

By integration with respect to the weight $\pi^{-1/2}\exp(-c_x^2)$ we find $\bar{u}(x, s)$ the Laplace transform of the mass velocity

$$\bar{u}(x, s) = u_0\pi^{1/2}(s+1)\int_0^{\infty} \frac{X_A(-v, s)\exp[-(s+1)(x/v) + v^2]}{[p(v, s)]^2 + \pi^2 v^2}\, dv, \qquad (32)$$

$$\bar{u}(x, s) = \frac{u_0(s + 1) \exp[-(s + 1)x/v_0]}{s v_0 X_B(v_0, s)}$$

$$- u_0 \pi^{1/2}(s + 1) \int_0^\infty \frac{(v_0 + v)X_B(-v, s) \exp[-(s + 1)(x/v) + v^2]}{[p(v, s)]^2 + \pi^2 v^2} \, dv \quad (33)$$

for s, respectively, outside and inside the γ-curve (and $\operatorname{Re} s \geqslant -1$).

It is important to note (Cercignani and Sernagiotto, 1964) that $\bar{u}(x, s)$ defined by Eqs. (32) and (33) outside and inside the γ-curve, is an analytical function also through this curve; this allows the integration paths in reversing the Laplace transform to be deformed as usual, also crossing the γ-curve, provided that in every region the appropriate expression is used. The segment $(-1, 0)$ of the real axis is easily seen to be a discontinuity line, because of the choice of v_0.

In order to get the expression for the Laplace transform of the shearing stress, we have to integrate Eqs. (29) and (30) with respect to the weight $\rho_0 \pi^{-1/2} c_x \exp(-c_x^2)$. We have

$$\bar{\tau}(x, s) = \rho_0 u_0 s \pi^{1/2} \int_0^\infty \frac{v X_A(-v, s) \exp[-(s + 1)(x/v) + v^2]}{[p(v, s)]^2 + \pi^2 v^2} \, dv, \quad (34)$$

$$\bar{\tau}(x, s) = \rho_0 u_0 \frac{\exp[-(s + 1)x/v_0]}{X_B(v_0, s)}$$

$$- \rho_0 u_0 s \pi^{1/2} \int_0^\infty \frac{v(v_0 + v)X_B(-v, s) \exp[-(s + 1)(x/v) + v^2]}{[p(v, s)]^2 + \pi^2 v^2} \, dv. \quad (35)$$

The function $\bar{\tau}(x, s)$ so defined for s outside and inside the γ-curve (and $\operatorname{Re} s \geqslant -1$) turns out to be analytic also across this curve, and discontinuous across the segment $(-1, 0)$ of the real axis.

V. Integration Paths for the Inverse Transformation

According to well-known theorems on Laplace transform, the y-component of the mass velocity and the xz-component of the stress tensor are given by the integrals

$$u(x, t) = (2\pi i)^{-1} \int_{a-i\infty}^{a+i\infty} e^{st} \bar{u}(x, s) \, ds, \quad (36)$$

$$\tau(x, t) = (2\pi i)^{-1} \int_{a-i\infty}^{a+i\infty} e^{st} \bar{\tau}(x, s) \, ds, \quad (37)$$

where $\bar{u}(x, s)$ and $\bar{\tau}(x, s)$ are given by Eqs. (32) and (34) and the path of integration is a vertical straight line to the right of γ.

Owing to the analyticity properties of $\bar{u}(x, s)$ and $\bar{\tau}(x, s)$ the previous path of integration in the s-plane can be deformed to a path indented on the

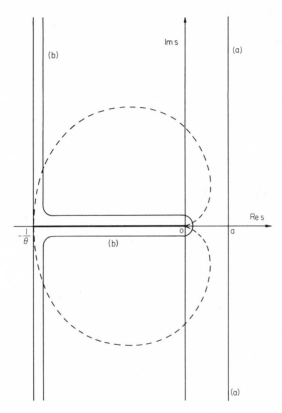

FIG. 2. Integration paths in the s-plane.

segment $(-1, 0)$ of the real axis and along the vertical straight line $\text{Re}(s + 1) = 0$ (see Fig. 2). Therefore we shall have

$$u(x, t) = (2\pi i)^{-1} \int_{-1-i\infty}^{-1+i\infty} e^{st}\bar{u}(x, s)\, ds - (2\pi i)^{-1} \int_{-1}^{0} e^{st} D(x, s)\, ds, \quad (38)$$

$$\tau(x, t) = (2\pi i)^{-1} \int_{-1-i\infty}^{-1+i\infty} e^{st}\bar{\tau}(x, s)\, ds - (2\pi i)^{-1} \int_{-1}^{0} e^{st} \Delta(x, s)\, ds, \quad (39)$$

where $D(x, s)$ and $\Delta(x, s)$ are the jumps, respectively, of $\bar{u}(x, s)$ and $\bar{\tau}(x, s)$ across the segment $(-1, 0)$ of the real axis in the s-plane. Such jumps are easily evaluated to be

$$D(x, s) = \frac{u_0(s + 1) \exp[-(s + 1)x/v_0]}{sv_0 X_B(v_0, s)} - \frac{u_0(s + 1) \exp[-(s + 1)x/v_0{}^*]}{sv_0{}^* X_B(v_0{}^*, s)}$$
$$- u_0\pi^{1/2}(s + 1)$$
$$\times \int_0^\infty \frac{(v_0 - v_0{}^*)X_B(-v, s) \exp[-(s + 1)(x/v) + v^2]}{[p(v, s)]^2 + \pi^2 v^2} \, dv, \tag{40}$$

$$\Delta(x, s) = \rho_0 u_0 \frac{\exp[-(s + 1)x/v_0]}{X_B(v_0, s)} - \rho_0 u_0 \frac{\exp[-(s + 1)x/v_0{}^*]}{X_B(v_0{}^*, s)}$$
$$- \rho_0 u_0 s\pi^{1/2}$$
$$\times \int_0^\infty \frac{v(v_0 - v_0{}^*)X_B(-v, s) \exp[-(s + 1)(x/v) + v^2]}{[p(v, s)]^2 + \pi^2 v^2} \, dv. \tag{41}$$

Here * denotes complex conjugate and $v_0(s)$ for s on the real axis means

$$\lim_{\varepsilon \to 0^+} v_0(s + i\varepsilon).$$

[it is clear that $v_0{}^* = \lim_{\varepsilon \to 0^+} v_0(s - i\varepsilon)$].

VI. Analytical Evaluation of Mass Velocity and Shear Stress on the Plate

On the plate, i.e., for $x = 0$, Eq. (32) becomes

$$\bar{u}(0, s) = u_0\pi^{1/2}(s + 1) \int_0^\infty \frac{X_A(-v, s) \exp(v^2)}{[p(v, s)]^2 + \pi^2 v^2} \, dv. \tag{42}$$

Now it is seen (see Appendix) that the following identity holds:

$$\frac{1}{X_A(-v, s)} = 1 - s\pi^{1/2} \int_0^\infty \frac{t \exp(t^2)X_A(-t, s)}{\{[p(t, s)]^2 + \pi^2 t^2\}(t + v)} \, dt. \tag{43}$$

For $v = 0$ Eq. (43) gives

$$\frac{1}{X_A(0, s)} = 1 - s\pi^{1/2} \int_0^\infty \frac{\exp(t^2)X_A(-t, s)}{[p(t, s)]^2 + \pi^2 t^2} \, dt. \tag{44}$$

On the other hand, for every complex v the following identity is easily seen to hold:

$$X_A(v, s)X_A(-v, s) = [(s + 1)/s]M(v, s) \tag{45}$$

where

$$M(v, s) = \exp(-v^2)[p(v, s) \pm \pi i v][\pi^{1/2}(s + 1)]^{-1}. \tag{46}$$

Here the plus and minus signs indicate whether v is in the upper or lower half plane, respectively. Letting $v \to 0$ Eq. (45) gives

$$X_A(0, s) = [(s + 1)/s]^{1/2}. \tag{47}$$

Therefore Eqs. (44) and (47) inserted in Eq. (42) give

$$\bar{u}(0, s) = u_0[(s + 1)/s]\{1 - [s/(s + 1)]^{1/2}\}. \tag{48}$$

Now one can easily determine the inverse transform of Eq. (48) by taking into account that its right-hand side has two branch points at $s = 0$ and $s = -1$:

$$u(0, t)/u_0 = 1 - (\pi i)^{-1} \int_0^{-1} [(s + 1)/s]^{1/2} e^{st} \, ds. \tag{49}$$

Changing the variable of integration from s to $-v$ gives

$$u(0, t)/u_0 = 1 - \pi^{-1} \int_0^1 [(1 - v)/v]^{1/2} e^{-vt} \, dv. \tag{50}$$

In such a way the mass velocity on the plate has been expressed in a simple analytical form valid for every t.

An expansion in power series of Eq. (50) gives

$$\frac{u(0, t)}{u_0} = 1 - \sum_0^\infty \frac{(-1)^n(2n)!}{(n!)^3(n + 1)2^{2n+1}} \, t^n. \tag{51}$$

This formula is particularly useful for numerical calculation when t is small.

Another useful manipulation of Eq. (50) will now be described. Let us differentiate Eq. (50) with respect to t:

$$\dot{u}(0, t) = (u_0/\pi) \int_0^1 [v(1 - v)]^{1/2} e^{-vt} \, dv. \tag{52}$$

The integral in Eq. (52) is easily evaluated by means of Bessel functions

$$\dot{u}(_0, t) = (u_0/2t)e^{-t/2} I_1(t/2) \tag{53}$$

where I_1 denotes as usual the modified Bessel function of the first kind of order one.

The function $u(0, t)$ is now got from Eq. (53) by simple integration

$$u(0, t)/u_0 = \tfrac{1}{2} + \tfrac{1}{2} \int_0^{t/2} (e^{-u}/u) I_1(u) \, du \tag{54}$$

where the value $u(0, 0) = \tfrac{1}{2}$ has been taken from Eq. (51).

By using Eqs. (51) and (54) a simple numerical calculation was set up for evaluating the mass velocity on the plate; the result is shown in Fig. 3 and in Table I. Please note that t is here measured in θ units.

TABLE I

VELOCITY ON THE PLATE
vs. t/θ

$u(0, t)/u_0$	t/θ
0.500000	0.000
0.515149	0.125
0.529394	0.250
0.555435	0.500
0.599270	1.000
0.634519	1.500
0.663233	2.000
0.686972	2.500
0.706865	3.000
0.723746	3.500
0.738238	4.000
0.769235	5.375
0.786153	6.375
0.799908	7.375
0.811353	8.375
0.821059	9.375
0.829421	10.375
0.858718	15.375
0.876789	20.375
0.889344	25.375
0.898717	30.375
0.912006	40.375

Analogously, for evaluating the shear stress on the plate, i.e., for $x = 0$, Eqs. (34) and (35) will be presently reduced to a simpler form. In fact, from Eq. (43) we get the following relation:

$$s\pi^{1/2} \int_0^\infty \frac{t \exp(t^2) X_A(-t, s)}{[p(t, s)]^2 + \pi^2 t^2} \, dt = \lim_{v \to \infty} v\left(1 - \frac{1}{X_A(-v, s)}\right). \quad (55)$$

On the other hand, Eq. (22) gives

$$X_A(-v, s) \simeq 1 - v^{-1}\left[\pi^{-1} \int_0^\infty \tan^{-1}[\pi t/p(t, s)] \, dt\right] \quad (56)$$

when $v \to \infty$. Now substituting Eqs. (55) and (56) into Eq. (34) we get for $x = 0$ the final expression

$$\bar{\tau}(0, s) = \rho_0 u_0 Q(s) \quad (57)$$

where

$$Q(s) = \pi^{-1} \int_0^\infty \tan^{-1}[\pi t/p(t, s)] \, dt. \quad (58)$$

In the same manner we shall reduce Eq. (35) for $x = 0$.

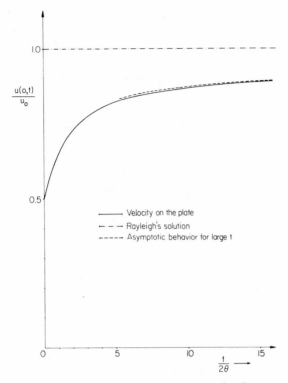

FIG. 3. Evolution of the mass velocity at the plate.

Now it is seen (see Appendix) that the following identity [analogous to Eq. (43)] holds:

$$\frac{1}{X_B(-v, s)} = -v + Q(s) - s\pi^{1/2} \int_0^\infty \frac{t(v_0{}^2 - t^2)X_B(-v, s)\exp(t^2)}{\{[p(t, s)]^2 + \pi^2 t^2\}(t + v)}\, dt. \quad (59)$$

Putting $-v = v_0$ into Eq. (59) gives

$$s\pi^{1/2} \int_0^\infty \frac{t(v_0 + t)X_B(-v, s)\exp(t^2)}{[p(t, s)]^2 + \pi^2 t^2}\, dt = \frac{1}{X_B(v_0, s)} - v_0 - Q(s). \quad (60)$$

Therefore Eq. (35) for $x = 0$ becomes

$$\bar{\tau}(0, s) = \rho_0 u_0 [v_0(s) + Q(s)]. \quad (61)$$

Equations (57) and (61) give the Laplace transform of the shear stress on the plate for s outside and inside the γ-curve, respectively. They are consistent since, as is easily seen, the integral $Q(s)$ suffers a jump equal to $v_0(s)$ crossing the γ-curve. So $\bar{\tau}(x, s)$ is analytical in the whole complex plane with a cut along the segment $(-1, 0)$ of the real axis, because of the discontinuity of

$v_0(s)$ on this line. Then inverse transformation gives

$$\tau(0, t) = \rho_0 u_0 (\pi i)^{-1} \int_0^{-1} v_0(s) e^{st} \, ds. \tag{62}$$

By taking into account that $v_0(s)$ is given by Eq. (19) and is purely imaginary when s is on the real axis, we can transform Eq. (62) as follows:

$$\tau(0, t) = \rho_0 u_0 \pi^{-1} \int_0^\infty [1 - \beta(\alpha)(1 + 2\alpha^2)] e^{-\beta(\alpha)t} \, d\alpha \tag{63}$$

where

$$\beta(\alpha) = 1 - \pi^{1/2} \alpha \exp(\alpha^2) \, \text{erfc}(\alpha). \tag{64}$$

Here, as usual, $\text{erfc}(\alpha)$ denotes the complementary error function, i.e.,

$$\text{erfc}(\alpha) = 2\pi^{-1} \int_\alpha^\infty \exp(-x^2) \, dx. \tag{65}$$

TABLE II

SHEAR STRESS ON THE PLATE
vs. t/θ

$\tau(0, t)/(\rho_0 u_0/2\pi^{\frac{1}{2}})$	t/θ
1.000000	0.00
0.898082	0.50
0.832385	1.00
0.777190	1.50
0.730287	2.00
0.639290	3.25
0.585181	4.25
0.542134	5.25
0.507004	6.25
0.477719	7.25
0.452871	8.25
0.431469	9.25
0.412800	10.25
0.396338	11.25
0.381684	12.25
0.368534	13.25
0.356650	14.25
0.345842	15.25
0.335957	16.25
0.326873	17.25
0.318486	18.25
0.310713	19.25
0.303481	20.25
0.296732	21.25
0.290414	22.25

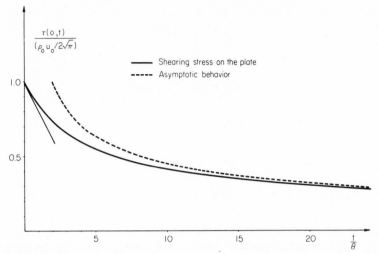

FIG. 4. Evolution of the shearing stress at the plate. The tangent to the curve at $t/\theta = 0$ is also drawn.

Equation (63) has been used for the numerical evaluation of the shear stress on the plate.

The behavior of the shear stress on the plate is tabulated in Table II and plotted in Fig. 4, where also previous results are reported for comparison. Besides, from Eq. (63) one can evaluate analytically the derivative of the stress on the plate for $t = 0$; the result is in agreement with the value recently given by Yoshio Sone (1964).

VII. Asymptotic Expansion for Large Knudsen Numbers

In this section we shall find an asymptotic expansion of our exact solution for mass velocity in the range of small t and arbitrary x/t.

It is useful to reintroduce the usual units for x and t, i.e., to replace them by x/θ and t/θ in Eq. (32). Accordingly we shall have

$$\bar{u}(x, s) = u_0 \theta \pi^{1/2} (s\theta + 1) \int_0^\infty \frac{X_A(-v, s) \exp[-(s\theta + 1)(x/\theta v) + v^2]}{[p(v, s)]^2 + \pi^2 v^2} \, dv \qquad (66)$$

where the transformation $t \to t/\theta$ has been accompanied by $s \to s\theta$ in such a way that the usual Laplace transform formulas hold in the new units.

We now give an asymptotic expansion of Eq. (66) up to terms of order $1/\theta$; viz.,

$$\frac{\bar{u}(x, s)}{u_0} \approx \frac{1}{s\pi^{1/2}} \int_0^\infty \left[1 + \frac{B(v) - 2R(v)}{s\theta} - \frac{x}{\theta v}\right] \exp[-s(x/v) - v^2] \, dv \qquad (67)$$

where

$$B(v) = 1 + \pi^{-1/2} \int_0^\infty \frac{u \exp(-u^2)}{u + v} \, du, \tag{68}$$

and

$$R(v) = 1 - 2v \exp(-v^2) \int_0^v \exp(u^2) \, du. \tag{69}$$

Then by performing the inverse transformation of Eq. (68) we get, up to terms of order t/θ,

$$u(x, t)/u_0 \approx \tfrac{1}{2} \operatorname{erfc}(x/t)$$
$$+ (t/\theta)\pi^{-1/2} \int_{x/t}^\infty [(B(v) - 2R(v))1 - (x/tv) - (x/tv)] \exp(-v^2) \, dv. \tag{70}$$

Equation (70) gives for t/θ small the behavior of the mass velocity for all values of x/t. Note that the term of zero order in Eq. (70) coincides with the solution by Yang and Lees (1960).

The manipulation of Eq. (70) is made easier by noting that $B(v)$ can be expressed as

$$B(v) = \tfrac{3}{2} - v\pi^{-1/2}$$
$$\times \left[\pi^{1/2} \int_0^v \exp(u^2) \, du - \int_0^v \frac{\exp(u^2) - 1}{u} \, du - \tfrac{1}{2}\gamma - \ln v \right] \exp(-v^2) \tag{71}$$

where $\gamma = 0.5772157 \ldots$ is Euler-Mascheroni's constant (Whittaker and Watson, 1958, p. 235). In fact by using Eq. (71) we can get from Eq. (70) useful asymptotic expansions for both small and large x/t values, which provide a satisfactory representation of Eq. (70) for every x/t.

For small x/t we have, up to the order $(x/t)^3$,

$$u(x, t)/u_0 \approx F(x/t) + (t/\theta)G(x/t) \tag{72}$$

where

$$F(x/t) = \tfrac{1}{2} - \pi^{-1/2}[(x/t) - \tfrac{1}{3}(x/t)^3], \tag{73}$$

and

$$G(x/t) = \tfrac{1}{8} + \tfrac{1}{2}\pi^{-1/2}(x/t)[\ln(x/t) + 1 + \tfrac{1}{2}\gamma - \sqrt{2}\ln(\sqrt{2} + 1)]$$
$$+ \pi^{-1}(x/t)^2[\tfrac{1}{4} + \tfrac{1}{2}\gamma - \ln(x/t)]. \tag{74}$$

On the other hand, for large x/t we have

$$u(x, t)/u_0 \approx \tfrac{1}{2}\pi^{-1/2} \exp(-x^2/t^2)(t/x)\{1 - \tfrac{1}{2}(t/x)^2 \tag{75}$$
$$- (t/\theta)[1 - \tfrac{3}{2}(t/x)^2 - \tfrac{1}{4}\pi^{-1/2}(t/x)^3]\}.$$

We note that the first terms of these expansions have been given independently in a recent note by Yoshio Sone (1964) through a perturbation method on the free-molecular flow solution.

An analogous procedure can be applied to evaluate the shear stress. First, reintroducing usual units for t and x in Eq. (34) gives

$$\bar{\tau}(x, s) = \theta^2 \rho_0 u_0 s \pi^{1/2} \int_0^\infty \frac{v X_A(-v, s\theta) \exp[-(s\theta + 1)(x/\theta v) + v^2]}{[p(v, s\theta)]^2 + \pi^2 v^2} \, dv. \quad (76)$$

Expanding in powers of $1/\theta$ gives

$$\bar{\tau}(x, s) \simeq \frac{\rho_0 u_0}{s \pi^{1/2}} \int_0^\infty \left\{ v + \frac{v}{s\theta} [B(v) - 2R(v) - 1] - (x/\theta) \right\} \exp(-v^2) \, dv. \quad (77)$$

Then by inverse transformation, we get up to terms of order t/θ:

$$\tau(x, t) \simeq \tfrac{1}{2} \rho_0 u_0 \pi^{-1/2} \exp(-x^2/t^2) + \rho_0 u_0 \pi^{-1/2}(t/\theta) \left\{ \int_{x/t}^\infty v \exp(-v^2)[B(v) \right.$$

$$\left. - 2R(v) - 1] \, dv - (x/t) \int_{x/t}^\infty \exp(-v^2)[B(v) - 2R(v)] \, dv \right\}. \quad (78)$$

The zero-order term coincides with Yang and Lees' result (1960). Equation (78) can be manipulated to give expressions for $\tau(x, t)$, valid when $x/t \ll 1$ or $x/t \gg 1$.

VIII. Asymptotic Expansion for Small Knudsen Numbers

In this section we shall find an asymptotic expansion of our exact solution in the range of large t (continuum limit).

To this end we shall use Eq. (38) which, in terms of the usual units and through Eqs. (32) and (33), can be written as

$$\frac{u(x, t)}{u_0} = (2\pi i)^{-1} \int_0^{-1/\theta} e^{st} \left[\frac{(s\theta + 1) \exp[-(s\theta + 1)(x/\theta v_0)]}{s v_0^* X_B(v_0^*, s\theta)} \right.$$

$$- \frac{(s\theta + 1) \exp[-(s\theta + 1)(x/\theta v_0^*)]}{s v_0^* X_B(v_0^*, s\theta)} - \theta \pi^{1/2}(s\theta + 1)$$

$$\left. \times \int_0^\infty \frac{(v_0 - v_0^*) X_B(-v, s\theta) \exp[-(s\theta + 1)(x/\theta v) + v^2]}{[p(v, s\theta)]^2 + \pi^2 v^2} \, dv \right] ds$$

$$+ (2\pi i)^{-1} \int_{-(1/\theta) - i\infty}^{-(1/\theta) + i\infty} e^{st} \bar{u}(x, s) \, ds \quad (79)$$

where $\bar{u}(x, s)$ is given by Eq. (66). The last term is easily seen to be asymptotically zero, since it is of order $e^{-t/\theta}$ when $\theta \to 0$. Therefore it will be neglected in the following expansion procedure.

From Eq. (19) we easily find for small θ

$$v_0(s\theta) \simeq (2s\theta)^{-1/2}. \tag{80}$$

Furthermore, one can expand $X_B(v_0)$ up to terms of order $1/v_0{}^2$:

$$X_B(v_0, s\theta) \approx (1/v_0) - (Q_1/v_0{}^2) \tag{81}$$

where $Q_1 \equiv Q(0)$ is given by Eq. (58).

Substituting Eq. (81) in Eq. (79) gives

$$\frac{u(x, t)}{u_0} \approx (2\pi i)^{-1} \int_0^{-\infty} e^{st} \left[\frac{e^{(-x/\theta v_0)}}{s(1 - Q_1/v_0)} - \frac{e^{(x/\theta v_0)}}{s(1 + Q_1/v_0)} \right.$$

$$\left. - 2v_0 \theta \pi^{1/2} \int_0^\infty \frac{X_B(-v, 0) \exp[(-x/\theta v) + v^2]}{[p_0(v)]^2 + \pi^2 v^2} \, dv \right] ds \tag{82}$$

where $p_0(v) \equiv p(v, 0)$. Using Eq. (80) and inverse transformation gives, up to terms of order $t^{-1/2}$,

$$\frac{u(x, t)}{u_0} \approx 1 - \frac{2x}{\sqrt{2\pi\theta t}} + \sqrt{\frac{2\theta}{\pi t}} Q_1 - \sqrt{\frac{\theta}{2t}} \int_0^\infty \frac{X_B(-v, 0) \exp[(-x/\theta v) + v^2]}{[p_0(v)]^2 + \pi^2 v^2} \, dv. \tag{83}$$

Since, in our units the kinematic viscosity coefficient, v, is related to θ by $\theta = 2v$, Eq. (83) can be written as follows:

$$\frac{u(x, t)}{u_0} \approx 1 - \frac{x}{(\pi v t)^{1/2}} + \frac{2vQ_1}{(\pi v t)^{1/2}} - \left(\frac{v}{t}\right)^{1/2}$$

$$\times \int_0^\infty \frac{X_B(-v, 0) \exp[(-x/\theta v) + v^2]}{[p_0(v)]^2 + \pi^2 v^2} \, dv. \tag{84}$$

Equation (84) can now be compared with the results given by Gross and Jackson (1958) and Schaaf (1950). This comparison shows that the slip coefficient must be

$$z = -2vQ_1 \equiv -2l\pi^{-1/2}Q_1 \tag{85}$$

where l is the mean free path related to the viscosity coefficient μ by the relation

$$l = (\mu/p)(\tfrac{1}{2}\pi RT)^{1/2} \tag{86}$$

(here $p = \rho RT$ is the pressure). The result given by Eq. (85) agrees with the previous one by Cercignani (1962) for steady problems.

The last term in Eq. (84) gives the boundary layer effect already found by Gross and Jackson (1958) in a qualitative form. As is seen, Eq. (86) shows a dependence on x more complicated than a simply exponential one (as found by Gross and Jackson). The last term in Eq. (84) can be written as

$$\left(\frac{v}{2t}\right)^{1/2} \int_0^\infty \frac{\exp\left[-\pi^{1/2} \int_0^\infty \ln(t+v) \frac{\exp(t^2)\,dt}{[p_0(t)]^2 + \pi^2 t^2} - \frac{x}{\theta v} + v^2\right]}{[p_0(v)]^2 + \pi^2 v^2}\, dv$$

$$= (v/2t)^{1/2} I(x/\theta). \quad (87)$$

It is to be noted that the boundary layer structure is described by the same function as in a steady problem (see, e.g., Cercignani, 1964a); in particular the microscopic slip coefficient is given by

$$z_{micro} = 2^{-1/2}\theta \equiv (2\pi^{-1})^{1/2}l, \quad (88)$$

in agreement with the value found for steady problems (Cercignani, 1964b).

The integral $I(x/\theta)$ appearing in Eq. (87) was calculated for $0 < x/\theta < 10$; the result is shown in Fig. 5 and Table III.

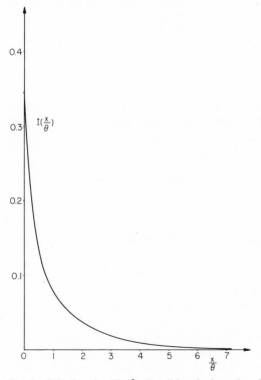

FIG. 5. Graph of the function $I(x/\theta)$, describing the boundary layer.

TABLE III

Values Calculated for Fig. 5

$I(x/\theta)$	x/θ
0.347721	0.
0.136617	0.5
0.079814	1.0
0.053642	1.5
0.037321	2.0
0.026169	2.5
0.018383	3.0
0.012921	3.5
0.009085	4.0
0.006391	4.5
0.004498	5.0
0.003167	5.5
0.002232	6.0
0.001574	6.5
0.001111	7.0
0.000786	7.5
0.000556	8.0
0.000395	8.5
0.000281	9.0
0.000200	9.5
0.000143	10.0

It can also be shown that this integral is related to the function $G(x/\theta)$ tabulated by Willis (1960) through a quite different calculation; the relation reads as follows:

$$I(x/\theta) = 2\pi^{-1/2}[G(x/\theta) - (z/\theta)] \qquad (89)$$

where $z = (1.1466)l$ is the slip coefficient for the BGK model (Albertoni *et al.*, 1963).

IX. Comparison with the Half-Range Polynomial Solution

In this section we shall consider the results given by Gross and Jackson (1958) and compare them with ours.

First, it must be noticed that Gross and Jackson give numerical results only for rigid sphere molecules. However the corresponding results both for Maxwellian molecules and the BGK model can be easily found, by using calculations due to Ziering (1960) and by direct evaluation, respectively.

We note that, although they use an approximate method (half-range polynomials expansion), Gross and Jackson do not work out the final result, but restrict themselves to an asymptotic analysis in the limits of short and long times, as we also did for our exact solution.

In the limit of short times, the result of Gross and Jackson is evidently inaccurate; this is due to the inadequacy of a polynomial expansion for describing the initial evolution of the velocity distribution.

In the limit of long times, Gross and Jackson find

$$u(x, t)/u_0 \approx 1 - [x/(\pi v t)^{1/2}] - 1.24(l/\pi t)^{1/2} + 0.292(l/\pi t)^{1/2}e^{-cx} \quad (90)$$

where l is the Maxwell mean free path for rigid sphere molecules and $c = 7.86/l$ (it appears that the printed value $c = l^{-1}(6.86)$ is a misprint).

For Maxwell molecules the previous term has a similar form with different, values for the numerical constants. By using the results given by Ziering (1960), we found in particular $c = 3.03/l$. It is to be noted that the boundary layer for Maxwellian molecules is thicker than for rigid sphere molecules (approximately two times).

For the BGK model the boundary layer is even thicker since $c = 1.88/\theta$. This, of course, relates to the half-range polynomial expansion up to first degree in c_x.

The qualitative agreement of Eqs. (84) and (90) should be noted; the most interesting difference consists of the fact that the simple exponential behavior of the boundary layer term in Eq. (90) corresponds to a more sophisticated dependence on the spatial variable in Eq. (84). Concerning this point one can note that a half-range polynomial expansion up to first degree in c_x gives necessarily an exponential behavior of the boundary layer term.

X. Concluding Remarks

The linearized Rayleigh's problem has been solved exactly for the whole range of Knudsen numbers. In addition to the general expression of the solution, we have given useful expansions for limiting cases and simple analytical formulas for velocity and stress on the plate. By the use of these equations we have also obtained numerical results for quantities of particular interest.

Among the various results we have obtained, we stress the fact that for large times the boundary layer is exactly described by the same function as in steady problems; in particular the value of the slip coefficient resulting from this time dependent problem is exactly the same as that for steady problems.

ACKNOWLEDGMENTS

The authors are grateful to professor S. Albertoni for his assistance and encouragement in developing this research. One of them (F.S.) is also indebted to C.N.R. for having partially supported this research through a grant.

Appendix

In this appendix we demonstrate identities (43) and (59) of the main text. In fact, Eq. (45) gives for real positive v

$$\frac{1}{X_A^+(v, s)} - \frac{1}{X_A^-(v, s)} = X_A(-v, s)\frac{s}{s + 1}\left[\frac{1}{M^+(v, s)} - \frac{1}{M^-(v, s)}\right]; \quad (A.1)$$

here, for any function $g(z)$, $g^\pm(v) = \lim_{\varepsilon \to 0} g(v \pm i\varepsilon)$. Equation (46) then gives

$$\frac{1}{X_A^+(v, s)} - \frac{1}{X_A^-(v, s)} = -2\pi i s \pi^{1/2}\frac{v \exp(v^2)X_A(-v, s)}{[p(v, s)]^2 + \pi^2 v^2}. \quad (A.2)$$

But $X_A(z, s) = 1 + O(1/z)$ when $z \to \infty$ (for complex z); accordingly $[X_A(z, s)]^{-1} = 1 + O(1/z)$. Therefore, Eq. (A.2) gives by means of Plemelj's formulas (Muskhelishvili, 1953)

$$\frac{1}{X_A(z, s)} = 1 - s\pi^{1/2}\int_0^\infty \frac{t \exp(t^2)X_A(-t, s)\, dt}{\{[p(t, s)]^2 + \pi^2 t^2\}(t - z)}. \quad (A.3)$$

This equation coincides with Eq. (43) of the main text, with z replaced by $-v$. Analogously, we can demonstrate that Eq. (59) of the main text holds. In fact $X_B(-v, s)$ satisfies the identity analogous to Eq. (45),

$$X_B(z, s)X_B(-z, s) = [(s + 1)]/s[M(z, s)/(v_0^2 - z^2)] \quad (A.4)$$

Consequently for real positive v we have the following identity analogous to Eq. (A.2):

$$\frac{1}{X_B^+(v, s)} - \frac{1}{X_B^-(v, s)} = -2\pi i s \pi^{1/2}(v_0^2 - v^2)\frac{v X_B(-v, s) \exp(v^2)}{[p(v, s)]^2 + \pi^2 v^2}. \quad (A.5)$$

But it is easily seen from Eqs. (26) and (58) of the main text that for every complex z we have

$$X_B(z, s) = z^{-1} - z^{-2}Q(s) + O(z^{-2}). \quad (A.6)$$

Accordingly one can apply the Plemelj formulas to

$$(1/X_B) - z - Q(s)$$

and find

$$\frac{1}{X_B(z, s)} = z + Q(s) - s\pi^{1/2}\int_0^\infty \frac{t \exp(t^2)(v_0^2 - t^2)X_B(-t, s)}{\{[p(t, s)]^2 + \pi^2 t^2\}(t - z)}\, dt. \quad (A.7)$$

This equation coincides with Eq. (59) of the main text, with z replaced by $-v$.

REFERENCES

Albertoni, S., Cercignani, C., and Gotusso, L. (1963). *Phys. Fluids* **6**, 993.

Bhatnagar, P. L., Gross, E. P., and Krook, M. (1954). *Phys. Fluids* **94**, 511.

Cercignani, C., (1962). *Ann. Phys.* **20**, 219.

Cercignani, C., (1964a). The Kramers problem for a not completely diffusing wall. *J. Math. Anal. Appl.* (to be published.)

Cercignani, C. (1964b). Plane Couette flow according to the method of elementary solutions *J. Math. Anal. Appl.* (to be published).

Cercignani, C. (1964c). Plane Poiseuille flow according to the method of elementary solutions. *J. Math. Anal. Appl.* (to be published).

Cercignani, C., and Sernagiotto, F. (1964). The method of elementary solutions for time-dependent problems in linearized kinetic theory. *Ann. Phys.* (*N.Y.*) **30**, 154.

Gross, E. P., and Jackson, E. A. (1958). *Phys. Fluids* **1**, 318.

Muskhelishvili, N. I. (1953). "Singular Integral Equations." Noordhoff, Groningen, the Netherlands.

Pekeris, C. L., Altermann, Z., Finkelstein, L., and Frankowski, K. (1962). *Phys. Fluids* **5**, 1608.

Rayleigh, J. W. Strutt, Lord (1911). *In* "Scientific Papers," Vol. VI, p. 29. Cambridge Univ. Press, London and New York.

Schaaf, S. A. (1950). Univ. of California. Inst. Eng. Res. Rept. NO HE-150-66.

Sirovich, L., and Thurber, J. (1963). *In* "Rarefied Gas Dynamics" (J. A. Laurmann, ed.), Vol. I, p. 159. Academic Press, New York.

Wang Chang, C. S., and Uhlenbeck, G. E. (1952). Eng. Res. Inst. Univ. of Michigan ONR Contract N60 nr-23222.

Whittaker, E. T., and Watson, G. N., (1927). "A Course of Modern Analysis." Cambridge Univ. Press, London and New York.

Willis, D. R. (1960). KTH AERO TN 52. Stockholm.

Yang, H. T., and Lees, L. (1956). *J. Math. and Phys.* **35**, 195

Yang, H. T., and Lees, L. (1960). *In* "Rarefied Gas Dynamics" (F. M. Devienne, ed.), p. 201. Pergamon Press, London.

Yoshio Sone (1964). *Phys. Fluids* **7**, 470.

Ziering, S. (1960). *Phys. Fluids* **3**, 503.

Bimodal Two-Stream Distribution and Compressible Couette Flow

JÜRGEN W. BECK

Institute for Fluid Mechanics, Technical University of Munich, Germany

A short description of the existing solutions for the flow of rarefied gases is given. Using the line-of-sight principle, a new and more general formulation for the velocity distribution function (viz., the bimodal two-stream distribution) is proposed, which appears to be particularly appropriate for nonlinear cases. The proposed method is applied to plane compressible Couette flow. In this case, the solutions can be expressed explicitly. Good agreement with other theoretical and experimental results is observed.

I. Introduction

A general theoretical treatment of the flow of rarefied gases has to proceed from the Boltzmann equation:

$$\partial f/\partial t + \boldsymbol{\xi} \cdot \nabla_r f + \mathbf{F} \cdot \nabla_\xi f = (\partial f/\partial t)_{\text{coll}}. \tag{1}$$

It must be noted, that this basic equation is exactly valid only for point molecules with sufficiently high rarefaction. The two limiting cases $\mathrm{Kn} = 0$ (continuum flow) and $\mathrm{Kn} \to \infty$ (free molecular flow) can be derived from Eq. (1). In addition, the transition between these two cases is of great interest in practical aerodynamics. Solutions of Eq. (1) valid for the entire range of Knudsen numbers are desirable.

There are several approximate solutions of the Boltzmann equation. For the so-called normal solutions, there exists a one-to-one correspondence between the distribution function and the macroscopic state. This method was developed by Hilbert, Enskog, and Chapman, see e.g. Chapman and Cowling (1960). The first approximation is equivalent to the Navier-Stokes equations. The second approximation (Burnett equations) and higher approximations are also obtained by this method. However, the validity of these latter for stronger rarefaction is questionable. Moreover, these equations are very unwieldy. A method, which is more applicable to practical cases, was proposed by Grad (1949). Using Hermite polynomials, it leads to the simplest case of the 13-moment approximation. From here start the works of Wang Chang and Uhlenbeck (1953), Mott-Smith (1954), and Gross et al. (1957). The latter use for the sake of simplicity the Krook model instead of the collision integral on the right-hand side of Eq. (1). In the regime of near-free-molecular flow, the distribution function can be expanded in powers of the Knudsen number. The related approaches of Heinemann (1948), Keller (1948), and Wang Chang (1950) are based on the work of Jaffé (1930). For large Knudsen numbers, Willis (1958) developed a method which is valid for molecules with finite total cross-section. Recently some interesting results were obtained by Smolderen (1965). For practical cases, the use of the transport equation seems to be most suitable. Generally, no closed system of equations can be derived from it. However, introducing a finite number of physically significant space and/or time functions into the velocity distribution function, an approximate solution can be given which is valid for the entire range of Knudsen numbers.

II. Directional Dependence of the Velocity Distribution Function

In every flow problem, not only macroscopic boundary conditions must be satisfied, but also microscopic ones related to the velocity distribution function. Owing to the reflection characteristics of solid boundaries, a discontinuity in the distribution function is introduced by every wall. This discontinuity is propagated into the surrounding flow field and, as a result of molecular encounters, is attenuated with increasing distance from the wall, i.e., for $Kn \neq \infty$. Therefore, in each point of the flow field, the distribution function will have dissimilar contributions depending on the direction of the molecular velocity considered. This is the reason why the approximate solutions with continuous full-range distributions (Hilbert-Enskog-Chapman, 13-moment, and others) are not appropriate in the vicinity of a wall.

A suitable model is provided by the line-of-sight principle proposed by Lees (1959), in which two molecular streams, represented by $\hat{f}$ and $\check{f}$, are distinguished at every point of space as shown in Fig. 1. Obviously, this physical picture is exactly valid for free molecular flow, where $\hat{f} = f_w$ denotes the distribution function of the molecules emitted from the wall, and $\check{f} = f_\infty$ denotes the one for free flow. However, the continuum behavior is also reproduced correctly, as the two functions $\hat{f}$ and $\check{f}$ will be similar at distances many free paths away from the body, i.e., after many encounters suffered by the molecules emitted from the wall. Thereby, the distribution function achieves a full-range character. The transition between these two cases is illustrated schematically in Fig. 2, where the distribution function (or any

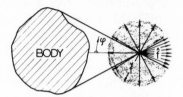

FIG. 1. Line-of-sight principle.

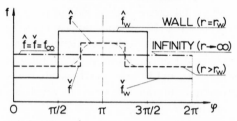

FIG. 2. Directional dependence of the velocity distribution function f (schematic).

related quantity) is plotted against the angle φ. It must be emphasized that this concept is a model only. Certainly, slight deviations from the line-of-sight concept may occur in practice as indicated in Fig. 2. This difficulty can be avoided by using other assumptions for the directional dependence. For example, with the relaxation-type procedure proposed by Shen (1963), the distribution function of the emitted molecules is attenuated exponentially with increasing distance from the body. Simultaneously, at a corresponding rate, the full-range distribution grows representing the correct continuum behavior. Similar to this is the work of Takao (1961).

In the following we shall use the line-of-sight principle. There are two main reasons for this choice: firstly, a comparatively simple solution is possible with this model; thus, a more general assumption for the distribution function can be made (see Section III); and secondly, deviations (as indicated in Fig. 2) shall tend to integrate out for the determination of macroscopic quantities, which are to be taken as mean values over the whole range $0 \leqslant \varphi \leqslant 2\pi$.

III. Formulation with Bimodal Two-Stream Distribution

To get a solution for the entire range of Knudsen numbers, we fall back upon the transport equation which is obtained by multiplying the Boltzmann equation (1) with a molecular property Φ and integrating over the whole velocity space. In case of Φ depending on the molecular velocity ξ only, the transport equation can be written in the steady case ($\partial/\partial t \equiv 0$) without external field of force ($\mathbf{F} \equiv 0$) as

$$\nabla_r \int \Phi\langle\xi\rangle \xi f\langle\xi, \mathbf{r}\rangle \, d\xi = \int \Phi\langle\xi\rangle (\partial f/\partial t)_{\text{coll}} \, d\xi = n \, \Delta\overline{\Phi}. \tag{2}$$

The assumption for $f\langle\xi, \mathbf{r}\rangle$ is to be physically significant and mathematically not too complicated. Introducing in this formulation k unknown space-dependent functions, k moment equations must be used for the determination of these functions, i.e., k different values of Φ must be introduced into Eq. (2). This number must be larger than the number of conservation equations, which result from the lowest values of Φ (viz., the summational invariants $\Phi_s = m$, $\Phi_s = m\xi$ and $\Phi_s = m\xi^2/2$, where $\Delta\overline{\Phi}_s \equiv 0$), so that the effect of rarefaction can be introduced through $\Delta\overline{\Phi}$ into the system of equations. As was shown by Maxwell (1867), the right-hand side of Eq. (2) is independent of the form of the distribution function, if Maxwellian molecules (repulsive force field $\sim r^{-5}$) are chosen. Then it can be expressed in terms of macroscopic flow quantities, e.g.,

$$\Phi = m\xi_j\xi_k: \qquad n \, \Delta\overline{\Phi} = p p_{jk}/\mu_c, \tag{3}$$

$$\Phi = \xi_j m\xi^2/2: \qquad n \, \Delta\overline{\Phi} = (p/\mu_c)(-2q_j/3 + \sum_k p_{jk}u_k), \tag{4}$$

where μ_c denotes the classical coefficient of viscosity based on a local full-range Maxwellian.

As to the distribution function itself, Lees (1959) takes for each of the two streams $\hat{f}$ and $\check{f}$ a local Maxwellian. With this assumption, ten unknown space-dependent functions are introduced. This assumption contains the limiting cases $\text{Kn} = 0$ and $\text{Kn} \to \infty$. However, the choice of local Maxwellians seems to be somewhat arbitrary, especially for large Knudsen numbers (or at distances of the order of λ from the body).

Therefore, a more general formulation for f is proposed in this paper choosing for each of the two streams $\hat{f}$ and $\check{f}$ a mixing formula. In this way, a bimodal two-stream distribution can be written as

$$\hat{f}\langle\xi, \mathbf{r}\rangle = \alpha\langle\mathbf{r}\rangle \cdot f_1\langle\xi, \mathbf{r}\rangle + \beta\langle\mathbf{r}\rangle \cdot f_2\langle\xi, \mathbf{r}\rangle,$$
$$\check{f}\langle\xi, \mathbf{r}\rangle = \gamma\langle\mathbf{r}\rangle \cdot f_1\langle\xi, \mathbf{r}\rangle + \delta\langle\mathbf{r}\rangle \cdot f_2\langle\xi, \mathbf{r}\rangle. \tag{5}$$

It is convenient to choose local Maxwellians for the two functions f_1 and f_2, namely,

$$f_{1,2}\langle\xi, \mathbf{r}\rangle = \frac{n_{1,2}\langle\mathbf{r}\rangle}{(2\pi R T_{1,2}\langle\mathbf{r}\rangle)^{3/2}} \exp\left\{-\frac{(\xi - \mathbf{u}_{1,2}\langle\mathbf{r}\rangle)^2}{2R T_{1,2}\langle\mathbf{r}\rangle}\right\}. \tag{6}$$

The influence functions α, β, γ, and δ determine the mixing ratio. The advantage of the assumption (5) lies in the greater generality of the distribution functions obtained and in a considerably better representation of the physical behavior in the range of higher Knudsen numbers. Especially the typical double maximum in the distribution function can be reproduced, which occurs for strongly different temperatures, i.e. in nonlinear cases. Treating the one-dimensional shock wave, Mott-Smith (1951) mixed two constant full-range distributions. He obtained good results especially for very strong waves, i.e., large temperature ratios.

The formulation (5) contains altogether twelve unknown space-dependent functions, namely u_1, u_2, T_1, T_2, αn_1, βn_2, γn_1, δn_2. It is sufficient to evaluate the last four functions as products rather than the functions themselves. If no simplification is made, a system of twelve differential equations (five conservation equations and seven additional moment equations) must be solved in the general three-dimensional case. The boundary conditions for a body in an infinitely extended flow field can be formulated easily:

$$\mathbf{r} = \mathbf{r}_w: \qquad \alpha \langle \mathbf{r}_w \rangle = 1; \qquad \beta \langle \mathbf{r}_w \rangle = 0; \qquad f_1 \langle \boldsymbol{\xi}, \mathbf{r}_w \rangle = f_w \langle \boldsymbol{\xi} \rangle,$$
$$\mathbf{r} \to \infty: \qquad \gamma \langle \infty \rangle = 0; \qquad \delta \langle \infty \rangle = 1; \qquad f_2 \langle \boldsymbol{\xi}, \infty \rangle = f_\infty \langle \boldsymbol{\xi} \rangle. \tag{7}$$

The boundary conditions for a closed geometry are similar to the above ones, see e.g. Section IV, B.

With the formulation (5) several simplifications are possible. Firstly, it can be seen, that the assumption of Lees (1959) is contained as a special case with

$$\alpha \equiv 1; \qquad \beta \equiv 0;$$
$$\gamma \equiv 0; \qquad \delta \equiv 1; \qquad \text{for all } \mathbf{r}.$$

However, there is still another special case deducible from Eq. (5), namely $f_1 = f_w = $ constant and $f_2 = f_\infty = $ constant with the space dependence of the velocity distribution function determined by the four influence functions. The boundary conditions can be satisfied easily (Section IV, B). The choice of constant functions f_1 and f_2 is useful only for very simple geometries, as otherwise the number of variables is not sufficient for the description of the effect of rarefaction. In more general cases, a simplification can be performed by keeping some parameters in f_1 and f_2 [see Eq. (6)] as constants, so that very few additional moment equations are required. In the general three-dimensional case, the entities n_1, u_1 and n_2, u_2 may be kept as constants (values at the wall and at infinity, respectively), and only the temperatures $T_1 \langle \mathbf{r} \rangle$ and $T_2 \langle \mathbf{r} \rangle$ are considered as space-dependent. With this, there are only six unknown functions which are determined by the five conservation equations and one additional moment equation (using Lees's two-stream Maxwellian, a system of altogether ten equations must be solved in the general three-dimensional case). The formulation of Eq. (5) serves to satisfy the boundary conditions without exception, i.e., regardless of the extent of simplification performed in the above manner.

IV. Application to Compressible Couette Flow

The formulation (5) with bimodal two-stream distribution shall now be applied to plane compressible Couette flow for which results from other schemes are available for comparison. The geometry of the well-known configuration and the coordinate system are shown in Fig. 3. The two infinitely extended

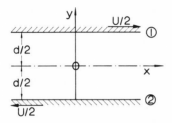

FIG. 3. Geometry of plane Couette flow.

plates are separated by a distance d. The upper plate (index " 1 ") moves with the constant velocity $U/2$ in the positive x-direction, the lower one (index " 2 ") in the opposite direction. Assuming completely diffuse reflection from the walls, the distribution functions for the emitted molecules can be written as

$$f_{1,2} = \frac{n_{1,2}}{(2\pi RT_{1,2})^{3/2}} \exp\left\{ -\frac{(\xi_x \mp U/2)^2 + \xi_y^2 + \xi_z^2}{2RT_{1,2}} \right\}. \tag{8}$$

The upper sign holds for plate " 1," the lower sign for plate " 2." The values of the densities and temperatures at the walls are denoted by $n_{1,2}$ and $T_{1,2}$, respectively.

A. System of Equations

The simplest solution is obtained by taking $f_1 = $ constant and $f_2 = $ constant, viz., the values at the walls from Eq. (8). The cones-of-sight from Fig. 1 degenerate to half-spaces everywhere, and the molecular distribution function can be written as

$$\xi_y > 0: \quad \hat{f}\langle y \rangle = \alpha\langle y \rangle \cdot f_1 + \beta\langle y \rangle \cdot f_2,$$
$$\xi_y < 0: \quad \check{f}\langle y \rangle = \gamma\langle y \rangle \cdot f_1 + \delta\langle y \rangle \cdot f_2. \tag{9}$$

As $\partial/\partial x \equiv \partial/\partial z \equiv 0$, Eq. (2) is simplified to

$$(\partial/\partial y) \int \Phi \xi_y f\langle y \rangle \, d\xi = n \cdot \Delta\overline{\Phi}. \tag{10}$$

For the summational invariants $\Delta\overline{\Phi}_s \equiv 0$, and hence

$$\int \Phi_s \xi_y f\langle y \rangle \, d\xi = \text{const.} \tag{11}$$

The integrals appearing in Eqs. (10) and (11) have the following significance:

$$\int (\cdots) f \, d\xi = \int_\uparrow (\cdots) \hat{f} \, d\xi + \int_\downarrow (\cdots) \check{f} \, d\xi$$

$$= \int_{-\infty}^{+\infty} \int_0^{+\infty} \int_{-\infty}^{+\infty} (\cdots) \hat{f} \, d\xi_x \, d\xi_y \, d\xi_z + \int_{-\infty}^{+\infty} \int_{-\infty}^0 \int_{-\infty}^{+\infty} (\cdots) \check{f} \, d\xi_x \, d\xi_y \, d\xi_z. \tag{12}$$

Different values of Φ are introduced now into Eq. (10) or (11). Firstly, taking $\Phi_s = m$, Eq. (11) yields

$$\int_\uparrow \xi_y \hat{f} \, d\xi + \int_\downarrow \xi_y \check{f} \, d\xi = 0. \tag{13}$$

The kinematic boundary condition $\int \xi_y f \, d\xi = 0$ has already been satisfied by equating the right-hand side of Eq. (13) to zero. After integration, Eq. (13) gives

$$n_1 (RT_1/2\pi)^{1/2}(\alpha - \gamma) + n_2 (RT_2/2\pi)^{1/2}(\beta - \delta) = 0. \tag{14}$$

Introducing the dimensionless ratios

$$v = n_1/n_2 \qquad \text{and} \qquad \tau = T_1/T_2, \tag{15}$$

Eq. (14) transforms to

$$v\tau^{1/2}(\alpha - \gamma) + (\beta - \delta) = 0. \tag{16}$$

Secondly, $\Phi_s = m\xi_x$ yields from Eq. (11)

$$\int_\uparrow \xi_x \xi_y \hat{f} \, d\xi + \int_\downarrow \xi_x \xi_y \check{f} \, d\xi = -p_{xy}/m \tag{17}$$

and after integration,

$$v\tau^{1/2}(\alpha - \gamma) - (\beta - \delta) = \zeta_1 \tag{18}$$

where

$$\zeta_1 = -2(2\pi)^{1/2} p_{xy}/(mn_2 U(RT_2)^{1/2}). \tag{19}$$

Thirdly, in similar manner, putting $\Phi_s = m\xi_y$ into Eq. (11), it can be written as

$$\int_\uparrow \xi_y{}^2 \hat{f} \, d\xi + \int_\downarrow \xi_y{}^2 \check{f} \, d\xi = -P_{yy}/m. \tag{20}$$

After integration, Eq. (20) results as

$$v\tau(\alpha + \gamma) + (\beta + \delta) = \zeta_2. \tag{21}$$

where

$$\zeta_2 = -2P_{yy}/(mn_2RT_2). \tag{22}$$

Fourthly, the energy equation is obtained by introducing $\Phi_s = m\xi^2/2$ into Eq. (11) as

$$\int_\uparrow \xi_y\xi^2 \hat{f} \, d\xi + \int_\downarrow \xi_y\xi^2 \check{f} \, d\xi = (2/m)(q_y - up_{xy}). \tag{23}$$

Upon integration

$$v\tau^{1/2}(\tau + \kappa \, \text{Ma}^2/16)(\alpha - \gamma) + (1 + \kappa \, \text{Ma}^2/16)(\beta - \delta) = \zeta_3 \tag{24}$$

where

$$\zeta_3 = \left(\frac{\pi}{2}\right)^{1/2} \frac{(q_y - up_{xy})}{mn_2(RT_2)^{3/2}}. \tag{25}$$

and

$$\text{Ma} = U/(\kappa RT_2)^{1/2}. \tag{26}$$

From Eq. (16) and (18) it follows that

$$(\alpha - \gamma) = \zeta_1/(2v\tau^{1/2}) \tag{27}$$

and

$$(\beta - \delta) = -\zeta_1/2. \tag{28}$$

Introducing these two values into Eq. (24), it can be seen that

$$\zeta_3 = (\tau - 1)\zeta_1/2 \tag{29}$$

whence, after inserting the values (19) and (25),

$$q_y = up_{xy}\left[1 - \frac{U}{u}\frac{2(\tau - 1)}{\kappa \, \text{Ma}^2}\right]. \tag{30}$$

With this relation, Eq. (24) is satisfied automatically, and one additional moment equation may be used. Therefore, finally introducing $\Phi = m\xi_x\xi_y$ into Eq. (10):

$$(d/dy)\left[\int_\uparrow \xi_x\xi_y{}^2 \hat{f} \, d\xi + \int_\downarrow \xi_x\xi_y{}^2 \check{f} \, d\xi\right] = pp_{xy}/(m\mu_c) \tag{31}$$

is obtained. Using the dimensionless coordinate

$$\eta = y/d \tag{32}$$

and carrying out the integration, Eq. (31) yields after rearranging

$$(d/d\eta)[v\tau(\alpha + \gamma) - (\beta + \delta)] + (\zeta_1/2\,\text{Kn})[v(\alpha + \gamma) + (\beta + \delta)] = 0 \tag{33}$$

where

$$\text{Kn} = (\pi\kappa/2)^{1/2}\text{Ma}/\text{Re} \qquad \text{and} \qquad \text{Re} = U\,dmn_2/\mu_{c_2}. \tag{34}$$

The four unknown functions α, β, γ, and δ of $\eta = y/d$ must satisfy Eqs. (16), (18), (21), and (33), since Eq. (24) is satisfied already through the relation (29).

B. Boundary Conditions and Solution

It is assumed that the molecules leave the surface with a Maxwellian distribution in equilibrium with the wall. Therefore, the boundary conditions can be written as

$$\begin{aligned}
y = +\tfrac{1}{2}d, \quad \eta = +\tfrac{1}{2}: \quad &\check{f} = f_1; \quad \gamma\langle +\tfrac{1}{2}\rangle = 1; \quad \delta\langle +\tfrac{1}{2}\rangle = 0, \\
y = -\tfrac{1}{2}d, \quad \eta = -\tfrac{1}{2}: \quad &\hat{f} = f_2; \quad \alpha\langle -\tfrac{1}{2}\rangle = 0; \quad \beta\langle -\tfrac{1}{2}\rangle = 1.
\end{aligned} \tag{35}$$

The temperatures of the walls are given. The quantity n_2 specifies the density level. There remain four constant parameters to be determined: v, ζ_1, ζ_2 and the integration constant which arises from Eq. (33). These four values are determined uniquely by the boundary conditions (35).

The solution of the system of Eqs. (16), (18), (21), and (33) is basically not difficult and will not be described here. Eliminating the integration constant arising from Eq. (33) by use of one of the boundary conditions (35), the solutions for the influence functions are obtained:

$$\alpha = \frac{\zeta_2}{2v(\tau - 1)} + \frac{\zeta_1}{4v\tau^{1/2}} - \frac{1}{v\tau}\left(1 + \frac{\zeta_1}{4} + \frac{\zeta_2}{2(\tau - 1)}\right)\exp\left\{\frac{\zeta_1(\tau - 1)}{4\tau\,\text{Kn}}(\tfrac{1}{2} + \eta)\right\}, \tag{36}$$

$$\beta = \left(1 + \frac{\zeta_1}{4} + \frac{\zeta_2}{2(\tau - 1)}\right)\exp\left\{\frac{\zeta_1(\tau - 1)}{4\tau\,\text{Kn}}(\tfrac{1}{2} + \eta)\right\} - \frac{\zeta_2}{2(\tau - 1)} - \frac{\zeta_1}{4}, \tag{37}$$

$$\gamma = \alpha - \zeta_1/(2v\tau^{1/2}), \tag{38}$$

$$\delta = \beta + \zeta_1/2. \tag{39}$$

Now using the remaining boundary conditions (35), the following three equations for the determination of v, ζ_1, and ζ_2 are obtained:

$$\zeta_2 = 2 - \zeta_1(\tau^{1/2} - 1)/2, \tag{40}$$

$$v = 1/\tau - \zeta_1(\tau^{1/2} - 1)/(2\tau) = (\zeta_2 - 1)/\tau, \tag{41}$$

$$\text{Kn} = \zeta_1(\tau - 1)\left[4\tau \ln \frac{4 - \zeta_1(\tau + \tau^{1/2} - 2)}{4\tau + \zeta_1(\tau - \tau^{1/2})}\right]^{-1}. \tag{42}$$

The relation (42) is shown in Fig. 9, where ζ_1 is connected with the drag coefficient through Eq. (61). Equations (36)–(39) along with (40)–(42) represent the complete solution of the problem.

The macroscopic quantities of the flow are obtained directly from their definitions:

$$n = \int f \, d\xi, \tag{43}$$

$$u = (1/n) \int \xi_x f \, d\xi, \tag{44}$$

as

$$n/n_2 = \rho/\rho_2 = \tfrac{1}{2}[v(\alpha + \gamma) + (\beta + \delta)], \tag{45}$$

$$u/U = \tfrac{1}{2}[v(\alpha + \gamma) - (\beta + \delta)]/[v(\alpha + \gamma) + (\beta + \delta)]. \tag{46}$$

The expression for the temperature in terms of the influence functions is somewhat longer and will not be cited here.

C. Special Cases

Firstly, the symmetrical case ($\tau = T_1/T_2 = 1$) is considered. For this case Eqs. (40)–(42) are simplified to

$$v = 1; \qquad \zeta_1 = -4\,\text{Kn}/(1 + 2\,\text{Kn}); \qquad \zeta_2 = 2. \tag{47}$$

Inserting these values into Eqs. (36)–(39), Eq. (45) gives

$$n/n_2 = 1 = \text{const}, \tag{48}$$

and Eq. (46) results as

$$u/U = \eta/(1 + 2\,\text{Kn}) \qquad \text{for} \quad \tau = 1, \tag{49}$$

which is surprisingly simple.

For the case of free molecular flow ($\text{Kn} \to \infty$) one obtains

$$v = 1/\tau^{1/2}; \qquad \zeta_1 = -2; \qquad \zeta_2 = 1 + \tau^{1/2}, \tag{50}$$

and therefore

$$n/n_2 = (1 + \tau^{-1/2})/2 = \text{const} \tag{51}$$

$$u/U = \tfrac{1}{2}(1 - \tau^{1/2})/(1 + \tau^{1/2}) = \text{const} \qquad \text{for} \quad \text{Kn} \to \infty, \tag{52}$$

since $\alpha = \delta = 0 = \text{constant}$ and $\beta = \gamma = 1 = \text{constant}$. Finally, the result for

continuum flow (Kn = 0) is

$$v = 1/\tau; \qquad \zeta_1 = 0; \qquad \zeta_2 = 2; \tag{53}$$

and

$$n/n_2 = (1/\tau)^{\frac{1}{2}+\eta}, \tag{54}$$

$$u/U = \frac{2 - (\tau + 1)(1/\tau)^{\frac{1}{2}+\eta}}{2(\tau - 1)(1/\tau)^{\frac{1}{2}+\eta}} \qquad \text{for} \quad Kn = 0. \tag{55}$$

It can easily be verified that the classical boundary condition (no slip) is reproduced by Eq. (55):

$$\begin{aligned}
\eta &= -\tfrac{1}{2}: \qquad u/U = -\tfrac{1}{2}, \\
\eta &= +\tfrac{1}{2}: \qquad u/U = +\tfrac{1}{2}.
\end{aligned} \tag{56}$$

D. Results and Discussion

Typical variations of the influence functions α, β, γ, and δ with the co-ordinate $\eta = y/d$ for the temperature ratio $\tau = T_1/T_2 = 4$ are shown in Figs. 4a and 4b. The Knudsen number appears as a parameter. For Kn = ∞

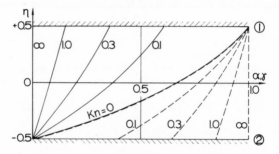

FIG. 4a. Influence functions α (full curves) and γ (dashed curves) for temperature ratio $\tau = T_1/T_2 = 4$.

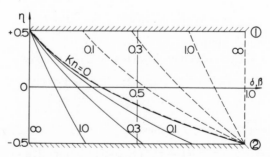

FIG. 4b. Influence functions δ (full curves) and β (dashed curves) for temperature ratio $\tau = T_1/T_2 = 4$.

the influence functions are constants. For $Kn = 0$, a full-range distribution occurs anywhere. However, this full-range distribution must, in general, not be Maxwellian. Therefore, it is not to be expected that the continuum behavior is reproduced exactly. The boundary conditions for $Kn = 0$, namely, the vanishing of slip velocity and temperature jump, are nevertheless satisfied in any case. The simplification (viz., f_1 and f_2 each to be constant) is apparently too strong. However, it is believed, that even this simple solution gives good results for large Knudsen numbers and large temperature ratios, as the double maximum in the distribution function can be reproduced.

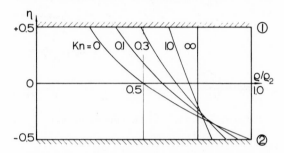

FIG. 5. Density profile for temperature ratio $\tau = T_1/T_2 = 4$.

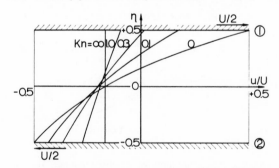

FIG. 6. Velocity profile for temperature ratio $\tau = T_1/T_2 = 4$.

The density and velocity profiles are shown in Figs. 5 and 6, respectively, both for $\tau = 4$. These curves do not depend on the Mach number. Of course, temperature and heat flux density, which are not cited here, do depend on Mach number. It should be noted, that the Mach number dependence of the results of Lees and Liu (1960) is only very weak.

Finally, the dimensionless slip velocity

$$\Delta u/(U/2) = |u\langle\eta_w\rangle - u_w|/(U/2), \qquad (57)$$

and the temperature jump for $Ma = 3$ (divided by the wall temperature T_2)

$$\Delta T/T_2 = (T\langle\eta_w\rangle - T_w)/T_2, \qquad (58)$$

are shown in Figs. 7 and 8, respectively, as functions of the Knudsen number for the temperature ratios $\tau = 1$ and $\tau = 4$. A comparison with the results of Lees and Liu shows that the solution given here yields a greater slip velocity

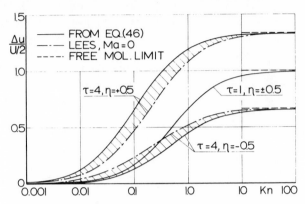

FIG. 7. Slip velocity vs. Knudsen number.

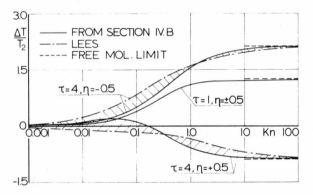

FIG. 8. Temperature jump vs. Knudsen number, Ma $= 3$.

at the wall with the higher temperature, and a smaller one at the wall with the lower temperature. The drag coefficient,

$$C_D = p_{xy}/(\rho_2 U^2/2) = -\zeta_1/[(2\pi\kappa)^{1/2}\text{Ma}], \tag{59}$$

is obtained from Eq. (19). Dividing Eq. (59) by the value for free molecular flow

$$C_{D_f} = (2/\pi\kappa)^{1/2}/\text{Ma} \tag{60}$$

gives

$$C_D/C_{D_f} = -\zeta_1/2. \tag{61}$$

Therefore, this ratio can be obtained immediately from Eq. (42) and is shown

in Fig. 9 as function of the Knudsen number for the whole range of temperature ratios. For comparison, the Navier-Stokes solution for $Ma = 0$ and the

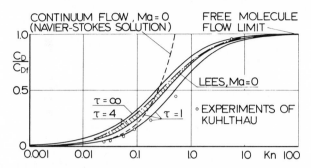

FIG. 9. Drag coefficient vs. Knudsen number.

result of Lees and Liu for $\tau = 4$ are also plotted. Good agreement with the
experimental results of Kuhlthau (1953) for $\tau = 1$ is observed.

E. More General Formulations

In order to improve the results of Section IV for the range of small Knudsen
numbers, a more general formulation has been applied using variable tem-
peratures $T_1\langle\eta\rangle$ and $T_2\langle\eta\rangle$ in Eq. (9), while the remaining parameters in
$f_{1,2}$ are kept as constants. This gives a system of six equations for the Couette
flow. Also, the most general case with variable temperatures and velocities
shall be used to yield a system of eight equations for the Couette flow. The
related results shall be presented in a later paper.

V. Conclusion

Using the line-of-sight principle for the description of the directional dependence of the distribution function, the formulation (5) yields distribution
functions which satisfy the boundary conditions and are especially appropriate
for nonlinear cases. Simplifications can be deduced easily from (5). Applying
the proposed approach to the Couette flow, results are obtained, which can be
expressed explicitly. Slip velocity and temperature jump are in reasonable
agreement with the earlier results obtained by Lees and Liu (1959). The comparison concerning the drag coefficient is also satisfactory. Further, the
experimental results of Kuhlthau (1953) are well confirmed. The proposed
approximate method is valid for the entire range of Knudsen numbers.

ACKNOWLEDGMENTS

The author is grateful to Professor Dr.-Ing. E. Truckenbrodt for his valuable suggestions and his support during the work. The research was sponsored by the Deutsche Forschungsgemeinschaft.

List of Symbols

C_D Drag coefficient, Eq. (60)
d Distance between plates
f Velocity distribution function
F External field of force
Kn Knudsen number, Eq. (34)
m Molecular mass
Ma Mach number, Eq. (26)
n Number density
p Hydrostatic pressure
p_{jk} Pressure tensor
P_{jj} Diagonal element of nondivergent pressure tensor $= -p + p_{jj}$
q Heat flux vector
r Position vector in coordinate space
R Specific gas constant
Re Reynolds number, Eq. (34)
T Temperature
u Macroscopic velocity

U Relative velocity of plates
x, y, z Rectangular coordinates
$\alpha, \beta, \gamma, \delta$ Influence functions
$\zeta_1, \zeta_2, \zeta_3$ Integration constants, Eqs. (19), (22), (25), respectively
η Dimensionless coordinate $= y/d$
κ Ratio of specific heats
λ Mean free path
μ_c "classical" viscosity coefficient
ν Density ratio $= n_1/n_2$
ξ Molecular velocity vector
ρ Density
τ Temperature ratio $= T_1/T_2$
φ Angle according to Fig. 1
Φ Molecular property
∇_r Nabla vector in coordinate space
∇_ξ Nabla vector in velocity space

INDICES

coll Due to collisions
f Free molecule conditions
s Summational invariant
w Wall
∞ Freestream conditions

$\hat{}$ Molecular stream according to Fig. 1
$\check{}$ Molecular stream according to Fig. 1
$\langle\cdots\rangle$ Angular brackets indicate functional dependence

REFERENCES

Beck, J. W. (1964). *In* "AGARDograph No. 87." NATO, Paris
Chapman, S., and Cowling, T. G. (1960). " The Mathematical Theory of Non-Uniform Gases." Cambridge Univ. Press, London and New York.
Grad, H. (1949). *Communs. Pure Appl. Math.* **2**, 331.
Gross, E. P., Jackson, E. A., and Ziering, S. (1957). *Ann. Phys. (N.Y.)* **1**, 141.
Heinemann, M. (1948). *Communs. Pure Appl. Math.* **1**, 259.
Jaffé, G. (1930). *Ann. Physik* **6**, 195.
Keller, J. B. (1948). *Communs. Pure Appl. Math.* **1**, 275.
Kuhlthau, A. R. (1953). *In* "Proc. 3rd Midwestern Con. Fluid Mech.," pp.495-514. Univ. of Minnesota.

Lees, L. (1959). GALCIT Hypersonic Research Project, Memo. No. 51.

Lees, L., and Liu, C. Y. (1960). GALCIT Hypersonic Research Project, Memo. No. 58.

Maxwell, J. C. (1867). *Phil. Trans. Roy. Soc. London* **157**, 49.

Mott-Smith, H. M. (1951). *Phys. Rev.* **82**, 885.

Mott-Smith, H. M. (1954). M.I.T. Lincoln, Lab., Group Rept. V-2.

Shen, S. F. (1963). *In* "Rarefied Gas Dynamics" (J. A. Laurmann, ed.), Vol. II, pp.112-131. Academic Press, New York.

Smolderen, J. J. (1965). This volume, p.277, private communication.

Takao, K. (1961). *In* "Rarefied Gas Dynamics" (L. Talbot ed.), pp.465-473. Academic Press, New York.

Wang Chang, C. S. (1950). Univ. Mich., Eng. Res. Inst. Rept. CM 654.

Wang Chang, C. S., and Uhlenbeck, G. E. (1953). Univ. Mich., Eng. Res. Inst. Rept. M 999.

Wang Chang, C. S., and Uhlenbeck, G. E. (1954). Univ. Mich., Eng. Res. Inst. Rept. 1999-1-T.

Willis, D. R. (1958). Princeton Univ., Aeronaut. Eng. Lab., Rept. 440.

A Discrete Ordinate Technique
for the Linearized Boltzmann Equation
with Application to Couette Flow[1]

BERNARD HAMEL AND MURRAY WACHMAN

Space Sciences Laboratory General Electric Company, King of Prussia, Pennsylvania

A numerical method is formulated for the solution of the distribution function of the Boltzmann equation. The method developed in this paper is one of discrete ordinates. Numerical approximations are developed for the linearized Boltzmann collision integral for hard sphere molecules. The resulting discrete ordinate differential equations are then solved for the case of linearized Couette flow and the results are found to be in qualitative agreement with previous work.

I. Introduction

In studying the problems of rarefied gas dynamics, one must generally have recourse to the Boltzmann transport equation. For the general case, one has a nonlinear, integro-differential equation, the integral involving a fivefold integration. In the linear problem one can simplify this integral by linearization and reduce the order of integration from five to three; however, even for this simplified case, the integro-differential equation presents formidable mathematical difficulties. To treat this problem thus far, various investigators (Bhatnagar *et al.*, 1954; Welander, 1954) have either postulated models which replace the complicated collision integrals or have utilized moment methods to obtain approximate solutions to the moments of the Boltzmann equation (Gross *et al.*, 1957; Lees, 1959). In the present work, in contradistinction to the previous investigations, we adopt the point of view that a numerical method be formulated for the solution of the distribution function of the Boltzmann equation. Utilizing this point of view we need make

[1] This work was supported by the USAF Office of Scientific Research under Contract No. AF 49(638)-1283.

approximations to the Boltzmann equation only in the sense of numerical truncations.

The numerical method developed here is one of discrete ordinates. This approach involves analyzing the linearized Boltzmann equation for hard sphere molecules at discrete points in velocity space. We treat the collision integral as a finite sum through the use of Gauss quadrature formulas, choosing the set of discrete points in velocity space so that they coincide with the set of points used to perform the quadrature. The choice of a quadrature formula (and discrete ordinate points in velocity space) is in general not simple; it is determined by the character of the integral being approximated, especially by the weight function under the integral and the properties of the integrand.

It is important to point out that the discrete ordinate approach has been perfected to a high degree of sophistication in radiative and neutron transport theory. The scattering integrals encountered there generally involve only one integration and are of a simple form thereby allowing a straightforward application of the quadrature formulas. The Boltzmann collision integral of rarefied gas dynamics, however, involves a quite complex quadrature, and the extension of the discrete ordinate technique to the rarefied gas dynamics problem is not straightforward. It should be emphasized that, thus far, the only other attempt to extend the discrete ordinate method to this problem has been made by Broadwell (1963a, b). Broadwell replaces the collision integral by a finite sum, employing the assumptions of constant molecular speed and constant mean free path. Broadwell does not however take account of the fact that approximation of the collision integral by a finite sum must be equivalent to the application of a numerical quadrature formula to the integral. In fact the assumptions made by Broadwell are equivalent to a quite crude formula, with the property that all quadrature coefficients are equal. The solution given by Broadwell (1963b) for the linearized Couette flow of hard sphere molecules reflects this low order approximation. These results do not exhibit the Knudsen layer for small Knudsen numbers and are quite inaccurate in the limit of large Knudsen numbers. These inaccuracies can only be corrected by a fuller appreciation of the quadrature approximation inherent in expressing the collision integral as a finite sum, rather than in adding more discrete ordinate points within the same procedure.

In the present work numerical approximations are developed (Section II) for the linearized Boltzmann collision integral of hard sphere molecules. The resulting discrete ordinate differential equations are then solved for the case of linearized Couette flow (Section III). The numerical results obtained for linearized Couette flow are discussed in Section IV, and are seen to be in qualitative agreement with previous work (Gross and Ziering, 1958; Cercignani, 1963). In fact, because of the relatively large number of discrete points used here, and the flexibility afforded by the technique, it is reasonable to assert that the results reported here have greater accuracy than the previously published work on the linearized Couette flow of hard sphere molecules (Gross and Ziering, 1958; Cercignani, 1963).

II. Approximation to the Linearized Boltzmann Integral for Hard Sphere Molecules

In this section a quadrature approximation will be developed for the linearized Boltzmann integral for hard sphere molecules. This approximation will enable us to replace the linearized Boltzmann equation by a closed system of linear differential equations which is flexible enough to apply to a wide range of linearized, rarefied gas dynamic problems.

For hard sphere molecules the linearized Boltzmann integral takes the form (Gross and Ziering, 1958)

$$\lambda^{-1}[J(\varphi(\mathbf{c}, \mathbf{r}, t))] = -n_0 \overline{K}(\mathbf{c})\varphi(\mathbf{c}, \mathbf{r}, t)$$

$$+ \int_{-\infty}^{\infty} \exp(-c_1{}^2) K(\mathbf{c}, \mathbf{c}_1)\varphi(\mathbf{c}_1, \mathbf{r}, t)\, d\mathbf{c}_1 \qquad (1)$$

where the perturbation distribution function $\varphi(\mathbf{c}, \mathbf{r}, t)$ is

$$f(\mathbf{c}, \mathbf{r}, t) = n_0(h/\pi)^{3/2} \exp(-c^2)[1 + \varphi(\mathbf{c}, \mathbf{r}, t)]; \qquad |\varphi(\mathbf{c})| \ll 1, \qquad (2)$$

and

$$\overline{K}(\mathbf{c}, \mathbf{c}_1) = \sigma^2 \pi^{1/2}\left\{-|\mathbf{c}_1 - \mathbf{c}| + \frac{2}{|\mathbf{c}_1 - \mathbf{c}|} \exp\left[\left(\frac{\mathbf{c}_1 \times \mathbf{c}}{|\mathbf{c}_1 - \mathbf{c}|}\right)^2\right]\right\},$$

$$\overline{K}(\mathbf{c}) = \pi^{1/2}\sigma^2\{\pi^{1/2}(1/|\mathbf{c}|)[c^2 + \tfrac{1}{2}] \operatorname{erf}|\mathbf{c}| + \exp(-c^{\,2})\} \qquad (3)$$

where σ is the diameter of the hard sphere molecule, λ is the mean free path, the vector $\mathbf{c}$ is the nondimensional velocity ($\mathbf{c} = \mathbf{c}/c_{\text{th}}$), $h = (2kT/m)^{\frac{1}{2}}$, n_0 is a constant density, and $\mathbf{c}_1$ represents the velocity of the colliding molecules (therefore $\mathbf{c}_1$ is the variable of integration). Note that $J(\varphi)$ as defined above is nondimensional.

An approximating formula is now constructed for $J(\varphi)$ at discrete velocity points $\mathbf{c}$, by evaluating the integral in Eq. (1) by means of Gauss quadrature. It should be noticed that if the integral in Eq. (1) is evaluated by Gauss quadratures the variable of integration $\mathbf{c}_1$ will have components which are roots of the particular Gauss quadrature, although the vectors $\mathbf{c}$ are still arbitrary. This results in an expression for $J(\varphi)$ in terms of values of the unknown function φ, evaluated at discrete velocity points $\mathbf{c}_1$ and $\mathbf{c}$. The choice of a Gauss quadrature formula is in general not simple. It is determined by the region of integration, by the weight function under the integral and by the properties of the integrand.

To choose the quadrature formulas it will be necessary to consider certain features of the collision integral as well as some aspects of kinetic theory boundary value problems. It should be noticed in Eq. (3) that $K(\mathbf{c}, \mathbf{c}_1)$ has a singularity at $\mathbf{c} = \mathbf{c}_1$. It is therefore necessary in our numerical scheme to design a grid so that the set of $\{\mathbf{c}\}$ and the set of $\{\mathbf{c}_1\}$ have no common members. Our solution to this problem is to take two distinct Gauss quadrature formulas, one whose roots will be the components of the set of $\{\mathbf{c}\}$ and the other whose roots will be the components of the set $\{\mathbf{c}_1\}$. At first we evaluate $J(\varphi(\mathbf{c}))$ on a set of values of $\mathbf{c}$, which are the roots of one quadrature formula, while $\mathbf{c}_1$ as a variable of integration ranges over the roots of the other quadrature formula. The roles of the two formulas are then reversed. This results in a closed symmetric system. Other considerations leading to the choice of two distinct formulas involve the physics of the boundary value problems. If we consider boundary value problems (such as Couette flow) it is clear that at the boundary, $\varphi(\mathbf{c})$ will be a discontinuous function of $\mathbf{c} \cdot \mathbf{n}$ ($\mathbf{n}$ is a unit vector normal to the boundary); however, in the interior of the regions considered, intermolecular collisions will smooth this behavior and the function will be full-range in velocity space. From this point of view in order to approximate this dual character of φ it is expedient to choose the two distinct Gauss quadratures, so that one is half-range and the other is full-range. In this way we can in some sense approximate the physical behavior of φ, especially if one used the plane of discontinuity in velocity space to define the half-range regions.

Since the weight function in Eq. (1) is of the form: $\exp(|-\mathbf{c}|^2)$, we choose for the full range formula the Gauss-Hermite approximation. For the half-range formula we employ the Gauss-Laguerre formula. Although this formula is designed for a weight function of the form: $\exp(-\mathbf{c})$, we shall show how to adjust the conventional Gauss-Laguerre formula so that a half-range integral with weight function $\exp(-\mathbf{c}^2)$ may be integrated.

Let us first consider the Gauss-Hermite full-range formula. If H_i, $i = 1, ...,$ $2m$, are the roots of the Hermite polynomials, then m of these roots are negative and m are positive. Equation (1) may then be approximated by

$$\lambda^{-1} J(\varphi(\Lambda)) = -n_0 \overline{K}(\Lambda)\varphi(\Lambda)$$

$$+ \sum_{i=1}^{2m} h_i \sum_{j=1}^{2m} h_j \sum_{k=1}^{2m} h_k [K(\Lambda; (H_k, H_j, H_i))\varphi(H_k, H_j, H_i)] \quad (4)$$

where h_i, h_j, h_k are Hermite quadrature coefficients and $\Lambda \neq (H_k, H_j, H_i)$ (since Λ are to be taken proportional[2] to roots of the half range quadrature

---

[2] The reason for proportionality will become clear later.

formulas). To perform the three-dimensional integration of Eq. (1) three applications of the one-dimensional Gauss-Hermite formulas are utilized.

For the second quadrature formula we employ the modified Gauss-Laguerre formula. We first divide the integral specified in Eq. (1) into eight half-range integrals:

$$
\int_{-\infty}^{\infty}\int_{-\infty}^{\infty}\int_{-\infty}^{\infty} = \int_{0}^{\infty}\int_{0}^{\infty}\int_{0}^{\infty} + \int_{-\infty}^{0}\int_{0}^{\infty}\int_{0}^{\infty} + \int_{0}^{\infty}\int_{-\infty}^{0}\int_{0}^{\infty} + \int_{-\infty}^{0}\int_{-\infty}^{0}\int_{0}^{\infty}
$$
$$
+ \int_{0}^{\infty}\int_{0}^{\infty}\int_{-\infty}^{0} + \int_{-\infty}^{0}\int_{0}^{\infty}\int_{-\infty}^{0} + \int_{0}^{\infty}\int_{-\infty}^{0}\int_{-\infty}^{0}
$$
$$
+ \int_{-\infty}^{0}\int_{-\infty}^{0}\int_{-\infty}^{0}.
\tag{5}
$$

We introduce the transformation $\Lambda = \mu \mathbf{W}$, where $\mathbf{W}$ has Laguerre roots for components and μ is a constant which is used to adjust our integrand [which has an $\exp(-|c|^2)$ weight function] to a Laguerre-Gauss quadrature. The choice of μ will be made clear in Section IV. Equation (1) can then be written in the form

$$
\lambda^{-1}J(\varphi(\mathbf{H})) = n_0 \bar{K}(\mathbf{H})\varphi(\mathbf{H})
$$
$$
+ \mu^3 \int_{-\infty}^{\infty} \exp[-(|W_x| + |W_y| + |W_z|)]
$$
$$
\times \exp[-|\mu\mathbf{W}|^2 + |W_x| + |W_y| + |W_z|]K(\mathbf{H}; (\mu W_x, \mu W_y, \mu W_z))
$$
$$
\times \varphi(\mu W_x, \mu W_y, \mu W_z)\, d\mathbf{W}.
\tag{6}
$$

Using Eq. (5) we can rearrange Eq. (6) in the following way to account for the fact that the Laguerre integration is performed in the range $0 \leqslant W \leqslant \infty$:

$$
\lambda^{-1}J(\varphi(\mathbf{H})) = n_0 \bar{K}(\mathbf{H})\varphi(\mathbf{H})
$$
$$
+ \mu^3 \int_{0}^{\infty} \exp(-|W_x| - |W_y| - |W_z|)
$$
$$
\times \Bigg\{ \exp(-|\Lambda|^2 + |W_x| + |W_y| + |W_z|) \sum_{i=0}^{1} \sum_{j=0}^{1} \sum_{k=0}^{1}
$$
$$
\times K(\mathbf{H}; ((-1)^i\Lambda_x, (-1)^j\Lambda_y, (-1)^k\Lambda_z))
$$
$$
\times \varphi((-1)^i\Lambda_x, (-1)^j\Lambda_j, (-1)^k\Lambda_z)\Bigg\}\, d\mathbf{W}.
\tag{7}
$$

The integral in Eq. (7) now has the proper weight function, $\exp(-|W_x| - |W_y| - |W_z|)$, and the region of integration is half-range. We can now employ a Gauss-Laguerre integration formula where the Laguerre roots will be W_i, $i = 1, ..., m$. If we consider that we have $2m$ Laguerre roots, i.e., W_i, $i = 1, ..., m$ and $-W_i$, $i = 1, ..., m$ then Eq. (1) can be approximated in the following manner:

$$\lambda^{-1} J(\varphi(\mathbf{H})) = -n_0 \overline{K}(\mathbf{H}) \varphi(\mathbf{H})$$

$$+ \mu^3 \sum_{i=1}^{2m} l_i \sum_{j=1}^{2m} l_j \sum_{k=1}^{2m} l_k$$

$$\times \exp[-\mu^2(W_k{}^2 + W_j{}^2 + W_i{}^2) + |W_k| + |W_j| + |W_i|]$$

$$\times K(\mathbf{H}; \mu(W_k, W_j, W_i)) \varphi(\mu(W_k, W_j, W_i)) \tag{8}$$

where $l_i = l_{m+i}$ are the Laguerre quadrature coefficients. It is obvious that one need not always take the two quadrature formulas to be a threefold Laguerre versus a threefold Hermite. It is sometimes advantageous from the physical point of view to weigh the integration in favor of one scheme. A mixing of schemes is clearly possible, as long as the set $\{\mathbf{c}\}$ does not have a member in common with the set $\{\mathbf{c}_1\}$.

Thus far we have established full-range Hermite and half-range Laguerre quadrature formulas and have indicated how they would be utilized to form a closed system of differential equations. The system is closed because an equation exists for φ at each discrete velocity ordinate at which $J(\varphi)$ is evaluated.

Let us assume that this set of $2(2m)^3$ values of φ has been given some linear order through the ordering of the $\mathbf{H}_i$ and Λ_i, i.e., has been put in one-to-one correspondence with the integers from 1 to $2(2m)^3$. This will allow us to write our system of differential equations in matrix form. First let us denote in Eq. (8)

$$\mu^3 l_i l_j l_k \exp[-\mu^2(W_k{}^2 + W_j{}^2 + W_i{}^2) + |W_k^2| + |W_j| + |W_i|]$$

$$\times K(\mathbf{H}_s; \mu(W_k, W_j, W_i)) = \beta_{S,\tau}$$

where S and τ are the indices that are determined by the ordering of $\mathbf{H}_S$ and $\Lambda_\tau = \mu(W_k, W_j, W_i)$; $S, \tau = 1, ..., (2m)^3$. Let us also denote in Eq. (8)

$$-n_0 \overline{K}(\mathbf{H}_S) = B_S.$$

A similar procedure can be used for Eq. (4), i.e., we denote

$$h_i h_j h_k K(\Lambda_S; (H_k, H_j, H_i)) = \gamma_{S,\tau}$$

and

$$-n_0 \overline{K}(\Lambda_S) = \Gamma_S.$$

Equation (1) can then be approximated by the following set of equations:

$$\lambda^{-1} J[\varphi(H_S)] = \frac{d\varphi}{dt}(\mathbf{H}_S) = B_S \varphi(\mathbf{H}_S) + \sum_{\tau=1}^{(2m)^3} \beta_{S,\,\tau} \varphi(\mathbf{\Lambda}_\tau), \quad S = 1, ..., (2m)^3,$$

$$\lambda^{-1} J[\varphi(\Lambda_S)] = \frac{d\varphi}{dt}(\mathbf{\Lambda}_S) = \Gamma_S \varphi(\mathbf{\Lambda}_S) + \sum_{\tau=1}^{(2m)^3} \gamma_{S,\,\tau} \varphi(\mathbf{H}_\tau), \quad S = 1, ..., (2m)^3$$

(9)

where

$$\frac{d}{dt} = \frac{\partial}{\partial t} + \mathbf{c} \cdot \frac{\partial}{\partial \mathbf{x}} + \mathbf{a} \cdot \frac{\partial}{\partial \mathbf{v}}.$$

Equation (9) may be written in the following matrix form where the matrix A is a $[2(2m)^3] \times [2(2m)^3]$ matrix:

$$\begin{pmatrix} \dfrac{d\varphi}{dt}(\mathbf{H}_S) \\[2mm] \dfrac{d\varphi}{dt}(\mathbf{\Lambda}_S) \end{pmatrix} = A \begin{pmatrix} \varphi(\mathbf{H}_S) \\[2mm] \varphi(\mathbf{\Lambda}_S) \end{pmatrix}.$$

(10)

The matrix A is composed of four matrices, each $(2m)^3 \times (2m)^3$:

$$A = \left(\begin{array}{c|c} A_{11} & A_{12} \\ \hline A_{21} & A_{22} \end{array} \right)$$

where

$$A_{11} = \begin{pmatrix} B_1 & & & 0 \\ & B_2 & & \\ & & \cdot & \\ & & & \cdot \\ 0 & & & B_{(2m)^3} \end{pmatrix} \qquad \text{is a diagonal matrix,}$$

$$A_{22} = \begin{pmatrix} \Gamma_1 & & & 0 \\ & \Gamma_2 & & \\ & & \cdot & \\ & & & \cdot \\ 0 & & & \Gamma_{(2m)^3} \end{pmatrix} \qquad \text{is a diagonal matrix;}$$

$$A_{12} = \begin{pmatrix} \beta_{11} & \beta_{12} & \cdots & \beta_{1(2m)^3} \\ \beta_{21} & \beta_{22} & \cdots & \beta_{2(2m)^3} \\ \vdots & \vdots & & \vdots \\ \beta_{(2m)^3 1} & \beta_{(2m)^3 2} & \cdots & \beta_{(2m)^3 (2m)^3} \end{pmatrix},$$

$$A_{21} = \begin{pmatrix} \gamma_{11} & \gamma_{12} & \cdots & \gamma_{1(2m)^3} \\ \gamma_{21} & \gamma_{22} & \cdots & \gamma_{2(2m)^3} \\ \vdots & \vdots & & \vdots \\ \gamma_{(2m)^3 1} & \gamma_{(2m)^3 2} & \cdots & \gamma_{(2m)^3 (2m)^3} \end{pmatrix}.$$

In Section III, the solution to Eq. (10) subject to an appropriate set of boundary conditions for linearized Couette flow is discussed.

III. The Boundary Value Problem for Linearized Couette Flow

In this section we show how the system of Eq. (10) makes it possible to solve the *boundary value problem* for linearized Couette flow in an explicit form (within the numerical approximation). This boundary value problem is shown to be reduceable to the solution of a set of $(2m)^3$ *linear algebraic* equations in the φ's.

Let us make the following assumption for the Couette flow problem.

1. Planar steady flow.
2. Plates have a common temperature T_0.
3. Upper plate moves with velocity $U'/2$ in the y direction, lower plate moves with velocity $-U'/2$ in the y direction.
4. $U' \ll c_{th}$ (c_{th} denotes the thermal velocity).
5. Hard sphere molecules with finite cross sections.
6. Diffuse reflection of molecules at each plate.

It can then be shown (e.g., Gross and Ziering, 1958) that the Boltzmann equation takes the linearized form

$$c_x \frac{d\varphi}{dx}(x, \mathbf{c}) = \alpha J[\varphi(x, \mathbf{c})] \tag{11}$$

when φ and $J(\varphi)$ are defined in Eqs. (1) and (2), c_x is taken to be c_x/c_{th}, x is taken to be x/d, and $\alpha = n_0\sigma^2\pi d = d/\lambda$, which is the reciprocal of the Knudsen number. The linearized boundary conditions for Eq. (11) are taken to be

$$f = af^{(0)}(1 + Uc_y), \quad c_x < 0, \quad x = \tfrac{1}{2}, \tag{12}$$

$$f = bf^{(0)}(1 - Uc_y), \quad c_x > 0, \quad x = -\tfrac{1}{2},$$

$$f^{(0)} = n_0(h/\pi)^{3/2} \exp(-c^2) \tag{13}$$

where c_x and c_y are the x and y component of $\mathbf{c}$ and $U = U'/c_{th}$.

To determine the constants a and b one must satisfy the conditions that the number of particles between the plates be constant and that there be no mass flow in the x direction. From conditions of symmetry (see Fig. 1): $\varphi(x, c_x) = -\varphi(-x, -c_x)$ and $a = b$. In addition since $U' \ll c_{th}$, one has a constant density, n_0, between the plates, so that $a = b = 1$.

The boundary conditions therefore become

$$\varphi(\tfrac{1}{2}, \mathbf{c}) = +Uc_y, \quad c_x < 0,$$

$$\varphi(-\tfrac{1}{2}, \mathbf{c}) = -Uc_y, \quad c_x > 0.$$

It can now be observed that if $d\varphi(\mathbf{c})/dt = c_x \, d\varphi(\mathbf{c})/dx$, Eq. (10) becomes

$$\begin{pmatrix} H_{xs} \dfrac{d\varphi}{dx}(\mathbf{H}_s) \\[2mm] \Lambda_{xs} \dfrac{d\varphi}{dx}(\Lambda_s) \end{pmatrix} = \alpha A \begin{pmatrix} \varphi(\mathbf{H}_s) \\[2mm] \varphi(\Lambda_s) \end{pmatrix} \tag{14}$$

where H_{xs} and Λ_{xs} are the x components of $\mathbf{H}_s$ and Λ_s, respectively. It is then seen that if we divide each of the $(2m)^3$ upper rows of αA by this corresponding

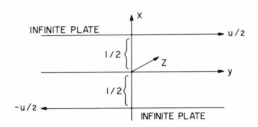

FIG. 1. Couette flow.

H_{xs} and each of the $(2m)^3$ lower rows of αA by the corresponding Λ_{xs} we will get a matrix $\alpha A'$ and the relation

$$\begin{pmatrix} \dfrac{d\varphi}{dx}(\mathbf{H}_s) \\[2mm] \dfrac{d\varphi}{dx}(\Lambda_s) \end{pmatrix} = \alpha A' \begin{pmatrix} \varphi(\mathbf{H}_s) \\[2mm] \varphi(\Lambda_s) \end{pmatrix}. \tag{15}$$

The matrix $\alpha A'$ is composed of elements which are functions of the velocity. Therefore, relative to the variable x, the matrix $\alpha A'$ has constant coefficients. Equation (15) has a solution of the form

$$\begin{pmatrix} \varphi(x, \mathbf{H}_s) \\ \varphi(x, \Lambda_s) \end{pmatrix} = e^{\alpha A'(x - x_0)} \begin{pmatrix} \varphi(x_0, \mathbf{H}_s) \\ \varphi(x_0, \Lambda_s) \end{pmatrix}. \tag{16}$$

Assume that with the ordering adopted for the Couette flow problem the first $(2m)^3/2$ of both the H_s, and Λ_s have the positive x component. We then wish to solve Eq. (16) with boundary conditions

$$\begin{aligned} x_0 &= -\tfrac{1}{2}, & \varphi &= -Uc_y, & c_x &> 0, \\ x &= \tfrac{1}{2}, & \varphi &= +Uc_y, & c_x &< 0. \end{aligned} \tag{17}$$

If one examines the formal solution [Eq. (16)] and the boundary conditions [Eq. (17)], it can be observed that at each boundary only half the distribution function is known. One can therefore not treat Eq. (16) as the solution to an initial value problem because one lacks a complete knowledge of the distribution function on any boundary.

In what follows Eq. (16) is rearranged so that the unknown part of the distribution function at each boundary is expressed as a linear algebraic map of the known boundary value. The entire solution of the problem is thus resolved by a solution of a system of linear algebraic equations.

It is convenient at this time to think of the matrix $\Omega = \exp[\alpha A'(x - x_0)]$ as being divided into 16 distinct equal sections with $(2m)^6/4$ element in each. We do this in the following way. Consider the first $(2m)^3/2$ columns of Ω. According to the way the $\varphi(\mathbf{H}_s)$ were ordered, the first $(2m)^3/2$ columns of Ω will multiply the $\varphi(\mathbf{H}_s)$ such that $H_{xs} > 0$. The next $(2m)^3/2$ columns will multiply the $\varphi(\mathbf{H}_s)$ with $H_{xs} < 0$. The third block of $(2m)^3/2$ columns will multiply the $\varphi(\Lambda_s)$ with $\Lambda_{xs} > 0$ and the last block of $(2m)^3/2$ will multiply the $\varphi(\Lambda_s)$ with $\Lambda_{xs} < 0$. We therefore have sectioned Ω into four blocks of columns. We divide the rows in a similar manner, i.e., according to whether $d\varphi(\mathbf{H}_s)/dx$ has $H_{xs} > 0$ or $H_{xs} < 0$ and $d\varphi(\Lambda_s)/dx$ has $\Lambda_{xs} > 0$ or $\Lambda_{xs} < 0$. The combined effect is the division of Ω into 16 sections which we label below:

$$\Omega = \begin{pmatrix} [1] & [2] & [3] & [4] \\ [5] & [6] & [7] & [8] \\ [9] & [10] & [11] & [12] \\ [13] & [14] & [15] & [16] \end{pmatrix}.$$

This concept of ordering and sectioning has been designed, as we shall soon see, to formulate our particular boundary value problem. Using the boundary conditions (Eq. (17)) in Eq. (16) we see that the boundary value problem acquires the following form:

$$(2m)^3/2\begin{cases} \varphi(\tfrac{1}{2}, \mathbf{H}_s) \\ U H_{ys} \\ \varphi(\tfrac{1}{2}, \Lambda_s) \\ U \Lambda_{ys} \end{cases} = \begin{pmatrix} [1] & [2] & [3] & [4] \\ [5] & [6] & [7] & [8] \\ [9] & [10] & [11] & [12] \\ [13] & [14] & [15] & [16] \end{pmatrix} \begin{pmatrix} -U H_{ys} \\ \varphi(-\tfrac{1}{2}, \mathbf{H}_s) \\ -U \Lambda_{ys} \\ \varphi(-\tfrac{1}{2}, \Lambda_s) \end{pmatrix}. \quad (18)$$

If we now denote the ith, $(2m)^3/2 \times (2m)^3/2$ matrix in each of the 16 sections of Ω by $[i]$, Eq. (18) may be written in the following way where all the unknowns are taken to one side and all the knowns to the other:

$$\begin{pmatrix} [1]U H_{ys} + [3]U\Lambda_{ys} \\ (I + [5])U H_{ys} + [7]U\Lambda_{ys} \\ [9]U H_{ys} + [11]U\Lambda_{ys} \\ [13]U H_{ys} + (I + [15])U\Lambda_{ys} \end{pmatrix} = \begin{pmatrix} -I & [2] & 0 & [4] \\ 0 & [6] & 0 & [8] \\ 0 & [10] & -I & [12] \\ 0 & [14] & 0 & [16] \end{pmatrix} \begin{pmatrix} \varphi(\tfrac{1}{2}, \mathbf{H}_s) \\ \varphi(-\tfrac{1}{2}, \mathbf{H}_s) \\ \varphi(\tfrac{1}{2}, \Lambda_s) \\ \varphi(-\tfrac{1}{2}, \Lambda_s) \end{pmatrix}$$
$$(19)$$

where I is the $(2m)^3/2 \times (2m)^3/2$ unit matrix and zero indicates the $(2m)^3/2 \times (2m)^3/2$ null matrix.

Equation (19) is a pure algebraic relationship. It is a system of $2(2m)^3$ linear equations in $2(2m)^3$ unknowns, i.e., the unknowns are the distribution function evaluated at discrete points in velocity space on the boundaries. This relation could even be further simplified because in Eq. (19) the second and fourth sets of $(2m)^3/2$ equations are independent of the first and third sets. We then have the $(2m)^3$ linear equations

$$\begin{pmatrix} (I + [5])UH_{ys} + [7]U\Lambda_{ys} \\ [13]UH_{ys} + (I + [15])U\Lambda_{ys} \end{pmatrix} = \begin{pmatrix} [6] & [8] \\ [14] & [16] \end{pmatrix}\begin{pmatrix} \varphi(-\tfrac{1}{2}, \mathbf{H}_s) \\ \varphi(-\tfrac{1}{2}, \mathbf{\Lambda}_s) \end{pmatrix}. \quad (20)$$

The solution to these linear algebraic equations represents the solution to the entire Couette flow boundary value problem.

It should also be noticed not only that we now have the φ on discrete velocity points, but that these points also are roots of quadrature formulas. This makes it extremely convenient for the computation of the moments. For example

$$\frac{c_{th}^{-2}p_{xy}}{n_0 m} = \pi^{-3/2} \int_{-\infty}^{\infty} \exp(-|\mathbf{c}|^2)\varphi(x, \mathbf{c})c_y c_x \, d\mathbf{c}$$

$$\approx \sum_{i=1}^{2m} h_i \sum_{j=1}^{2m} h_j \sum_{k=1}^{2m} h_k H_k H_j \varphi(x, \mathbf{H}_r),$$

$$c_{th}^{-1}(q_y(x)) = \pi^{-3/2} \int_{-\infty}^{\infty} \exp(-\mathbf{c}^2)\varphi(x, \mathbf{c})c_y \, d\mathbf{c} \approx \sum_{i=1}^{2m} h_i \sum_{j=1}^{2m} h_j \sum_{k=1}^{2m} h_k H_j \varphi(x, \mathbf{H}_r)$$

where

$$c_{th} = \left(\frac{2kT_0}{m}\right)^{1/2}. \quad (21)$$

Once we know the value of $\varphi(x, \mathbf{H}_s)$ and $\varphi(x, \mathbf{\Lambda}_s)$ at $x = \pm\tfrac{1}{2}$ we can use the transformation

$$\begin{pmatrix} \varphi(x, \mathbf{H}_s) \\ \varphi(x, \mathbf{\Lambda}_s) \end{pmatrix} = e^{\alpha A'(x-\frac{1}{2})}\begin{pmatrix} \varphi(-\tfrac{1}{2}, \mathbf{H}_s) \\ \varphi(-\tfrac{1}{2}, \mathbf{\Lambda}_s) \end{pmatrix} \quad (22)$$

to get the values of $\varphi(x, \mathbf{H}_s)$, $\varphi(x, \mathbf{\Lambda}_s)$ at any x in $\tfrac{1}{2} > x > -\tfrac{1}{2}$. These values will still be at discrete velocity points which are quadrature roots and we can easily compute the moments at these values of x.

IV. Results

A. The Moments

In the previous sections a discrete ordinate approximation for the linearized Boltzmann integral for hard sphere molecules has been presented and the resulting system of linear differential equations has been applied to the problem of Couette flow. In this section the results of the calculations for the Couette flow are given. These calculations are based on the approximation obtained by taking $m = 2$ (i.e., a four point quadrature) in Sections II and III. In Eq. (20), this results in a 64×64 matrix which is within the capability of present matrix solving routines. The resulting net is then a 64 point grid for φ in each of the Laguerre and Hermite quadratures. These results are discussed in the light of approximations inherent in the present work and are compared with results obtained in previous investigations (Gross and Ziering, 1958; Cercignani, 1963). Calculations have been performed for both the macroscopic quantities of interest: shear stress, and flow velocity, and for the microscopic distribution function. We first discuss the calculation of the shear stress and flow velocity and compare with the previous work.

To calculate the macroscopic stress and velocity, we employ the definitions

$$\frac{p_{xy}}{mn_0(2kT_0/m)} = \int \exp(-c^2)\varphi c_x c_y \, d^3c,$$

$$\frac{q_y}{(2kT_0/m)^{1/2}} = \int \exp(-c^2)\varphi c_y \, d^3c. \tag{23}$$

An application of a quadrature formula to these integrals will now enable us to use the calculated values of φ at the discrete quadrature points [see Eq. (21)]. We therefore calculate p_{xy} and q_y by utilizing Eqs. (20) and (22) for φ, and applying a quadrature formula to Eq. (23). (See Tables I and II.) In Figs. 2 and 3 we plot p_{xy}, and q_y ($x = 0$) as functions of α, and in Fig. 4 $q_y(x)$ is plotted versus x with α as a parameter.

A significant feature of the discrete ordinate technique developed here is the simultaneous use of two distinct quadrature formulas. The flexibility introduced by using two formulas allows us to modify the quadrature expressions to take account of the varying influence of the boundaries and of intermolecular collisions as one goes from high to low Knudsen number.

In the limit of high Knudsen numbers, $\alpha \leqslant \frac{1}{2}$, particles reflected from the boundaries are important and the distribution function is markedly half-range. The use of half-range quadrature formulas therefore becomes necessary

TABLE I

MACROSCOPIC STRESS
$p_{xy}/(p_{xy})_{\text{t.m.}}$

α	LHH-LLL	LLL-HHH	HHL-HHH
1/256	0.996		
1/128	0.992		
1/64	0.985		
1/32	0.971		
1/16	0.947		
1/8	0.908		
1/4	0.853		
1/2	0.778		
1	0.647	0.587	
2		0.441	0.461
4			0.274

in this regime and the quadratures are performed with a formula heavily weighted with half-range roots. The quadrature formulas have roots specified by: LLL and LHH (L indicates a set of half-range Laguerre roots, H a set of full-range Hermite roots; the ordering indicates x, y, z integration).

As discussed in Appendix A, approximate expressions can be obtained (as $\alpha \to 0$) for φ, enabling a calculation of $\lim p_{xy}$ as $\alpha \to 0$ and $\lim \partial p_{xy}/\partial \alpha$ as

TABLE II

MACROSCOPIC VELOCITY AT BOTTOM PLATE
q_y $(x = 0)$
Free Molecule: q_y $(x = 0) = 0$
Continuum: q_y $(x = 0) = 5.0 \times 10^{-3}$

α	LHH-LLL	LLL-HHH	HHL-HHH
1/256	$-4.4068041 \times 10^{-5}$		
1/128	$-8.6870153 \times 10^{-5}$		
1/64	$-1.6889957 \times 10^{-4}$		
1/32	$-3.2001814 \times 10^{-4}$		
1/16	$-5.7933009 \times 10^{-4}$		
1/8	$-9.7485042 \times 10^{-4}$		
1/4	$-1.4812426 \times 10^{-3}$		
1/2	$-2.0048441 \times 10^{-3}$		
1	$-2.4994552 \times 10^{-3}$	$-2.5478463 \times 10^{-3}$	
2		$-3.26037092 \times 10^{-3}$	$-3.0763354 \times 10^{-3}$
4			$-3.9818682 \times 10^{-3}$

$\alpha \to 0$ (for details see Appendix A). By adjusting the variable factor μ (which appears in the definition of the half-range polynomials) we come within 7% of the exact $\lim p_{xy}$ as $\alpha \to 0$, and 7% of the $\lim \partial p_{xy}/\partial \alpha$ as $\alpha \to 0$ obtained

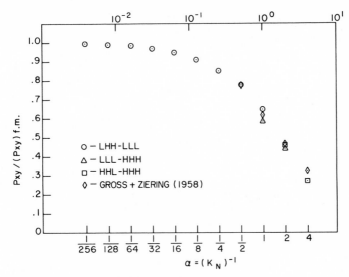

FIG. 2. Macroscopic stress versus α.

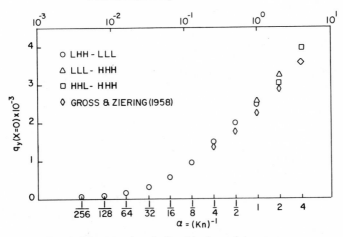

FIG. 3. Macroscopic velocity at bottom plate versus α.

from Knudsen iteration. It should, however, be noted that if μ were adjusted to give the exact $\lim p_{xy}$ as $\alpha \to 0$, then $\lim \partial p_{xy}/\partial \alpha$ as $\alpha \to 0$ would differ from the value obtained with Knudsen iteration by some 15%. This perhaps would be equally satisfactory since the relationship between $\lim \partial p_{xy}/\partial \alpha$ as $\alpha \to 0$ as

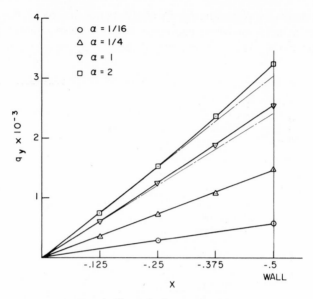

FIG. 4. Flow velocity q_{xy} versus x.

obtained by Knudsen iteration and the true exact value $\lim \partial p_{xy}/\partial \alpha$ as $\alpha \to 0$ is not yet clear. The departure from the exact $\alpha \to 0$ values are mainly explainable by the fact that the quadrature formula, LLL; LHH utilized in this limit, is not purely half-range. The full-range Hermite components are mainly responsible for the errors as $\alpha \to 0$.

As particles which have undergone intermolecular collisions become of the same importance as particles reflected from the boundaries, the distribution function tends to become more full range. To account for this tendency, in the Knudsen number range: $1 \leqslant \alpha \leqslant 2$, we use a quadrature scheme which is: $LLL - HHH$, in other words the half-range and full-range formulas are equally weighted. As the Knudsen number increases still further intermolecular collisions become dominant, and except for a small region near the boundary (Knudsen layer), the distribution function is markedly full-range. Therefore, for $\alpha \geqslant 2$ we choose $HHH - HHL$. The results obtained for large α are typical of what one expects in this regime. In Fig. 4 we note that as α increases the flow velocity profile begins to exhibit the characteristic Knudsen layer in the vicinity of the boundary and becomes linear as one approaches the center-line. As pointed out in Appendix B, accurate results are presented here only for $\alpha \leqslant 4$. Although the techniques introduced are still sound, the computational procedure adopted give rise to numerical difficulties as α increases, and so make calculations for very large α a function of the computing machine. It is interesting to point out that the procedure for the division of the Couette flow problem into Knudsen number regimes and the use of varying combinations of full-range and half-range quadratures for each regime is analogous to a method proposed by Krook (1959) for the nonlinear rarefied gas dynamics problem. Krook suggests the use of various combinations of full-range and half-range polynomial expansions for the different Knudsen number regimes. In this way the effects on the distribution function of the boundaries and intermolecular collisions can be accounted for. The flexibility of the discrete ordinate technique in allowing for varying combinations of quadrature formulas within the same formalism is one of its distinct advantages and may be quite useful in analyzing linearized problems in more than one dimension.

The analogy between polynomial expansions and discrete ordinate techniques that was alluded to above was made quite clearly in an earlier paper by Krook (1955). In the paper Krook proves that the discrete ordinate approximation for the distribution function is equivalent to a truncation of the moments by a polynomial expansion. From this paper it would appear that a one-dimensional discrete ordinate method using n points would be equivalent to a polynomial expansion of n terms. Judging from these remarks it would seem that the three dimensional grid of 64 discrete ordinate points utilized here represents a rather high order polynomial expansion, with the added flexibility of allowing for adjustment of the expansions to suit each Knudsen number regime.

It should be remarked, however, that in the present work as $\alpha \rightarrow 0$, the behavior of φ, as a function of c_x, is not polynomial like. In fact, we observe (see Appendix A), that $\varphi(c_{x_i}) \sim \exp(\alpha/c_{x_i})$. This is somewhat remarkable (e.g., Gross and Ziering, 1958) because one does not expect such behavior (for $\alpha \rightarrow 0$) from the polynomial like approximation upon which the present work is based.

It is on this point that the present work seems to differ qualitatively from the moment methods. This difference seems attributable to the fact that the differential equations for φ are solved first and the moments are then computed by a quadrature. In the moment methods φ is expressed first as a polynomial expansion and the moment coefficients are then computed from the moment equations. The important point here is that in the present work the behavior of φ is not smeared out by first averaging (taking moments), φ is formally solved in Eq. (16) and it is this expression that is approximated.

B. Comparison with Other Work

To date, the most accurate analysis of the linearized Couette flow of hard sphere molecules has been given by Gross and Ziering (1958) with certain corrections added by Cercignani (1963). Gross and Ziering assume a half-range polynomial of the form:

$$\varphi^{\pm}(\mathbf{c}, x) = a_0^{\pm}(x)c_y + a_1^{\pm}(x)c_y c_x \tag{24}$$

where $a_0^\pm$ and $a_1^\pm$ are the half-range space-dependent coefficients which are determined from the half-range moment equations. This approach yields results for hard sphere molecules, which are exact for p_{xy} and $\partial p_{xy}/\partial\alpha$ (Knudsen iteration) in the limit as $\alpha \to 0$; however, as $\alpha \to \infty$ the half-range coefficients do not become equal. Cercignani explains this difficulty by noting that Eq. (1) is incomplete, however, if one adds a factor $b(|\mathbf{c}|)$ so that Eq. (24) reads

$$\varphi^\pm(\mathbf{c}, x) = a_0^\pm(x)c_y + a_1^\pm(x)b(|\mathbf{c}|)c_y c_x, \qquad (25)$$

the Chapman and Enskog full-range solution is recovered as $\alpha \to \infty$. Cercignani does not, however, utilize Eq. (25) to perform calculations over the entire range of α. He assumes that the numerical differences introduced over all α by the factor $b(|\mathbf{c}|)$ will be small. This is reasonable, although it would be of interest to see the effects produced by this correction. Therefore, in comparing our results with those of Gross and Ziering (1958) it must be remembered that their results were generated with Eq. (24) and do not include the factor $b(|\mathbf{c}|)$ which is introduced by Cercignani.

In the limit of $\alpha \to 0$, the purely half-range expansion [Eq. (24)] of Gross and Ziering exactly satisfies the boundary conditions, giving the exact value of $\lim p_{xy}$ as $\alpha \to 0$ and the Knudsen iteration value of $\lim \partial p_{xy}/\partial\alpha$ as $\alpha \to 0$. However, as pointed out by Gross and Ziering, the behavior of φ as a function of c_x, as $\alpha \to 0$, for polynomial expansions is not correct. Comparing this with the present work we note that here: $\varphi(c_{x_i}) \sim \exp(\alpha/c_{x_i})$ as $\alpha \to 0$. In addition by examining Figs. 2 and 3 we can see that the numerical differences, for $\alpha \leqslant \frac{1}{2}$, between Gross and Ziering (1958) and the present work are quite small (provided p_{xy} in the present work is normalized by $(p_{xy})_{\text{f.m.}}$).

For $\alpha \geqslant \frac{1}{2}$ we can expect that the large number of roots utilized (i.e., high order expansion) and the advantageous mixture of half-range and full-range roots enable one to obtain more accurate results. In fact the largest departures of the present results from those of Gross and Ziering are seen to occur for $\alpha > \frac{1}{2}$. In summary one can say of this comparison, that for $\alpha < \frac{1}{2}$ the purely half-range expansion of Gross and Ziering should give quite accurate results (except as regards the dependence of φ on c_x) while for $\alpha > \frac{1}{2}$, the flexibility and larger number of terms possible with the present method make it attractive.

C. Calculations for φ

An interesting aspect of the present calculation is that the perturbation distribution function is computed directly for the quadrature points. An examination of the results for the $\varphi(\mathbf{c}_i)$ are interesting because they enable one to check the symmetries and conservation laws and in addition to show graphically the evolution of the distribution function as one goes from the

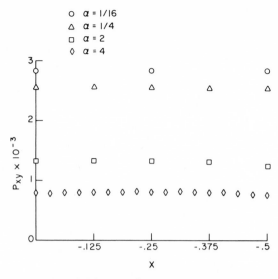

FIG. 5. Macroscopic stress p_{xy} versus x.

free molecule to the continuum regime. It is of interest to note that several symmetries are present. The first such symmetry can be written as $\varphi(x, c_y) = -\varphi(x, -c_y)$; this indicates that φ behaves as a polynomial in odd powers of c_y. Secondly, we observe that $\varphi(x, c_z) = \varphi(x, -c_z)$, and $\varphi(x, c_x) = -\varphi(-x, -c_x)$. In addition, from Fig. 5 we note that the numerical results for p_{xy},

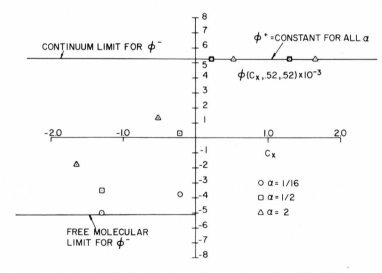

FIG. 6. Perturbation distribution function at bottom plate, $\varphi(c_x, 0.52, 0.52)$, versus c_x.

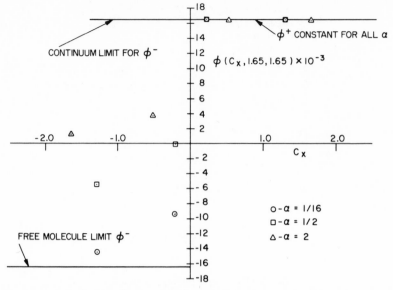

FIG. 7. Perturbation distribution function at bottom plate, $\varphi(c_x, 1.65, 1.65)$, versus c_x.

give a value which is a constant between the plates. The above symmetries and constancy of p_{xy} show that the numerical results preserve the conservation laws for the linearized Couette flow.

In Figs. 6 and 7 we show the perturbation distribution function, φ, at the bottom plate as a function of c_x. It is interesting to observe the half-range

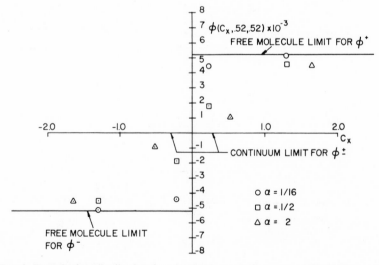

FIG. 8. Perturbation distribution function at the centerline, $\varphi(c_x, 0.52, 0.52)$ versus c_x.

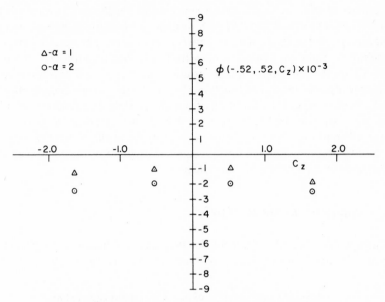

FIG. 9. Effect of the z velocity component at the centerline.

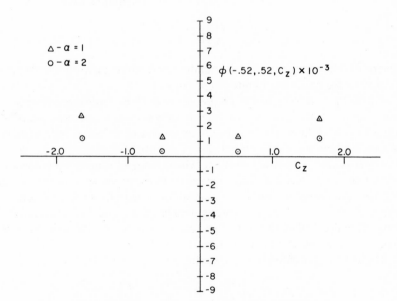

FIG. 10. Effect of the $-z$ velocity component at the bottom plate.

character of φ at the boundary for small α and the progress toward the continuum limit as α increases. In Fig. 8 we again see φ plotted versus c_x, but now the points are at the centerline between the plates. The results here quite graphically show the evolution of φ from a half-range character at small α to a Chapman and Enskog linear variation with c_x at $\alpha = 2$. In Figs. 9 and 10 we have also plotted φ as a function of c_z; this is of interest because all other investigators neglect the variation of φ with c_z, while the present work allows for this variation. In Fig. 9 we note that at the centerline there exists, for practical purposes, little variation with c_z, while at the plate (Fig. 10) there is more variation, although it too is small. This confirms the two dimensional character of the Couette flow problem.

Appendix A: Small α Limit

This appendix describes the behavior of φ as $\alpha \to 0$ and how relation (16) is used to compute $\lim p_{xy}(x)$ as $\alpha \to 0$ and $\lim \partial p_{xy}(x)/\partial \alpha$ as $\alpha \to 0$:

$$\lim_{\alpha \to 0} p_{xy}(x) = \pi^{-3/2} \int_{-\infty}^{\infty} \exp(-c^2) c_y c_x [\lim_{\alpha \to 0} \varphi(x, \mathbf{c})] \, d\mathbf{c}.$$

Since $\lim \exp[\alpha A'(x - x_0)]$ as $\alpha \to 0$ is I, we can therefore write for φ:

$$\lim_{\alpha \to 0} \begin{pmatrix} \varphi(x, \mathbf{H}_s) \\ \varphi(x, \boldsymbol{\Lambda}_s) \end{pmatrix} = \begin{pmatrix} \varphi(x_0, \mathbf{H}_s) \\ \varphi(x_0, \boldsymbol{\Lambda}_s) \end{pmatrix} \tag{26}$$

where I is the unit matrix. The boundary conditions then supply all the information we need to compute $\lim p_{xy}(x)$ as $\alpha \to 0$.

The method to compute $\lim \partial p_{xy}(x)/\partial \alpha$ as $\alpha \to 0$ is a little more complicated and requires some discussion of the behavior of φ. Upon examination of Eq. (16) one observes that except for the matrix A' (which is independent of α) the solution $\varphi(c_{x_i})$ is essentially an exponential function of α/c_{x_i}. Since A' is a matrix that is constant over the whole range of Knudsen numbers it is clear that it is indeed the factor $\exp(\alpha/c_{x_i})$ that determines how the solution changes with Knudsen number. It should be noted that since c_{x_i} is a parameter and not a variable, it is always possible to expand the exponential for small α, and calculate the slope: $\lim \partial p_{xy}(x)/\partial \alpha$ as $\alpha \to 0$. Let us assume that since α is small we can therefore take: $e^{\alpha A'} \approx I + \alpha A'$.

Let us further subdivide A' as we did Ω:

$$A' = \begin{pmatrix} A_1' & A_2' & A_3' & A_4' \\ A_5' & A_6' & A_7' & A_8' \\ A_9' & A_{10}' & A_{11}' & A_{12}' \\ A_{13}' & A_{14}' & A_{15}' & A_{16}' \end{pmatrix}.$$

Since we have assumed $\Omega = I + \alpha A'$ we can write the partial derivative of Eq. (20) with respect to α in the following way:

$$\frac{\partial}{\partial \alpha}\begin{pmatrix} (I + \alpha A_5')UH_{ys} + \alpha A_7'U\Lambda_{ys} \\ \alpha A'_{13}UH_{ys} + (I + \alpha A'_{15})U\Lambda_{ys} \end{pmatrix}$$

$$= \begin{pmatrix} A_6' & A_8' \\ A'_{14} & A'_{16} \end{pmatrix}\begin{pmatrix} \varphi(-\tfrac{1}{2}, \mathbf{H}_s) \\ \varphi(-\tfrac{1}{2}, \mathbf{\Lambda}_s) \end{pmatrix} + \begin{pmatrix} I + \alpha A_6' & \alpha A_8' \\ \alpha A'_{14} & I + \alpha A'_{16} \end{pmatrix}$$

$$\times \begin{pmatrix} \dfrac{\partial}{\partial \alpha}\, \varphi(-\tfrac{1}{2}, \mathbf{H}_s) \\[2mm] \dfrac{\partial}{\partial \alpha}\, \varphi(-\tfrac{1}{2}, \mathbf{\Lambda}_s) \end{pmatrix}. \qquad (27)$$

However, since $\lim \varphi(-\tfrac{1}{2}, \mathbf{c}_s)$ as $\alpha \to 0$ is $-Uc_{ys}$, and,

$$\lim_{\alpha \to 0} \frac{\partial}{\partial \alpha}\begin{pmatrix} (I + \alpha A_5')UH_{ys} + \alpha A_7'U\Lambda_{ys} \\ \alpha A'_{13}UH_{ys} + (I + \alpha A'_{15})U\Lambda_{ys} \end{pmatrix} = \begin{pmatrix} A_5'UH_{ys} + A_7'U\Lambda_{ys} \\ A'_{13}UH_{ys} + A'_{15}U\Lambda_{ys} \end{pmatrix},$$

Eq. (27) then gives

$$\lim_{\alpha \to 0}\begin{pmatrix} \dfrac{\partial}{\partial \alpha}\, \varphi(-\tfrac{1}{2}, \mathbf{H}_s) \\[2mm] \dfrac{\partial}{\partial \alpha}\, \varphi(-\tfrac{1}{2}, \mathbf{\Lambda}_s) \end{pmatrix} = \begin{pmatrix} (A_5' + A_6')UH_{ys} + (A_7' + A_8')U\Lambda_{ys} \\ (A'_{13} + A'_{14})UH_{ys} + (A'_{15} + A'_{16})U\Lambda_{ys} \end{pmatrix}.$$

Thus we have $\lim \partial\varphi/\partial\alpha$ as $\alpha \to 0$ at the discrete velocity points which are roots of our quadrature formulas. Since

$$\lim_{\alpha \to 0} \frac{\partial p_{xy}}{\partial \alpha} = \pi^{-3/2} \int_{-\infty}^{\infty} \exp(-|\mathbf{c}|^2)\lim_{\alpha \to 0}\frac{\partial\varphi}{\partial\alpha}\, c_y c_z\, d\mathbf{c} \qquad (28)$$

we can then apply the quadrature formulas to Eq. (28) and compute $\lim \partial p_x/\partial \alpha$ as $\alpha \to 0$.

Appendix B. The Case where $\alpha > 1$

When $\alpha > 1$ the elements of the matrix $e^{\alpha A'}$ become large compared to 1. It then becomes evident that the matrix in Eq. (19) will become more and more ill-conditioned[3] as α grows. This is clear because the even submatrices,

---

[3] An ill-conditioned matrix is a matrix whose determinant is small compared to the magnitude of its row or column vectors. This means that the rows (or columns) are nearly linearly dependent.

[2] to [16], become so large that the matrix I is comparatively insignificant. We can then expect that whatever solution we can possibly extract will lose significant digits with increasing α. Any such solution φ, can only be expected to be valid within a numerically zero[4] eigenvector of the matrix. That is, there will exist solutions φ_1 to Eq. (20) where

$$\begin{pmatrix} [6] & [8] \\ [14] & [16] \end{pmatrix} \begin{pmatrix} \varphi_1(-\frac{1}{2}, \mathbf{H}_s) \\ \varphi_1(-\frac{1}{2}, \Lambda_s) \end{pmatrix} \approx 10^{-m} \begin{pmatrix} (I + [5])UH_{ys} + [7]U\Lambda_{ys} \\ [13]UH_{ys} + (I + [15])U\Lambda_{ys} \end{pmatrix}$$

where m denotes the number of significant digits in the computation, while φ_1 will be of the same order as φ.

Since it is known theoretically that five zero eigenvectors φ_i, $i = 1, ..., 5$ exist, one must find a solution $\bar{\varphi} = \varphi + \sum_{i=1}^{5} b_i\varphi_i$ such that $\sum_{i=1}^{5} b_i\varphi_i$ is a numerically zero eigenvector and where $\bar{\varphi}$ satisfies the following conditions:

(1) $p_{xy}(x)$ when calculated with $\bar{\varphi}$ is constant for all values of x between the plates.

(2) $q_y(x)$ decreases monotomically from the $x = \frac{1}{2}$ plate and attains the value zero at $x = 0$.

In the numerical calculation of the Couette flow reasonable answers were obtainable only for the cases of $\alpha = 2$ and $\alpha = 4$. For $\alpha = 8$ so many significant digits were lost as to give inconsistent results even at the wall.

In the case of $\alpha = 2$ the only adjustment to be made with the zero eigenvectors involved the fact that $q_y(x)$ was not quite zero at the center line, when computed with φ. This adjustment was managed quite easily with zero eigenvectors.

For $\alpha = 4$, p_{xy} and q_y when computed with φ alone behaved properly in the vicinity of the boundary. However as one proceeded to the center line especially from the point $x = 0.375$ ($= \frac{1}{2} - (1/2\alpha)$) p_{xy} and q_y behaved erratically. Five independent numerically zero eigenvalues were then found and the following five equations were solved for the b_i:

$$q_{y_0}(x_4) + \sum_{i=1}^{5} b_i q_{y_i}(x_4) = 0$$

$$p_{xy_0}(x_j) + \sum_{i=1}^{5} b_i p_{xy_i}(x_j) = p_{y_0} \qquad (x = 0.5)$$

where $x_1 = 0.375$, $x_2 = 0.25$, $x_3 = 0.175$, $x_4 = 0$, and q_{y_0}, p_{y_0} represent quantities calculated with φ alone and q_{y_i}, p_{xy_i} represents quantities calculated with φ_i. These results show their validity in the following ways:

(1) $\displaystyle\sum_{i=1}^{5} b_i\varphi_i$ remains a numerically zero eigenvalue

[4] In an n-decimal-place machine, x is numerically zero compared to y if $10^{-n}y \cong x$.

$$(2) \quad p_{xy}(x) = p_{xy_0}(x) + \sum_{i=1}^{5} b_i p_{xy_i}(x) \qquad \text{remains constant and equal to } p_{xy_0}$$

$(x = 0.5)$ in the entire range $0.5 \geqslant x \geqslant 0$;

$$(3) \quad q_y(x) = q_{y_0}(x) + \sum_{i=1}^{5} b_i q_{y_i}(x) \qquad \text{behaves reasonably in the entire range}$$

$0.5 \geqslant x \geqslant 0$.

REFERENCES

Bhatnagar, P. L., Gross, E. P., and Krook, M. (1954). *Phys. Rev.* **94**, 511.

Broadwell, J. E. (1963a). " Study of Rarefied Shear Flow by the Discrete Velocity Method." STL Rep. 9813-6001-RU000.

Broadwell, J. E. (1963b). "Application of a Discrete Velocity Model to the Boltzmann Equation in Shear Flows." STL Rep. 9813-6004-RU000.

Cercignani, C. (1963). *Nuovo cimento* **27**, 1240.

Gross, E. P., Jackson, E. A., and Ziering, S. (1957). *Ann. Phys. (N.Y.)* **1**, 141.

Gross, E. P., and Ziering, S. (1958). *Phys. Fluids* **1**, 215.

Krook, M. (1955). *J. Astrophys.* **122**, 488.

Krook, M. (1959). *J. Fluid Mech.* **6** 523.

Lees, L. (1959). "A Kinetic Theory Description of Rarefied Gas Flows." Calif. Inst. of Technol., Guggenheim Aeronaut. Lab. Rep. No. 51.

Welander, P. (1954). *Arkiv fysik* **7**, 44.

Kinetic Theory of the Leading Edge[1]

SIGI ZIERING, LAN-KEH CHI, AND RONALD FANTE

Space Sciences, Inc., Waltham, Massachusetts

The interaction of a finite plate with a streaming gas is considered by using the Bhatnagar, Gross, and Krook equation of statistical mechanics. In order to describe the near free molecule domain accurately, the distribution function is separated into various domains. The collisionless forms of the distribution functions are constructed and briefly discussed. When collisions are retained, integral solutions are constructed for the various parts of the distribution function. These have to be solved either by numerical methods or by approximation schemes. Various limiting cases are treated and discussed. Specific numerical results for a linearized iterative treatment in the near free molecule domain are presented.

I. Introduction

To the researcher more familiar with kinetic theory than with continuum mechanics, it seems that the piecewise fitting together of free stream, shock wave, inviscid, and boundary layer regions is at best a cumbersome and highly limited procedure. The advent of high speed digital computers and our simultaneous increased understanding of simplified "model" transport equations seem to make a renewed attack by kinetic theory worthwhile (Bhatnagar *et al.*, 1954; Gross and Jackson, 1959). Equally important, today's space goals extend the physical environment with which a hypersonic vehicle interacts, from collision dominated fluids (continuum domain) all the way to collisionless fluids (free molecule flow domain). The treatment of the latter limit, however, is always *a priori* ruled out in fluid mechanical treatments.

While some previous work by kinetic theory has been done yielding solutions that span all flow regimes, these were restricted in the main due to (1) strong linearization (that is, subsonic flow, small temperature gradients,

---

[1] Work supported by the U.S. Air Force Office of Scientific Research.

etc.) and (2) consideration of one-dimensional flow problems (Couette, Poiseuille, etc.). With these restrictions, however, many refinements and techniques have been developed to adequately span the complete density field (or more accurately, range of Knudsen number λ/d, where d is a characteristic length of the physical body and λ the mean free path). Moreover, these one-dimensional solutions have not been restricted to "Model" transport equations, but have in certain instances been successfully applied to the complete Boltzmann equation (Grad, 1949; Wang Chang and Uhlenbeck, 1949, 1953, 1954; Mott-Smith, 1951, 1954; Welander, 1953; Gross *et al.*, 1957; Gross and Jackson, 1958, 1959; Gross and Ziering, 1958, 1959; Willis, 1958, 1961; Lees, 1959; Ziering, 1960).

In this paper we would like to apply and extend these methods to a specific two-dimensional transport problem. Problems in three-dimensional geometries will not be considered here, however, the same methods can be applied, and in certain cases symmetry considerations about a particular flow direction can be exploited to reduce the dimensions from three to two. The most intriguing two-dimensional flow problem is that associated with an analysis of the leading edge. Blunt bodies and other shapes provide for smoother adjustment of the physical parameters in contrast to the abrupt transition associated with the singularity of the leading edge. Thus our concern throughout this paper will be with the problem of the leading edge. All the techniques developed, however, can be extended to different two and three-dimensional flow problems. For this purpose considerable effort is made to carefully define the mathematical and physical framework for analysis, and to explicitly point out specific assumptions and simplifications in the following two sections (Section II and III). In Section IV we apply an iterative scheme to obtain solutions in the near free molecule domain. We are also attempting iteration schemes on the equations evolved in Section III, by starting from the other extreme limit, continuum flow. The results, however, are not complete. Some preliminary results are presented in Appendix C. A survey and discussion of results is presented in Section V.

II. Statement of the Problem

In Fig. 1 we consider a stream of particles moving in the positive x direction with specified physical parameters at $x = -\infty$; that is, flow velocity U_∞, density n_∞, and temperature T_∞. At the origin of our coordinate system we assume a plate of infinite dimension in the z direction located on the positive x axis $(0 < x < L; y = 0; -\infty < z < \infty)$ of length L. We would like to investigate by kinetic theory to what extent the particle distribution function and the physically meaningful moments are modified by the presence of the

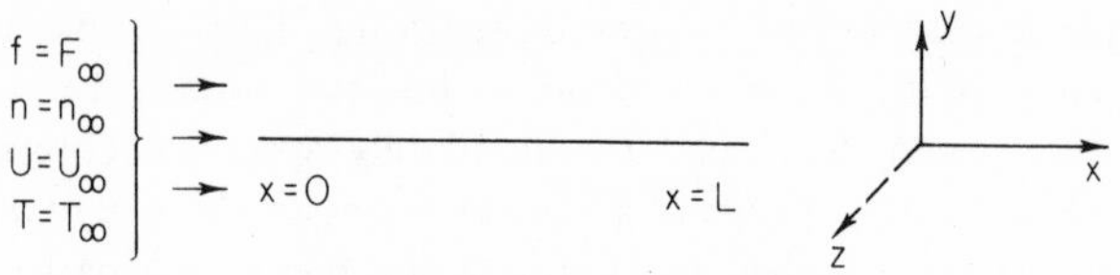

FIG. 1. Coordinate system.

plate. To simplify the analysis at the outset we neglect all dependencies both on z and c_z. Without any appeal to boundary layer or continuum fluid mechanics the problem breaks into the following specific tasks: (a) the appropriate statistical equations to be used; (b) boundary conditions— prescription of molecular interactions with the plate, and specification of the distribution function of the incoming stream $f(x = -\infty) = F_\infty$, and c) specification of symmetry conditions. A combination and specification of all these tasks should then define uniquely the mathematical framework for analysis. The mathematical analysis itself ultimately depends on the skill of the researcher and the various approximations introduced in order to obtain analytical results and should be compared with corresponding results obtained from continuum theory if the region of validity extends to both the particular approximations and the continuum theory (or its offspring boundary layer theory). Thus the use of a modified Boltzmann equation below (BGK equation), and the specification of average gas-solid interaction parameters (accommodation coefficients) seems to us not a serious restriction imposed on the formulation of the problem. Indeed it can be argued that both these restrictions are inherently better and more detailed than the gross equations of continuum flow, and have been shown to reproduce continuum-like equations.

A. Statistical Equations

We assume that the Bhatnagar *et al.* (1954) single relaxation model governs because of its inherent simplification in the collision term (mainly as a consequence of linearizing the bilinear collision term in the distribution function of the Boltzmann equation into a linear collision term). Obvious limitations of the simple BGK model, as for instance disagreement with kinetic theory on the ratio of viscosity to heat conduction coefficients, will be accepted in the sense that more sophisticated models of the BGK equation can be and have been constructed which will correct those deficiencies and yet keep the collision term considerably simpler than the full collision integrals of the Boltzmann equation. Previous analysis of the BGK equation has also indicated that this mathematically more accessible equation does retain the essential features of a kinetic treatment, thus allowing the solutions to span the complete domain from free molecular flow to continuum flow.

For the two-dimensional problems of interest we write the BGK equation as

$$\frac{\partial f}{\partial t} + v_x \frac{\partial f}{\partial x} + v_y \frac{\partial f}{\partial y} = \frac{n}{\tau} \{f_{eq} - f\} \tag{1}$$

where τ is a constant collision time, and

$$f_{eq} = n(\mathbf{x}, t)\left(\frac{m}{2\pi k T(\mathbf{x}, t)}\right)^{3/2} \exp\left[-\frac{m}{2kT(\mathbf{x}, t)}(\mathbf{v} - \mathbf{q}(\mathbf{x}, t))^2\right]$$

$$n(\mathbf{x}, t) \equiv \int f \, d\mathbf{v},$$

$$\mathbf{q}(\mathbf{x}, t) \equiv n^{-1} \int \mathbf{v} f \, d\mathbf{v},$$

$$P_{ij}(\mathbf{x}, t) \equiv m \int (v_i - q_i)(v_j - q_j) f \, d\mathbf{v},$$

$$T(\mathbf{x}, t) = \frac{m}{3n(\mathbf{x}, t)k} \int (\mathbf{v} - \mathbf{q}(\mathbf{x}, t))^2 \, d\mathbf{v}, \quad \text{etc.}$$

(For a detailed discussion of the BGK equation see Bhatnagar *et al.*, 1954.) Under steady state conditions $\partial f/\partial t = 0$ and hence we write the equivalent set of characteristic equations

$$\frac{dx}{v_x} = \frac{dy}{v_y} = \frac{df}{(n/\tau)\{f_{eq} - f\}}. \tag{2}$$

On integrating the first set we find $x = ly + a$ where $l \equiv c_x/c_y = \cot \alpha$ and a is a constant of integration. If we now substitute $n(x, y) = n(ly + a, y)$ and do likewise for f and f_{eq} we can integrate the second set of equations to obtain

$$f = \int_B^y \frac{n(y')}{\tau v_y} f_{eq}(y') \exp\left\{-\int_{y'}^y \frac{n(y'')}{\tau v_y} \, dy''\right\} dy' + H f_B \exp\left\{-\int_B^y \frac{n(y'')}{\tau v_y} \, dy''\right\} \tag{3}$$

where $H = H(xv_y - yv_x)$.

We have of course implicitly assumed in the above formulation that it will be possible to substitute the characteristic equation $x = ly + a$ both in n, and f_{eq}. This is a restrictive but not serious limitation and, as will be discussed below, the most likely procedure for effecting solutions of this equation is to iterate starting either from the continuum limit or the free molecular flow limit. In either case the x, y dependence of the solution is known, and thus we may proceed with the above substitution eliminating x in terms of y. We also have preferred to express our solution in terms of y only. This is completely arbitrary and an equally valid equation in x space could have been obtained. The particular selection is governed by the specific boundary and symmetry conditions as discussed below.

B. Symmetry Conditions

As stated previously we can restrict ourselves to the positive y space by invoking symmetry conditions; that is,

$$f(v_x, v_y, v_z, x, y, z) = f(v_x, -v_y, v_z, x, -y, z). \tag{4}$$

This symmetry condition will govern the solution as well as the corresponding boundary conditions, provided the corresponding changes in the definition of the solid angle are made as well.

C. Boundary Conditions

It is our firm conviction that the accurate treatment of theories spanning both free molecular flow and continuum flow must by necessity allow for distribution functions tailored to go into specific distribution functions over a limited part of the velocity phase consistent with microscopic boundary conditions. The necessarily discontinuous nature of the distribution functions have been discussed at great length by various authors. In one-dimensional problems the breakup of the distribution function is straightforward along a line parallel in velocity space to the boundaries. The extension to more than one geometry presents complications in that the discontinuity exists in a more complex form mixing both spatial and velocity coordinates. To construct the particular distribution functions to be chosen, we insist that they be able to duplicate the extreme free molecular form. As discussed in the above cited work, this formulation does not in any way violate an acceptable and consistent solution in the continuum domain.

As stated before, we assume that the particles stream along the positive x axis, originating from a distance far enough upstream ($x \to -\infty$) where they have known properties. That is, our distribution function far upstream ($x \to -\infty$) is as follows:

$$f(x = -\infty, y) = F_\infty = n_\infty \left(\frac{m}{2\pi kT_\infty}\right)^{3/2} \exp\left[-\frac{m}{2kT_\infty}(\mathbf{v} - \mathbf{i}u_\infty)^2\right] \tag{5}$$

where $\mathbf{i}$ is a unit vector in the x direction. The other boundary conditions by necessity are those on the plate, and within uncertainties as to quantum mechanical interactions and the use of gross accommodation coefficients, one writes

$$f^+(v_x, v_y, y = 0, x) = \beta f_w{}^+ + (1 - \beta)f^-(v_x, -v_y, y = 0, x), \qquad v_y > 0 \tag{6}$$

where f^+ and f^- refer, respectively, to those particles moving away and toward the wall ($v_x > 0$, and $v_x < 0$, respectively). $f_w{}^+$ is the distribution function for those particles diffusely emitted from the wall with the characteristic wall parameters (temperature, and flow velocity if any) and β is the accommodation coefficient for diffuse reflection. The fraction $(1 - \beta)$ pertains to those particles which merely exchange their normal velocity vector upon interacting with the wall.

A great simplification results if we assume that all particles interact diffusely with the wall (that is, $\beta = 1$). This is a customary assumption based on experimentally observed results that $\beta \approx 1$. For large Mach number flow, however, this may be a bad approximation in our specific application. Then the particles emitted from the plate should have a preferred persistence of flow velocity in the x direction. Furthermore, there could be significant and uneven heating of the plate in the downstream direction which should reflect itself in that the plate temperature should be an increasing function of x. All these refinements, however, will be neglected in the present analysis, and the incorporation of these effects should not unduly complicate our simplified analysis below.

Returning to our basic inquiry as to the form of the distribution function in free molecule flow (no collisions) we find that all particles at any point in physical space can be assigned to two classes, namely, those originating from the infinity distribution (F_∞), and those coming from the plate (f_p). For simplicity, we shall restrict our discussion to the positive y space only, the extension to negative y space can easily be accomplished by symmetry arguments. In Fig. 2 we illustrate the complete division of the distribution function

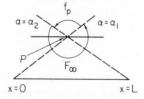

FIG. 2. Free molecular distribution functions. Finite plate.

at point P in accordance with the free molecular criteria. At point P in physical space we construct a line parallel to the plate (x axis) through point P and set up a polar coordinate system with points $x = y = 0$ as origin. We now state that

$$f = f_p, \qquad \alpha_1 < \alpha < \alpha_2,$$
$$= F_\infty, \qquad \alpha_2 < \alpha < 2\pi \quad \text{and} \quad 0 < \alpha < \alpha_1.$$

It is clear that for $y = 0$ and $0 < x < L$ one finds $\alpha_1 = 0$ and $\alpha_2 = \pi$. For $x < 0$, $y = 0$ one finds $\alpha_1 = \alpha_2 = \pi$ and hence all particles on the negative x axis belong to the $f = F_\infty$ distribution. Similarly for $x > L$ and $y = 0$, $\alpha_1 = \alpha_2 = 0$ and again (as it should be in the absence of collisions), all particles on the positive x axis ($x > L$) belong to the infinity distribution. In particular, if one considered a semi-infinite plate ($L \to \infty$) then $\alpha_2 \to \pi$. The free-molecular analysis in the above manner has been done by two of the present authors (L.C. and S.Z.) and was done independently and in more detail by Chuan and Yang (1963). The reader is referred to the publication of the latter authors for full particulars. The solution although straightforward, is not a simple one.

We have demonstrated that the boundary conditions (and hence the free-molecular solution) dictates the use of highly specialized distribution functions. The most essential difference from one-dimensional problems is that the discontinuity in velocity space (α_1, α_2) is a strong function of the particular location in physical space. In a sense then, this is an extension of the half-range or two-fluid concept and indeed has been advocated by Lees (1959) and others as the line of sight principle.

A final boundary condition to be invoked is that there is no accumulation of particles on the plate; that is,

$$\int_{-\infty}^{\infty} v_y f(y = 0) \, d\mathbf{v} = 0. \tag{7}$$

The above boundary conditions, and in particular the specification of the plate distribution function, make our choice of y coordinates an obvious one to work with. The remaining boundary condition of the distribution function and state variables at $x = -\infty$ is hard to tamper with. In a collision dominated gas the effect of the plate could mathematically speaking be present however insignificant at $y = \pm \infty$ especially in the domain $x > 0$. It is therefore a safer procedure to retain this boundary condition in x space. As will be shown below, no particular difficulties are encountered with this particular boundary condition.

Having stated in detail the kinetic equation and the dictates of the boundary conditions on the form of the solution we can now in the next section combine this information to discuss the particular method of analysis.

III. Method of Analysis

We now consider Eq. (3) in the light of our previous discussion of the boundary conditions. To begin with, we limit our analysis by simplifying Eq. (3) for the following two reasons: (1) to illustrate in as simple a manner as possible and without loss of generality the specific subdivision of the distribution function in the light of Section C and (2) to effect analytic solutions under linearized subsonic conditions. All this is done not because the answers are very meaningful for practical applications, but to determine as precisely and accurately as possible sensible solutions of limited validity. These results together with the more exact formulation, it is hoped, will then be used as the basis for numerical high-speed machine calculations for the non-linear hypersonic problem of the leading edge.

Under these circumstances we then remove the remaining trace of the bilinear form of the distribution function in the collision integral and assume that n/τ is a constant n_∞/τ. (This still retains, however, nonlinear contributions arising from taking moments of the distribution function, unless further linearizations are effected.) At the same time it is convenient to introduce dimensionless variables, specifically

$$\mathbf{c} = \left(\frac{m}{2kT_\infty}\right)^{1/2}\mathbf{v} \quad \text{and} \quad \mathbf{u} = \left(\frac{m}{2kT_\infty}\right)^{1/2}\mathbf{q}.$$

We also define an upstream mean free path λ such that

$$\lambda = \frac{\tau}{n_\infty}\left(\frac{2kT_\infty}{m}\right)^{1/2}.$$

With these definitions we write Eq. (3) as

$$f = e^{-y/\lambda c_y}\int_B^y \frac{f_{eq}(y', ly' + a)}{\lambda c_y} e^{y'/\lambda c_y}\, dy' + Hf_B e^{-(y-B)/\lambda c_y}. \tag{8}$$

For the problem of the finite plate care has to be taken that our solutions are well behaved because (1) a different limiting value for B has to be assigned to each part of the distribution function and (2) c_y can be both positive and negative so that the infinity distribution has to be further separated into two parts in order to avoid divergencies. The three different domains for the distribution function are illustrated in Fig. 3. We therefore write

$$f = f_\mathrm{I}, \quad \text{for} \quad 0 < \alpha < \alpha_1, \quad \text{and} \quad \alpha_2 < \alpha < \pi,$$
$$= f_\mathrm{II}, \qquad \alpha_1 < \alpha < \alpha_2,$$
$$= f_\mathrm{III}. \qquad \pi < \alpha < 2\pi.$$

In the collisionless case $f_\mathrm{I} = f_\mathrm{III} = F_\infty$ and $f_\mathrm{II} = f_p$. For collision-dominated phenomena, however, $f_\mathrm{I}, f_\mathrm{II}$ and f_III are now to be determined as functions of x and y. Equation (8) now separates as follows:

$$f_\mathrm{I} = e^{-y/\lambda c_y}\int_{-\infty}^y \frac{f_{eq}(y', ly' + a)}{\lambda c_y} e^{y'/\lambda c_y}\, dy' + H_\mathrm{I} f_{-\infty} e^{-(y+\infty)/\lambda c_y} \tag{9}$$

$$\text{for} \quad 0 < \alpha < \alpha_1 \quad \text{and} \quad \alpha_2 < \alpha < \pi,$$

$$f_{\text{II}} = e^{-y/\lambda c_y} \int_0^y \frac{f_{\text{eq}}(y', ly' + a)}{\lambda c_y} e^{y'/\lambda c_y} \, dy' + H_{\text{II}} f_p e^{-y/\lambda c_y} \tag{10}$$

$$\text{for} \quad \alpha_1 < \alpha < \alpha_2,$$

$$f_{\text{III}} = e^{-y/\lambda c_y} \int_\infty^y \frac{f_{\text{eq}}(y', ly' + a)}{\lambda c_y} e^{y'/\lambda c_y} \, dy' + H_{\text{III}} f_\infty e^{-(y-\infty)/\lambda c_y} \tag{11}$$

$$\text{for} \quad \pi < \alpha < 2\pi.$$

Our reason for separating f_{I} and f_{III} now becomes apparent. It is quite evident that the exponent $\exp[-(y + \infty)/\lambda c_y]$ in the second term of f_{I} is bounded for $-\infty < y < \infty$ as long as c_y is positive. Likewise the exponent

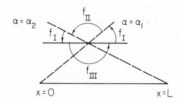

FIG. 3. Domain of velocity distribution functions for the finite plate.

$\exp[-(y - \infty)/\lambda c_y]$ is bounded for $-\infty < y < \infty$ as long as c_y is negative in f_{III}. In Appendix A we further show that the integral parts of the solution are bounded.

The final part of the paper will now attempt to solve Eqs. (9)–(11) together with boundary conditions (5)–(7).

The most obvious approaches are to start iterative schemes both from the collisionless solution and from the continuum solution. Until now we have not implicitly stated a detailed form for the function f_{eq} in anticipation of expecting to use f_{eq} as the quantity to be iterated. Willis (1958, 1961), starting from the collisionless solution, has used this scheme on related problems. The iteration schemes from the extreme solutions (free molecule and continuum) do not necessarily satisfy the conservation equations in the first iteration.

Another approach which will not be considered in this paper, is to construct integral equations for the moments of the distribution functions and iterate those equations. This would at the same time satisfy the conservation laws. Consider for instance the customary form of f_{eq} as a displaced locally Maxwellian distribution:

$$f_{\text{eq}} = \bar{n}(x, y) \left(\frac{m}{2\pi k \bar{T}(x, y)} \right)^{3/2} \exp - \left[\frac{m}{2k \bar{T}(x, y)} (\mathbf{v} - \mathbf{i}\bar{q}(x, y))^2 \right]. \tag{12}$$

Writing Eqs. (9)–(11) in operator form

$$f_i = \Gamma_i(f_{eq}), \qquad i = \text{I, II, III,}$$

then we find

$$n(x, y) = \pi^{-3/2} \int_{-\infty}^{\infty} d\mathbf{c}\{\Gamma_{\text{I}}(f_{eq}) + \Gamma_{\text{II}}(f_{eq}) + \Gamma_{\text{III}}(f_{eq})\}. \tag{13}$$

At the same time because of the form of f_{eq} [Eq. (12)]

$$n(x, y) = \pi^{-3/2} \int_{-\infty}^{\infty} f_{eq}\, d\mathbf{c} = \bar{n},$$

which will assure in this case that the particle number conservation law is satisfied. By taking respective moments, similar equations for higher moments can be obtained and by choice one can thus enforce the conservation laws of momentum and energy. Equation (13) and related moment equations can also be subjected to variational techniques.

An equally satisfactory approach is to obtain a solution by different techniques, (as for instance the analysis of a limited number of moment equations of the BGK equation) after which one proceeds to iterate this solution in Eqs. (9)–(11).

In the following we shall simplify the problem further by linearizing the distribution function [that is, subsonic flow $q_{\infty} < (2kT_{\infty}/m)^{1/2}$] and iterate from the free molecule solution.

IV. Iteration of Free Molecular Flow Solution

We use the BGK transport equation [Eq. (1)] and linearize it as follows:

$$n' = n_{\infty}(1 + n); \qquad T' = T_{\infty}(1 + T),$$

assuming that $n \ll 1$, $T \ll 1$, $q \ll 1$, and

$$\bar{f} = n_{\infty}(m/2\pi kT_{\infty})^{3/2} \exp(-c^2).$$

We write

$$f_{eq} = \bar{f}(1 + 2c_x q_{\infty} + \phi_{eq}),$$
$$f = \bar{f}(1 + 2c_x q_{\infty} + \phi). \tag{14}$$

With all these substitutions in Eq. (1) we obtain (Gross et al., 1957)

$$c_x \frac{\partial \phi}{\partial x} + c_y \frac{\partial \phi}{\partial y} = \frac{1}{\lambda}(\phi_{eq} - \phi) \tag{15}$$

where

$$\phi_{eq} = n + (c^2 - \tfrac{3}{2})T + 2c_x(q_x - q_{\infty}) + 2c_y q_y. \tag{16}$$

In terms of ϕ the deviations of the physical parameters are

$$n = \pi^{-3/2} \int \phi \exp(-c^2)\, d\mathbf{c}, \tag{17}$$

$$\mathbf{q} = q_\infty \mathbf{i} + \pi^{-3/2} \int \phi \mathbf{c} \exp(-c^2)\, d\mathbf{c}, \tag{18}$$

$$n + T = \tfrac{2}{3}\pi^{-3/2} \int \phi c^2 \exp(-c^2)\, d\mathbf{c}. \tag{19}$$

The boundary conditions [Eqs. (5)–(7)] in terms of ϕ are

$$\phi \to 0, \qquad \text{as} \quad x \to -\infty, \tag{20}$$

$$\phi = \lim_{y \to 0} H(xc_y - yc_x) - 1 - 2c_x q_\infty, \tag{21}$$

for $c_y > 0$, and on $y = 0, L > x > 0$,

$$\int \phi c_y \exp(-c^2)\, d\mathbf{c} = 0, \qquad \text{on} \quad y = 0. \tag{22}$$

The function H is independent of $\mathbf{c}$ when $y = 0$, $L > x > 0$, and should be determined by Eq. (22).

We will now solve Eq. (15) by an iteration scheme similar to the one used by Willis (1958, 1961). First, the free molecular solution $\varphi^{(0)}$ will be found by solving

$$c_x \frac{\partial \phi^{(0)}}{\partial x} + c_y \frac{\partial \phi^{(0)}}{\partial y} = 0 \tag{23}$$

subject to the above boundary conditions. With $\varphi^{(0)}$ known, we may choose $\phi_{\text{eq}}^{(0)}$ consistent with Eqs. (16)–(19), and then obtain $\phi^{(1)}$ from Eq. (15) with $\phi_{\text{eq}} = \phi_{\text{eq}}^{(0)}$. In principle, this process may be repeated by solving

$$c_x \frac{\partial \phi^{(s)}}{\partial x} + c_y \frac{\partial \phi^{(s)}}{\partial y} = \lambda^{-1}(-\phi^{(s)} + \phi_{\text{eq}}^{(s-1)}), \qquad s = 1, 2, \ldots. \tag{24}$$

Up to date, it has not been established that the sequence $(\phi^{(s)})$ is uniformly convergent, except in the case of linearized plane Couette flow, using the BGK equation (Willis, 1958, 1961). Here, we assume that this sequence is uniformly convergent for the leading edge problem under consideration. It is interesting to note that the conservation laws will be satisfied if the sequence $(\phi^{(s)})$ tends to a limit uniformly.

It is easy to see that the linearized free molecular flow distribution is given by (see Fig. 4)

$$\phi = \phi^{(0)} = \begin{cases} 0, & \alpha_2 > \alpha > \alpha_1, \\ -2c_x q_\infty + O(q_\infty{}^2), & \text{all other } \alpha, \end{cases}$$

where

$$c_x = \bar{c} \cos \alpha, \qquad c_y = \bar{c} \sin \alpha, \qquad \bar{c}^2 = c_x^2 + c_y^2,$$

$$\tan \alpha_1 = y/x, \qquad \tan \alpha_2 = y/(x - L).$$

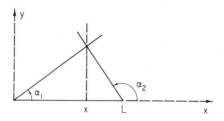

FIG. 4. Spatial coordinate system.

Substituting $\phi^{(0)}$ into Eqs. (17)–(19), we obtain

$$n^{(0)} = \frac{q_\infty}{2\pi^{1/2}} (\sin \alpha_1 - \sin \alpha_2) + O(q_\infty^2), \tag{25}$$

$$q_x^{(0)} = \frac{q_\infty}{2\pi} (2\pi + \alpha_1 - \alpha_2 + \sin \alpha_1 \cos \alpha_1 - \sin \alpha_2 \cos \alpha_2) + O(q_\infty^2), \tag{26}$$

$$q_y^{(0)} = \frac{q_\infty}{2\pi} (\sin^2 \alpha_1 - \sin^2 \alpha_2) + O(q_\infty^2), \tag{27}$$

$$T^{(0)} = \frac{q_\infty}{6\pi^{1/2}} (\sin \alpha_1 - \sin \alpha_2) + O(q_\infty^2). \tag{28}$$

These results have also been checked against the more extensive expressions obtained by Chuan and Yang (1963). Therefore, Eq. (16) suggests that $\phi_{eq}^{(0)}$ may be taken as

$$\phi_{eq}^{(0)} = q_\infty \{\pi^{-1/2}(\tfrac{1}{4} + \tfrac{1}{6}c^2)(\sin \alpha_1 - \sin \alpha_2) + (c_x/\pi)(\alpha_1 - \alpha_2 + \sin \alpha_1 \cos \alpha_1$$
$$- \sin \alpha_2 \cos \alpha_2) + (c_y/\pi)(\sin^2 \alpha_1 - \sin^2 \alpha_2) + O(q_\infty^2)\}. \tag{29}$$

Hence the first iteration $\phi^{(1)}$ (hereafter the superscript unity will be dropped from $\phi^{(1)}$) satisfies

$$c_x \frac{\partial \phi}{\partial x} + c_y \frac{\partial \phi}{\partial y} = \lambda^{-1}(-\phi + \phi_{eq}^{(0)})$$

$$= \lambda^{-1}\{-\phi + q_\infty[\pi^{-1/2}(\tfrac{1}{4} + \tfrac{1}{6}c^2)(\sin \alpha_1 - \sin \alpha_2)$$
$$+ (c_x/\pi)(\alpha_1 - \alpha_2 + \sin \alpha_1 \cos \alpha_1 - \sin \alpha_2 \cos \alpha_2)$$
$$+ (c_y/\pi)(\sin^2 \alpha_1 - \sin^2 \alpha_2)]\}. \tag{30}$$

Using the method of characteristics as in Eq. (2), and incorporating the boundary conditions Eqs. (20)–(22), we find that the solution of Eq. (30), in analogy with Eqs. (9)–(11) of Section II can be written as follows:

$$\phi = \phi_{\mathrm{I}} = e^{-y/\lambda c_y} \int_{-\infty}^{y} \frac{1}{\lambda c_y} e^{y'/\lambda c_y} \phi_{\mathrm{eq}}^{(0)}(ly' + a, y', \mathbf{c})\, dy'$$

$$\text{for} \quad 0 < \alpha < \alpha_1, \quad \alpha_2 < \alpha < \pi, \quad (31)$$

$$\phi = \phi_{\mathrm{II}} = e^{-y/\lambda c_y} \int_{0}^{y} \frac{1}{\lambda c_y} e^{y'/\lambda c_y} \phi_{\mathrm{eq}}^{(0)}(ly' + a, y', \mathbf{c})\, dy'$$

$$+ (H - 1 - 2c_x q_\infty) e^{-y/\lambda c_y}$$

$$\text{for} \quad \alpha_1 < \alpha < \alpha_2, \quad (32)$$

and

$$\phi = \phi_{\mathrm{III}} = e^{-y/\lambda c_y} \int_{\infty}^{y} \frac{1}{\lambda c_y} e^{y'/\lambda c_y} \phi_{\mathrm{eq}}^{(0)}(ly' + a, y', \mathbf{c})\, dy'$$

$$\text{for} \quad \pi < \alpha < 2\pi. \quad (33)$$

In the following discussion, we are only interested in the distribution function on the plate $y = 0$, $0 < x < L$. On the plate $\alpha_1 = 0$, $\alpha_2 = \pi$, hence ϕ_{I} makes no contribution, as expected, to the distribution function, and

$$\phi_{\mathrm{II}} = H - 1 - 2c_x q_\infty, \qquad \pi > \alpha > 0. \quad (34)$$

It is shown in Appendix B that on the plate

$$\phi_{\mathrm{III}} = q_\infty \left\{ \left[\frac{1}{\pi^{1/2}} \left(\frac{1}{4} + \frac{c^2}{6} \right) \frac{1}{\bar{c}} - \frac{2}{\pi} \right] \left[\frac{x}{\lambda} \log \frac{x}{\lambda} + \left(\frac{L}{\lambda} - \frac{x}{\lambda} \right) \log \left(\frac{L}{\lambda} - \frac{x}{\lambda} \right) \right] \right\}$$

$$\times \sin \alpha \cos \alpha + O\!\left(\frac{x}{\lambda} \right). \quad (35)$$

In the above calculations we have integrated the free molecular $\phi_{\mathrm{eq}}^{(0)}$ from $y' = \infty$ to $y' = 0$ [see for example Eqs. (B.1)]. Of course, this is not strictly correct since the free molecular ϕ_{eq} is not valid for all y. That is for $|y|$ less than a mean free path the free molecular $\phi_{\mathrm{eq}}^{(0)}$ is valid, while for $|y|$ of order of a mean free path some transitional $\phi_{\mathrm{eq}}^{(0)}$ should be used, and for $|y|$ much greater than a mean free path the continuum $\phi_{\mathrm{eq}}^{(0)}$ should be inserted into Eqs. (B.1). For the solutions on a plate of length $L \ll \lambda$ it appears reasonable to make the approximation of using the free molecular solution for all y, and our solutions become increasingly better as L/λ becomes smaller. However, if one were solving the case of a plate of length much greater than a mean free path (as, for example, the semi-infinite plate) then it is clear that the use of the free molecular $\phi_{\mathrm{eq}}^{(0)}$ for all y will give results which are not strictly correct. In that case however, repeated iteration will improve the accuracy and domain of validity of the solution.

Since the boundary conditions specify ϕ_{II} on the plate, and since ϕ_I vanishes on the plate, we can calculate the quantities of physical interests. It is found that on the plate, $n = T = q_y = 0$, and

$$q_x = q_\infty \left\{ \frac{1}{2} - \frac{1}{6\pi^{3/2}} \left[\frac{x}{\lambda} \log \frac{x}{\lambda} + \left(\frac{L}{\lambda} - \frac{x}{\lambda} \right) \log \left(\frac{L}{\lambda} - \frac{x}{\lambda} \right) + O\left(\frac{x}{\lambda} \right) \right] \right\},$$

$$p_{xy} = \frac{n_\infty k T_\infty}{\pi^{1/2}} q_\infty \left\{ -1 + \left(\frac{5\pi^{1/2}}{96} - \frac{1}{4\pi^{1/2}} \right) \right.$$
$$\left. \times \left[\frac{x}{\lambda} \log \frac{x}{\lambda} + \left(\frac{L}{\lambda} - \frac{x}{\lambda} \right) \log \left(\frac{L}{\lambda} - \frac{x}{\lambda} \right) \right] + O\left(\frac{x}{\lambda} \right) \right\}.$$

An extension of the above calculations for the flow properties off the plate, would make all quantities (that is n, q_y, and T) nonzero.

V. Summary

A considerable part of this report has been devoted to the formulation of a kinetic theory approach to the problem of the leading edge. As pointed out in the introduction we regard the finite plate problem as a testing case for more general geometries in two and three dimensions. In this sense we believe that our work establishes, that a unified kinetic theory treatment spanning the domains from continuum theory, (through the intermediate regimes of slip-flow and transition), and extending into the free molecule regime is entirely possible and feasible. Whether it is practical, and can eventually be reduced to provide engineering answers and guidance, cannot be determined without additional and more extensive analysis than has been accomplished here.

In Section IV we presented analytical results which should be valid in the near free molecule regime and calculated the flow properties on the plate itself. This particular calculation can be extended to distances of the order of a mean free path away from the plate by an extension of the techniques applied in Section IV (and in Appendix B). Whether such a limited extension provides much more insight is questionable, and therefore has not been pursued here. Our motivation rather, has been to complete at least one iteration by the method proposed, and secondly to verify the expected non-analytic behavior of the solution in the near free molecule flow domain found in one-dimensional problems (Willis, 1958, 1961).

Willis (1958, 1961) considered the related problem of uniform flow impinging perpendicularly on a finite plate. He found that the leading term of the distribution function is proportional to $K \log K$, where K is the inverse of the Knudsen number. In his analysis the leading term is independent of the position on the plate. Willis contends that only the term corresponding to

$\alpha_1 - \alpha_2$ in the present paper (Section IV) is essential in $\phi_{eq}^{(0)}$. As is demonstrated here, all the other terms in $\phi_{eq}^{(0)}$, such as for instance $\sin \alpha_1 - \sin \alpha_2$, etc., are as essential as the term $\alpha_1 - \alpha_2$.

The iteration from the continuum limit is also possible, although not reported in this report in detail. We have with limited success iterated continuum solutions due to Lewis and Carrier (1949) and Laurmann (1961). The second is perhaps a more promising solution to iterate with, as Laurmann has built slip boundary conditions into his solution. Some preliminary results on the iteration of Laurmann's solution are presented in Appendix C.

We have concluded at this stage that brute force iterations from either of the extreme flow regimes, while possible in principle, are marginal in the expected analytic return. We have therefore searched for alternatives which might be classified as follows:

(1) An "inspired guess" at a reasonable distribution function for $f_{eq}(x, y)$ which could be handled mathematically (that is integrated formally) and yet in a crude sense be physically meaningful.

(2) Machine calculations either on the nonlinear or linear equations set up in this report for the distribution functions themselves, or for the integral equations governing the moments (see Section III).

(3) A solution obtained by methods other than integral equations, retaining however the appropriate division of the distribution functions as governed by the free molecule distribution and set forth in this report.

(4) Utilizing the results, if any, obtained by a method other than integral techniques and iterating the solution to correct for the nonanalytic behavior near the boundary.

The third approach has considerable promise, in that we have obtained preliminary results by moment techniques. These have been obtained for the linearized BGK equation and will be reported on shortly in a subsequent publication. Depending on the complexity of this as yet incomplete analysis, we may try to iterate these results in accordance with the fourth alternative.

We are also attempting high speed computer solutions of the equations evolved in this report, which could iterate the solutions to sufficient order to assure compliance with the conservation laws. We are most intrigued, however, (although unsuccessful to date) by an inspired guess in the spirit of Mott-Smith's (1951, 1954) bimodal "Ansatz," which would yield analytically accessible results.

Although the mathematical analysis seems rather formidable and difficult, one should keep in mind the alternative of piecewise fitting together and matching various solutions. A most challenging test for kinetic theory treatments will be the prediction of the attached shock wave for hypersonic flow. As a matter of fact, the collisionless treatment by Chuan and Yang

(1963) for the hypersonic density and flow velocity profiles (for $M = 8$, where M is the Mach number) indicates regions of rapid changes of these flow variables near the plate. Indeed, the success of the one-dimensional bimodal kinetic theory analysis of shock waves by Mott-Smith indicates the plausibility of this approach. The key to the bimodal approach is the mixing of the two extreme distribution functions (boundary conditions) governing processes far upstream and downstream respectively. In the same manner one would expect that the mixing of the two distribution functions in the leading edge formulation of this report (plate distribution f_p, and upstream distribution F_∞) would provide the mechanism for yielding a shock structure modified by the geometry of the problem. It remains to be seen through further analytical work whether this conjecture has merit, and can yield practical answers.

Appendix A

Here it is shown that

$$I(\infty) = \lim_{y \to \infty} e^{-y/\lambda c_y} \int_\infty^y e^{y'/\lambda c_y} f(y') \, dy' \to 0, \qquad (A.1)$$

provided $\lim_{y \to \infty} |f(y)| < M$. To prove this we write

$$I(y) = \lim_{l \to \infty} e^{-y/\lambda c_y} \int_l^y e^{y'/\lambda c_y} f(y') \, dy'. \qquad (A.2)$$

Now let $y = l + \varepsilon$ so that the limit as $y \to \infty$ corresponds to $\varepsilon \to 0$. Thus,

$$I(\infty) = \lim_{l \to \infty, \, \varepsilon \to 0} e^{-(l+\varepsilon)/\lambda c_y} \int_l^{l+\varepsilon} e^{y'/\lambda c_y} f(y') \, dy'. \qquad (A.3)$$

Since ε is small,

$$\int_l^{l+\varepsilon} f(y') e^{y'/\lambda c_y} \, dy' \approx \varepsilon f(l) e^{l/\lambda c_y}$$

so that Eq. (A.3) becomes

$$I(\infty) = \lim_{l \to \infty, \, \varepsilon \to 0} \varepsilon e^{-\varepsilon/\lambda c_y} f(l). \qquad (A.4)$$

Provided $\lim_{l \to \infty} |f(l)| < M$ then from Eq. (A.4) it is readily seen that $I(\infty) \to 0$.

Appendix B

To demonstrate the evaluation of integrals of the type occurring in Section IV, we choose Eq. (33) to evaluate a typical term on the plate ($y = 0$):

$$I = \frac{1}{\lambda c_y} \int_\infty^0 e^{y'/\lambda c_y}(\sin \alpha_1 - \sin \alpha_2) \, dy'. \tag{B.1}$$

From Fig. 4

$$\sin \alpha_1 - \sin \alpha_2 = \frac{y}{[x^2 + y^2]^{1/2}} - \frac{y}{[(L - x)^2 + y^2]^{1/2}}$$

$$= \int_0^L \frac{y(x_0 - x)}{[(x_0 - x)^2 + y^2]^{3/2}} \, dx_0. \tag{B.2}$$

Hence from Eqs. (B.1) and (B.2)

$$I = -\frac{1}{\lambda c_y} \int_0^\infty e^{y'/\lambda c_y} y' \, dy' \int_0^L \frac{(x_0 - ly' - a)}{[(x_0 - ly' - a)^2 + y'^2]^{3/2}} \, dx_0. \tag{B.3}$$

Making the transformation

$$\rho \cos \Psi = y', \qquad \rho \sin \Psi = x_0 - a,$$

and reducing the transformed integral in a straightforward fashion, we obtain

$$I = \int_0^\infty \frac{1 + lt}{[(1 + l^2)t^2 + 2lt + 1]^{3/2}} e^{-at/\lambda|c_y|} \, dt$$

$$- \int_0^\infty \frac{1 - lt}{[(1 + l^2)t^2 - 2lt + 1]^{3/2}} e^{-(L-a)t/\lambda|c_y|} \, dt. \tag{B.4}$$

The first integral can be rewritten as

$$J = \frac{1}{(1 + l^2)^3 |c_y|^2} \int_0^\infty \frac{1 + l|c_y|t}{[t^2 - 2t\bar{c}^{-1} \cos \alpha + \bar{c}^{-2}]^{3/2}} e^{-at/\lambda} \, dt. \tag{B.5}$$

On the plate $a = x$. When $\mu \equiv x/\lambda$ is small, we may choose t_1 such that $1/\mu > t_1 > 1$. Then

$$J = \frac{1}{(1 + l^2)^3 |c_y|^2} \int_0^{t_1} \frac{1 + l|c_y|t}{[t^2 - 2t\bar{c}^{-1} \cos \alpha + \bar{c}^{-2}]^{3/2}} \cdot [1 - \mu t + \tfrac{1}{2}\mu^2 t^2 + \cdots] \, dt$$

$$+ \int_{t_1}^\infty e^{-\mu t}(1 + l|c_y|t)t^{-3}[1 + \cdots] \, dt$$

$$= (1 + l^2)^{-1/2} + \bar{c}^{-1} \cos \alpha \sin \alpha \mu \log \mu + O(\mu). \tag{B.6}$$

Similarly, when $(L - x)/\lambda$ is small,

$$\int_0^\infty \frac{1 - lt}{[(1 + l^2)t^2 - 2lt + 1]^{3/2}} e^{-(L-a)t/\lambda|c_y|} dt$$

$$= (1 + l^2)^{-1/2} - \bar{c}^{-1} \cos \alpha \sin \alpha((L/\lambda) - \mu) \log((L/\lambda) - \mu) + O(\mu). \quad \text{(B.7)}$$

Thus we write

$$I = \bar{c}^{-1} \cos \alpha \sin \alpha[\mu \log \mu + ((L/\lambda) - \mu) \log((L/\lambda) - \mu)] + O(\mu). \quad \text{(B.8)}$$

By a similar calculation, we find that

$$\frac{1}{\lambda c_y} \int_\infty^0 e^{y'/\lambda c_y}[(c_x/\pi)(\alpha_1 - \alpha_2 + \sin \alpha_1 \cos \alpha_1 - \sin \alpha_2 \cos \alpha_2)$$

$$+ (c_y/\pi)(\sin^2 \alpha_1 - \sin^2 \alpha_2)] \, dy'$$

$$= -2\pi^{-1} \cos \alpha \sin \alpha[\mu \log \mu + ((L/\lambda) - \mu) \log((L/\lambda) - \mu)] + O(\mu),$$

from which we obtain Eq. (35).

Appendix C

In this appendix are presented some preliminary results for the nearly continuum flow along a flat plate of length L, which have been obtained by iterating the solution obtained by Laurmann (1960) for incompressible flow. In performing these calculations we have assumed that the moments n, T, and q_y contribute negligibly on the r.h.s. of the BGK equation. For q_x we have used the expression for the flow velocity obtained by Laurmann; that is,

$$q_x = -\frac{v}{\pi a_1 L} \left\{ \frac{U}{v} \int_0^L \exp\left[\frac{U}{2v}(x - t)\right] K_0\left[\frac{U}{2v}[(x - t)^2 + y^2]^{1/2}\right] dt \right.$$

$$+ \exp\left[\frac{U}{2v}(x - L)\right] K_0\left[\frac{U}{2v}[(x - L)^2 + y^2]^{1/2}\right]$$

$$\left. - \exp\left[\frac{U}{2v} x\right] K_0\left[\frac{U}{2v}(x^2 + y^2)^{1/2}\right] + \frac{1}{2} \ln\left[\frac{x^2 + y^2}{(x - L)^2 + y^2}\right] \right\} \quad \text{(C.1)}$$

where

$$a_1 = (2 - \eta)/\eta, \qquad \eta = \text{Maxwell reflection coefficient,}$$

$$v = C_s\lambda(2/\pi\gamma)^{1/2}, \qquad C_s = \text{sound speed,}$$

$$U = \text{free stream velocity}, \qquad K_0 = \text{modified Bessel function.}$$

We shall obtain the perturbation ϕ in the distribution of incoming particles evaluated along the plate. Once this is known the calculation of the outgoing distribution is trivial. Thus in accordance with Eq. (33) we write

$$-\phi_{\mathrm{III}}(y = 0) = +\lambda c_y^{-1} \int_0^\infty 2c_x q_x(y', x = ly' + a)e^{y'/\lambda c_y} \, dy' \qquad (C.2)$$

where

$$[a]_{y=0} = x$$

In order to perform the integrations in Eq. (C.2) it is necessary to realize that due to the exponential in Eq. (C.2) the principal contributions, assuming c_y is of order unity compared with λ, will come for (strictly speaking the continuum solution should not be used in Eq. (C.2) for $y' < \lambda$. However, we shall assume that it is approximately valid in this domain. Hence the results obtained for ϕ_{III} should be interpreted as valid in an order of magnitude sense) $y' \sim \lambda$, and hence large values of y (i.e., $y \gg \lambda$) will contribute very little to the integral. Thus if it is assumed that $a = x$ is much greater than a mean free path, it is reasonable to expand the square roots occurring in K_0 in Eq. (1). First consider the integral obtained when the third term in Eq. (C.1) is substituted into Eq. (C.2). This is

$$-I_3 = \frac{P}{\lambda c_y} \int_0^\infty \exp\left(\frac{y}{\lambda c_y}\right) \exp\left(\frac{q_\infty(ly' + a)}{2\kappa\lambda}\right)$$

$$\times K_0\left[\frac{q_\infty}{2\kappa\lambda}[(1 + l^2)y^2 + 2aly + a^2]^{1/2}\right] dy$$

$$\approx \frac{P}{\lambda c_y} \int_0^\infty \exp\left(\frac{y}{\lambda c_y}\right) \exp\left(\frac{q_\infty(ly' + a)}{2\kappa\lambda}\right) K_0\left[\frac{q_\infty}{2\kappa\lambda}|a|[1 + \cdots]\right] dy \qquad (C.3)$$

where $q_\infty = U/C_s$; $P = v/\pi a_1 L$ and where it has been assumed that $|l| \sim |$, or smaller. Now if x, q_∞, and λ are such that $q_\infty x/2\kappa\lambda \gg 1$, we can use the asymptotic expansion for K_0 to obtain as the leading term in I_3:

$$-I_3 \to -P\left(\frac{\pi\kappa\lambda}{q_\infty x}\right)^{1/2} 2xc_x + \cdots \qquad (C.4)$$

Similarly the second and fourth terms become

$$-I_2 \to +P\left(\frac{\pi\kappa\lambda}{q_\infty(L - x)}\right)^{1/2} 2c_x \exp\left(-\frac{q_\infty(L - x)}{\kappa\lambda}\right) + \cdots, \qquad (C.5)$$

$$-I_4 \to +\log[x/(L - x)]2c_x + \cdots. \qquad (C.6)$$

The only difficulty is the first term in Eq. (C.1). Here, one must first perform the integral over t and then over y'. The integral over t can be rewritten as

$$\overline{T} = -\frac{U}{\pi a_1 L} \exp\left(\frac{q_\infty(ly + a)}{2\kappa\lambda}\right) \int_0^L dt \exp\left(-\frac{q_\infty t}{2\kappa\lambda}\right)$$

$$\times K_0\left[\frac{q_\infty}{2\kappa\lambda}[(1 + l^2)y^2 + 2aly + a^2 - 2tly - 2at + t^2]^{1/2}\right].$$

The above integral can be split into two parts, one from $t = 0$ to $t = a$, and the other from a to L. In the first integral $a > t$ and hence we can expand the square root in t/a, assuming $l = |c_x/c_y|$ is of order unity.

Similarly in the second integral we have expanded in a/t. If this is done and only the leading terms are retained we obtain (again using the asymptotic expression for K_0)

$$\overline{T} = \frac{2\kappa\lambda C_s}{\pi a_1 L} \exp\left(\frac{q_\infty ly}{2\kappa\lambda}\right)\left[\exp\left(-\frac{q_\infty a}{2\kappa\lambda}\right) - 1\right]\left(\frac{\pi\kappa\lambda}{q_\infty x}\right)^{1/2}$$

$$- \frac{2\sqrt{\pi}\kappa\lambda C_s}{\pi a_1 L} \exp\left(\frac{q_\infty(ly + x)}{2\kappa\lambda}\right)\left[\Phi\left(\frac{q_\infty L}{\kappa\lambda}\right)^{1/2} - \Phi\left(\frac{q_\infty x}{\kappa\lambda}\right)^{1/2}\right] \quad (C.7)$$

where

$$\Phi(\xi) = \int_{-\infty}^\xi \exp(-z^2)\, dz.$$

If Eq. (C.7) is substituted into Eq. (C.2) to obtain the contribution of this integral to ϕ_{III} we obtain (we have used our previous assumption that $q_\infty a/2\kappa\lambda \ll 1$ and the further assumption that $|1/\lambda c_y| > q_\infty l/2\kappa\lambda$; the latter assumption was necessary in order to ensure that the integral on y' is bounded) as the leading terms

$$-I_1 = \frac{2\kappa\lambda C_s}{\pi a_1 L} 2c_x\left(\frac{\pi\kappa\lambda}{q_\infty x}\right)^{1/2}$$

$$+ \frac{4\kappa\lambda\pi^{1/2}c_x C_s}{\pi a_1 L} \exp\left(\frac{q_\infty x}{2\kappa\lambda}\right)\left[\Phi\left(\frac{q_\infty L}{\kappa\lambda}\right)^{1/2} - \Phi\left(\frac{q_\infty x}{\kappa\lambda}\right)^{1/2}\right]. \quad (C.8)$$

Combining all the terms we obtain finally for ϕ_{III}

$$-\phi_{III} = \frac{2c_x C_s \lambda\kappa}{\pi a_1 L}\left\{\left(\frac{\pi\kappa\lambda}{q_\infty x}\right)^{1/2} + \log\frac{x}{L - x}\right.$$

$$\left. + 2\pi^{1/2} \exp\left(+\frac{q_\infty x}{2\kappa\lambda}\right)\left[\Phi\left(\frac{q_\infty L}{\kappa\lambda}\right)^{1/2} - \Phi\left(\frac{q_\infty x}{\kappa\lambda}\right)^{1/2}\right]\right\} \quad (C.9)$$

where in writing Eq. (C.9) we have neglected the contribution from I_2 since it is exponentially small.

It is now important to point out some of the limitations under which the preceding analysis is valid. The most stringent assumption was that $|l|$ is of order unity or smaller. This implies that our results are not valid for very small c_y, nor very large c_x. The latter restriction is not too serious since large velocities contribute very little to the moments, but the restriction on c_y is more important. It is possible to develop an expression for ϕ_{III} valid in this regime, but this will be deferred to a future paper. In addition, Eq. (C.9) is not valid within a mean free path of the leading or trailing edges. The former limitation has been pointed out in the text, while the latter is inherent in the mathematical simplifications leading to Eqs. (C.5) and (C.6). Of course, one should not expect to obtain the correct solution within a mean free path of the leading edge in any case, since we have iterated from the continuum solution. That is, within a mean free path of the leading edge it is more reasonable to iterate from the free molecular solution and hence the behavior of ϕ_{III} near the leading edge is given by Eq. (35) in the main text.

We have not presented expressions for the moments of ϕ_{III}, because, as stated previously, the solutions for small c have not been fully obtained, and it is not yet clear how important a contribution the small velocity range of ϕ_{III} will make to the moments. The full results will be presented in a future note.

REFERENCES

Bhatnagar, P. L., Gross, E. P., and Krook, M. (1954). *Phys. Rev.* **94**, 511-525.

Chuan, R. L., and Yang, H. T. (1963). "Hypersonic Low Density Wakes." Univ. of Southern California Eng. Center Rept. 93-101.

Grad, H. (1949). *Communs. Pure Appl. Math.* **2**, 331-407.

Gross, E. P., and Jackson, E. A. (1959). *Phys. Fluids* **2**, 432-441.

Gross, E. P., Jackson, E. A., and Ziering, S. (1957). *Ann. Phys. (N.Y.)* **1**, 141-167.

Gross, E. P., and Ziering, S. (1958). *Phys. Fluids* **1**, 215-224.

Gross, E. P., and Ziering, S. (1959). *Phys. Fluids* **2**, 701-712.

Gross, E. P., and Jackson E. A. (1958). *Phys. Fluids* **1**, 318-328.

Laurmann, J. A. (1960). *In* "Rarefied Gas Dynamics" (F. M. Devienne, ed.), pp. 293-316. Pergamon Press, New York.

Lees, L. (1959). GALCIT Memo. No. 51.

Lewis, J. A., and Carrier, J. F. (1949). *Q. Appl. Math.* **7**, 228-234.

Mott-Smith, H. M. (1954). M.I.T., Lincoln Lab., Group Rept. V-2.

Mott-Smith, H. M. (1951). *Phys. Rev.* **82**, 885-892.

Wang Chang, C. S., and Uhlenbeck, G. E. (1949). Univ. of Michigan Eng. Res. Inst. Rept. C. M. 579.

Wang Chang, C. S., and Uhlenbeck, G. E. (1953). Univ. of Michigan Eng. Res. Inst. Rept. M999.

Wang Chang, C. S., and Uhlenbeck, G. E. (1954). Univ. of Michigan Eng. Res. Inst. Rept. 1999-1-T.

Welander, P. (1953). *Arkiv fysik.* **7**, 507.

Willis, D. R. (1958). Princeton Univ. Aeronautical Eng. Rept. 440.

Willis, D. R. (1960). *In* " Rarefied Gas Dynamics " (F. M. Devienne, ed.), 246-257. Pergamon Press, New York.

Ziering, S. (1960). *Phys. Fluids* 3, 503-509.

The Incipient Continuum Flow Near the Leading Edge of a Flat Plate[1]

JACK MORITO II AND ROBERT E. STREET

The Boeing Company, and Department of Aeronautics and Astronautics, University of Washington, Seattle, Washington

In the flow over a sharp flat plate the Navier-Stokes equations with first order slip are assumed to hold in the regime between the near-free-molecular flow at the leading edge and the boundary layer flow further downstream. Expansion of the variables in powers of $\varepsilon = (\gamma^{\frac{1}{2}} M_\infty)^{-\frac{1}{2}}$ leads to the conclusion that to first order, the flow downstream of the shock wave is described by a system of almost inviscid equations, only one viscous term occurring, but next to the plate surface the compressible boundary layer equations hold. If $\mu \propto T^\omega$, no slip occurs to the first order if $\omega = \frac{1}{2}$, but if $\omega \geq \frac{3}{4}$ there are slip effects. These equations are solved and the outer solution matched to the inner solution along the interfacial streamline originating at the point on the shock wave where its slope is a maximum. Comparison of the heat transfer coefficient is made with experiment.

I. Introduction

The theory presented here is an attempt to devise an explanation of the transition from the near-free-molecular flow at the leading edge of a sharp flat plate in a rarefied hypersonic flow to the continuum boundary layer flow further downstream. The flow regime thus corresponds to the transition zone of Charwat (1961). Charwat's sketch, with modifications, is shown here as Fig. 1 to illustrate the flow regimes under discussion, with Charwat's transition zone renamed the viscous regime in accordance with the definition of Oguchi (1961, 1963) and Street (1961). In this regime the Navier-Stokes equations are assumed to be valid together with first order slip boundary

---

[1] This work was supported in part by the National Science Foundation under Grant NSF-G24294.

conditions, in accordance with the belief that no better system of equations is known to exist.

It might be possible to numerically integrate the Navier-Stokes equations but, as the shock wave shape and position are unknown and the boundary between the first collision regime and the viscous regime is not specified

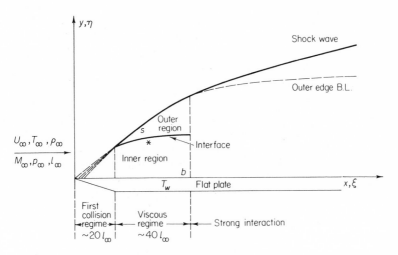

FIG. 1. Flow model.

a priori, this method of solution is hardly feasible. Instead, in order to get a feel for the order of magnitude of the terms and to find a relatively simple solution, we propose to expand the Navier-Stokes equations in powers of a small parameter and to solve the first order approximation equations only. Other approximations are made as well:

1. The effect of shock wave thickness is ignored. Thus the Rankine Hugoniot conditions are taken across the shock wave.

2. The Prandtl number is taken to be unity.

3. The exponent ω in the power law for the variation of the coefficients of viscosity and thermal conductivity with temperature is constant.

4. The component of velocity v in the y direciton is assumed to have simple linear dependence upon the stream function ψ.

Some years ago Li and Nagamatsu derived the boundary layer equations from the Navier-Stokes equations by means of essentially an expansion of the flow quantities in powers of M^{-1}, where M_∞ is the free-stream Mach number. We have tried to generalize this expansion as shown in the next section.

II. The Navier-Stokes Equations and Their Expansion in Powers of a Parameter

With coordinates x and y chosen as in Fig. 1 with origin at the leading edge of the flat plate, we assume the usual well known equations of motion of a two-dimensional, steady-state, compressible flow of an ideal gas. These are the equation of state, equation of continuity, the two equations of momentum in the x and y directions and the energy equation for the five unknowns, pressure p, density ρ, temperature T, and the components of velocity u, v in the x, y directions, respectively. The flow properties in the uniform stream ahead of the plate are assumed to be constant and will be denoted by subscript ∞. Then we arbitrarily choose a small parameter ε defined by $\varepsilon^2 = (\gamma^{1/2} M_\infty)^{-1}$. Because of the well-known kinetic theory relation between the coefficient of viscosity μ and the mean free path l, this parameter can also be expressed in terms of the free-stream Reynolds number Re_{l_∞} based upon the mean free path l_∞ which is assumed larger than the leading edge thickness or

$$\varepsilon^2 = (\gamma^{1/2} M_\infty)^{-1} = 1.25/\mathrm{Re}_{l_\infty}. \tag{1}$$

The subscript is left off a γ and will also be omitted from the symbols c_p, c_v and Pr since all of these quantities, the specific heats, their ratio and the Prandtl number are assumed constant throughout the flow, at least to the order of approximation which will be considered.

Although ε is really small only at very large Mach numbers, we will actually consider comparison with experiments in the range from 15 to 25 for M_∞ for which $\varepsilon \approx 0.2$, so even to obtain rough results it may be necessary to go to terms in ε^2. This will turn out to be necessary only in the region next to the surface of the plate, the inner region of Fig. 1.

The viscous flow regime is assumed at first to extend outward all of the way from the plate surface to the shock wave. In this regime the absolute values of x are quite small and, although y is possibly some order of magnitude less than x, it may not be as small compared to x as in the boundary layer flow further downstream. Hence, we choose two constant exponents m and n to make both ξ and η new dimensionless coordinates with l_∞ as reference length according to the definition

$$\xi = \varepsilon^m (x/l_\infty); \qquad \eta = \varepsilon^{m-n}(y/l_\infty). \tag{2}$$

The numerical values of m and n will be chosen later so as to make ξ and η both of order unity. In the equations of motion the partial differentiation operators become

$$\frac{\partial}{\partial x} = \frac{\varepsilon^m}{l_\infty} \frac{\partial}{\partial \xi}; \qquad \frac{\partial}{\partial y} = \frac{\varepsilon^{m-n}}{l_\infty} \frac{\partial}{\partial \eta}. \tag{3}$$

The kinematic and thermodynamic variables are expanded in powers of ε:

$$u = U_\infty[u_1(\xi, \eta) + \varepsilon u_2(\xi, \eta) + \cdots],$$
$$v = \varepsilon^n U_\infty[v_1(\xi, \eta) + \varepsilon v_2(\xi, \eta) + \cdots],$$
$$p = \varepsilon^{-\beta} p_\infty[p_1(\xi, \eta) + \varepsilon p_2(\xi, \eta) + \cdots], \qquad \alpha, \beta \text{ constant} \qquad (4)$$
$$\rho = \varepsilon^{-\alpha} \rho_\infty[\rho_1(\xi, \eta) + \varepsilon \rho_2(\xi, \eta) + \cdots],$$
$$T = \varepsilon^{-(\beta-\alpha)} T_\infty[t_1(\xi, \eta) + \varepsilon t_2(\xi, \eta) + \cdots].$$

The coefficients of shear viscosity, bulk viscosity, and thermal conductivity are all assumed to be power functions of the temperature or $\mu/\mu_\infty = C_\infty(T/T_\infty)^\omega$, etc., where ω is a constant, $\frac{1}{2} \leqslant \omega \leqslant 1$. Then, if $\mu_1(t_1) = C_\infty t_1^\omega$, $\mu_1'(t_1) = \omega C_\infty t_1^{\omega-1}$, $\lambda_1(t_1) = C_\infty t_1^\omega$, etc., we obtain the expansions

$$\mu = \varepsilon^{-\omega(\beta-\alpha)} \mu_\infty[\mu_1(t_1) + \varepsilon t_2 \mu_1'(t_1) + \cdots],$$
$$\lambda = \varepsilon^{-\omega(\beta-\alpha)} \mu_\infty[\lambda_1(t_1) + \varepsilon t_2 \lambda_1'(t_1) + \cdots], \qquad (5)$$
$$k = \varepsilon^{-\omega(\beta-\alpha)} k_\infty[k_1(t_1) + \varepsilon t_2 k_1'(t_1) + \cdots].$$

When expressions (3)–(5) are substituted into the equations of motion certain dimensionless combinations of the free stream properties occur which can be expressed in terms of ε. These are

$$\frac{p_\infty}{\rho_\infty U_\infty^2} = \frac{1}{\gamma M_\infty^2} = \varepsilon^4, \qquad \frac{\mu_\infty}{\rho_\infty U_\infty l_\infty} = \frac{1}{\mathrm{Re}_{l_\infty}} = 0.8\varepsilon^2,$$

$$\frac{k_\infty}{c_p \rho_\infty U_\infty l_\infty} = \frac{1}{\mathrm{Pr}\,\mathrm{Re}_{l_\infty}} = 0.8 \frac{\varepsilon^2}{\mathrm{Pr}}, \qquad \frac{p_\infty}{\rho_\infty c_p T_\infty} = \frac{\gamma - 1}{\gamma},$$

$$\frac{\mu_\infty U_\infty}{\rho_\infty l_\infty c_p T_\infty} = \frac{(\gamma - 1)M_\infty^2}{\mathrm{Re}_{l_\infty}} = \frac{\gamma - 1}{\gamma} \frac{0.8}{\varepsilon^2}, \qquad (6)$$

$$\frac{k_\infty T_\infty}{\mu_\infty U_\infty^2} = \frac{1}{(\gamma - 1)M_\infty^2\,\mathrm{Pr}} = \frac{\gamma}{\gamma - 1} \frac{\varepsilon^4}{\mathrm{Pr}}.$$

When $\gamma = 1.4$ and $15 < M_\infty < 25$ we see that $0.8(\gamma - 1)/\gamma \approx \varepsilon$ so

$$\frac{p_\infty}{\rho_\infty c_p T} \approx 1.25\varepsilon, \qquad \frac{\mu_\infty U_\infty}{\rho_\infty l_\infty c_p T_\infty} \approx \varepsilon^{-1}, \qquad \frac{k_\infty T_\infty}{\mu_\infty U_\infty^2} \approx \frac{0.8}{\mathrm{Pr}} \varepsilon^3, \qquad (7)$$

will be used in place of the expressions in terms of γ given in Eq. (6).

Retaining only the first two terms in expansions (4) and (5), the equations of motion take on the dimensionless form

$$p_1 + \varepsilon p_2 = (\rho_1 + \varepsilon \rho_2)(t_1 + \varepsilon t_2), \qquad (8)$$

$$\frac{\partial}{\partial \xi}[(\rho_1 + \varepsilon \rho_2)(u_1 + \varepsilon u_2)] + \frac{\partial}{\partial \eta}[(\rho_1 + \varepsilon \rho_2)(v_1 + \varepsilon v_2)] = 0, \qquad (9)$$

$$(\rho_1 + \varepsilon\rho_2)\left[(u_1 + \varepsilon u_2)\frac{\partial}{\partial\xi}(u_1 + \varepsilon u_2) + (v_1 + \varepsilon v_2)\frac{\partial}{\partial\eta}(u_1 + \varepsilon u_2)\right]$$

$$+ \varepsilon^{4-\beta+\alpha}\frac{\partial}{\partial\xi}(p_1 + \varepsilon p_2)$$

$$= 0.8\varepsilon^{m-\omega(\beta-\alpha)+\alpha+2-2n}\frac{\partial}{\partial\eta}\left\{(\mu_1 + \varepsilon t_2\mu_1')\left[\frac{\partial}{\partial\eta}(\mu_1 + \varepsilon u_2) + \varepsilon^{2n}\frac{\partial}{\partial\xi}(v_1 + \varepsilon v_2)\right]\right\}$$

$$+ 0.8\varepsilon^{m-\omega(\beta-\alpha)+\alpha+2}\frac{\partial}{\partial\xi}\left\{(\lambda_1 + \varepsilon t_2\lambda_1')\left[\frac{\partial}{\partial\xi}(u_1 + \varepsilon u_2) + \frac{\partial}{\partial\eta}(v_1 + \varepsilon v_2)\right]\right.$$

$$\left. + 2(\mu_1 + \varepsilon t_2\mu_1')\frac{\partial}{\partial\xi}(u_1 + \varepsilon u_2)\right\}, \tag{10}$$

$$(\rho_1 + \varepsilon\rho_2)\left[(u_1 + \varepsilon u_2)\frac{\partial}{\partial\xi}(v_1 + \varepsilon v_2) + (v_1 + \varepsilon v_2)\frac{\partial}{\partial\eta}(v_1 + \varepsilon v_2)\right]$$

$$+ \varepsilon^{4-\beta+\alpha-2n}\frac{\partial}{\partial\eta}(p_1 + \varepsilon p_2)$$

$$= 0.8\varepsilon^{m-\omega(\beta-\alpha)+\alpha+2-2n}\left\{\frac{\partial}{\partial\xi}\left[(\mu_1 + \varepsilon t_2\mu_1')\left(\frac{\partial}{\partial\eta}(u_1 + \varepsilon u_2)\right.\right.\right.$$

$$\left.\left. + \varepsilon^{2n}\frac{\partial}{\partial\xi}(v_1 + \varepsilon v_2)\right)\right] + \frac{\partial}{\partial\eta}\left[(\lambda_1 + \varepsilon t_2\lambda_1')\left(\frac{\partial}{\partial\xi}(u_1 + \varepsilon u_2) + \frac{\partial}{\partial\eta}(v_1 + \varepsilon v_2)\right)\right.$$

$$\left.\left. + 2(\mu_1 + \varepsilon t_2\mu_1')\frac{\partial}{\partial\eta}(v_1 + \varepsilon v_2)\right]\right\}, \tag{11}$$

$$(\rho_1 + \varepsilon\rho_2)\left[(u_1 + \varepsilon u_2)\frac{\partial}{\partial\xi}(t_1 + \varepsilon t_2) + (v_1 + \varepsilon v_2)\frac{\partial}{\partial\eta}(t_1 + \varepsilon t_2)\right]$$

$$= 1.25\varepsilon\left[(u_1 + \varepsilon u_2)\frac{\partial}{\partial\xi}(p_1 + \varepsilon p_2) + (v_1 + \varepsilon v_2)\frac{\partial}{\partial\eta}(p_1 + \varepsilon p_2)\right]$$

$$+ \frac{0.8}{\text{Pr}}\varepsilon^{m-\omega(\beta-\alpha)+\alpha+2-2n}\left\{\frac{\partial}{\partial\eta}\left[(k_1 + \varepsilon t_2k_1')\frac{\partial}{\partial\eta}(t_1 + \varepsilon t_2)\right]\right.$$

$$\left. + \varepsilon^{2n}\frac{\partial}{\partial\xi}\left[(k_1 + \varepsilon t_2k_1')\frac{\partial}{\partial\xi}(t_1 + \varepsilon t_2)\right]\right\}$$

$$+ \varepsilon^{m-\omega(\beta-\alpha)+\beta-1-2n}\left\{(\mu_1 + \varepsilon t_2\mu_1')\left[\frac{\partial}{\partial\eta}(u_1 + \varepsilon u_2) + \varepsilon^{2n}\frac{\partial}{\partial\xi}(v_1 + \varepsilon v_2)\right]^2\right.$$

$$+ 2\varepsilon^{2n}(\mu_1 + \varepsilon t_2\mu_1')\left[\left\{\frac{\partial}{\partial\xi}(u_1 + \varepsilon u_2)\right\}^2 + \left\{\frac{\partial}{\partial\eta}(v_1 + \varepsilon v_2)\right\}^2\right]$$

$$\left. + \varepsilon^{2n}(\lambda_1 + \varepsilon t_2\lambda_1')\left[\frac{\partial}{\partial\xi}(u_1 + \varepsilon u_2) + \frac{\partial}{\partial\eta}(v_1 + \varepsilon v_2)\right]^2\right\}. \tag{12}$$

So far these equations are exact, no approximation having been made, except that $0.8(\gamma - 1)/\gamma \approx \varepsilon$. The next step is to determine the numerical values of the constants α, β, n, and m so that the terms in Eqs. (8)–(12) can be rearranged in increasing powers of ε and the various orders of approximation determined.

The experimental shock tunnel data of Nagamatsu *et al.* (1960, 1961, 1962) and of Vidal and Wittliff (1963) indicate a pressure maximum near the leading edge which we assume is within the viscous flow regime. Since the maximum pressure ratio $p/p_\infty \sim O(\gamma^{1/2} M_\infty) \sim \varepsilon^{-2}$ downstream of the shock wave we take $\beta = 2$. Although the density ratio across the shock wave itself is of the order of ε^{-1}, the pressure rises between the shock wave and the plate surface and the density decreases. Hence $\alpha < 1$, and since $T_\infty / T_w \sim \varepsilon^2$, it appears reasonable to take $\alpha = 0$. The choice of n is considerably more difficult. Since the viscous layer reaches from the plate surface to the shock wave, we do not expect y to be so very small compared to x as in boundary layer theory. The shock wave slope is

$$\theta_s \sim \frac{y_s}{x} \sim \varepsilon^n$$

and according to Newtonian flow theory

$$c_p = \frac{2}{\gamma M_\infty{}^2} \left(\frac{p}{p_\infty} - 1 \right) \approx 2\theta_s{}^2 \sim 2\varepsilon^{2n}$$

so $p/p_\infty \sim \gamma M_\infty{}^2 \varepsilon^{2n} = \varepsilon^{2n-4}$. However, $p/p_\infty = O(\varepsilon^{-2})$ and so $n = 1$ would seem to be a proper choice. Thus the layer is thicker than in the boundary layer case for which $n = 2$.

With $\alpha = 0$, $\beta = 2$ and $n = 1$ we still have to decide on the value of the exponent m. Since $x \sim O(l_\infty \varepsilon^{-m})$, the value of m determines the position of the flow regime downstream of the leading edge in multiples of the mean-free-path of the free-stream gas. If $m = 1$ and $\varepsilon = 0.2$, then $x \sim 5l_\infty$ which would put us somewhere in the free-molecule flow regime. However, if $m \geqslant 2$ then $x \geqslant 25l_\infty$ which seems more reasonable. Also an observation of the right-hand sides of Eqs. (10)–(12) shows the predominant term to be $\varepsilon^{m-2\omega-1} \mu_1 u_{1_\eta}$ in Eq. (12), so if $m = 2\omega \leqslant 2$ we have the first approximation term to be $u_{1_\eta} = 0$ or $u_1 = u_1(\xi)$, indicating perfect slip as in free-molecule flow. But if we take $m = 2\omega + 1$, this term on the right-hand side of Eq. (12) will be of the same order as the convection terms on the left-hand side and it will be the only viscous term in the first approximation to the equations of motion.

Note the critical dependence of m on the value of ω. If $\omega = \frac{1}{2}$, as is often assumed, m is smaller than if $\omega = \frac{3}{4}$ or 1. It will be seen later that the choice of ω determines whether or not slip at the plate surface is a first or second order phenomena as well. Also from the above discussion it is clear that, if viscous terms do not appear in the first order approximation, it is not going to be possible to satisfy the boundary conditions at the plate surface. Hence, we are led to conceive of an outer region of the viscous flow regime in which the equations obtained by the above choice of exponents are valid and an inner region in which the exponents are chosen so as to lead to the boundary layer equations. The solutions in the two regions will be matched along an interface between the two regions (Fig. 1).

III. The Equations in the Outer Region and Their Solution

With the choice $\alpha = 0$, $\beta = 2$, $n = 1$ and $m = 2\omega + 1$ made above we can express the terms in Eqs. (8)–(12) in increasing positive powers of ε. The terms independent of ε then give us the first order approximation to the full equations. Transformed back to the original physical variables they are

$$p = R\rho T, \qquad \frac{\partial}{\partial x}(\rho u) + \frac{\partial}{\partial y}(\rho v) = 0,$$

$$u\frac{\partial u}{\partial x} + v\frac{\partial u}{\partial y} = 0, \qquad \rho u\frac{\partial v}{\partial x} + \rho v\frac{\partial v}{\partial y} + \frac{\partial p}{\partial y} = 0,$$

$$\rho c_p\left(u\frac{\partial T}{\partial x} + v\frac{\partial T}{\partial y}\right) = \mu\left(\frac{\partial u}{\partial y}\right)^2. \tag{14}$$

Since Eqs. (13) are nonviscous and independent of Eq. (14) they are solved first and then Eq. (14) is used to find the temperature. We eliminate the continuity equation by assuming a stream function $\psi(x, y)$ such that

$$\rho u = \partial\psi/\partial y, \qquad \rho v = -\partial\psi/\partial x. \tag{15}$$

The von Mises transformation is applied in which x, ψ are taken as new independent variables in place of x and y. The two momentum equations become

$$\partial u/\partial x = 0, \qquad \partial p/\partial\psi = -\partial v/\partial x. \tag{16}$$

Also we have along each streamline

$$\partial y/\partial x = v/u, \qquad \partial y/\partial\psi = 1/\rho u, \tag{17}$$

and the stream function at the shock wave is

$$\psi_s = \rho_\infty U_\infty y_s(x). \tag{18}$$

From the first of Eqs. (16) we have $u = u(\psi)$ or u is constant along each streamline, $\psi = $ constant. Applying the usual shock wave conditions results in

$$u = u_s(\psi) = u_s(y)|_{y=y_s(x)}, \tag{19}$$

where subscript s denotes the value of the quantity just after the shock wave.

In order to solve the second of Eqs. (16) we assume a particular simple form for $v(x, \psi)$. It is a linear function of ψ or

$$v(x, \psi) = v_s(x)\frac{\psi}{\psi_s} = \frac{v_s(x)\psi}{\rho_\infty U_\infty y_s(x)}. \tag{20}$$

We differentiate Eq. (20) with respect to x and then integrate with respect to ψ, taking into account the boundary condition at the shock wave, to obtain

$$\frac{p(x, \psi)}{p_\infty} = \frac{p_s(x)}{p_\infty} + \frac{\gamma M_\infty^{\ 2}}{2U_\infty}\left[v_s(x)\frac{dy_s}{dx} - y_s(x)\frac{dv_s}{dx}\right]\left[1 - \frac{y_s^2(\psi)}{y_s^2(x)}\right]. \tag{21}$$

The temperature equation (14) is transformed by the von Mises transformation into

$$\frac{\partial T}{\partial x} = \frac{\rho\mu u}{c_p}\left(\frac{\partial u}{\partial \psi}\right)^2. \tag{22}$$

Since

$$\frac{\partial u}{\partial \psi} = \frac{1}{\rho_\infty U_\infty}\left(\frac{\partial u}{\partial y}\right)_s \quad \text{and} \quad \frac{\rho\mu}{c_p} = \frac{\mu_\infty p T^{\omega-1}}{c_p R T_\infty^{\ \omega}}$$

we have

$$\frac{\partial T}{\partial x} = \frac{\mu_\infty}{c_p R T_\infty^{\ \omega}}\frac{u_s}{(\rho_\infty U_\infty)^2}\left(\frac{\partial u_s}{\partial y_s}\right)^2 p(x, \psi)T^{\omega-1}. \tag{23}$$

Substitution of Eq. (21) into Eq. (23) gives a simple differential equation for T in which the variables are separable. The integration of this differential equation is carried out along a streamline giving

$$T(x, \psi) = T_s(\psi) + \left[\frac{(2-\omega)\mu_\infty u_s(\psi)}{(\rho_\infty U_\infty)^2 c_p R T_\infty^{\ \omega}}\left(\frac{\partial u_s}{\partial y_s}\right)^2 \int_{\psi=\text{const}} p(x, \psi)\,dx\right]^{1/(2-\omega)} \tag{24}$$

This equation is not valid at the plate surface because the term $T_s(\psi)$ is then obtained from the free-molecule flow theory. The value of $T_s(\psi)$ at $x = l_\infty/\varepsilon^{2\omega}$ is the value at the beginning of continuum flow. The value of ψ at this point is assumed to be the inner limit of the outer region. Details of the derivation of Eqs. (21) and (24) have been given by Ii (1964).

The initial values of the flow in the outer region are obtained from the hypersonic approximations giving the flow condition just downstream of the shock wave

$$\frac{p_s(x)}{p_\infty} = \frac{2\gamma}{\gamma+1}M_\infty^{\ 2}\theta_s^{\ 2}(x), \qquad \frac{u_s(x)}{U_\infty} = 1 - \frac{2}{\gamma+1}\theta_s^{\ 2}(x),$$

$$\frac{v_s(x)}{U_\infty} = \frac{2}{\gamma+1}\theta_s(x). \tag{25}$$

IV. The Equations in the Inner Region and Their Solution

In order to satisfy either the slip or no-slip conditions at the plate surface we must derive and solve a system of equations containing more terms involving the coefficients of heat conduction and viscosity. Also the velocity gradient is larger next to the plate, so we would expect the boundary layer equations should be the governing equations in what we term the inner region. That this is so follows from a reconsideration of the values of the exponents of the expansions made in Section II.

The inner region is thinner so $n > 1$ and the pressure is higher but the density is lower. Therefore, we take $\alpha = 0$ as before but take $\beta = 2 + \omega$. The position of the layer is the same so $m = 2\omega + 1$ again. To determine n we examine the terms on the right-hand side of Eq. (12). Again the predominant term is the viscous dissipation term with the exponent of ε equal to $m - \omega(\beta - \alpha) + \beta - 1 - 2n$ which becomes $\omega(1 - \omega) + 2(1 - n)$. This vanishes if $n = 1 + \frac{1}{2}\omega(1 - \omega)$, and then the exponent of ε for the conduction term becomes $1 - \omega$ which is also the exponent of the predominant viscous term in the x-momentum Eq. (10). If $\omega = 1$, we then obtain the boundary layer equations for the first approximation but, if $\omega = \frac{1}{2}$, we still obtain the boundary layer equations by retaining terms to the order of $\varepsilon^{1/2}$ but neglecting terms of order $\varepsilon^{3/4}$. The pressure gradient term in Eq. (10) is of order ε at least and can be neglected. Thus we have the usual boundary layer equations but without a pressure gradient term in the x direction,

$$p = R\rho T, \qquad \frac{\partial}{\partial x}(\rho u) + \frac{\partial}{\partial y}(\rho v) = 0, \qquad (26)$$

$$\rho u \frac{\partial u}{\partial x} + \rho v \frac{\partial u}{\partial y} = \frac{\partial}{\partial y}\left(\mu \frac{\partial u}{\partial y}\right), \qquad \frac{\partial p}{\partial y} = 0, \qquad (27)$$

$$\rho c_p\left(u \frac{\partial T}{\partial x} + v \frac{\partial T}{\partial y}\right) = \frac{\partial}{\partial y}\left(k \frac{\partial T}{\partial y}\right) + \mu\left(\frac{\partial u}{\partial y}\right)^2. \qquad (28)$$

The solution of these equations must match the outer solution at the interface where $y = y^*(x)$ and it must fair into Charwat's solution at the downstream boundary of the near-free-molecule flow over the leading edge. Finally the solution must satisfy either no-slip or the slip conditions at the plate surface. We examine the latter first. The first order slip and jump conditions at the plate are

$$u_b = u(x, 0) = \bar{a}_1\lambda_b(\partial u/\partial y)_{y=0},$$
$$T_b = T(x, 0) = T_w + \bar{c}_1\lambda_b(\partial T/\partial y)_{y=0}, \qquad (29)$$

where

$$\lambda = (\mu/p)(RT)^{1/2} \approx 0.8l,$$

$$\bar{a}_1 = \frac{2-\sigma}{\sigma}\left(\frac{\pi}{2}\right)^{1/2}, \qquad \bar{c}_1 = \frac{2\gamma}{\gamma+1}\frac{1}{\mathrm{Pr}}\frac{2-\alpha}{\alpha}\left(\frac{\pi}{2}\right)^{1/2}.$$

The subscript b denotes conditions in the gas at the surface, σ is the molecular reflection coefficient and α is the thermal accommodation coefficient; both α and σ being assumed constant, they will be taken equal to unity.

When the expressions for the flow quantities given by Eqs. (4) and (5) are substituted into Eq. (29) we obtain

$$u_1(x,0) + \varepsilon u_2(x,0) + \cdots = 0.8\bar{a}_1\varepsilon^{1-\frac{1}{2}\omega^2}\left[\frac{\mu_1}{p_1} t_1^{1/2} \frac{\partial u_1}{\partial \eta}\bigg|_{\eta=0} + O(\varepsilon)\right]$$

$$t_1(x,0) + \varepsilon t_2(x,0) + \cdots = \varepsilon^{2+\omega}\frac{T_w}{T_\infty} + 0.8\bar{c}_1\varepsilon^{1-\frac{1}{2}\omega^2}\left[\frac{\mu_1}{p_1} t_1^{1/2} \frac{\partial t_1}{\partial \eta}\bigg|_{\eta=0} + O(\varepsilon)\right],$$

which shows that slip effects are significant only if $\omega = 1$ and are of second order if $\omega < \frac{3}{4}$. Also the term T_w in the temperature jump is of higher order unless, as in shock tunnel experiments, $T_w/T_\infty \geqslant \varepsilon^{-3}$.

The boundary conditions at the interface where $y = y^*$ are $u_i = u_0 = u_s^* =$ constant along a stream line and $T_i = T_0 = T^*(x)$ where subscripts i and 0 refer to inner and outer regions, respectively. The initial conditions at $x = x^*$ where continuum flow starts will be introduced later.

In order to solve Eqs. (26)–(28) we introduce the Howarth type transformation used by Jain and Li (1963) in which the new independent variables are taken to be

$$\xi(x) = \int_0^x \rho_b\mu_b u^*\, dx, \qquad \eta(x,y) = (u^*/\xi)\int_0^y \rho\, dy. \tag{30}$$

[These are not the same as the dimensionless variables defined by Eq. (2).] Introduce a stream function ψ so that the continuity equation (26) is satisfied by letting

$$\partial\psi/\partial y = \rho u, \qquad \partial\psi/\partial x = -\rho v. \tag{15}$$

If $H = c_p T + \frac{1}{2}u^2$ is the total enthalpy, we can introduce the new dependent variables f and g defined by

$$\psi(\xi,\eta) = \xi f(\xi,\eta), \qquad H/H^* = g(\xi,\eta), \tag{31}$$

and carry out the transformation of Eqs. (27)–(28) resulting in

$$(Nf_{\eta\eta})_\eta + \xi f f_{\eta\eta} = \xi^2(f_\eta f_{\xi\eta} - f_\xi f_{\eta\eta}), \tag{32}$$

$$\left\{\frac{N}{\mathrm{Pr}}\left[g_\eta - (1-\mathrm{Pr})\frac{u^{*2}}{2H^*}(f_\eta^2)_\eta\right]\right\}_\eta + \xi f g_\eta = \xi^2(f_\eta g_\xi - f_\xi g_\eta) \tag{33}$$

where $N = (\rho\mu)/(\rho_b\mu_b) = (T/T_b)^{\omega-1}$ since $p = $ constant across the inner region of the viscous layer. Subscripts ξ, η denote partial differentiation with respect to ξ and η, respectively.

The conservation of mass flow through the inner region requires that

$$\rho_\infty U_\infty y_s^* = \int_0^{y^*} \rho u \, dy = \xi f(\xi, \eta^*). \tag{34}$$

This relation gives the ordinate η^* of the interface streamline when the initial ordinate y_s^* at the shock wave is known. It is more useful to rewrite Eq. (34) as a relation between the initial shock wave slope θ_s^* and $f(\xi^*, \eta_s^*)$. Using the approximations $\theta_s^* = y_s^*/x$ and $\xi^*/x = (d\xi/dx)_{\xi^*}$, the relation is

$$\frac{\rho_\infty U_\infty \theta_s^*}{\rho_b\mu_b u_s^*} = f(\xi^*, \eta_s^*). \tag{35}$$

Other conditions on the interface streamline are

$$f_\eta(\xi, \eta^*) = 1, \qquad g(\xi, \eta^*) = 1. \tag{36}$$

At the plate surface there is no slip if $\omega = \frac{1}{2}$ and the boundary condition is

$$f_\eta(\xi, 0) = 0, \qquad g(\xi, 0) = H_w/H^*; \qquad \omega = \frac{1}{2}. \tag{37}$$

For $\omega = 1$ we take the first order slip conditions given by Eq. (29) and transform them into the new notation obtaining the form indicated by Street (1961)

$$f_\eta(\xi, 0) = \zeta(\xi)f_{\eta\eta}(\xi, 0), \qquad T_b = T_w + (\bar{c}_1/\bar{a}_1)\zeta(\xi)T_\eta(\xi, 0), \qquad \omega = 1 \tag{38}$$

where

$$\zeta(\xi) = \bar{a}_1 u^* \mu_b (RT_b)^{-1/2}\xi^{-1} = D^*\xi^{-1}(T_b/T^*)^{1/2} \tag{39}$$

Here

$$D^* \equiv \bar{a}_1\rho^*\lambda^* u^* = \bar{a}_1[\mu^* u_s^*/(RT^*)^{1/2}].$$

Also

$$f(\xi, 0) = f_\xi(\xi, 0) = 0.$$

Jain and Li (1963) have solved Eq. (32) for the no-slip case with $\omega = \frac{1}{2}$ and $\mathrm{Pr} = 1$ by the use of a Görtler series

$$f(\xi, \eta) = \sum_{n=0}^\infty \xi^n f_n(\eta), \tag{40}$$

neglecting terms in ξ^2 and higher powers of ξ. They also took Crocco's integral as the solution of Eq. (33) since the pressure term drops out of the equations for f_0 and f_1. Street (1961) made the usual Howarth-Dorodnitsyn transformation so his Görtler series was in powers of $z = (2\xi)^{1/2}$ but with slip boundary conditions, $\omega = 1$ and arbitrary but constant Prandtl number.

Crocco's integral was not used and three terms in both series for $f(z, \eta)$ and $g(z, \eta)$ were found, to the second power in ξ.

Here we have the same differential equations as Jain and Li but we consider the case where $\omega = 1$ and hence use the slip boundary conditions (38). Then Crocco's integral does not apply so we assume for $g(\xi, \eta)$ the Görtler series

$$g(\xi, \eta) = \sum_{n=0}^{\infty} \xi^n g_n(\eta), \qquad (41)$$

and calculate terms to the order of ξ^2. Since this is only a first order approach, we also take $\Pr = 1$ so that Eq. (33) simplifies somewhat. Also with $\omega = 1$, $N = 1$ the substitution of Eqs. (40) and (41) into Eqs. (32) and (33) leads to ordinary linear differential equations for the six functions f_0, f_1, f_2, g_0, g_1, g_2.

We omit details of the solution which follows the method used by Street (1961) and can be found in Ii (1964). In summary, the technique is to expand the boundary conditions in powers of ξ as well and, using the relation

$$T/T^* = (1 + \Delta^*)g(\xi, \eta) - \Delta^* f_\eta^2(\xi, \eta),$$

where $\Delta^* = \frac{1}{2}(\gamma - 1)M^{*2} \approx \frac{1}{2}(\gamma - 1)M_s^{*2}$, which is valid for $C_p = $ constant, obtain the expansions

$$T_b/T^* = a_0 + a_1\xi + a_2\xi^2 + \cdots, \qquad (T_b/T^*)^{1/2} = b_0 + b_1\xi + b_2\xi^2 + \cdots.$$

Then it is easy to obtain the boundary conditions on f_n and g_n for $n = 0, 1, 2$. With these boundary conditions the solutions of the six ordinary differential equations are simple polynomials in η, giving

$$f(\xi, \eta) = \eta - (\eta^* - \tfrac{1}{2}\eta)\frac{\eta'\xi}{D^*} + \frac{\eta^*}{2D^*}(\eta^{*2} - \tfrac{1}{3}\eta^2)\eta\xi^2$$
$$+ \left[1 - \frac{1}{2}\frac{\bar{a}_1}{\bar{c}_1}\left(1 - \frac{T_w}{T^*}\right)\right]\frac{\eta^*}{D^{*2}}(\eta^* - \tfrac{1}{2}\eta)\eta\xi^2 + O(\xi^3), \qquad (42)$$

$$g(\xi, \eta) = 1 - \left[\frac{\bar{a}_1}{\bar{c}_1}\left(1 - \frac{T_w}{T^*}\right) + 2\Delta^*\right]\left[\frac{(\eta^* - \eta)\xi}{(1 + \Delta^*)D^*} - \frac{\eta^*(\eta^{*2} - \eta^2)\xi^2}{2(1 + \Delta^*)D^*}\right]$$
$$- \left\{\frac{\bar{a}_1}{\bar{c}_1}\left(1 - \frac{T_w}{T^*}\right)\left[\Delta^* - \frac{1}{2}\frac{\bar{a}_1}{\bar{c}_1}\left(1 + \frac{T_w}{T^*}\right)\right] - 4\Delta^*\right\}\frac{\eta^*(\eta^* - \eta)\xi^2}{(1 + \Delta^*)D^{*2}}$$
$$+ O(\xi^3). \qquad (43)$$

The value of T^* is obtained from Eq. (24) when $\omega = 1$ as

$$\frac{T^*(x)}{T_s^*} = 1 + \frac{\gamma - 1}{\mathrm{Re}_\infty} M_s^{*2} \frac{U_\infty}{u_s^*}\left(\frac{\partial}{\partial y_s}\frac{u_s^*}{U_\infty}\right)^2 \int_{y=y^*} \frac{p^*(x)}{p_\infty}\,dx = 1 + \kappa(x) \qquad (44)$$

where $\mathrm{Re}_\infty = \rho_\infty U_\infty/\mu_\infty$ and $\kappa(x)$ is the temperature correction.

V. Matching of Inner and Outer Solutions

Having obtained solutions in the inner and outer regions they have to be matched at their common boundary which is a stream surface starting at the line on the shock wave at position x^*, y_s^* as shown in Fig. 2. This position is the down-stream boundary of the near-free-molecule flow at the leading

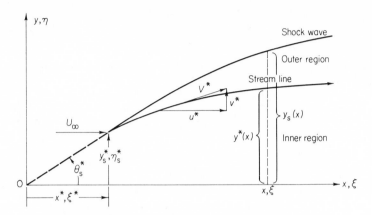

FIG. 2. Matching configuration showing coordinate notation.

edge. From the discussion in Section II we saw that when $m = 2\omega$ we were in the near-free-molecule flow regime. Assuming $\xi = 1$ in Eq. (2) is the downstream limit, we take for x^* the value

$$x^* = l_\infty \varepsilon^{-2\omega} = l_\infty (\gamma^{1/2} M_\infty)^\omega = \gamma^{1/2} M_\infty l_\infty , \qquad \text{since} \quad \omega = 1. \quad (45)$$

Assuming the pressure distribution at the plate surface is

$$p_w(x)/p_\infty = P_m F(\bar{x}) \tag{46}$$

where $P_m = p_{\max}/p_\infty$ and $\bar{x} = x/x^* \geqslant 1$, we can use the hypersonic approximations given by Eq. (25) in Eq. (21) to find p_s/p_∞ and hence the shock wave slope $\theta_s(x)$ is given by

$$\theta_s^2(\bar{x}) = \theta_s^{*2}[\tfrac{2}{3}F(\bar{x}) + \tfrac{1}{3}\bar{x}^{-2} + \cdots]. \tag{47}$$

Charwat (1963) gives an expression for the maximum pressure on the surface which is used to determine θ_s^{*2}. If the same approximations are made in Eq. (44) we obtain the temperature distribution along the interface streamline in the form

$$\frac{T^*(\bar{x})}{T_s^*} = 1 + 2\frac{\gamma - 1}{\gamma + 1}\frac{M_s^{*2}}{(\gamma^{1/2}M_\infty)^3}\frac{P_m^2}{\text{Re}_{l_\infty}}\left(\frac{dF(\bar{x})}{d\bar{x}}\right)^2 \int_1^{\bar{x}} F(\bar{x})\,d\bar{x}. \tag{48}$$

Substituting the solution for f from Eq. (42) into Eq. (34) gives a quartic equation in $\xi\eta^*/D^*$,

$$\left(\frac{\xi\eta^*}{D^*}\right)^4 + \frac{3}{2}K_{T^*}\frac{\xi}{D^{*2}}\left(\frac{\xi\eta^*}{D^*}\right)^3 - \frac{3}{2}\frac{\xi}{D^{*2}}\left(\frac{\xi\eta^*}{D^*}\right)^2$$

$$+ \frac{3\xi}{D^{*2}}\left(\frac{\xi\eta^*}{D^*}\right) - \frac{3\xi}{D^{*2}}\frac{\rho_\infty U_\infty y_s^*}{D^*} = 0, \quad (49)$$

where

$$K_{T^*}(\bar{x}) = 1 - \tfrac{1}{2}(\bar{a}_1/\bar{c}_1)[1 - (T_w/T^*)], \qquad D^*(\bar{x}) = \bar{a}_1\gamma^{1/2}\mu_s^*M_s^*(T^*/T_s^*)^{1/2}.$$

The solution of Eq. (49) gives $\xi\eta^*/D^*$ as a function of the variable ξ/D^{*2}. ξ is obtained from Eq. (30) by integration along the interface using the fact that $\rho_b\mu_b = \rho^*\mu^*$ in this case where $\omega = 1$. The result is

$$\xi = \rho_s^*\mu_s^*u_s^*x^*X(\bar{x}),$$

where

$$X(\bar{x}) = 1 + \int_1^{\bar{x}} F(\bar{x})\,d\bar{x}.$$

Then

$$\frac{D^*}{\xi^{1/2}} = \frac{\bar{a}_1\gamma^{1/2}M_s^*}{(\mathrm{Re}_x^*)^{1/2}}\left(\frac{T^*}{T_s^*}\right)^{1/2}, \qquad \text{if} \qquad \mathrm{Re}_x^* = \frac{\rho_s^*u_s^*x^*}{\mu_s^*}X(\bar{x}). \quad (50)$$

The calculations are now clear although quite tedious. We assume a pressure distribution and determine the function $F(\bar{x})$. The shock-wave shape follows from Charwat's solution and Eq. (47). Knowing this we use Eq. (25) to obtain the variables behind the shock and Eqs. (19)–(21), (24) to determine the solution in the outer region. Then the known variation of the quantities along the dividing streamline $y^*(x)$ give us the solution for the inner region. Equation (42) determines the velocity profile in the inner region through the equation

$$u/u_s^* = f_\eta(\xi, \eta),$$

while Eq. (19) gives it in the outer region.

VI. The Skin Friction and Heat Transfer

These quantities are of the greater physical interest and the heat transfer at least can be checked experimentally. Also we can show that the determination of the skin friction coefficient and heat transfer coefficient do not depend upon having a complete solution of the flow problem. Only the values of the variables along the dividing streamline $y^*(x)$ are needed.

The wall shear stress when $\omega = 1$ and hence $N = 1$ can be transformed into the ξ, η variables giving

$$\tau_w = \mu_b \left(\frac{\partial u}{\partial y}\right)_{y=0} = \frac{\rho^* \mu^* u_s^{*2}}{\xi} f_{\eta\eta}(\xi, 0).$$

The local skin friction coefficient is then taken as

$$C_f = \frac{2\tau_w}{\rho_\infty u_\infty^2} = 2 \frac{p^* \rho_s^*}{p_s^* \rho_\infty} \frac{1}{\bar{a}_1 \gamma^{1/2} M_s^*} \left(\frac{T_s^*}{T^*}\right)^{1/2} \left[1 - K_{T^*} \frac{\xi\eta^*}{D^*} + O(\xi^2 \eta^{*2})\right]. \quad (51)$$

In the near-free-molecule limit when $\xi \to 0$ the first term in Eq. (51) becomes the Charwat (1963) value

$$(C_f)_{\text{FM}} = \frac{2}{\bar{a}_1 (\gamma)^{1/2} M_\infty}$$

The maximum local shear coefficient, $(C_f)_m$, which is a near-free-molecule limit, is assumed to be obtained by $p^* \to p_s^*$, $T^* \to T_s^*$, and by neglecting the term $\xi\eta^*/D^*$ so that

$$(C_f)_m = \frac{2}{\bar{a}_1 (\gamma)^{1/2} M_s^*} \frac{\rho_s^*}{\rho_\infty}.$$

Similarly the heat flux from the plate surface is

$$-q_b = (k \, \partial T/\partial y + \mu u \, \partial u/\partial y)_{y=0} = (\rho^* \mu^*/\xi) u_s^* H^* g_\eta(\xi, 0),$$

if $\text{Pr} = 1$. Using the solution given by Eq. (43) and defining the heat transfer coefficient used by Nagamatsu

$$C_h = \frac{-q_b}{\rho_\infty U_\infty c_p (T_0 - T_w)},$$

we obtain

$$C_h = \frac{\rho_s^*}{\rho_\infty} \frac{p^*}{p_s^*} \frac{u_s^*}{U_\infty} \frac{(T_s^*/T^*)_{H^*}^{1/2} [(\bar{a}_1/\bar{c}_1)(1 - (T_w/T^*)) + 2\Delta^*]}{C_p (T_0 - T_w)(1 + \Delta^*) \bar{a}_1 (\gamma)^{1/2} M_s^*}$$

$$\times \left[1 - K_{H^*} \frac{\xi\eta^*}{D^*} + O(\xi^2 \eta^{*2})\right] \quad (52)$$

where

$$K_{H^*} = \frac{4\Delta^* - (\bar{a}_1/\bar{c}_1)(1 - (T_w/T^*))\{\Delta^* - \frac{1}{2}(\bar{a}_1/\bar{c}_1)(1 + (T_w/T^*))\}}{2\Delta^* + (\bar{a}_1/\bar{c}_1)(1 - (T_w/T^*))}.$$

In the free-molecule limit $\xi \to 0$, $p^* \to p_\infty$, $T^* \to T_\infty$, and $H^* \to H_\infty$. Assuming $M^2 \gg 1$, $H_\infty = C_p T_0$, and $u^* \approx U_\infty$ we find

$$(C_h)_{\text{FM}} = \frac{1}{1 - T_w/T_0} \frac{2}{\bar{a}_1 (\gamma)^{1/2} M_\infty}.$$

The maximum heat transfer coefficient, $(C_h)_m$, can be obtained by $p^* \to p_s^*$, $T^* \to T_s^*$, and by neglecting the term $\xi\eta^*/D^*$. Assuming $M_s^* \gg 1$, $H_s^* \approx C_p T_0$, and $u^* \approx U_\infty$, we find

$$(C_h)_m \approx \frac{\rho_s^*}{\rho_\infty} \frac{1}{1 - T_w/T_0} \frac{2}{\bar{a}_1(\gamma)^{1/2} M_s^*}.$$

VII. Discussion

Although fairly rough in its order of approximation, the approach to the leading edge problem presented here does seem to give reasonable results. For any given pressure distribution over the flat plate the detailed flow

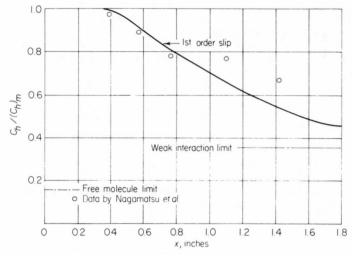

FIG. 3. Heat transfer coefficient for $M_\infty = 15.2$, $T_0 = 6640°R$, $T_w/T_0 = 0.08$ compared with experiment.

pattern can be constructed without too much difficulty. Since only heat transfer measurements are available, one such example is worked out using Eq. (52). This is the case $M_\infty = 15.2$, $T_0 = 6640°R$ for which data are available in Nagamatsu et al. (1962). The results plotted in Fig. 3 show remarkably good agreement between the theory and experiment. Only the weak interaction limit is shown downstream, since the data of Vidal and Wittliff (1963) implied that the strong interaction region was of less importance and possibly not necessary to explain transition from leading edge flow to boundary layer flow. In this case $F(\bar{x})$ was the measured pressure distribution of Nagamatsu et al. A more thorough comparison with theory and experiment can be found in Ii (1964).

It is not expected that further refinement in the calculations will improve the results. Although the experimental data of Nagamatsu and associates indicates that the best value of ω is of the order of $7/8$, any value of $\omega < 1$ adds considerable analytic difficulty to finding the inner solution. Also the Görtler type series used is not well known for good convergence, especially when ξ is as large as it is. A more realistic choice of Prandtl number could be made without adding much more labor to the calculation.

REFERENCES

Charwat, A. F. (1961). In "Rarefied Gas Dynamics" (L. Talbot, ed.), pp. 553-578. Academic Press, New York.

Charwat, A. F. (1963). Rand Corp. R.M. 2553-PR.

Ii, J. Morito (1964). Ph.D. Dissertation, Univ. of Washington.

Jain, A. C., and Li, T. Y. (1963). ARL 63-161.

Nagamatsu, H. T., and Sheer, R. E., Jr. (1960). *ARS (Amer. Rocket Soc.) J.* **30**, 454-462.

Nagamatsu, H. T., Sheer, R. E., Jr., and Schmid, J. R. (1961) *ARS (Amer. Rocket Soc.) J.* **31**, 902-910.

Nagamatsu, H. T., Weil, J. A., and Sheer, R. E., Jr. (1962). *ARS (Amer. Rocket Soc.) J.* **32**, 533-541.

Oguchi, H. (1961). In "Rarefied Gas Dynamics" (L. Talbot, ed.), pp. 501-524. Academic Press, New York.

Oguchi, H. (1963). In "Rarefied Gas Dynamics" (J. A. Laurmann, ed.), Vol. II, pp. 181-193. Academic Press, New York.

Street, R. E. (1961). Boeing Sci. Research Lab. Rept. No. 49.

Street, R. E. (1962). Addendum, Tech. Memo. No. 8.

Vidal, R. J., and Wittliff, C. E. (1963). In "Rarefied Gas Dynamics" (J. A. Laurmann, ed.), Vol. II, pp. 343-378. Academic Press, New York.

TRANSITION FLOW—EXPERIMENTAL

Recent Experimental and Theoretical Extensions of Nearly Free Molecular Flow[1]

G. J. MASLACH, D. ROGER WILLIS, S. TANG, AND D. KO

University of California, Berkeley, California

A new comparison is made between experimental results for cylinder and flat strip models in near free molecule flow and corresponding theoretical results. It is found that a new relation between the Knudsen number and the natural rarefaction parameter occurring in the theoretical calculations leads to much better agreement between experiment and theory than was observed in similar comparisons presented at the previous symposium.

I. Introduction

At the last symposium Schaaf and Maslach (1963) presented experimental cylinder drag results which were obtained at sufficiently high Knudsen numbers and with small enough scatter in the data to make a meaningful comparison with the theories then available (Lunc and Lubonski, 1956; Baker and Charwat, 1958; Willis, 1959) for high Knudsen number flows. A large discrepancy between theory and experiment was noted at that time. As theoretical results were not then available for a cylinder the comparison was based on results for a two-dimensional strip normal to the flow. However, it was felt that this geometric effect would not significantly change the qualitative nature of the comparison.

Since the last meeting the following steps have been taken in an attempt to reconcile the results of theory and experiment. Firstly, new experimental results have been obtained (Section II). Secondly, theoretical calculations have been performed for the cylinder (Taub, 1965). Thirdly, a method different from that of Schaaf and Maslach (1963) has been used to relate the Knudsen

[1] This work was sponsored by the Office of Naval Research under Contract Nonr–222(45), and the National Science Foundation under Grant P–13802.

number to the parameter which arises in those theoretical calculations where a statistical model is used to represent the intermolecular collision process. This is discussed in Section III.

II. New Experimental Results

Since 1962 a continuing program of drag force measurement in the near free molecule and free molecule regimes has been carried out at Berkeley extending the range of flow conditions to higher Mach numbers and utilizing both

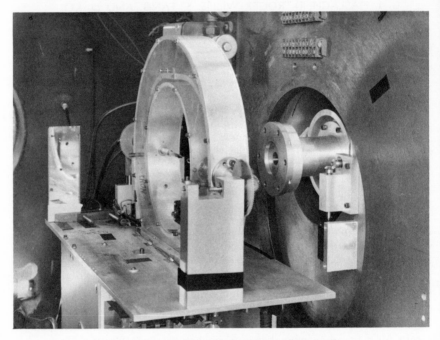

FIG. 1. Model, balance, and nozzle in wind tunnel.

cylindrical and flat strip models. Essentially, the same experimental methods have been used as were previously described (Maslach and Schaaf, 1963), but with an improved balance mechanism, Fig. 1, and the use of free jet testing techniques to achieve higher Mach numbers at lower densities. The extensive precautions taken to determine precisely the characteristics of the flow fields issuing from these simple convergent nozzles are the subject of a separate paper (Ashkenas and Sherman, 1965).

Cylinder drag data were obtained at Mach numbers of approximately 6,

8, and 10 with a range of Knudsen numbers from approximately 1 to 32 (Tang, 1964). Flat strip drag data for the model normal to the flow were obtained at approximately the same Mach numbers with a similar range of Knudsen numbers (Ko, 1964).

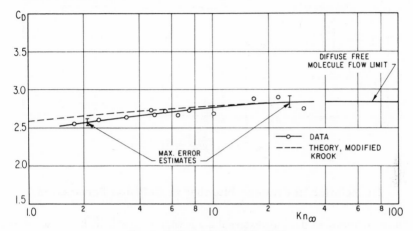

FIG. 2. Cylinder drag at $M = 9.85$.

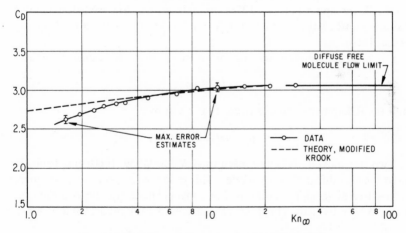

FIG. 3. Drag of a two-dimensional strip at $M \approx 10.09$.

All results approach diffuse free molecule flow limiting conditions for high Knudsen numbers; typical data are shown in Figs. 2 and 3. Previous results at a Mach number of approximately 5.92 using uniform flow field testing techniques were essentially duplicated (the maximum discrepancy being 2.8%) utilizing the free jet testing methods, Fig. 4.

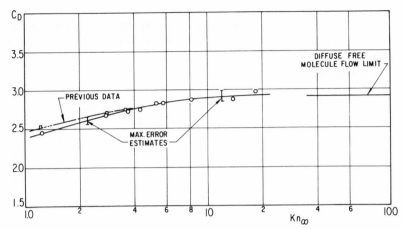

FIG. 4. Cylinder drag at $M = 5.92$.

III. Relation of Knudsen Number to Collision Parameters

All calculations to date for external aerodynamic problems have used either perfectly elastic spheres to represent the collision process (Lunc and Lubonski, 1956; Baker and Charwat, 1958) or replaced the Maxwell-Boltzmann collision operator with a statistical type model (Willis, 1959, 1960; Taub, 1964; Rose, 1964).

For hard sphere molecules the mean free path is given unambiguously by

$$\lambda = (\sqrt{2}\pi n \sigma^2)^{-1}, \tag{1}$$

and the (Chapman-Enskog) viscosity is given by

$$\mu = \rho\lambda(2kT/\pi m)^{1/2}, \tag{2}$$

Two statistical models have been used. Willis (1959, 1960) and Taub (1964) used the "modified Krook" model. This model was specifically designed for nearly free molecular conditions. For convenience a brief description is given in the Appendix. Rose (1964) uses the original Krook model (Bhatnagar *et al.*, 1954).

Nearly free molecular analyses using either of these models give results in terms of a "natural" small parameter $\alpha = \delta n_\infty (D/2)(m/2kT_b)^{1/2}$. In this relation D is a typical body dimension, n_∞ the number density at infinity, δ is a constant appearing in the model (such that $1/\delta n_\infty$ is the relaxation time for the translational degrees of freedom), and T_b is the temperature characterizing the Maxwell distribution which the molecules reflected from the body are assumed to possess.

In comparing theory with experiment we must relate α to the free stream Knudsen number. Schaaf and Maslach (1963) used the following relation:

$$\alpha = 0.6 S_b / \text{Kn}_\infty, \tag{3}$$

where $S^2 = m U_\infty^2 / 2kT$ and $\text{Kn}_\infty = \lambda_\infty / D$. This relation is empirical and was obtained by a comparison of high Mach number strip drag results using the modified Krook model and hard sphere molecules.

A very different result is obtained if we choose to define a mean free path from the viscosity formula of Eq. (3). This formula is only valid for near equilibrium conditions, i.e., far from the body. For the simple Krook model we have the result

$$\mu_\infty = k T_\infty / \delta, \tag{4}$$

and hence

$$\alpha = (\pi^{1/2}/4)(T_\infty / T_b)^{1/2} / \text{Kn}_\infty. \tag{5}$$

There will be a large difference between the results of Eqs. (3) and (5) if the speed ratio S_∞ is not close to unity. For the modified Krook model the meaning of the viscosity is not so clear as the model is specifically designed for nonequilibrium situations. However, we propose to use the relation in Eq. (5) for this case also.

There are, of course, several other ways in which α could be related to Kn_∞. The physical arguments underlying both the first collision methods and the order of magnitude analyses using the first iterate method with the model equations suggest that the main source of correction to the free molecular drag, etc., comes from collisions between molecules leaving the body and free stream molecules. A relation between α and Kn_∞ might then be developed by studying the rate of such collisions. This will not be attempted here.

IV. Comparison between Theory and Experiment

Unless specifically stated otherwise we use Eq. (5) to relate α and Kn_∞ for those theoretical results that use the statistical models.

A. Cylinder and Two-Dimensional Strip Drag

The theoretical results, based on the modified Krook model, are of the form

$$C_D = C_{Dfm} + H(S_\infty, S_b)(\alpha \ln \alpha). \tag{6}$$

The method used is that of integral iteration (Willis, 1959). The function

TABLE I

VALUES OF $H(S_\infty, S_b)$ [EQ. (6)]

M_∞	S_∞	S_b	H (cylinder)	H (strip)
1.96	1.64	1.17	1.218	1.644
4.00	3.34	1.55	1.162	1.666
5.92	4.95	1.66	1.148	1.660
9.85	8.24	1.71	1.166	—
10.09	8.44	1.69	—	1.656

H is given in Table I for typical values of S_∞ and S_b used in the drag experiments. It should be noted that terms of order α have been neglected compared to those of order $\alpha \ln \alpha$. This naturally limits the range of validity of the theory significantly. Typical comparisons of the data with the theoretical results are shown in Figs. 3 and 5. For the cylinder we show the effect of the two interpretations of the α-Kn_∞ relation. It is obvious that the agreement is far superior using the mean free path based on viscosity, i.e., Eq. (5).

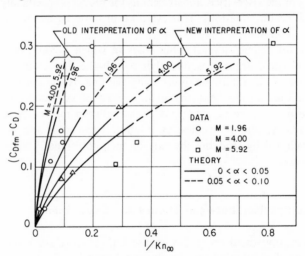

FIG. 5. Comparison of theory and experiment for cylinder drag.

B. Cylinder Equilibrium Temperature

The cylinder equilibrium temperature can be calculated from results given by Taub (1965) for the heat transfer corrections. The calculation must be performed using the value of S_b, uniquely determined by S_∞, which corresponds to zero heat transfer for the free molecular flow. Using the modified Krook model we obtain the following result for the normalized equilibrium temperature:

$$\eta^* = \frac{T_{eq} - T_{eq}(Kn_\infty = 0)}{T_{eq}(Kn_\infty = \infty) - T_{eq}(Kn_\infty = 0)} = 1 + (\alpha \ln \alpha)G(S_\infty, S_b). \quad (7)$$

Assuming a monatomic gas, a recovery factor of unity in continuum conditions, and supersonic flow, we have approximately

$$T_{eq}(Kn_\infty = 0)/T_{eq}[Kn_\infty = \infty] = (1 + 0.4S_\infty^2)(T_\infty/T_{eq}[Kn = \infty]). \quad (8)$$

Using this result and the standard formula for $(T_\infty/T_{eq}[Kn = \infty])$ for a cylinder (Schaaf, 1963) we obtain

$$S_\infty = 2, \quad S_b = 1.12, \quad G = 0.190;$$
$$S_\infty = 4, \quad S_b = 1.31, \quad G = 0.304; \quad (9)$$
$$S_\infty = 5, \quad S_b = 1.35, \quad G = 0.340.$$

These results are plotted in Fig. 6 using Eq. (5) to relate α to Kn_∞. The data are taken from Dewey (1961). Also shown is the result given by Schaaf and Maslach (1963), namely,

$$\eta^* = 1 - (0.88/Kn_\infty)(\ln Kn_\infty), \quad (10)$$

which was obtained from results in (Willis, 1959) using hard sphere molecules with S_∞ approaching infinity. The modified Krook results fall within the scatter bounds of the data for $Kn_\infty \gtrsim 5$. While this agreement is scarcely

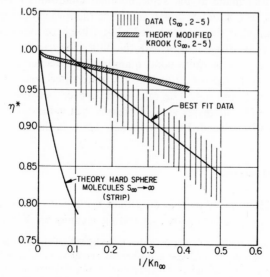

FIG. 6. Comparison of theory and experiment, cylinder equilibrium temperature.

good, it is far better than the gross discrepancy between the result of Eq. (10) and the data.

The value of G is quite sensitive to the assumption regarding the recovery factor under continuum conditions and may be expected to vary significantly for diatomic gases. There is also some question regarding the Prandtl number implied by the model.

C. Sphere Drag

Sphere drag has been predicted by first collision (Baker and Charwat, 1958) and first iterate (Willis, 1960) methods. Recently Rose (1964) derived an expression for the drag by a much different analytical method involving the use of the linearized Krook equation and Fourier transform techniques. All the above results were for large free stream Mach number and $S_b \gtrsim 2$. Rearranging all the results in terms of Kn_∞, we find[2]

$$C_D - C_{Dfm} = -(0.24S_b + 1.06)/Kn_\infty \qquad \text{(Baker and Charwat),} \qquad \text{(11a)}$$

$$= -(0.165S_b + 1.44 - 1.13/S_b)/(S_\infty Kn_\infty) \qquad \text{(Willis),} \qquad \text{(11b)}$$

$$= -(0.33S_b - 0.12)/S_\infty Kn_\infty \qquad \text{(Rose).} \qquad \text{(11c)}$$

Equation (11b) is obtained by fitting numerical results for $S_b \geqslant 2$.

We have compared the theories with typical data given by Kinslow and Potter (1963) in Fig. 7. (We have plotted mean values when more than one measurement was made at the same nominal conditions.) The data were obtained for $S_\infty = 8.8$ and $S_b \geqslant 4.4$, so all the theories should be applicable.

It can be seen that the results based on hard sphere molecules (Eq. 11a) are again in serious disagreement with the data. The results for both Krook models, however, are in quite good quantitative agreement with the data. These remarks hold true for all of Kinslow and Potter's data with $S_b = 6.25$ (Fig. 7), 5.85, 5.0, and 4.4. The relative difference between the results of Eqs. (11b) and (11c) increases as S_b decreases, but values of S_b significantly lower than 4.4 will be needed to discriminate between the results.

V. Conclusions

1. New cylinder and flat strip drag data for models normal to the flow have been obtained utilizing free jet testing techniques. For similar Mach

[2] Formula (11a) is slightly different from that given by Schaaf and Maslach (1963) due to a difference in expressing one of Baker and Charwat's parameters in terms of Kn_∞ and S_b. Equation (11b) corrects a typographical error in a corresponding equation in a paper by Willis (1960).

numbers the data essentially duplicate those obtained in previous work using uniform flow field testing techniques.

2. For the drag of a cylinder or two-dimensional strip the data have been obtained for sufficiently high Knudsen number and with sufficiently low scatter to provide a test of the theoretical predictions.

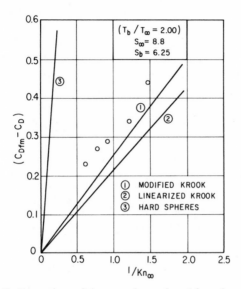

FIG. 7. Comparison of theory and experiment for sphere drag.

3. The theoretical results obtained from the first iterate method, using the modified Krook model to represent the collision process, and determining the mean free path from viscosity in the gas far from the body, are in reasonable agreement with experimental data for cylinder, two-dimensional strip, and sphere drag. For the cylinder equilibrium temperature the agreement is only fair, but at least $(T_{eq} - T_{eq}[Kn_\infty = \infty])$ has the correct order of magnitude for $Kn_\infty \gtrsim 5$.

4. Results obtained using the linearized Krook model (Rose, 1964) are also in reasonable agreement with the sphere drag data of Kinslow and Potter (1963).

5. Theoretical results using hard sphere molecules to represent the collision process do not agree with the above cited experimental data.

6. A more definitive comparison could be obtained if the theoretical calculations for the two-dimensional bodies were extended to include the terms of order $(1/Kn_\infty)$ as well as $(1/Kn_\infty) \ln (Kn_\infty)$, and if the sphere drag results could be obtained at higher Knudsen numbers and for a wider range of body to free stream temperature ratios.

Appendix. The Modified Krook Model

The simple Krook model (Bhatnagar *et al.*, 1954) considers all collisions at a point statistically and makes no distinctions between the various types of collisions that occur. This appears, intuitively, to be too simple a representation for a nearly free molecular flow where the distribution function has very different properties depending on whether or not the molecular velocity is within the solid angle subtended by the body and directed away from the body. As a step toward the Maxwell-Boltzmann type of collision operator, where all possible types of collisions are considered, we propose the following model, specifically designed for nonequilibrium conditions. The molecules at any point $\mathbf{r}$ are divided into two classes. Those whose molecular velocities (ξ) lie in the outward drawn solid angle subtended by the body are called class b and all other molecules are called class c. The collision term becomes

$$(\partial f_b/\partial t)_{\text{coll}} = -\delta f_b(n_b w_{bb} + n_c w_{bc})$$
$$+ \delta(n_b{}^2 w_{bb}\Phi_{bb} + 2n_b n_c w_{bc}\Phi_{bc} + n_c{}^2 w_{cc}\Phi_{cc}), \qquad \text{(A.1)}$$

where δ is a constant, w_{bb}, $w_{bc} = w_{cb}$, w_{cc} are functions of $\mathbf{r}$ only and

$$\Phi_{ij} = (m/2k\pi T_{ij})^{3/2} \exp(-[m/2kT_{ij}][\xi - \mathbf{u}_{ij}]^2). \qquad \text{(A.2)}$$

[The equation for f_c is given by exchanging b and c in Eq. (A.1)]. The other parameters are given by net conservation considerations as

$$n_i = \iiint_{\Omega_i} f \, d^3\xi,$$

$$2\mathbf{u}_{ij} = (n_i)^{-1} \iiint_{\Omega_i} f\xi \, d^3\xi + (n_j)^{-1} \iiint_{\Omega_j} f\xi \, d^3\xi, \qquad \text{(A.3)}$$

$$6kT_{ij}/m = (n_i)^{-1} \iiint_{\Omega_i} f(\xi - \mathbf{u}_{ij})^2 \, d^3\xi + (n_j)^{-1} \iiint_{\Omega_j} f(\xi - \mathbf{u}_{ij})^2 \, d^3\xi,$$

where Ω_i and Ω_j are the corresponding solid angles. All results presented in the main text were obtained with w set equal to unity. In this case the collision rate is independent of the relative velocity and there are some similarities to the Maxwell-Boltzmann collision operator with Maxwell molecules.

REFERENCES

Ashkenas, H., and Sherman, F. S. (1965). Volume II of this Symposium, p. 84.
Baker, R. M. L., Jr., and Charwat, A. F. (1958). *Phys. Fluids* 1, 73.
Bhatnagar, P. L., Gross, E. P., and Krook, M. (1954). *Phys. Rev.* 94, 511.

Dewey, C. F., Jr. (1961). *ARS (American Rocket Soc.) J.* **31**, 1709–1717.

Kinslow, M., and Potter, J. L. (1963). *AIAA J.* **1**, 2467–2474.

Ko, D. R., (1964). Univ. Calif., Berkeley Aero. Sci. Rept. AS-64-4.

Lunc, M., and Lubonski, J. (1956). *Arch. Mech. Stosowanej* **8**, 597–616.

Maslach, G. J., and Schaaf, S. A. (1963). *Phys. Fluids* **6**, 315.

Rose, M. H. (1964). *Phys. Fluids* **7**, 1262.

Schaaf, S. A. (1963). *In* "Handbuch der Physik" (S. Flugge/Freiburg, eds.) Vol. VIII/2, p. 606. Springer-Verlag, Berlin.

Schaaf, S. A., and Maslach, G. J. (1963). *In* "Rarefied Gas Dynamics" (J. A. Laurmann, ed.), Vol. 2, pp. 317–327. Academic Press, New York.

Tang, S. (1964). Univ. Calif., Berkeley Aero Sci. Rept. AS-64-3.

Taub, P. (1965). MSE Thesis, Princeton Univ., Aero. Eng. Dept.

Wilis, D. R. (1959). Ph.D. Thesis, Princeton Univ., Aero. Eng. Dept.

Willis, D. R. (1960). General Electric Co., Space Sci. Lab. TIS R60SD399.

Drag Measurements in Slip and Transition Flow

H. COUDEVILLE, P. TREPAUD, AND E. A. BRUN

Laboratoire d'Aérothermique du C.N.R.S., Meudon, France

At the third International Rarefied Gas Dynamics Symposium we presented an initial experimental report on the drag of a grid of wires in a rarefied gas flow. We have now given greater emphasis to the finite size of the grid and improved the equipment in order to obtain more accurate results. New facilities were also used to measure the drag of isolated cylinders and strips. Finally, the measurements have been extended from low speeds to supersonic flow conditions.

I. Drag at Low Speeds

A. Methods of Measurement

Measurements were made not only with the aid of the rotating arm device, previously described by Brun *et al.* (1963), but also in a wind tunnel where the conditions of pressure and speed were the same. The purpose of making the same measurements in two different devices is as follows: with the rotating arm, speed measurements are very accurate, but it is difficult to obtain accurate measurements of very small drag; on the other hand, in a tunnel, it is possible to make use of very sensitive and accurate balances, but it is difficult to measure speeds at very low pressures. Consequently, it is useful to compare the results obtained with both methods in order to check their accuracy.

In the very rare cases where slight differences occurred, we gave preference to the results obtained with the rotating arm since this device which is described in detail in a laboratory report by Coudeville (1964) has been considerably improved (Fig. 1). The torsion angle is now measured by an optical method instead of with an electromagnetic device which tended to develop a

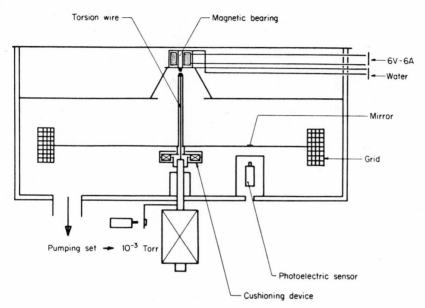

FIG. 1. Rotating arm apparatus.

slight retarding moment. But, more important, the use of a magnetic suspension has eliminated all dry friction during the rotation of the arm.

Measurements were taken at speeds up to 70 m/sec and at pressures between 5 and 5×10^{-3} mm Hg.

B. Drag of Isolated Cylinders

Using the rotating arm method and at the pressures mentioned above, we measured the drag of a cylinder 1 mm in diameter for a molecular speed ratio of $S = 0.027$ and that of a cylinder 3.2 mm in diameter for molecular speed ratios of $S = 0.013$, 0.027, 0.054, and 0.107. In the tunnel we used cylinders of the same diameters with molecular speed ratios of $S = 0.027$, 0.054, 0.107, and 0.197.

The curves in Fig. 2 show the drag coefficient,

$$C_D = F/\tfrac{1}{2}\rho U^2 A,$$

as a function of the Reynolds number $\mathrm{Re} = UD/\nu$ for various speed ratios, $S = U/s$, where ν is the kinematic viscosity and s is the most probable speed of the molecules.

The curves in Fig. 3 show the same coefficient as a function of the Knudsen number $K = \lambda/D$.

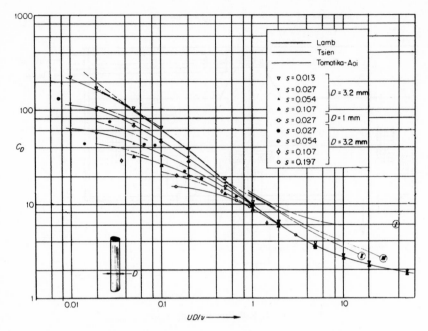

FIG. 2. Cylinder drag coefficient at low-speed ratios vs. Reynolds number.

If we examine the results relating to the molecular speed ratio $S = 0.027$, we will note that the experimental points obtained from cylinders of different diameters follow a single curve. This is proof that the coefficient C_D does in fact depend only on two dimensionless numbers (Re and S or K and S).

In Fig. 2, it can be seen that the curves merge at a Reynolds number greater than 3: the flow is of a continuum nature in this range of Reynolds numbers for all values of S. For the smallest value of $S(S = 0.013)$ the curve due to Lamb (1936), defined by the formula

$$C_D = \frac{8\pi}{\mathrm{Re}(2 - \log_e \mathrm{Re})},\qquad(1)$$

is confirmed for Reynolds numbers as low as $\mathrm{Re} = 0.1$.

The formula[1]

$$C_D = \frac{8\pi}{\mathrm{Re}(0.80 - \log_e \mathrm{Re}) + 4.33S}\qquad(2)$$

given by Tsien (1946) for slip flow provides an approximate representation of

_____

[1] This formula is based on the assumption that the fraction of diffusely reflected molecules is 0.9.

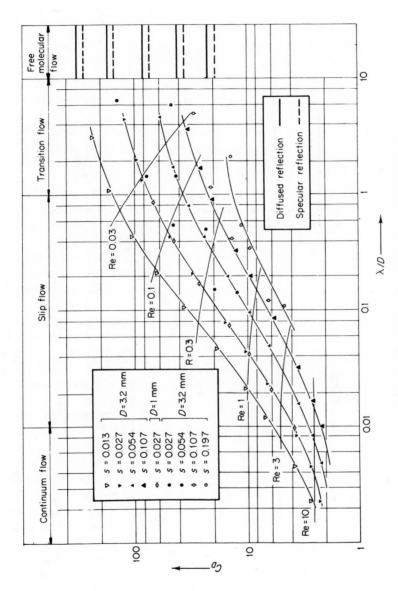

Fig. 3. Cylinder drag coefficient at low-speed ratios vs. Knudsen number.

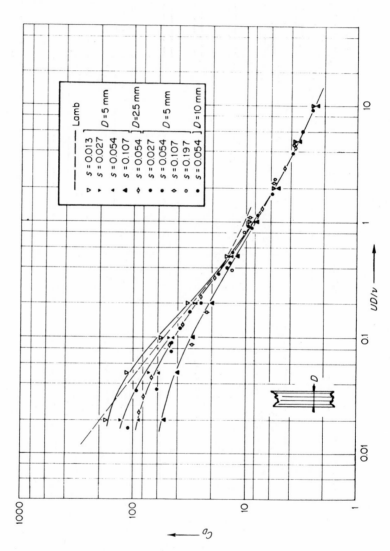

FIG. 4. Drag coefficient of flat strips vs. Reynolds number.

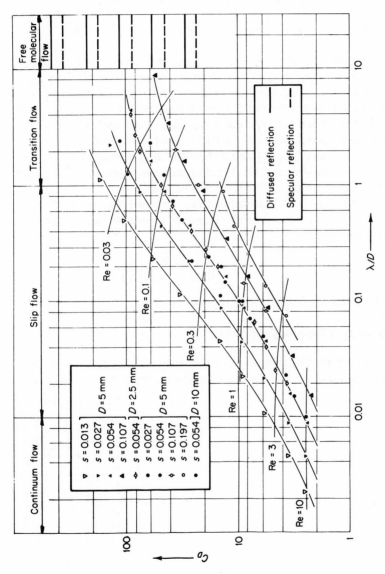

FIG. 5. Drag coefficient of flat strips vs. Knudsen number.

the experimental results beyond the continuum region, whereas the computations due to Brook and Reis (1963) lead to an inferior representation.

In Fig. 3 it can be seen that, from $K = 1$ onward, the curves flatten out and tend toward the limits characteristic of free molecular flow.

C. Drag of Isolated Rectangular Strips

Using the rotating arm method, and still within the same pressure range, we measured the drag of strips having a width of 2.5 and 10 mm, for a molecular speed ratio of $S = 0.027$, and of one strip having a width of 5 mm, for molecular speed ratios of $S = 0.013$, 0.027, 0.054, and 0.107.

In the tunnel, the experiment was carried out with a strip 5 mm wide, for molecular speed ratios of $S = 0.027$, 0.054, 0.107, and 0.197.

The curves of Figs. 4 and 5 show the drag coefficient as a function of the Reynolds number and the Knudsen number, respectively, the characteristic length D representing the width of the strip.

The results were identical to those obtained for the cylinders. It is to be noted, however, that in the continuum regime the drag coefficient for rectangular strips due to Lamb (1936),

$$C_D = \frac{8\pi}{\text{Re}(2.2 - \log_e \text{Re})},\qquad(3)$$

differs slightly from the experimental results.

D. Drag of Grids of Cylinders or Strips

1. **General Remarks.** Let us consider a grid of circular cylinders or strips as shown in Fig. 6: D is the diameter of the cylinders or the width of the strips,

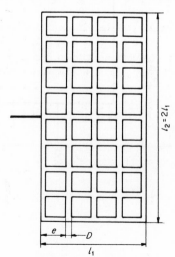

FIG. 6. Grid geometry.

e is their pitch, l_1 is the total width of the grid, and l_2 is the height of the grid. In the case of the cylinder we may reason as follows: when the pitch e is large in relation to the diameter D, the flow around each cylinder acts as if it were isolated and the drag F_∞ of each cylinder is independent of e. When, all other things being equal, the distance e is reduced, the drag will begin to vary from a certain value of e downward: there is interference between the cylinders. This interference is particularly significant in a flow of a rarefied gas.

The interpretation of the experimental results is rendered more difficult by the, obviously unavoidable, finite size of the surface of the grid to be studied. To simplify matters, we confined ourselves to the use of rectangular grids for which $l_2 = 2l_1$. In this case, the only geometric values which exert an effect on the drag are the diameter D, the pitch e, and the width l_1. Elementary considerations of dimensional analysis then lead us to the following formula for the drag coefficient:

$$C_{D_m} = f(\text{Re}, S, e/D, l_1/D). \tag{4}$$

The applicability of this formula is confirmed by the results obtained by using two geometrically similar grids whose dimensions are, respectively:

$$D = 3.2 \text{ mm}, \quad e = 32 \text{ mm}, \quad l_1 = 99.2 \text{ mm};$$

$$D = 1 \text{ mm}, \quad e = 10 \text{ mm}, \quad l_1 = 31 \text{ mm}.$$

Operating at constant speed (S is constant), it is found that, for these two grids, the curves which represent C_{D_m} as a function of Re are identical (Fig. 7).

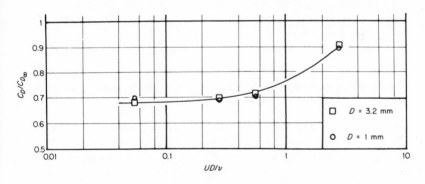

FIG. 7. Correlation of drag data for similar grids.

In order to exhibit the phenomena of interference, it is more convenient to employ the drag coefficient ratio C_{D_m}/C_{D_∞}, where C_{D_∞} denotes the coefficient which would be obtained if the distance e were large enough for each cylinder to be considered as being isolated. It is obvious, since

$$C_{D_\infty} = f(\text{Re}, S), \tag{5}$$

452   H. COUDEVILLE, P. TREPAUD, AND E. A. BRUN

that this ratio depends upon the same dimensionless numbers as the coefficient C_D, and consequently

$$C_{D_m}/C_{D_\infty} = f(\text{Re}, S; e/D, l_1/D). \tag{6}$$

The same reasoning applies for the case of a grid of rectangular strips with dimension D representing the width of the strips.

We studied the variation of the ratio C_{D_m}/C_{D_∞} as a function of the Reynolds number and for various values of the parameter e/D, keeping the parameters l_1/D and S constant. Grids formed of cylinders of diameter $D = 3.2$ mm were used. The grid width was 99.2 mm in one series, but the pitch e of the grids was varied and had the values 96, 48, 32, 24, and 9.6 mm. We also used grids having a width of $l_1 = 105$ mm, formed of strips of width $D = 5$ mm, with the pitch e of these grids being successively 100, 50, and 25 mm.

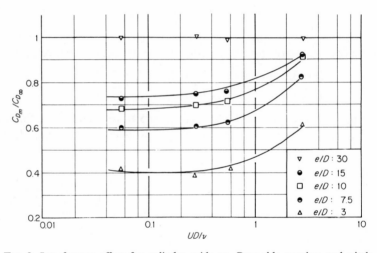

FIG. 8. Interference effect for cylinder grids vs. Reynolds number and pitch.

Figures 8 and 9 show the variations of the ratio C_{D_m}/C_{D_∞} as a function of the Reynolds number both for cylinders and strips. Two remarks can be made about these figures. Firstly, the ratio C_{D_m}/C_{D_∞} always increases with the Reynolds number and it retains a substantially constant value as long as the Reynolds number remains lower than 0.2. For larger values the ratio increases more and more rapidly, at least as long as the Reynolds number stays below 5. Secondly, the interference becomes appreciable when the value of the ratio e/D drops below 15. We shall study two cases in particular: that of weak interference which corresponds to a ratio e/D of at least 9 and that of strong interference which corresponds to a ratio e/D of 4 at most.

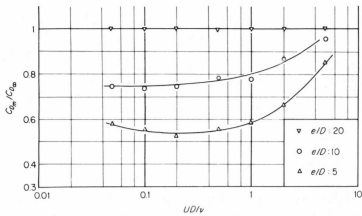

FIG. 9. Interference effect for flat strip grids vs. Reynolds number and pitch.

2. Weak Interference (e/D > 9). Figure 10 presents the drag coefficient for a grid of cylinders with $D = 3.2$ mm; $e = 32$ mm; $l_1 = 99.2$ mm as a function of Reynolds number and for various speed ratios. The same Reynolds number were obtained by adjusting the pressure for each speed ratio. It is apparent that the molecular speed ratio has only a negligible influence on interference as long as the latter remains weak ($e/D > 9$). Figure 11 shows similar results for a grid of strips with $D = 5$ mm; $e = 50$ mm; $l_1 = 105$ mm, and the same conclusion applies.

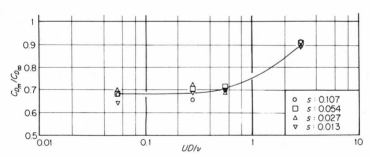

FIG. 10. Interference effect for cylinder grids vs. Reynolds number and speed ratio.

If the ratio e/D is large, it might be supposed that the interference experienced by a cylinder is due solely to cylinders immediately neighboring it. If we are to take into account the finite size of the grid, we are led to the conclusion that the effect of interference on the cylinders which form the edges of the grid is only half that for cylinders in the center of the grid.

Let L_i be the length of the cylinders inside the grid; L_b, the length of the cylinders on the edge of the grid; C_{D_m}, the average drag coefficient which is

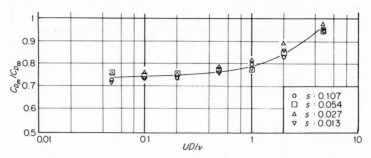

FIG. 11. Interference effect for flat strip grids vs. Reynolds number and speed ratio.

the coefficient we are to measure and C_D, the true drag coefficient which is that of the central areas of all cylinders forming the grid. We have then, obviously,

$$C_D = f(\text{Re}, S, e/D). \tag{7}$$

The previous hypothesis leads us easily to the equation

$$[L_i + (L_b/2)]C_D = (L_i + L_b)C_{D_m} - (L_b/2)C_{D_\alpha}.$$

Putting

$$\frac{L_b/2}{L_i + (L_b/2)} = \alpha, \tag{8}$$

we obtain

$$C_D = (1 + \alpha)C_{D_m} - \alpha C_{D_\infty}. \tag{9}$$

For grids of cylinders or strips all having the same parameter $e/D(e/D = 10)$ we varied the ratio l_1/D. In Fig. 12 (cylinders) and in Fig. 13 (strips), it can be seen that the average drag coefficient C_{D_m}, shown in full lines, varies with l_1/D for a given Reynolds number, but also that the calculation of the true drag coefficient C_D on the basis of Eq. (9) leads to a value independent of α and C_D (dashed curve). Thus, the curve which defines true interference depends only on the ratio e/D and not at all on the relative width of the grid. This

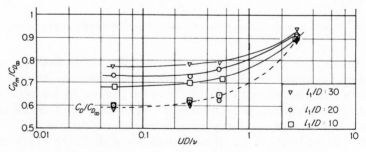

FIG. 12. Interference effect for various sizes of cylinder grids.

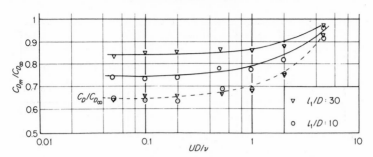

FIG. 13. Interference effect for various sizes of flat strip grids.

justifies, *a posteriori*, the hypothesis made to establish the formula of C_D in the case of weak interference [Eq. (9)]. It will furthermore be noted that the true interference coefficients have very similar values (when $e/D = 10$) for both grids of cylinders and grids of strips.

3. Strong Interference ($e/D < 4$). When a parameter e/D is lower than 4, it is preferable to compare the drag of the grid with that of a flat plate normal to the stream and of the same width l_1. We shall use a Reynolds number related to the width l, and we shall define a drag coefficient C_{D_r} related to the total surface area $A_0 = l_1 \cdot l_2$ of the grid. The coefficient C_{D_r} is linked to the coefficient C_{D_m} related to the cross-section A of all the cylinders in the grid through the following equation:

$$C_{D_r} = C_{D_m}(A/A_0). \tag{10}$$

The ratio of the coefficient C_{D_r} to the drag coefficient C_{D_p} of the flat plate with a width l_1 and a surface area, A_0, also represents the ratio of the drag F of the grid to the drag F_p of the flat plate with a width l_1 and the same surface area.

Figure 14 refers to two grids with a pitch e of 9.6 mm and made of cylinders of 3.2 mm in diameter (parameter $e/D = 3$). Their respective widths l_1 are 99.2 and 32 mm. The drag coefficients of the cylinders, C_{D_m}, of the grid, C_{D_r}, and of the flat plate, C_{D_p}, are presented as a function of the Reynolds number related to length l_1 of the grid. From the figure we observe firstly, that the results obtained with the two grids are approximately shown by a single curve, which proves that the coefficients are practically independent of the parameter l_1/D. Secondly, the ratio $k = C_{D_r}/C_{D_p}$ is constant when the cylinders of the grid are under slip conditions.

The coefficient k was found to be equal to 0.90 in the case of the grid made of cylinders with $D = 3.2$ mm and $e = 9.6$ mm. This coefficient was found to be equal to 0.95 in the case of a grid made of strips with $D = 5$ mm and $e = 10$ mm.

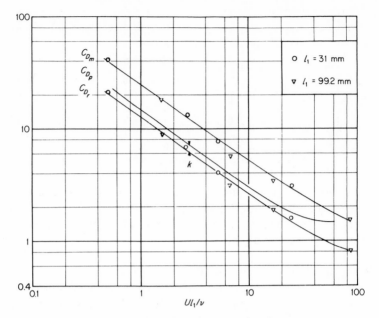

FIG. 14. Drag coefficient for strong interference.

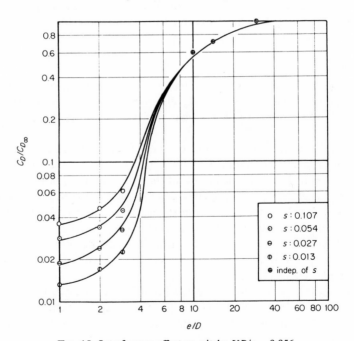

FIG. 15. Interference effect vs. pitch; $UD/\nu = 0.056$.

4. Summary of Results. In the case of slip flow conditions it is possible to determine the interference between cylinders and strips for grids of infinite size. Figures 15, 16, and 17 show, for Reynolds numbers of 0.056, 0.028, and

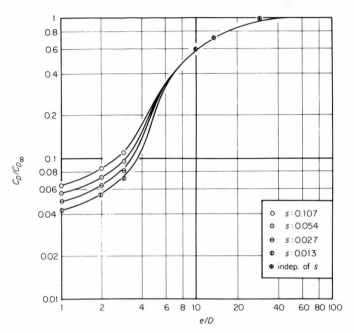

FIG. 16. Interference effect vs. pitch; $UD/\nu = 0.28$.

0.56, respectively, a summary of the results obtained. The figures present the ratio C_D/C_{D_∞} of the drag coefficient of cylinders or strips located in a large dimension grid to the drag coefficient of isolated cylinders or strips as a function of the parameter e/D.

II. Drag in Supersonic Flow

A. Measurements in Supersonic Rarefied Air Flow

The measurements in a supersonic flow of the drag of cylinders or strips, in isolated or interference configurations, were carried out in a low-density wind tunnel described by J. Kleman (1964). The flow characteristics were kept constant during the whole series of experiments. We report the results for the following test conditions: Mach number 2.31; pressure in the jet 16.7 μ Hg; stagnation temperature 18°C. The variation of the Knudsen number K was

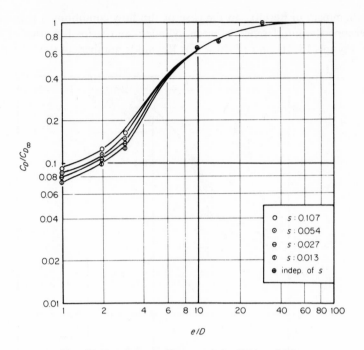

FIG. 17. Interference effect vs. pitch; $UD/\nu = 0.56$.

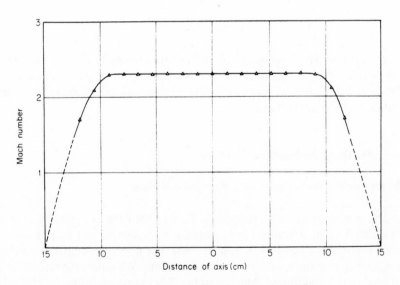

FIG. 18. Mach number profile of supersonic test flow.

obtained by modifying the characteristic length of the model being tested. In this way, it was possible to cover a very large part of the transition regime ($0.1 < K < 1.5$), because the core of the flow in which the Mach number was constant had a diameter of approximately 18 cm (Fig. 18).

The drag is measured with a torsion balance. The principle of the instrument is shown in diagram form in Fig. 19. The moment Fb of the force to be

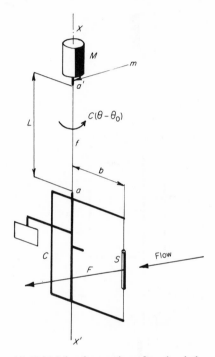

FIG. 19. Principle of operation of torsion balance.

measured about the axis $X'X$ is balanced by the torque of a wire of torsion constant C. At equilibrium, if the angle of torsion is $\theta - \theta_0$, the force is

$$F = C(\theta - \theta_0)/b. \tag{11}$$

The measuring balance consists essentially of a rigid frame C on which the test model S is fixed. This frame is suspended by a torsion wire f, 53 cm long, fixed at its other end to the shaft of a motor M, by a chuck m. When the tunnel is in operation, the wire must be twisted through an angle of $\theta - \theta_0$ in order to keep the test model in its initial position (no wind). The motor is placed inside the test chamber. It is controlled by a servosystem located outside the tunnel, which makes it possible to turn the motor M to the required angle.

Figure 20 gives a few further details concerning the balance. One way to attach the test model involves the use of two arms, *ab* and *de*. The end of each arm has a slot into which the wire holding the model can be pinched. An alternative method involves the use of an arm *fg* which is shorter than the previous arms. The model is attached at the end of this arm by a rod. An arm *ih* carries a brass plate *G* at one end. The plate is dipped in a container filled

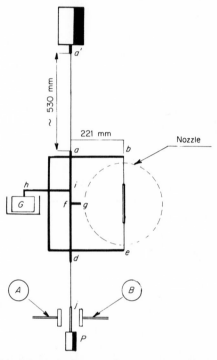

Fig. 20. Schematic diagram of construction of balance.

with butyl phtalate to damp the oscillations of the frame. The nylon wire *dj* supports a weight *P* of approximately 1 kg. During experiments, this weight is clamped between two jaws *A* and *B*, in order to avoid any motion of the balance assembly, but the torsion wire remains subjected to a constant stress which is initially determined by the weight *P*. The complete frame is enclosed in a box; only the wire (or rod) holding the model protrudes from this box through special slots.

After fixing the model on the balance and creating a vacuum in the tunnel, the model is brought into the exact, desired position in the test section by twisting the wire (this position is located 1 cm downstream of the exit plane of the nozzle) and the required angle of torsion is θ_0. Once steady conditions have been reached further twisting of the wire brings the model back into the same position. Let θ be the new angle of torsion. The force which acts on the model is then given by Eq. (11).

The operations to be carried out for each measurement depend on the method of attachment chosen.

a. Attachment by Rod. With a cylinder of diameter D or a strip of width D, measurements are taken for two lengths l_1 and l_2 of the cylinder or strip. If we subtract the two measured drags, we obtain the drag of a cylinder or strip of length $l_1 - l_2$ which acts like one element of a cylinder or strip of

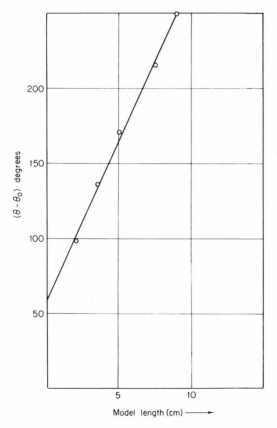

FIG. 21. Torsion angle as function of model length.

infinite length. Measurements are taken with $l_1 = 10$ cm and $l_2 = 2$ cm. This method is justified by the fact that the length of the cylinder or the strip has no influence on the value of the drag coefficient obtained; in other words, the force measured is a linear function of the length of the cylinder or the strip. This is shown, in particular, by Fig. 21 concerning a 10 mm wide strip of variable length.

b. Attachment by Wire. As in the preceding case, the drag measurements are taken for two lengths l_1 and l_2, but in this case, if we subtract the drags measured, we obtain the drag of one part of a cylinder or strip of length $l_1 - l_2$ diminished by the drag on a length $l_1 - l_2$ of the support wire. In order to eliminate the effect of the support wires, we take measurements with support wires having different diameters d. This allows the determination of the drag coefficient resulting from a simple subtraction of the drags obtained from the two model lengths as a function of d. When the diameter d tends towards zero, this coefficient tends toward the value of C_D for a cylinder of infinite length. Hence, it is simple to obtain this value of C_D by extrapolating the experimental results for different values of d to $d = 0$.

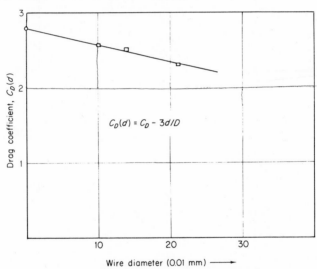

FIG. 22. Drag coefficient vs. diameter of the support wires.

Figure 22 gives the result obtained in the case of a cylinder of diameter $D = 1$ mm, when the diameter d of the support wire varies between 0.10 and 0.25 mm. The experimental points lie on a straight line given by the equation

$$C_D(d) = C_D - 3d/D, \tag{12}$$

which determines automatically the value of C_D. The linear law expressed in Eq. (12) shows that the drag coefficient of the support wire is constant and approximately equal to 3. If we assume that the flow around the support wire is a free molecular flow, then we reach approximately the same result.

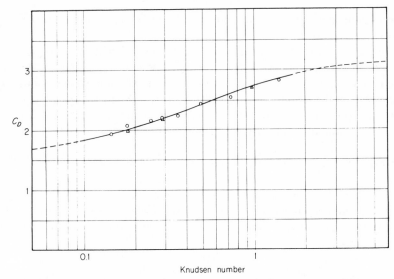

FIG. 23. Drag coefficient of cylinders vs. Knudsen number; $M = 2.31$.

B. Drag of Isolated Cylinders and Strips

Figures 23 and 24 show the variation of the drag coefficient as a function of the Knudsen number for isolated cylinders and strips of infinite length, respectively. On these figures, the triangles represent the experimental

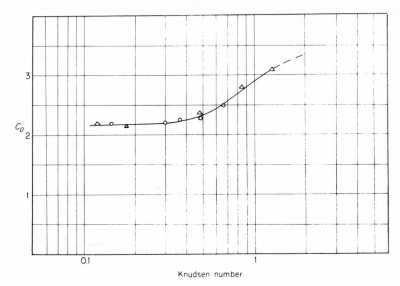

FIG. 24. Drag coefficient of flat strips vs. Knudsen number; $M = 2.31$.

points obtained with a rod attachment and the circles represent those obtained with wire suspension.

The curve for the strip model in Fig. 24 is quite different from that for the cylinder. The value of the coefficient remains practically constant when the Knudsen number is lower than 0.3, but increases more rapidly than that of the cylinder when the Knudsen number increases from 0.5 to 1.2.

It was noted that, in the range of Knudsen numbers explored, the drag varied very little for cylinder temperatures between 20° and 250°C.

C. Drag of Cylinders and Strips in Interference Configuration

Let us consider three identical circular cylinders (1), (2), and (3) of radius R set in a plane perpendicular to the flow axis. If the distance e between the axes of two consecutive cylinders is sufficiently small, the drag of cylinder (2)

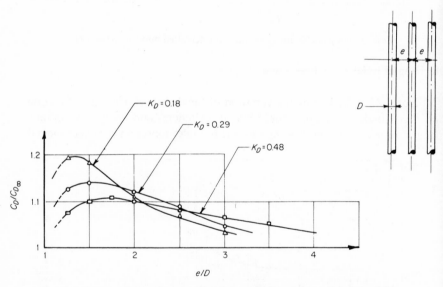

FIG. 25. Supersonic interference effect for a cylinder grid vs. pitch; $M = 2.31$.

is modified by the presence of the two other cylinders. We studied the influence of the relative pitch e/D on the drag coefficient C_D of the cylinder (2) for various Knudsen numbers.

The method of measurement involving the use of suspension wires is no longer valid here, since the suspension wire would be also influenced by the presence of the cylinders (1) and (3). We must therefore use the rod attachment and operate for two lengths l_1 and l_2 of the same cylinder, as was done for the measurement with an isolated cylinder. The lengths chosen were $l_1 = 10$ cm and $l_2 = 2$ cm.

Cylinders (1) and (3) have an approximate length of 30 cm. Each of them is fixed on articulated arms in order to obtain the parallelism of the three cylinders. These articulated arms are actuated by a micromanipulator system operated from outside the tunnel. It is thus possible to set the three cylinders in the same plane perpendicular to the axis of the nozzle and to position them within this plane with an accuracy of 0.01 mm.

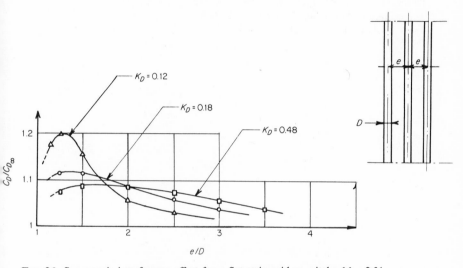

FIG. 26. Supersonic interference effect for a flat strip grid vs. pitch; $M = 2.31$.

When the cylinder (2) of length l_1 has been attached to the balance, the drag is measured as a function of the relative pitch e/D of the cylinders. By subtracting the drags corresponding to the two lengths l_1 and l_2, it is possible to obtain the drag of a part of length $(l_1 - l_2)$, of a cylinder of infinite length subjected to interference from two neighboring cylinders as a function of the relative pitch e/D of the cylinders.

Interference is characterised by the ratio C_D/C_{D_∞}, where C_D is the drag coefficient of the cylinder subjected to interference and C_{D_∞} is the drag coefficient of the isolated cylinder. Figures 25 and 26 which refer to cylinders and strips, respectively, show that, contrary to what happens in low-speed flow, interference produces an increase in drag. This increase reaches a maximum. The magnitude of this maximum becomes less as the pressure diminishes and the value of e/D corresponding to this maximum increases as the pressure diminishes.

REFERENCES

Brooks, W. B., and Reis, G. E. (1963). *In* "Rarefied Gas Dynamics" (J. Laurmann, ed.), Vol. II, pp. 291–302. Academic Press, New York.

Brun, E. A., Facy, L., and Trotel, J. (1963). *In* "Rarefied Gas Dynamics" (J. Laurmann, ed.), Vol. II, pp. 303–316. Academic Press, New York.

Coudeville, H. (1964). Rappt. 64–2 Lab. Aerotherm., Bellevue, Seine-et-Oise.

Kleman, J. (1964). Rappt. 64–5 Lab. Aerotherm., Bellevue, Seine-et-Oise.

Lamb, H. (1936). *Z. Angew Math. Phys.* **16**, 615

Tomotika, and Aoi (1950). *J. Mech. Appl. Math.*

Tsien, H. S. (1946). *J. Aeronaut. Sci.* **13**, 653.

Experimental Studies of Low-Density Effects in Hypersonic Wedge Flows[1]

R. J. VIDAL AND J. A. BARTZ

Cornell Aeronautical Laboratory, Inc., Buffalo, New York

Experimental heat transfer and pressure data are presented which extend from the classical thin boundary layer regime to near-free-molecule flow (Knudsen numbers based on ambient stream conditions as large as 5). These data are compared with viscous shock layer theory for heat transfer and with theory for the combined effects of wedge angle and boundary layer displacement to define the theoretical range of validity and to identify the low-density departures from boundary layer theory. It is noted that low-density effects are first evident in the pressure data. It is concluded that the cause of these departures cannot be identified within existing solutions based on the Navier-Stokes relations. It is hypothesized that the departure might stem from second-order (Burnett) molecular effects.

I. Introduction

A fundamental problem in rarefied gas flows over bodies is to describe the transition between the continuum situation and the free-molecule limit. One basic difficulty is that the governing relations for the flow have not been established. The Navier-Stokes relations, as derived from a continuum viewpoint, have been duplicated with kinetic theory as a first-order approximation in molecular mean free path. Second-order approximations in molecular mean free path have been derived (Burnett, 1935; Grad, 1949), but since there is no established continuum equivalent for these relations, the physical significance of the second-order terms is not clear. Consequently, the main effort has been to use the first-order (Navier-Stokes) approximation as the governing relations and to account for the fluid processes induced by the body that are consistent with these relations. The resulting solutions then require

[1] Sponsored by the U.S. Air Force Office of Scientific Research, Contract AF 49(638)-952.

experimental checks to determine their range of validity and to indicate where the next order of approximation might be required.

The purpose of this paper is to present heat transfer and pressure data obtained with two-dimensional wedge models (sharp leading edges) in the CAL six-foot hypersonic shock tunnel. These data virtually span the entire transition regime, extending from the classical thin boundary-layer regime to Knudsen numbers (based on ambient stream conditions) as large as 5. The intent here is to test the available theories dealing with wedges in a continuum flow in order to define their limits of validity, and to provide data in the transition regime. These wedge models are particularly useful in this transition regime for several reasons. First, the two-dimensional models, as compared with three-dimensional models, make it feasible to incorporate instrumentation closer to the leading edge and hence more closely approach the free-molecule limit. Second, the simple wedge configuration tends to suppress a variety of low-density fluid processes associated with blunt bodies that complicate the data interpretation. Third, by varying the wedge angle, it is possible to change the dominant low-density mechanism governing the initial departures from the continuum regime.

In the succeeding sections, the basis for the applicable theories will be briefly reviewed in order to indicate those items that could influence the observed low density departures. Following this, the experimental apparatus will be briefly described, leading to the presentation and discussion of the experimental data.

II. Wedge Theories

A. Boundary-Layer Displacement Theory

The problem of hypersonic viscous flow over a wedge has been considered for over a decade, and pioneering theoretical research was accomplished by Shen (1952), Pai (1953), and by Pai and Shen (1955). More recently Cheng *et al.* (1961) have presented a unified approach to this and related boundary layer problems which has a wide range of applicability. Cheng's theory for the thin boundary layer regime will be used for comparison with the data in the present paper.

Briefly, the basis for Cheng's theory is in the Navier-Stokes approximation which is specialized, for the case of large Mach numbers and small disturbances, to the boundary layer equations. Using the appropriate similarity transformation, these are reduced further to the Blasius equations for the case of $(\gamma - 1)/(\gamma + 1) \ll 1$ and/or a sufficiently small axial pressure gradient. In this way it is shown that if the shock layer is not fully viscous and if slip at the surface is negligible, there is a similarity between the transformed velocity profile, u/U_∞, and the transformed enthalpy profile, $H - H_\infty/H_w - H_\infty$.

There are several important conclusions to be noted in connection with this theory. First, because of the similarity in the governing tangential momentum and energy equations, it is possible to immediately write a general relation between the heat transfer to the surface and the local hydrostatic pressure:

$$M^3 C_H \equiv \frac{M^3 q}{\rho_\infty U_\infty (H_\infty - H_w)} = 0.332 M^3 \left(\frac{C_*}{\mathrm{Re}_L}\right)^{1/2} \frac{p/p_\infty}{\left[\int_0^x (p/p_\infty)(dx/L)\right]^{1/2}}. \quad (1)$$

The details of this computation can be obtained from Cheng's paper (1961). One implication of this result is that the heat transfer to the surface and the hydrostatic pressure at the surface are simple related. Within the framework of this theory, low-density departures from the theory should be observed simultaneously in both the heat transfer and the hydrostatic pressure at the surface.

The second important conclusion reached in this wedge theory is that the hydrostatic pressure on the compression side of the wedge is accurately given by the sum of the inviscid wedge pressure and the induced pressure due to boundary layer displacement. This leads to the following expression, consistent with the approximations used by Cheng:

$$p/p_\infty \approx \gamma M^2 \alpha^2 + \tfrac{1}{2}\sqrt{3}\gamma \bar\chi_\varepsilon,$$

$$\bar\chi_\varepsilon = \frac{\gamma - 1}{\gamma + 1}\left(0.664 + 1.73 \frac{T_w}{T_0}\right) M^3 \left(\frac{C_*}{\mathrm{Re}_x}\right)^{1/2}.$$

The form used in the present work includes a more accurate expression for an oblique shock wave:

$$p/p_\infty \approx [2\gamma/(\gamma + 1)]M^2 \sin^2 \theta + \tfrac{1}{2}\sqrt{3}\gamma \bar\chi_\varepsilon. \quad (2)$$

Substituting in Eq. (1) leads to the following expression for the surface heat transfer,

$$M^3 C_H = 0.166(3)^{1/4}\bar\chi(\gamma\bar\chi_\varepsilon)^{1/2} \frac{\left[1 + \dfrac{4}{\sqrt{3}(\gamma + 1)}\dfrac{M^2 \sin^2 \theta}{\bar\chi_\varepsilon}\right]}{\left[1 + \dfrac{2}{\sqrt{3}(\gamma + 1)}\dfrac{M^2 \sin^2 \theta}{\bar\chi_\varepsilon}\right]^{1/2}}, \quad (3)$$

where θ is the shock wave angle and is related to the wedge angle, α, through the oblique shock wave relations.

The third important item to be noted in connection with Cheng's theory concerns the range of validity for the theory. The model used should remain valid, within the Navier-Stokes approximation, as long as there is an essentially inviscid region behind the shock wave, and as long as the slip velocity and energy jump at the surface are small. The latter requires that the molecular mean free path be small at the surface.

Cheng's theory for the combined effects of wedge angle and boundary layer displacement has been experimentally checked, within its range of validity, as a part of comprehensive experimental research on heat transfer to sharp and blunted flat plates (Hall and Golian, 1960; Cheng et al., 1961). Pressure data obtained by Hall and Golian also confirmed the theory at zero wedge angle.

B. Viscous Shock-Layer Theory

More recently Cheng (1963) has extended his work on the wedge problem to allow for a fully viscous shock layer. This work, which is one part of a comprehensive treatment of the blunt-body problem, takes account of the transport effects, as they alter the boundary conditions at the shock wave. The development is based on the Navier-Stokes equations which are specialized to the viscous shock-layer equations. These differ from the boundary layer equations in that the normal and tangential pressure gradient terms are retained.

The details of this viscous shock-layer formulation can be obtained from the original paper (Cheng, 1963). Several points are of importance to the present work. First, the viscous shock layer problem is fundamentally nonsimilar since the boundary conditions to be satisfied at the shock wave are nonsimilar. The solutions given by Cheng were obtained using machine methods. These are restricted to large wedge semiangles (greater than about 20° but smaller than the shock wave detachment angle of about $42\frac{1}{2}°$). This restriction to large angles makes it possible to neglect viscous layer displacement effects and surface-slip effects. With these restrictions and within the Navier-Stokes model, the surface pressure is simply the hydrostatic pressure behind the oblique shock wave. The skin friction and heat transfer to the surface are less than the Blasius prediction since the transport effects at the shock wave convect away energy and tangential momentum.

The numerical solutions given by Cheng yield the Blasius solution in the limit of high Reynolds numbers. In addition, they yield the free-molecule limits for the case of vanishing Reynolds number. This low Reynolds number behavior evidently is due to the proper conservation of energy and momentum through the modified boundary conditions at the shock wave.

FIG. 1. CAL six-foot hypersonic shock tunnel.

III. Experimental Apparatus and Test Conditions

A. Apparatus

1. Tunnels. The low-density investigations were made in the CAL six-foot hypersonic shock tunnel shown in Fig. 1. In addition, certain high-density, low-Mach number experiments were made in the CAL 48 in. hypersonic shock tunnel to completely span the transition between the classical thin boundary layer regime and the strong interaction regime. These facilities have been discussed in connection with earlier low-density research (Vidal and Wittliff, 1963), describing the available range of test conditions, the mode of operation, the test section calibrations, the effects of nozzle thermochemical nonequilibrium, and the calculation of ambient test section conditions.

2. Flow Angularity. It was noted earlier (Vidal and Wittliff, 1963) that there was some uncertainty concerning the flow angularity in the tunnel test section which could influence the low-density data. Since that work, detailed angularity calibrations have been made using the small flat-plate model described below. This calibration exploits the extreme sensitivity of flat plate heat transfer to small wedge angles under near-free molecule conditions. Typically, a one-degree change in angle produces a 70% change in heat transfer. The flat plate heat transfer was measured over a range of positive and negative angles in order to determine the change in heat transfer with wedge angle and to determine the wedge angle where the heat transfer was independent of model rotation in the tunnel. These experiments showed the flow angularity was about $0.1°$ with an experimental uncertainty of $\pm 0.1°$. Consequently, it is concluded that the effects of flow angularity are negligible in these experiments.

3. Models. Two flat-plate models were used in the experimental wedge research (Fig. 2). The wedge flows were produced by pitching the models to various compression angles. The small-scale model, designed to investigate the leading-edge region, consisted of fourteen thin-film (platinum) thermometers mounted on a Pyrex glass plate. This glass plate was bonded to a steel plate. Typically, these thermometers were 0.02×0.25 in. and near the leading edge were spaced about 0.02 in. apart. All fourteen gages were located within about 1 in. from the leading edge, and under typical test conditions, five gages were within one ambient mean free path from the leading edge. The first gage was at the leading edge. The gage wire lead was a gold film about 2μ thick, leading to a conventional wire lead at the model extremities. The entire model was coated with titanium dioxide about 0.1μ thick to prevent electrical shorting in ionized flows. The operating principles of the thin-film

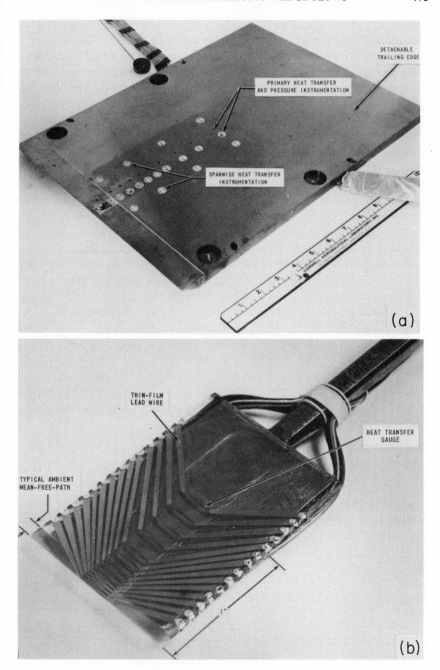

FIG. 2.(a) Large-scale flat plate model. (b) Small-scale flat plate model.

gage as well as the coated gage have been described in the literature (Hall and Hertzberg, 1958; Vidal, 1956, 1962), and will not be reviewed here.

The leading edge of the small-scale model was flat-faced with a thickness estimated to be 0.005 in. The wedge angle of the lower surface was 30°. During experiments at small wedge angles, it was found that the first gage indicated a heat transfer rate about twice that at the next station. It has been determined that this behavior was due to heat conduction from the blunt leading edge and the lower surface. Under free-molecule conditions, the heat transfer rates to the blunt leading edge and to the wedge lower surface are, respectively, sixty times and thirty times greater than that to the upper surface. Heat conduction calculations showed that this would cause a 100 % change in indicated heat transfer to the instrumented surface. Experiments were made with the instrumented surface shielded from the flow to measure the heating from both surfaces. These tests verified the above calculation. The data that were affected by this additional heating are not reported.

The large-scale flat plate model shown in Fig. 2 consisted of a steel plate with detachable leading and trailing edges. The model instrumentation included platinum thin-film resistance thermometers and piezoelectric pressure transducers. The model leading edge was a 30° wedge honed to a thickness of the order of 5×10^{-4} in. A complete description of this model, including chordwise and spanwise effects, lag time associated with pressure orifice size, and model support, is given by Vidal and Wittliff (1963). The effects due to a finite span and a finite chord were examined in the present research and found to be negligible except for wedge semiangles larger than 45°. The effects of a finite chord for these conditions will be discussed in the next section.

B. Low-Density Orifice Effects

The usual approach in interpreting pressure measurements is to assume the measured pressure is the local hydrostatic pressure at the surface. This is a valid assumption if the molecular mean free path at the surface is much smaller than the orifice diameter and/or the gas and surface are in thermal equilibrium. However, if the molecular mean free path is comparable to or greater than the orifice diameter and if the surface temperature differs from the gas temperature, a thermal transpiration effect is encountered. This effect can be explained by considering the limit where the mean free path is much larger than the orifice. Under such conditions, assuming no gradients in the gas, mass continuity requires that

$$\rho_w(T_w)^{1/2} = \rho_G(T_G)^{1/2},$$
$$p_w/p_G = (T_w/T_G)^{1/2}, \tag{4}$$

where the subscripts W and G refer to surface and gas conditions, respectively.

The above transpiration formulas apply only if the orifice diameter is much smaller than the molecular mean free path. In the present experiments the orifice diameter was comparable to the mean free path, and the measured pressure was corrected by using an empirical formula given by Knudsen (1927). Knudsen conducted a series of transpiration experiments with hydrogen in heated tubes in which the ratio of the tube diameter to the molecular mean free path was varied over a wide range. He found that all data correlated within about 4% with the formula

$$p_w/p_G = (T_w/T_G)^{1/2K(\lambda)},$$

$$K(\lambda) = \left[1 + 1.23 \frac{d}{\lambda_w}\left(\frac{1 + 1.575d/\lambda_w}{1 + 12.25d/\lambda_w}\right)\right]^2,$$ (5)

where d is the orifice diameter and λ_w is the molecular mean free path at the wall conditions. Knudsen's original experiments have been duplicated by Arney and Bailey (1962a, b) for air, argon, and helium, and have verified Knudsen's empirical formula with errors of less than 5%.

The pressure data from the present experiment have been corrected using Knudsen's formula, Eq. (5), and the gas temperature as calculated from the measured heat transfer rate. It can be shown, consistent with the Navier-Stokes approximation, that the gas temperature near a surface is

$$T_G = T_w + \frac{75\pi}{128}\lambda_G\frac{\partial T}{\partial y} + \frac{(\gamma - 1)u_G^2}{4\gamma C_p},$$ (6)

where C_p is the specific heat at constant pressure (Patterson, 1956). Within this approximation, the heat transfer to the surface is

$$q = -k_G\frac{\partial T}{\partial y} - \mu_G u_G\frac{\partial u}{\partial y}.$$ (7)

The gas temperature expressed in terms of the heat transfer rate is

$$C_pT_G = C_pT_w + \frac{75\pi}{128}\left(\frac{\lambda C_p}{k}\right)_G q + \frac{u_G^2}{4}\left(\frac{\gamma}{\gamma - 1} - \frac{15}{2}\text{Pr}\right).$$ (8)

The magnitude of the velocity terms in Eq. 8 has been estimated for the thin boundary layer regime, using Cheng's theory (1961) and was found to be less than 10% over the density range of interest. Consequently, they were neglected and the gas temperature was taken as

$$\left(\frac{T_G}{T_w}\right)^{1/2} = \frac{15}{8}\left(\frac{\pi(\gamma - 1)}{2\gamma}\right)^{1/2}\frac{\text{Pr}\,q}{(C_pT_w)^{1/2}}\frac{1}{p_G}.$$ (9)

Equations (5) and (9) were combined to obtain a relation for the ratio of the measured pressure to the gas pressure in terms of measured heat transfer rate and pressure which was used to correct for the orifice effects. The correction amounted to about 50% at the lowest density and a few per cent at the highest density.

There are two important assumptions inherent in this correction. First, Knudsen's experiments were made with long circular tubes, while the present data were obtained using relatively short tubes with approximately elliptical cross sections (length-to-width) ratio of 2. The effective diameter was taken to be the hydraulic diameter. The second approximation is the neglect of the gradients in the gas. Knudsen's experiments were made with tubes connecting constant temperature reservoirs, while in the present experiments the gas was markedly nonuniform. These two items introduce some doubt as to the relevance of Knudsen's tube correction for the orifice effect in the present data.

The applicability of Knudsen's semiempirical tube formula to the orifice effect has been checked with a direct measurement of surface pressure. One of the piezoelectric pressure transducers used in orifice measurements was modified so that the $\frac{1}{2}$-in. diaphragm was flush with the surface.[2] This instrument was mounted in the large-scale flat plate model, 5 in. from the leading edge and adjacent to an orifice transducer. The model was than tested at a low-density condition where orifice measurements indicated the chordwise variations in surface pressure were negligible (15% over an 8 in. length). The pressures measured by the adjacent orifice and surface pressure transducer differed by a factor of 1.64, as compared with a factor of 1.60 predicted with Knudsen's formula. Consequently, it is concluded that the present data, corrected with Knudsen's formula, can be interpreted as the surface pressure.

IV. Experimental Results

In the subsequent discussion, the experimental data will be presented and compared with the wedge theories described in Section II. The comparison first will be made with the viscous shock layer theory to demonstrate its accuracy and to explore its range of validity. Included are previously-reported data obtained at zero-angle of attack and at large wedge angles (Vidal and Wittliff, 1963; Vidal et. al., 1963).

A. Viscous Shock Layer Regime

The heat transfer data obtained with wedge semiangles of 2°, 5°, 10°, 20°, 30°, 40°, 45°, 60°, and 75° are compared with the viscous shock layer theory of Cheng (1963) in Fig. 3. Consider first the data obtained at wedge

[2] The flush-diaphragm transducer was developed earlier at CAL by Mr. R. MacArthur of the Applied Hypersonic Tunnel Department.

semiangles of 20°, 30°, and 40°, where the theory is expected to be valid. It can be seen that the data are in good agreement with the theory over the entire density range. The data tend to fall about 15% above the theory even in the high-Reynolds number (Blasius) limit ($\mathrm{Re}_x/\gamma M^2 C_* \cos \alpha > 1.0$), and approach the free-molecule limit at small Reynolds numbers. As the wedge semiangle

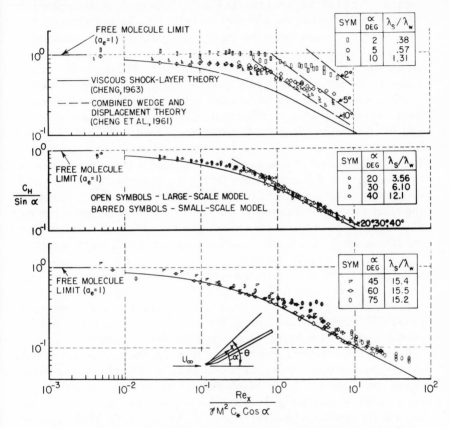

FIG. 3. Comparison of experiment and theory for viscous shock layer wedge flow.

is decreased ($\alpha = 10°, 5°, 2°$), the data tend to fall progressively above the theory in the high-Reynolds number limit, but tend to approach the correct free-molecule limit for a unit accommodation coefficient. It is believed that this behavior at high densities can be ascribed to viscous layer displacement effects which are neglected in the theory. That is, the theory assumes that the rate of growth of the viscous layer is negligible in comparison with the wedge semiangle. As a check on this displacement effect, the theory for the combined effects of wedge angle and boundary layer displacement given by

Cheng *et al.* (1961) has been used to estimate the heat transfer. The relation given in Eq. (3) was used here. It can be seen that the data tend towards that estimate in the high-Reynolds number limit, indicating the departures from the theory are, in part, due to displacement effects. The displacement theory for $\alpha = 20°$, $30°$, and $40°$ is essentially independent of wedge angle when plotted in terms of the parameters in Fig. 3. The estimate of the displacement effects is in good agreement with the data in the high-Reynolds number limit. Consequently, it is concluded that the 15% discrepancy between viscous-layer theory and experiments observed within the theoretical range of validity is largely due to boundary layer displacement effects. The departures at small wedge angles stem, at least in part, from the neglected displacement effects.

There is one further item to be noted in Fig. 3 in the comparison between displacement theory and experiment at small wedge angles. At $\alpha = 20°$, $30°$, and $40°$, the low-density effects first become apparent at $\mathrm{Re}_x/\gamma M^2 C_* \cos \alpha \lesssim 0.5$. In contrast, at $\alpha = 2°$, the low-density effects become apparent at $\mathrm{Re}_x/\gamma M^2 C_* \cos \alpha \lesssim 5.0$. One mechanism neglected in both the viscous shock layer theory and the displacement theory is slip at the surface. It can be demonstrated that the ratio of the shock wave transport effect to the surface slip effect varies approximately as the ratio of the molecular mean free path at the shock wave to that at the surface. This ratio has been calculated using the oblique shock wave relations and is tabulated in Fig. 3. It can be seen that for $\alpha = 20°$, $30°$, and $40°$, the ratio of the mean free paths is $3\frac{1}{2} < \lambda_s/\lambda_w < 12$ indicating that the shock wave transport effect is dominant for these wedge angles. However, for $\alpha \leqslant 10°$, the ratio of mean free paths is $\lambda_s/\lambda_w \leqslant 1.3$, indicating that slip effects at the surface are at least comparable in magnitude to the shock wave transport effects. In fact, at $\alpha = 2°$ the surface slip effects should be at least 3 to 4 times greater than the transport effects.

Before leaving the data obtained at small wedge angles, it should be noted that an approximate criterion can be derived for the lower limit of validity, in wedge semi-angle, for the viscous shock layer theory. The data and the comparisons with theory in Fig. 3 suggest that displacement effects are the major cause of the departures from the viscous shock layer theory. These departures are greatest at $\mathrm{Re}_x/\gamma M^2 C_* \cos \alpha \approx 1.0$. The displacement effects have been calculated at this value of the rarefaction parameter; they amount to 13 and 24% at $\alpha = 20°$ and $15°$, respectively. On this basis it is concluded that the viscous shock layer theory is accurate for wedge semiangles as small as $20°$.

It was noted in Section II that the viscous shock layer for wedge flows should be valid only if the shock wave is attached. This corresponds to a maximum wedge angle of $\alpha \approx 42\frac{1}{2}°$ for $M \to \infty$. The accuracy of this theory for detached shock waves was investigated with experiments at $\alpha = 45°$, $60°$, and $75°$, Fig. 3. It can be seen that the theory is generally quite accurate, underestimating the heat transfer by about 30% in the high Reynolds number limit. The data at low Reynolds numbers approach the free-molecule limit and agree quite well with the theory. One item to be noted is the distinct trailing edge effect in these data. For example, note the data obtained with the large model and the small model at $\alpha = 75°$. Those obtained near the trailing edge of the small model fall about 50% above the data from the center of the large model.

B. Boundary Layer Displacement Effects

It was noted in the discussion of Fig. 3 that displacement effects are important at small wedge angles. Since the viscous shock layer theory for large wedge angles predicts that the hydrostatic pressure at the surface should be that for an inviscid wedge, it is pertinent to compare all date with the

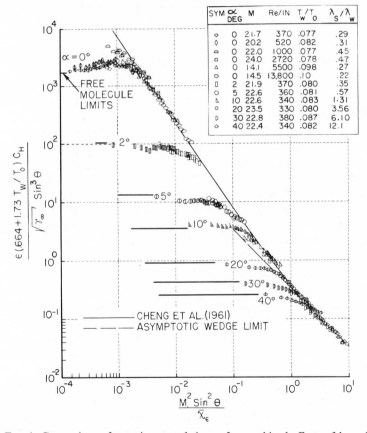

FIG. 4. Comparison of experiment and theory for combined effects of boundary-layer displacement and wedge angle.

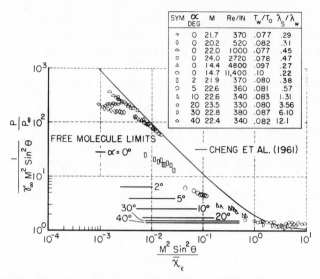

SYM	α DEG	M	Re/IN	T_w/T_0	λ_s/λ_w
◦	0	21.7	370	.077	.29
◊	0	20.2	520	.082	.31
◠	0	22.0	1000	.077	.45
□	0	24.0	2720	.078	.47
△	0	14.4	4800	.097	.27
○	0	14.7	11,400	.10	.22
◻	2	21.9	370	.080	.38
○	5	22.6	360	.081	.57
▵	10	22.6	340	.083	1.31
○	20	23.5	330	.080	3.56
◿	30	22.8	380	.087	6.10
◊	40	22.4	340	.082	12.1

FIG. 5. Comparison of experiment and theory for combined effects of boundary-layer displacement and wedge angle.

theory for the combined effects of wedge angle and boundary layer displacement (Cheng et al., 1961).

These comparisons (Figs. 4 and 5) include data for $\alpha = 0$ which were previously reported (Vidal and Wittliff, 1963). They have been included in these comparisons by assuming an arbitrarily small wedge angle ($\alpha = 10^{-2}$ rad). That is, the governing parameters for the combined wedge angle-displacement theory were evaluated at 10^{-2} rad. where wedge effects are negligibly small. The corresponding free-molecule limit was evaluated at the same wedge angle. The heat transfer data, Fig. 4, are in good agreement with the theory near the trailing edge (large values of $M^2 \sin^2 \theta / \bar{\chi}_\epsilon$), and the low density effects appear as the data fall below the theory near the leading edge. The data obtained at large wedge angles ($\alpha = 20°, 30°, 40°$) are seen to agree well with the wedge limit, and the displacement effects discussed earlier are apparent in this presentation. It should be noted that all data approach the appropriate free-molecule limit (unit accommodation coefficient). The interesting item here is that the data obtained at all finite wedge angles approach the free-molecule limits without overshoot. In contrast, the $\alpha = 0°$ data initially overshoot the free-molecule limit and approach it from above.

The corrected pressure data are compared with the theory for displacement and wedge effects in Fig. 5. Consider first the data obtained at large wedge angles ($\alpha = 20°, 30°, 40°$). It can be seen that these data are in reasonable agreement with the wedge limit $[(1/\gamma M^2 \sin^2 \theta)/(p/p_\infty) \approx 1.0]$, falling somewhat higher than this limit. This can be ascribed to the approximate relation

TABLE I

DISCREPANCY BETWEEN THEORY AND EXPERIMENT FOR
SURFACE PRESSURE AND HEAT TRANSFER

Wedge semiangle (deg)	$\dfrac{M^2 \sin^2 \theta}{\bar{\chi}_\varepsilon}$	$\dfrac{C_{HT} - C_{H\text{exp}}}{C_{HT}}$ (%)	$\dfrac{(p/p\infty)_T - (p/p\infty)_{\text{exp}}}{(p/p\infty)_T}$ (%)
40	2.0	0	0
30	1.2	0	28
20	0.7	0	35
10	0.2	0	60
5	0.12	0	64
2	0.03	0	69

used for pressure in the theory for the wedge limit. The theory predicts a significant boundary layer displacement for $\alpha = 20°$, while the data fall somewhat below this estimate. As the wedge angle is decreased further to 2°, the data depart further from the theory, differing by a factor of 3 to 4 at $\alpha = 2°$. However, the high-density data for $\alpha = 0°$ agree well with the theory. Consequently, it must be concluded that the theory is basically correct, and that these departures stem from a low-density effect not included in the theory.

These departures and those observed in the heat transfer are summarized in Table I. This tabulation lists the value of $M^2 \sin^2 \theta/\bar{\chi}_\varepsilon$ where the heat transfer first departs from the theory, and the magnitude of the departures in pressure at that value of the governing parameter. It can be seen both in Figs. 4 and 5 and in Table I that there is virtually no agreement in the point where low-density departures are first observed in the heat transfer and in the pressure. This behavior is surprising in view of the comments made in Section II. The theory is based upon similarity between the enthalpy and velocity profiles in the boundary layer. This similarity makes it possible to cast the expression for the heat transfer in terms of the hydrostatic pressure. From this relation it might be expected that the departures of heat transfer from theory might vary as the square root of the hydrostatic pressure. The data do not confirm this expectation. Further, this behavior does not seem to be associated with the shock layer becoming fully viscous since the effect is apparent in the $\alpha = 20°$ data. The data for $\alpha = 20°$ fall in the range of validity for the viscous shock layer theory, which predicts that the surface pressure is the hydrostatic pressure for the inviscid wedge. The observed effect might stem from the shock wave thickening or from a normal pressure gradient. Cheng (1963) has shown that in the viscous shock layer regime for wedges, the shock thickening effect and the normal pressure gradient are of higher order than the transport effects at the shock wave.

More recently Probstein and Pan (1964) have considered these effects in an analysis of the sharp flat plate at zero angle of attack using the Navier-Stokes approximation. They show that these effects, combined with first-order surface slip and shock wave transport effects, only produce a 25% departure from displacement theory. Finally, this behavior might be ascribed to a breakdown in the strong shock wave approximation, the limiting density ratio approximation, or the small disturbance approximation. However, if this were the case, the heat transfer should reflect this breakdown since the heat transfer is determined by the pressure distribution. It appears that the observed departures cannot be explained within the framework of existing Navier-Stokes analyses.

C. Additional Molecular Effects

The main feature apparent in the experimental data is that the low-density effects are first evident in the measured pressure. The pressure departs markedly from boundary layer theory in a range of the rarefaction parameter, $M^2 \sin^2 \theta / \bar{\chi}_\varepsilon$, where the heat transfer data are in good agreement with the same theory. This behavior could stem from several sources.

One possible cause of the observed behavior is in the interpretation of pressure. Boundary layer theory takes the surface pressure to be the local hydrostatic pressure in the gas; that is, the average value of the three normal stresses in the gas. The correct gas pressure is the stress in the gas normal to the surface. Within the Navier-Stokes approximation, this normal stress, in two dimensions, is

$$\frac{\sigma_y}{p} = 1 + \frac{2}{3} \frac{\mu}{p} \left(\frac{\partial u}{\partial x} - 2 \frac{\partial v}{\partial y} \right), \tag{10}$$

where σ_y is the normal stress adjacent to the surface. It can be seen that if the slip velocity at the surface is appreciable, the normal stress could differ from the hydrostatic pressure. The magnitude of the normal stress at the surface has been estimated using Cheng's (1961) results. The calculation shows the normal stress at the surface to be

$$\frac{\sigma_y}{p} = 1 - \frac{\varphi_{\eta\eta}\pi^{1/2}}{4(3)^{3/4}\delta^3} \left\{ \frac{(\gamma - 1)\dfrac{\bar{\chi}_\varepsilon}{M^2}\dfrac{T_w}{T_0}}{1 + \dfrac{2}{\sqrt{3}(\gamma + 1)}\dfrac{M^2 \sin^2 \theta}{\bar{\chi}_\varepsilon}} \right\}^{3/2}$$

$$\times \left\{ 1 + \frac{4}{3} \frac{\left[1 + \dfrac{2}{\sqrt{3}(\gamma + 1)}\dfrac{M^2 \sin^2 \theta}{\bar{\chi}_\varepsilon} \right]}{\left[1 + \dfrac{4}{\sqrt{3}(\gamma + 1)}\dfrac{M^2 \sin^2 \theta}{\bar{\chi}_\varepsilon} \right]^2} \right\}, \tag{11}$$

where $\varphi_{\eta\eta}$ is the slope of the Blasius profile at the surface and

$$\delta = \frac{\gamma - 1}{\gamma + 1}\left(0.664 + 1.73\frac{T_w}{T_0}\right).$$

For the cold-wall conditions of the present experiments, Eq. (11) is approximately

$$\frac{\sigma_y}{p} \approx 1 - \frac{1}{40}\left(\frac{\dfrac{\bar{\chi}_\varepsilon}{M^2}}{1 + \dfrac{2}{\sqrt{3}(\gamma + 1)}\dfrac{M^2\sin^2\theta}{\bar{\chi}_\varepsilon}}\right)^{3/2}$$

$$\times \left\{1 + \frac{4}{3}\frac{\left[1 + \dfrac{2}{\sqrt{3}(\gamma + 1)}\dfrac{M^2\sin^2\theta}{\bar{\chi}_\varepsilon}\right]}{\left[1 + \dfrac{4}{\sqrt{3}(\gamma + 1)}\dfrac{M^2\sin^2\theta}{\bar{\chi}_\varepsilon}\right]^2}\right\}. \tag{12}$$

To illustrate, consider Eq. (12) in the limit of dominant displacement effects (vanishing $M^2\sin^2\theta$). This limit corresponds to the largest low-density effects, and the first departures from boundary layer theory are observed at $\bar{\chi}_\varepsilon/M^2 \approx 2 \times 10^{-2}$. It can be seen that, within the Navier-Stokes approximation, the normal stress differs from the hydrostatic pressure by less than 0.1%. Consequently, it is concluded that, within the Navier-Stokes approximation, this difference is not the cause of the observed effects.

A second possible source of the observed departures in the pressure is in the transpiration correction applied to the data. It was noted in Section III, B that the correction was based upon Knudsen's experiments involving pseudo transpiration between constant-temperature reservoirs. In contrast, the present experiments involved pseudo transpiration with large gradients in the gas. The effects of these gradients on the pressure correction can be estimated, within the Navier-Stokes relations, by considering the transpiration effect for a nonuniform gas. The basis for this computation can be obtained from Patterson (1956) using the continuity requirement in the calculation of the slip boundary conditions. Neglecting the details of the calculation, it can be shown that, for an orifice diameter much smaller than the mean free path in the gas, the ratio of the measured pressure to the hydrostatic pressure in the gas in two dimensions is

$$\frac{p_w}{p_G} = \left(\frac{T_w}{T_G}\right)^{1/2}\left[1 + \frac{1}{3}\frac{\mu}{p}\left(\frac{\partial u}{\partial x} - 2\frac{\partial v}{\partial y}\right)\right]. \tag{13}$$

Comparing Eq. (13) with Eqs. (4) and (10), it can be seen that the correction term for the gradients in the gas is simply half of the correction term for the normal stress in the gas. Consequently, it is concluded that, within the Navier-Stokes approximation, the gradients have a negligible effect on the transpiration correction.

A third possible source of the observed departures in the pressure is second-order molecular effects. This possibility was first noted by Maxwell in 1879 in his paper, " On Stresses in Rarefied Gases Arising from Inequalities in Temperature." In particular, Maxwell retained certain second-order terms in a formal kinetic-theory development of the (first-order) Navier-Stokes relations to show that additional temperature terms appeared in the stress tensor. This second-order theory was subsequently completed by Burnett (1935) and by Grad (1949), retaining all second-order terms. If the second-order stress tensor is examined, it is found that the normal stress in the gas varies as

$$\frac{\sigma_y}{p} = 1 + \frac{2}{3}\frac{\mu}{p}\left(\frac{\partial u}{\partial x} - 2\frac{\partial v}{\partial y}\right) + \left(\frac{\mu}{p}\right)^2\left[C_1\left(\frac{\partial T}{\partial y}\right)^2 + C_2\frac{\partial^2 T}{\partial y^2} + \cdots\right], \quad (14)$$

where C_1 and C_2 are known constants. It was shown earlier that the first-order term in the normal stress is negligibly small for the cold wall conditions of the present experiments. The second-order terms can be large, however, owing to the high stagnation temperature and the low wall temperature. To illustrate, the temperature gradient near the wall in the present experiments is of the order of 5×10^4 °K/ft, which is large enough to make the second-order terms appreciable (10–30%). It is clear that second-order molecular effects cannot be neglected a priori, and that the observed departures between theory and experiment could indicate that the Navier-Stokes relations are inapplicable.

V. Concluding Remarks

Experimental heat transfer and pressure data obtained with wedge models in a hypersonic shock tunnel have been presented and compared with boundary layer theory and with viscous shock layer theory. These data, which virtually span the entire transition from continuum to near-free-molecule flows, show that the viscous shock layer theory for heat transfer is in error by less than 15% in the theoretical range of validity (wedge semiangles greater than 20° but less than that for shock wave detachment). The heat transfer data obtained with a detached shock wave show that the theory can be used to estimate heat transfer under these conditions with an error of less than 25% if the wedge trailing edge is sufficiently far downstream. For wedge half-angles of less than 20°, the data show that the viscous shock layer theory for heat transfer progressively breaks down with decreasing wedge angle. Comparisons with boundary layer theory in the high Reynolds number limit indicate the breakdown in the viscous shock layer theory is largely due to the neglect of the viscous layer thickness in comparison with the wedge thickness.

A comparison of the heat transfer data with boundary layer theory for the combined effects of wedge angle and boundary layer displacement show that the data are in good agreement with the theory in the high Reynolds number limit. The data depart near the leading edge and, for all wedge semiangles equal to or greater than 2°, approach the free-molecule limit from below that limit. In contrast, the pressure data agree with the theory at much larger Reynolds numbers. The discrepancies between theory and experiment at equal values of the rarefaction parameter are much larger for pressure than for heat transfer, and the cause of this behavior cannot be identified within existing solutions based upon the Navier-Stokes approximation. Cursory examination of the second-order relation for the normal stress near the surface indicates that second-order molecular effects could be significant in these experiments.

With respect to experimental techniques, it has been noted that appreciable orifice effects can be present in low-density experiments because of pseudo thermal transpiration effects. An empirical correction due to Knudsen has been applied to these data. A direct measurement of surface pressure, using a transducer with a flush diaphragm, shows that these corrected data can be interpreted as the surface pressure.

List of Symbols

a_e	Thermal accommodation coefficient	y	Distance measured normal to wedge surface
C_*	Modified Chapman-Rubesin constant, $\mu(T_*)/\mu_\infty \times T_\infty/T_*$	α	Wedge semiangle
C_H	Stanton number	γ	Ratio of specific heats
H	Total enthalpy	θ	Shock angle
M	Free stream Mach number	λ	Molecular mean free path
p	Hydrostatic pressure	μ	Viscosity
q	Heat flux per unit area	ρ	Density
Re_x	Reynolds number, $\rho_\infty U_\infty x/\mu_\infty$	σ_y	Normal stress in gas adjacent to surface
T	Temperature		
T_*	Modified reference temperature, $T_*/T_0 = (T_w/T_0) + \frac{1}{2}(1 - T_w/T_0) - \frac{1}{3}\cos^2\alpha$	$\bar\chi = M^3(C_*/Re_x)^{1/2}$	
		$\bar\chi_e = \dfrac{\gamma-1}{\gamma+1}\left(0.664 + 1.73\dfrac{T_w}{T_0}\right)M^3\left(\dfrac{C_*}{Re_x}\right)^{1/2}$	
U_∞	Free stream velocity	*Subscripts*	
u, v	Velocity components in x and y direction, respectively	∞	Free stream condition
		G	Gas condition
x	Distance along wedge, measured from the leading edge	W	Wall condition
		0	Reservoir condition

REFERENCES

Arney, G. D., and Bailey, A. B. (1962a). AEDC-TDR-62-26.
Arney, G. D., and Bailey, A. B. (1962b). AEDC-TDR-62-188.
Burnett, D. (1935). *Proc. London Math. Soc.* **40**, 382.
Cheng, H. K. (1963). CAL Rept. AF-1285-A-10.
Cheng, H. K., Hall, J. G., Golian, T. C., and Hertzberg, A. (1961). *J. Aerospace Sci.* **28**, 353.
Grad, H. (1949). *Communs. Pure Appl. Math.* **2**, 331.
Hall, J. G., and Hertzberg, A. (1958). *Jet Propulsion* **28**, 719.
Hall, J. G., and Golian, T. C. (1960). CAL Rept. AD-1052-A-10.
Knudsen, M. (1927). *Ann. Physik* **83**, 797.
Maxwell, J. C. (1879). *Phil. Trans. Roy. Soc. London* p. 231.
Pai, S. I. (1953). *J. Aeronaut. Sci.* **20**, 502.
Pai, S. I., and Shen, S. E. (1955). *In* "50 Jahre Grenzschichtforschung." Vieweg, Braunschweig.
Patterson, G. N. (1956). "Molecular Flow of Gases." Wiley, New York.
Probstein, R. F., and Pan, Y. S. (1964). *Intern. Symp. Fundamental Phenomena in Hypersonic Flow, Buffalo, New York, June* 25–26.
Shen, S. E. (1952). *J. Math. and Phys.* **31**, 192.
Vidal, R. J. (1956). CAL Rept. AD-917-A-1.
Vidal, R. J. (1962). CAL Rept. 114.
Vidal, R. J., and Wittliff, C. E. (1963). *In* "Rarefied Gas Dynamics" (J. Laurmann, ed.), Vol. II, p. 343. Academic Press, New York.
Vidal, R. J., Golian, T. C., and Bartz, J. A. (1963). AIAA Paper No. 63-435.

An Experimental Study of Surface and Flow Field Effects in Hypersonic Low Density Flow over a Flat Plate[1]

J. E. WALLACE AND A. F. BURKE

Cornell Aeronautical Laboratory, Inc., Buffalo, New York

An experimental study of the flow over sharp and blunt flat plates at zero angle of attack was conducted in the Cornell Aeronautical Laboratory 48-in. hypersonic shock tunnel at Mach numbers between 7 and 21, and at Reynolds numbers as low as 10^4 per foot. Measurements were made of surface skin friction, heat transfer, static pressure, and shock layer pitot pressure. In addition, the shock wave and boundary layer shapes were determined from schlieren photographs. The heat transfer and skin friction data taken on the sharp flat plate agreed quite well with the viscous interaction theories for $\bar{\chi} < 100$, but exhibited a rapid departure from the theories for $\bar{\chi} > 100$. At high values of $\bar{\chi}$, the simple free molecule flow relations $M_\infty C_H = \text{const}$, $M_\infty C_f = \text{const}$ predict the trend as well as the approximate magnitude of the data. For the blunt flat plates, no significant viscous interaction effects were apparent in either the surface or flow field data even though tests were conducted at Mach numbers as high as 21 and leading edge Reynolds numbers as low as 500. For these low-density test conditions, the combined bluntness-viscous interaction theory of Cheng predicts significant viscous interaction effects.

I. Introduction

In seeking an understanding of the complex phenomena of the low-density hypersonic flow regime it is desirable to obtain as many corroborating measurements as possible in an experimental program. A CAL-developed instrument for the direct measurement of skin friction under shock tunnel conditions has been used to augment previously employed pressure, heat

[1] The experimental studies reported herein were supported by the Aeronautical Systems Division (now Research and Technology Division) Air Force Systems Command, USAF (Contract Nos. AF 33(616)-8413, AF 33(657)-8662, and AF 33(657)-10423).

transfer, and schlieren instrumentation to investigate hypersonic, low-density flow over flat plate models with sharp and blunt leading edges. The experimental program spanned the range of flow regimes from thin boundary layer flow to near-free-molecule flow on the sharp flat plate and included conditions at which significant boundary layer interaction is theoretically predicted on a blunt leading edge ($\frac{1}{2}$-in. cylindrical) flat plate. Since theory is not well developed over much of the low-density flow regime, the present experimental results are correlated in a manner suitable to guide the further development of appropriate theory and hence are compared to the more conventional theoretical treatments in order to illustrate their limitations.

II. Experimental Apparatus

A. Shock Tunnel

The experimental investigations were conducted in the Cornell Aeronautical Laboratory 48-in. hypersonic shock tunnel, which utilizes helium or helium-air mixtures as the driver gas at initial temperatures up to 810°K. Effective maximum reservoir temperature and pressure of 3200°K and 4000 psi, respectively, may be obtained for tailored interface operation. The reservoir temperatures for the present investigations were kept high enough to avoid liquefaction at high expansion ratios, yet were sufficiently low that dissociation effects could be neglected.

Three basic expansion nozzle configurations were used to provide the appropriate test section conditions: (1) contoured nozzle "A," which terminates in a 24-in. exit diameter and covers the Mach number range 5.5 to 8.5, (2) contoured nozzle "D," which terminates in a 48-in. exit diameter and covers the Mach number range 12–17, and (3) 10.5° half-angle conical nozzle "E," which terminates in a 48-in. exit diameter and covers the Mach number range 12–25. All three nozzles have been calibrated using a pitot-pressure rake to span the test section for a range of incident shock Mach numbers, reservoir pressures and throat diameters. Uniform test cores of at least 12 in. in diameter were obtained under even the lowest density conditions of the present series of tests. In all cases, free-stream conditions were evaluated at the model leading edge. No attempt was made in the data correlations to account for the effects of the axial Mach number gradients of approximately 2.5%/ft in the conical nozzle.

B. Model and Instrumentation

The flat plate model used for these studies was 9 × 12 in. and $\frac{1}{2}$ in. thick, and was fitted with interchangeable leading edge pieces—a circular cylindrical leading edge of $\frac{1}{2}$-in. diameter and an effectively sharp leading edge (having a nose radius determined to be less than 0.0005 in.) with a 30° bevel angle on its underside. The plate was instrumented with heat transfer gages to within 0.375 in. of the sharp leading edge and with skin friction and pressure gages to within 0.75 in. of the sharp leading edge. Brief descriptions of the transducers used and their principle of operation are given below.

In the CAL direct measuring skin friction gage, surface shear is sensed by a flush-mounted $\frac{1}{2}$-in. diameter disk, the displacement of which stresses a piezoelectric crystal beam in bending. The gage has a sensitivity of 5 V/psi (shear) and is normally linear to better than 1 % up to 1 psi. Internal acceleration compensation keeps the acceleration sensitivity below 0.0003 psi per "g." The sensitivity of the gage to surface static pressure can normally be held to within 0.001 psi of indicated shear for 1.0 psi of surface pressure. The thermal sensitivity of the gage was negligible under the conditions of the test described here. The details of design, characteristics and calibration of the skin friction gage have been reported by MacArthur (1963).

The heat transfer gages used in the model were thin-film platinum resistance thermometers painted to a thickness of approximately 0.1 μ on a Pyrex glass substrate. The method of fabrication and calibration of these gages has been described by Vidal (1956, 1962). The heat transfer gage output was passed through an electrical analog network (Skinner, 1960) to convert the output voltage to one corresponding directly to the heat transfer rate.

Model pressures were measured with miniature ceramic piezoelectrical crystal transducers. Shielding of the sensing elements precludes thermal effects during the short test time. For the measurement of the very low pressures (as low as 0.0004 psi) experienced in certain portions of the current program, a dual-element transducer was used to reduce acceleration effects to 0.001 psi indicated per "g." The voltage output of each gage is calibrated against pressure applied through the model surface orifice after the gage has been installed in the model. Design, fabrication and calibration details are described by Martin et al. (1962).

The pitot pressure probes used to investigate the shock layer profiles of both sharp and blunt models were of rectangular opening 0.1 × 0.375 in. with the leading edges of the probe sharpened to less than 0.01 in. Pressures were sensed with the same basic type of piezoelectric pressure transducer as for surface measurements; in the probe the gage orifice was located approximately 0.75 in. from the mouth of the probe.

C. Test Conditions

The tunnel free-stream Mach number for each run was determined from air flow calibrations using the throat diameter of the nozzle, the incident shock Mach number and the average reservoir pressure. The other free-stream conditions were calculated using M_∞, incident shock Mach number and reservoir pressure as input quantities in a digital computer program for isentropic, equilibrium expansion in the nozzle. The program presumes vibrational equilibrium throughout.

III. Sharp Leading Edge Flat Plate

A. Pressure Distribution

The pressure distribution near the leading edge of a sharp flat plate in low density hypersonic flow has been studied experimentally by several investigators (Nagamatsu *et al.*, 1961; Vidal and Wittliff, 1963; Vidal *et al.*, 1963; Wallace and Burke, 1963). In general, it has been found that the data lie significantly below Lees' classical viscous interaction theories for $10 < \bar{\chi} < 80$ and exhibit an even sharper departure from the theory for $\bar{\chi} > 80$. Unfortunately, the various sets of data are not in good agreement with each other or with the several theories (Oguchi, 1960, 1963; Charwat, 1961; Aroesty, 1961) which have been proposed to account for the low density, leading edge effects. Since the pressure data obtained in the present study would not help significantly to clarify the current confused situation, no further discussion of the pressure distribution on the sharp plate will be given here.

B. Heat Transfer and Skin Friction

The sharp flat plate heat transfer and skin friction data have been compared with appropriate hypersonic flow theories which are applicable in the various low density flow regimes—namely, (1) weak viscous interaction theory, (2) strong viscous interaction theory, (3) strong viscous interaction with surface slip[2] (Aroesty, 1961), and (4) free molecular flow theory. For purposes of completeness, the various theoretical results for heat transfer, skin friction, and the skin friction to heat transfer ratio will be summarized.

1. Heat Transfer. Weak viscous interaction:

$$\frac{C_H(\text{Re}_{\infty_x})^{1/2}}{(C_*)^{1/2}} = \frac{0.332(1 + \beta\bar{\chi})}{(1 + 2\beta\bar{\chi})^{1/2}},$$

[2] The theoretical result for strong viscous interaction with surface slip on a highly cooled flat plate was obtained from Aroesty (1961), by assuming the fractional reduction due to slip was the same for a highly cooled plate as for an insulated plate. This yields a conservative estimate.

where

$$p/p_\infty = 1 + \beta(\bar{\chi}) + O(\bar{\chi}^2).$$

Strong viscous interaction[3]:

$$C_H(\mathrm{Re}_{\infty_x})^{1/2}/(C_*)^{1/2} = 0.0788[(1 + 2.5H_w/H_0)\bar{\chi}]^{1/2}.$$

Strong viscous interaction with surface slip[2]:

$$C_H(\mathrm{Re}_{\infty_x})^{1/2}/(C_*)^{1/2} = 0.0788[1 + 2.5(H_w/H_0)]^{1/2}[1 + O(M_\infty/(\mathrm{Re}_{\infty_x})^{1/2})].$$

Free molecule flow:

$$M_\infty C_H = \frac{1}{(2\pi\gamma)^{1/2}} \frac{a_c}{1 - (H_w/H_0)} \left[1 + \frac{\gamma + 1}{\gamma(\gamma - 1)M_\infty^2}\left(1 - \frac{T_w}{T_0}\right)\right],$$

where a_c is the thermal accommodation coefficient of the surface,

$$C_H = \dot{q}/\rho_\infty u_\infty(H_0 - H_w), \qquad \bar{\chi} \equiv M_\infty^3(C_*)^{1/2}/(\mathrm{Re}_{\infty_x})^{1/2},$$

$$C_* \equiv (\mu_*/T_*)(T_\infty/\mu_\infty), \qquad T_* = \tfrac{1}{6}T_0 + \tfrac{1}{2}T_w.$$

2. Skin Friction. Weak viscous interaction:

$$C_f(\mathrm{Re}_{\infty_x})^{1/2}/(C_*)^{1/2} = 0.664[1 + (3/\gamma^2)\beta^2\bar{\chi}].$$

Strong viscous interaction[3]:

$$C_f(\mathrm{Re}_{\infty_x})^{1/2}/(C_*)^{1/2} = 0.208[(1 + 2.5H_w/H_0)\bar{\chi}]^{1/2}.$$

Strong viscous interaction with surface slip[2]:

$$C_f(\mathrm{Re}_{\infty_x})^{1/2}/(C_*)^{1/2} = 0.208[(1 + 2.5H_w/H_0)\bar{\chi}]^{1/2}$$
$$\times \{1 - 0.85[(\gamma - 1)/\gamma]^{1/2}(\bar{\chi}^{1/2}/M_\infty)\}$$

Free molecule flow:

$$M_\infty C_f = (f_t/M_\infty)(2/\pi\gamma)^{1/2},$$

where f_t is tangential momentum accommodation coefficient of the surface,

$$C_f \equiv \tau/\tfrac{1}{2}\rho_\infty u_\infty^2.$$

3. Skin Friction-Heat Transfer Ratio. Weak viscous interaction (first order):

$$C_f/C_H = 2\{1 + 1.328[\tfrac{1}{4}(\gamma - 1)(1 + 2.5H_w/H_0)]^2\bar{\chi}\}.$$

Strong viscous interaction:

$$C_f/C_H = 2.64.$$

[3] The factor $(1 + 2.5H_w/H_0)$ in the strong interaction expressions for heat transfer and skin friction accounts accurately for wall enthalpy effects near $H_w/H_0 \approx 0$ only. For the insulated wall case, the factor results in an error of about 20%.

492 J. E. WALLACE AND A. F. BURKE

Strong viscous interaction with surface slip:

$$C_f/C_H = 2.64\{1 - 0.85[(\gamma - 1)/\gamma]^{1/2}(\bar\chi^{1/2}/M_\infty)\}.$$

Free molecule flow:

$$C_f/C_H = 2f_t/a_c.$$

The heat transfer, skin friction, and skin friction to heat transfer ratio data are shown compared with the various theories in Figs. 1, 2, and 3, respectively. The general characteristics of the heat transfer data-theory comparisons (Fig. 1) are the same as previously reported by Vidal and Wittliff (1963);

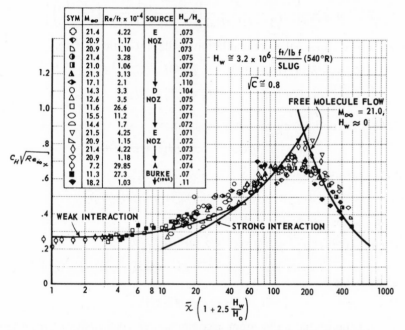

FIG. 1. Heat transfer distribution on a sharp flat plate at zero angle of attack.

Vidal et al. (1963); Nagamatsu et al. (1962); and Burke et al. (1962)—that is, the data lie slightly above the viscous interaction theories for $\bar\chi < 100$ and exhibit a sharp departure from the theories for $\bar\chi > 100$. At the high values of $\bar\chi$, the simple free molecule flow relation $M_\infty C_H = $ constant predicts the trend as well as the approximate magnitude of the data. The skin friction data (Fig. 2) compares well with the viscous interaction relations for $\bar\chi < 100$, but as in the case of heat transfer, it exhibits a sharp departure from the viscous interaction relations for $\bar\chi > 100$. The behavior of the skin friction data is similar to that of the heat transfer data, but because of the lack of skin friction data

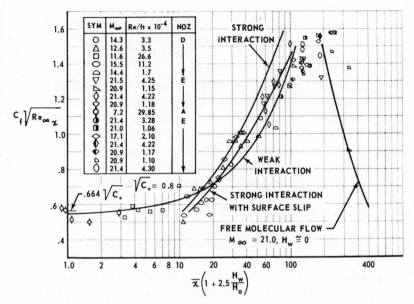

FIG. 2. Skin friction distribution on a sharp flat plate at zero angle of attack.

at $\bar{\chi}$ values greater than 200, it is not possible to conclude with a reasonable degree of certainty that the skin friction follows approximately the simple free molecule flow relation $M_\infty C_f =$ constant at the high values of $\bar{\chi}$. The data

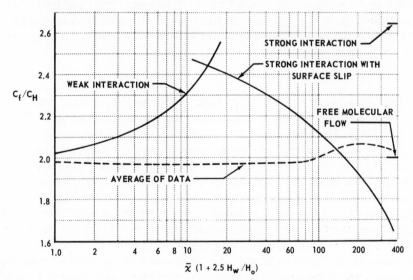

FIG. 3. Skin friction-heat transfer ratio for a sharp flat plate at zero angle of attack.

do suggest such a trend, however. The skin friction to heat transfer ratio data are shown in Fig. 3. Average data curves for both C_f and C_H were used to compute the experimental values of C_f/C_H. From Fig. 3 it is seen that the data yield C_f/C_H values near two for the complete range $1 < \bar{\chi} < 300$ of the tests. The increase of C_f/C_H above two predicted by the viscous interaction theories and the subsequent predicted decrease below two due to surface slip are not apparent in the data; however, it is quite possible that such trends could be masked by the data scatter. In general, it is felt that the agreement of the skin friction data with the various theories and its compatibility with the heat transfer data is quite good, especially since the skin friction transducer had not been used previously in hypersonic flow research studies.

C. Shock Wave and Boundary Layer Shapes

A detailed treatment of the flow field over a sharp plate including viscous interaction effects is given in Stewartson (1955). The referenced work is for an insulated plate, but the functional form of the solution is applicable to the cool wall case also. Hence the shock and boundary layer shapes are of the form

$$y_s/x \sim (\bar{\chi}^{1/2}/M_\infty)(1 + C_1/\bar{\chi}), \qquad \delta/x \sim (\bar{\chi}^{1/2}/M_\infty)(1 - C_2/\bar{\chi}),$$

where C_1, C_2 are positive constants. For $\bar{\chi} \gg 1$, the shock wave and the boundary layer have similar shapes. The ratio of the thicknesses (δ/y_s) was determined by Stewartson from a matching of the boundary layer and the inviscid outer flow. Since this ratio should not change with wall cooling, the ratio obtained by Stewartson for the insulated wall case will be assumed to apply to the cold wall case as well, or

$$(\delta/y_s)_{\bar{\chi} \gg 1} = 0.595.$$

The shock wave and boundary layer thicknesses have been read from schlieren photographs. Reproductions of the schlieren are given in Burke et al. (1962). The selection of the outer edges of both the shock and the boundary layer is arbitrary to some extent. In both cases the effective edges were taken as the outermost edge of the region of sudden change in light intensity. The shock wave and boundary layer thickness data have been correlated using the forms suggested by the theoretical work of Stewartson (1955). The effect of wall cooling is included by using the factor $[1 + 2.5H_w/H_0]^{1/2}$ taken from the first-order strong interaction theory (Hayes and Probstein, 1959). The correlations are shown in Fig. 4. In general, the boundary layer thickness results agree quite well with the theoretical predictions; even the negative slope of the data correlation curve with increasing values of $1/\bar{\chi}$ is as predicted. The shock slope results are not in such good agreement with the theoretical predictions especially at relatively large $\bar{\chi}$; however, the positive slope of the shock shape data correlation curve with $1/\bar{\chi}$ is as predicted. It is surprising that the boundary layer shape results are in good agreement with

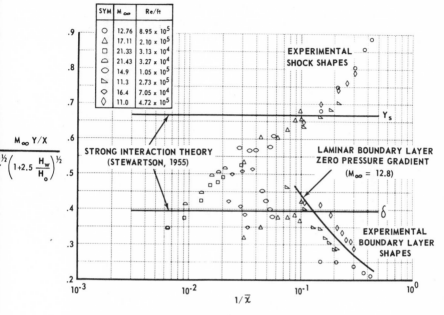

FIG. 4. Sharp flat plate shock and boundary layer shapes.

theory at relatively large $\bar{\chi}$, while the pressure distributions (Burke *et al.*, 1962) and the shock shape are not.

D. Shock Layer Pitot Pressure Distributions

The pitot pressure distributions (Fig. 5) across the shock layer at 10.5 in. from the leading edge of the sharp flat plate model were measured for tunnel test conditions which resulted in local $\bar{\chi}$ values (based on free-stream conditions) of 2, 9, 47, and 85. The distributions for local $\bar{\chi} = 2$ and 9 exhibited the classical shape postulated in the weak and strong viscous interaction theories: that is, a distinct boundary layer region, through which the pitot pressure decreases very rapidly approaching the static pressure at the wall, and a well-defined inviscid region, across which the pitot pressure varies rather slowly because of shock wave curvature alone. For local $\bar{\chi} = 47$ and 85, no distinct boundary layer and inviscid regions are apparent in the data. In those cases, the resultant effect of extreme shock wave curvature near the leading edge is to cause large Mach number gradients across the entire shock layer. It seems clear that external vorticity must be included in the boundary layer theory before a viscous interaction theory can be expected to adequately describe the flow field in this flow regime.

In Fig. 5, the boundary layer thicknesses δ determined from the correlations of schlieren photograph readings of boundary layer and shock wave shapes (Fig. 4) are marked for the cases of local $\bar{\chi} = 2$ and 9. In both cases the edge

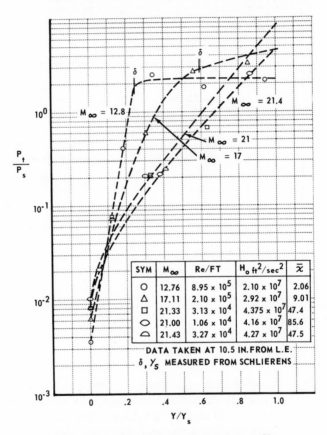

SYM	M_∞	Re/FT	$H_0 \, \text{ft}^2/\text{sec}^2$	$\bar{\chi}$
○	12.76	8.95×10^5	2.10×10^7	2.06
△	17.11	2.10×10^5	2.92×10^7	9.01
□	21.33	3.13×10^4	4.375×10^7	47.4
◇	21.00	1.06×10^4	4.16×10^7	85.6
△	21.43	3.27×10^4	4.27×10^7	47.5

DATA TAKEN AT 10.5 IN. FROM L.E.
δ, Y_s MEASURED FROM SCHLIERENS

FIG. 5. Sharp flat plate shock layer pitot profiles.

of the boundary layer inferred from reading schlieren photographs falls near the knee of the pitot pressure distribution curves. Hence both methods of determining the boundary layer thickness yield nearly the same result. This indicates that the interpretation of the schlieren photographs previously discussed in Section III, C was correct.

IV. Blunt Leading Edge Flat Plate

A. Surface Pressure Distribution

Numerous works are available on the prediction of the inviscid pressure distribution over a blunt plate in hypersonic flow, including correlations of solutions obtained by the method of characteristics (Baradell and Bertram, 1960) and various blast analogy solutions as reviewed by Lukasiewicz (1961). Typical results are:

Method of characteristics (Bertram and Baradell, 1960)

$$p/p_\infty = 0.113[M_\infty^3 C_{DN}/(x/d_0)]^{2/3} + 0.74. \tag{1}$$

Second order blast wave theory (Lukasiewicz, 1961)

$$p/p_\infty = 0.121[M_\infty^3 C_{DN}/(x/d_0)]^{2/3} + 0.56, \tag{2}$$

where C_{DN} is the nose drag coefficient, and d_0 is the leading edge diameter.

At the high densities and Reynolds numbers appropriate to thin boundary layers, these predictions are well substantiated by experiment. For sufficiently low densities, boundary layer interaction with the inviscid flow needs to be taken into account. Several theoretical approaches have been proposed, including the small $-\varepsilon$ (or γ close to one) entropy layer theory of Cheng et al. (1961), linear superposition techniques (Creager, 1957 and Burke et al., 1962), and hypersonic similarity addition of a viscous induced pressure increment to

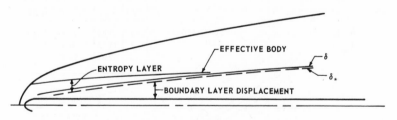

FIG. 6. Blunt body shock layer regions.

the bluntness-induced pressure (Bertram and Blackstone, 1961). In the analysis of Cheng et al. (1961), the effective body shape is taken at the edge of the entropy layer (gas processed by the strong bow shock) after it has been displaced by the boundary layer displacement thickness, δ^* (see Fig. 6). The solution is found as an expansion for small values of the limiting density ratio, $\varepsilon \equiv \rho_\infty/\rho$. Although the two asymptotic solutions for p/p_∞ (bluntness dominated flow at one end and viscous interaction dominated at the other) obtained by Cheng are not in good agreement with the blast wave or viscous interaction theories, it was found (Cheng et al., 1961) that a linear addition of the two asymptotic solutions was within 12% of the exact solution in the transition region. On the basis of this finding, it was proposed by Burke et al. (1962) that the "correct" blast wave and strong interaction solutions be simply superposed as an approximation of the Cheng theory in the form

$$p/p_\infty = 0.268\gamma K_\varepsilon^{2/3} + \tfrac{3}{8}\gamma^{1/2}(\gamma + 1)^{3/2}\bar\chi_\varepsilon. \tag{3}$$

The parameters

$$K_\varepsilon \equiv \varepsilon C_{D_N} M_\infty^{\,3}/(\chi/d_0), \qquad \bar\chi_\varepsilon \equiv \varepsilon(0.54 + 1.33 H_w/H_0)\bar\chi,$$

are essentially those of Cheng et al. (1963) with the displacement thickness dependence on wall temperature taken for the strong interaction pressure gradient rather than the zero-pressure gradient value (0.664 + 1.73H_w/H_0).

Previous experimental investigations (e.g., Hammitt et al., 1955; Henderson and Johnston, 1959; Bertram and Blackstock, 1961) of the pressure induced by the combined effects of bluntness and boundary layer interaction have found significant effects of boundary layer interaction on flat plates with blunted leading edges in reasonably good agreement with the theoretical predictions. The conditions of the present tests are distinguished from those of the previous investigations in several respects. The degree of bluntness in previous investigations has been small, so that measurements were taken at more than 100 nose diameters downstream in most cases; in the present case with a $\tfrac{1}{2}$ in. leading edge diameter the measurements are all made within 15 nose diameters

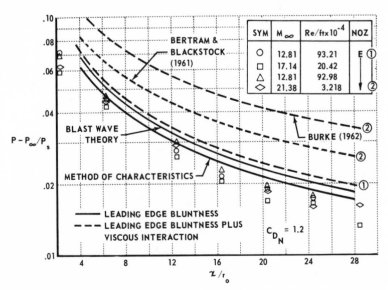

FIG. 7. Pressure distribution on a blunt flat plate at zero angle of attack.

of the leading edge. Previous studies have been conducted primarily in continuous flow facilities with the model at adiabatic wall conditions; the present shock tunnel tests are of short duration so that the model wall remains cold. Free-stream Mach numbers have been below 10 except for tests in helium; the present data are taken in air at Mach numbers up to 21. Finally, the unit Reynolds numbers of the present tests—as low as 10^4 per foot—are considerably lower than those of previous tests.

The ratio of measured pressure to free-stream pitot pressure is presented in Fig. 7. It is apparent that the inviscid theories, Eqs. (1) and (2), are in best agreement with the data in spite of the large increases in pressure due to boundary layer displacement predicted by the theory of Bertram and Blackstock (1961) and the approximation of Cheng's result by Burke et al. (1962). More will be said later regarding the absence of the predicted viscous interaction effect after further corroborating data have been presented.

B. Heat Transfer and Skin Friction

The locally similar boundary layer results (Hayes and Probstein, 1959) for heat transfer and skin friction,

$$\dot{q} = \rho_1 u_1 \mu_1 \frac{H_0 g'(0)}{(2\xi)^{1/2}} \quad \text{and} \quad \tau_w = \rho_1 u_1^2 \mu_1 \frac{f''(0)}{(2\xi)^{1/2}}, \tag{4}$$

can be written in terms of the shock Reynolds number based on nose radius, $\mathrm{Re}_{s_{r0}} \equiv (\rho_\infty u_\infty r_0)/\mu_s$, and the pressure distribution as

$$C_H(\mathrm{Re}_{s_{r0}})^{1/2} = \frac{g'(0)/1 - g_w}{[2\varepsilon I(x/r_0)]^{1/2}} \left(\frac{T_s}{T_w}\right)^{1-\omega} \frac{p_1}{p_s} \left[1 - \left(\frac{p_1}{p_s}\right)^{(\gamma-1)/\gamma}\right]^{1/2}, \tag{5}$$

and

$$C_f(\mathrm{Re}_{s_{r0}})^{1/2} = \frac{\sqrt{2} f''(0)}{[\varepsilon I(x/r_0)]^{1/2}} \left(\frac{T_s}{T_w}\right)^{1-\omega} \frac{p_1}{p_s} \left[1 - \left(\frac{p_1}{p_s}\right)^{(\gamma-1)/\gamma}\right]^{1/2}, \tag{6}$$

where

$$I(x/r_0) \equiv \int_0^{x/r_0} (p_1/p_s)^{(\omega\gamma+1-\omega)/\gamma} [1 - (p_1/p_s)^{(\gamma-1)/\gamma} \, d(x/r_0)]^{1/2}$$

$$g(\eta) \equiv H/H_0, \qquad f'(\eta) \equiv u/u_1,$$

$$\eta = \frac{u_1}{(2\xi)^{1/2}} \int \rho \, dy, \qquad \xi = \int \rho_1 u_1 \mu_1 \, dx, \qquad \mu \sim T^\omega.$$

Subscript 1 indicates local conditions at the edge of the boundary layer; subscript s denotes stagnation point conditions. This form presumes that the mass addition to the boundary layer is small enough that the local velocity and viscosity can be determined from the pressure distribution by assuming an isentropic expansion along the body from the nose. This assumption will be violated for high-Mach number, low-Reynolds number flows, but provides a convenient theory at more moderate conditions. A more exact calculation based on the correct local conditions at the edge of the boundary layer can be made using the IBM 704 program recently reported by Curtis *et al.* (1964), which matches the inviscid flow and boundary layer flows. That computer program will be utilized in future work to investigate the effects of mass addition to the boundary layer from the entropy layer.

Assuming the blast wave pressure distribution and making the approximations $U_1 = U_\infty$ and of a linear viscosity relation, Eqs. (5) and (6) can be written more simply as

$$C_H(\mathrm{Re}_{s_{r_0}})^{1/2} = 0.382[g'(0)/(1 - g_w)]C_{D_N}^{1/3}(x/r_0)^{-5/6}, \tag{7}$$

and

$$C_f(\mathrm{Re}_{s_{r_0}})^{1/2} = 0.764f''(0)C_{D_N}^{1/3}(x/r_0)^{-5/6}. \tag{8}$$

If in these expressions one substitutes the combined blast-wave and viscous interaction pressure result, Eq. (3), both the heat transfer and skin friction expressions, Eqs. (7) and (8), are modified by a factor

$$\frac{1 + 4.75(\bar{\chi}_\varepsilon/K_\varepsilon)^{2/3}}{[1 + 3.15(\bar{\chi}_\varepsilon/K_\varepsilon)^{2/3}]^{1/2}}.$$

In Fig. 8 the heat transfer results of the present tests are compared to the local similarity solution obtained by using a Newtonian Prandtl-Meyer blast wave pressure distribution in Eq. (4). The agreement of the local similarity solution with all of the data is quite good. The predicted effect of boundary layer interaction is shown for the range of test conditions of the present data. The effect of boundary layer interaction, as seen in the increment over the hypersonic linear approximation, Eq. (7), is no more distinguishable for the heat transfer data than it is for the pressure case, although the magnitude of the predicted effect is less for heat transfer than for pressure and therefore more easily obscured within the scatter of the data. The prime point, however, is the lack of any consistent trend with increasing Mach number and decreasing Reynolds number.

The same comparisons are made for skin friction in Fig. 9. The local similarity, linear viscosity, Pr = 1 boundary layer theory is in good agreement with the trend of the data as a function of x/r_0. However, the spread in the correlated data prevents any meaningful comparison with the increment in skin friction indicated by the boundary layer interaction theory as an increase over the hypersonic linear viscosity approximation. There is no clear trend with decreasing free-stream density.

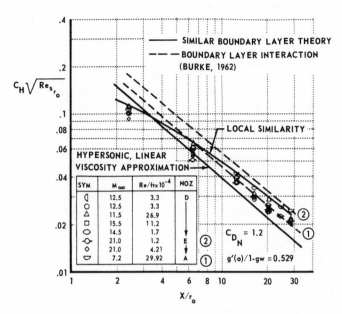

Fig. 8. Correlated heat transfer coefficient for a blunt flat plate at zero angle of attack.

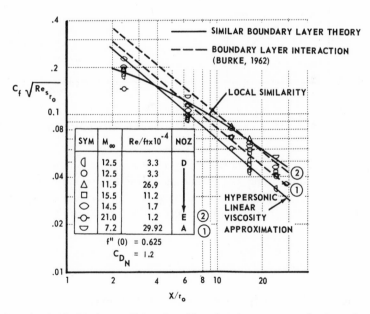

Fig. 9. Correlated skin friction coefficient for a blunt flat plate at zero angle of attack.

Using the expressions previously shown for the thin boundary layer, local similarity theory for the local skin friction, Eq. (8), and heat transfer, Eq. (7), the ratio of these coefficients becomes.

$$C_f/C_H = \{2f''(0)/[g'(0)/1 - g_w]\}(u_1/u_\infty)^{1/2}.$$

If the blast pressure, Eq. (2), and an isentropic expansion along the body from the stagnation point are again assumed, the result is

$$C_f/C_H = \{2f''(0)/[g'(0)/1 - g_w]\}\{1 - [0.15C_{D_N}^{2/3}(\chi/r_0)^{-2/3}]^{(\gamma-1)/\gamma}\}^{1/2}.$$

The spread in the skin friction data correlation is such that any attempt to fair an average curve through the data is somewhat subjective. However, "average" curves were faired through both the heat transfer and skin friction data correlations and the ratio taken to evaluate the Reynolds analogy

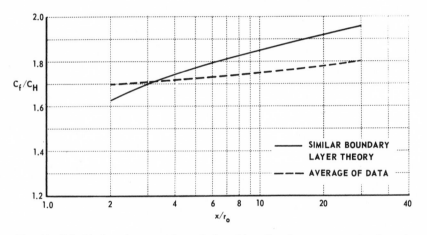

Fig. 10. Skin friction—heat transfer ratio for a blunt flat plate at zero angle of attack.

parameter, C_f/C_H. As shown in Fig. 10, the ratio so obtained shows approximately the same trend and magnitude as the theoretical expression, i.e., less than two but increasing over the range of x/r_0 considered. Again, these observations are not conclusive because of the spread in the skin friction data correlation.

C. Shock Shape

In accordance with the flow field model shown in Fig. 6 for analyzing the combined effects of bluntness and boundary layer displacement, it would be presumed that the shock should be displaced outward from the theoretical inviscid position. The shock shape for a blunt plate has been found (Lukasiewicz, 1961) in the second order blast wave theory to be

$$\frac{y}{r_0} = \frac{1.548 C_{D_N}^{1/3}(x/d_0)^{2/3}}{1 - 1.09[(x/d_0)/M_\infty^3 C_{D_N}]^{2/3}}.$$

The similar boundary layer solution for the boundary layer displacement thickness,

$$\delta_* = [(2\xi)^{1/2}/\rho_1 u_1] \int_0^\infty [(H_0/h)(g - f'^2) + f'^2 - f'] \, d\eta,$$

can be expressed (for $U_1 \approx U_\infty$, linear viscosity, blast wave pressure distribution, isentropic expansion along the body from the stagnation point) as

$$\delta_*/r_0 = (4.65/C_{D_N}^{1/3})(\varepsilon/\mathrm{Re}_{s_{r_0}})^{1/2}(x/r_0)^{5/6}(0.425 + H_w/H_0). \tag{9}$$

Schlieren photographs from the present tests on a 0.5-in. diameter leading edge blunt plate, augmented by schlieren photographs from a previous experimental program (Burke *et al.*, 1962) on a plate with a 0.122-in. diameter leading edge, were read and reduced to graphical form. Although no clear boundary layer was discernable from the schlieren photographs for either of the blunt plate models (0.5 in. diam. and 0.122 in. diam.), the shock shapes

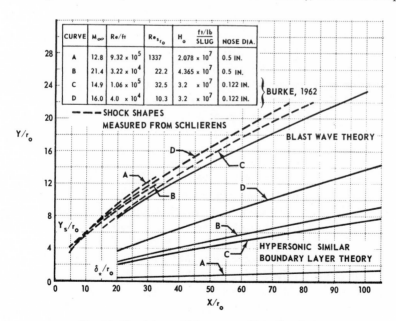

FIG. 11. Shock layer thickness on a blunt flat plate.

were easily readable. As shown in Fig. 11 the shock shapes are in quite good agreement with the inviscid blast wave theory and are not significantly displaced, in contradiction to the predicted "displacement" thickness of Eq. (9). This drastic reduction of boundary layer interaction is consistent with the observations made for the surface measurements of pressure and heat transfer. Although at low free-stream densities and high free-stream Mach numbers the boundary layer thickness may increase, compensating effects between the viscous and inviscid flow phenomena apparently mask any net effects of boundary layer growth. In reflecting on these observations it is noted that whereas the usual notion of displacement thickness assumes that a uniform flow would exist down to the body if there were no boundary layer, in the blunt flat plate case the gas density is high at the shock but drops rapidly toward the body. The conventional "displacement" arises from the substitution of a hot, low density gas region for the cooler, higher density gas in the inviscid flow next to the surface. In the blunt flat plate case, however, the inviscid gas near the body is of decreasing density toward the wall so that the flow external to the boundary layer could be little altered by the substitution of a boundary layer of comparably low density. This would be the case particularly at high M_∞ where the entropy rise across the nose bow shock is large.

D. Pitot Pressure Profiles

As shown by Burke et al. (1962), the blast wave local static density to free-stream density ratio, which is tabulated in the summary of blast wave theory by Lukasiewicz (1961), is approximately equal to the pitot pressure ratio p_t/p_s for very large Mach numbers [$\frac{1}{2}(\gamma - 1)M_\infty \gg 1$]. The quantity p_t indicates the pitot pressure as it would be measured by a pitot probe in the shock layer and p_s indicates the stagnation pressure at the nose of the blunt plate (equivalent to free-stream pitot pressure behind a normal shock). The shock layer pitot pressure profile is compared to the experimentally determined pitot pressures in Fig. 12, where p_t/p_s is shown versus the distance above the plate surface normalized by the local shock position (as determined from schlieren photographs). Data taken at 19.2 nose diameters downstream on the 0.5-in. diameter leading edge blunt plate of the present tests and at 79 nose diameters downstream on the 0.122-in. diameter leading edge blunt plate reported by Burke et al. (1962) are shown. The more highly expanded flow at the measurement station of the 0.122-in. diameter model shows the closer agreement with the blast wave profile. Any attempt to locate the extent of the boundary layer by looking for a change of slope in the pitot profile is obscured by the inviscid layer Mach number gradient, which in itself produces a considerable gradient in the pitot pressure. Furthermore, it is noted that, in contrast to the sharp plate pitot profiles, the pitot pressure profiles for the blunt plate over a wide range of Reynolds numbers do not reflect any sub-stantial alteration in the boundary layer region from the inviscid profile. This observation lends further support to the conjecture made earlier with regard to the possibility of compensating effects between inviscid and viscous flows.

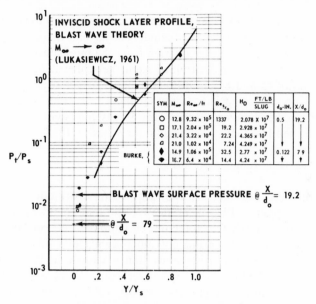

FIG. 12. Blunt flat plate shock layer pitot profiles.

It would appear that a detailed analysis of the inviscid-viscous interaction problem on blunt plates that can better account for the observed effects both on the surface and in the shock layer is very much needed.

V. Summary and Conclusions

A. Sharp Flat Plate Studies

1. The skin friction and heat transfer distributions on the sharp plate agree well with the weak and strong interaction theories for $\bar{\chi} < 100$, but show rapid departures from the theory for $\bar{\chi} > 100$. At large $\bar{\chi}$ values, the simple free molecule relations (e.g., $M_\infty C_f = $ constant) predict both the trend and approximate magnitude of the data. The experimental skin friction to heat transfer ratio C_f/C_H was about two for the entire $\bar{\chi}$ range of the tests.

2. The boundary layer thickness results determined from schlieren photo-graphs were in good agreement with the weak and strong viscous interaction

theories for $\bar{\chi} < 30$. No well-defined boundary layer edge was apparent on the schlieren for higher $\bar{\chi}$.

3. The shock shape results were not in good agreement with the strong interaction theory. The shock layer thickness was significantly less than predicted for $\bar{\chi} > 10$.

4. The measured shock layer pitot pressure distributions for local $\bar{\chi}$ values of 2 and 9 exhibited well-defined boundary layer and inviscid regions. The thickness of the boundary layer inferred from the pitot pressure data was in good agreement with that determined from the schlieren photographs. For local $\bar{\chi}$ values of 45 and 87, no distinct boundary layer region was apparent in the pitot pressure data indicating that shock curvature induced vorticity and Mach number gradients were large. This is consistent with the absence of a well-defined boundary layer edge in the schlieren for $\bar{\chi} > 30$.

B. Blunt Flat Plate Studies

1. The pressure, heat transfer and skin friction distributions on the blunt plate were well predicted by the blast-wave and thin boundary layer theories assuming local similarity for all the test conditions of the predicted study.

2. The shock wave shape did not differ significantly from the inviscid, blast-wave result even at test Reynolds numbers as low as 10^4/ft.

3. The combined bluntness-viscous interaction theory of Cheng predicts significant viscous interaction effects (e.g., up to 100% increments in pressure and 60% increments in heat transfer) at the low density free-stream conditions (for M_∞ up to 21.4) of the present tests. It is conjectured that the reason for the lack of agreement between the theory and the data is that the theory does not properly account for the swallowing of the high-temperature, low-density entropy layer into the boundary layer; for high free-stream Mach numbers, the density of the nearly normal shock-processed gas is sufficiently low that its net displacement effect may be nearly the same whether it be in the entropy layer or in the boundary layer.

4. The shock layer pitot pressure distributions did not exhibit any well-defined boundary layer displacement effect.

C. Skin Friction Instrumentation for Shock Tunnel Studies

1. The scatter in the skin friction measurements was larger than in the heat transfer measurements. Nonetheless, the skin friction data are consistent with those for the heat transfer. The agreement with simple flow theories, at test conditions where such agreement is expected on the basis of results obtained with the more highly developed heat transfer and pressure instrumentation, shows that the direct measuring skin friction gage is a useful tool for

hypersonic flow research in shock tunnels. As greater experience with the gage is obtained and refinements are made, its utility should be further increased.

REFERENCES

Aroesty, J. (1961). AF ARL Rept. No. 64.

Baradell, D. L., and Bertram, M. H. (1960). NASA TN-D-408.

Bertram, M. H., and Blackstock, T. A. (1961). NASA TN-D-798.

Burke, A. F., Smith, W. E., Dowling, E. D., and Carlson, D. R. (1962). ASD TDR 62-797, Part I.

Charwat, A. F. (1961). *In* "Rarefied Gas Dynamics" (L. Talbot, ed.), pp. 553–578. Academic Press, New York.

Cheng, H. K., Hall, J. G., Golian, T. C., and Hertzberg, A. (1961). *J. Aerospace Sci.* **28**, 353–381.

Creager, M. O. (1957). NACA TN 4142.

Curtis, J. T., Burke, A. F., Wallace, J. E., and Butler, F. E. (1964). CAL Rept. No. AA-1747-Y-1.

Hayes, W. D., and Probstein, R. F. (1959). "Hypersonic Flow Theory." Academic Press, New York.

Henderson, A., Jr., and Johnston, P. J. (1959). NASA Memo 5-8-59L.

Lukasiewicz, J. (1961). AEDC TR-61-4.

MacArthur, R. C. (1963). CAL Rept. No. 129.

Martin, J. F., Duryea, G. R., and Stevenson, L. M. (1962). *In* "Advances in Hypervelocity Techniques," pp. 145–186. Plenum Press, New York.

Nagamatsu, H. T., Sheer, R. E., and Schmid, J. R. (1961). *ARS (Am. Rocket Soc.) J.* **31**, 902–910.

Nagamatsu, H. T., Weil, J. A., and Sheer, R. E. (1962). *ARS (Am. Rocket Soc.) J.* **32**, 533–540.

Oguchi, H. (1960). AF ARL TN-60-133.

Oguchi, H. (1963). *In* "Rarefied Gas Dynamics" (J. A. Laurmann, ed.), Vol. II, pp. 553–578. Academic Press, New York.

Skinner, G. (1960). *ARS (Am. Rocket Soc.) J.* **30**, 569–570.

Stewartson, K. (1955). *J. Aeronaut. Sci.* **22**, 303–309.

Vidal, R. J. (1950). WADC TN 56-315 (Also CAL Rept. No. AD-917-A-1).

Vidal, R. J. (1962). CAL Rept. No. 114.

Vidal, R. J., and Wittliff, C. E. (1963). *In* "Rarefied Gas Dynamics" (J. Laurmann, ed.), Vol. II, pp. 343–378. Academic Press, New York.

Vidal, R. J., Golian, T. C., and Bartz, J. A. (1962). AIAA Preprint No. 63-435.

Wallace, J. E., and Burke, A. F. (1963). AF ASD-TDR-63-772.

Some Exploratory Experimental Studies of Hypersonic Low Density Effects on Flat Plates and Cones

I. E. VAS, J. MCDOUGALL, G. KOPPENWALLNER,[1] AND
S. M. BOGDONOFF

Gas Dynamics Laboratory, Princeton University, Princeton, New Jersey

The present paper covers the first phase of a series of flow experiments on sharp flat plates, and sharp and blunted cones of 5°, 10° and 15° included angle at a Mach number of about 25 with both hot and cold wall conditions. The experiments were performed in a high-pressure, heated-nitrogen hypersonic wind tunnel, and consisted primarily of surface pressure measurements in a regime where slip effects are expected. Comparisons of the results with pertinent theories are presented.

I. Introduction

Over the past decade, the area of low-density flows at low-Mach numbers has been relatively well explored. A considerable number of major contributions have been made in this field between continuum and free molecular flows. Only recently has this low-density effort been extended into the hypersonic regime. Some continuous facilities have been built which have reached as high as Mach 10, but the really high-Mach number work has been done primarily in shock tunnels at Cornell Aeronautical Laboratory and General Electric Company. Practical considerations of actual bodies which experienced flight conditions in which hypersonic flow and low-density effects are important have stimulated a more detailed study of deviations from the continuum flow at very high-Mach numbers. Just as the problem of extrapolation of continuum supersonic flow theory to hypersonic speeds was questioned, now the extensive low-density supersonic results have to be examined in the light of the very strong entropy and pressure gradients which are characteristic of hypersonic flight.

---

[1] *Permanent address:* Aerodynamische Versuchsanstalt, Gottingen, Germany.

From the theoretical point of view, the general flow picture for hypersonic flight at low density has usually been built around the approximation of a cold wall. This is a good approximation for blunt bodies, but for flat plates and cones this is not necessarily so. In some research equipment now being used to study such flows (if the models are exposed for long test times) or in flight, where high surface temperatures may be required for radiation cooling, the "cold wall" approximation may not be valid.

As part of a long range study of hypersonic low-density flows over simple bodies, the Gas Dynamics Laboratory at Princeton University has developed a series of hot nitrogen hypersonic wind tunnels which operate continuously at stagnation temperatures to 3000°K and stagnation pressures from 300 to 5000 psi at Mach numbers from 15 to 26. These facilities are currently being used to study the flow over a wide range of configurations (both two- and three-dimensional). Stagnation conditions and Mach number are used to vary the flow field parameters while body geometry and wall temperature (variable from 300° to 1200°K) control the boundary layer and wall conditions. The choice of operating conditions permits rarefaction effects to be limited or concentrated in the stream, the shock layer, or in the boundary layer, as desired.

The present paper covers the first phase of the studies of sharp flat plates and sharp and blunted cones, at a Mach number of about 25 with both hot and cold wall conditions. These studies were carried out in tunnel N-3, the high pressure facility, and consist primarily of surface pressure distributions in a regime where slip effects are expected. Detailed heat transfer and boundary layer surveys and optical observations are either underway or will be programmed shortly. Comparison of the results with pertinent theories and other observations are presented. Owing to space requirements only some typical results will be included.

The hot nitrogen facilities were developed under a Princeton University Research Grant and exploited as hypersonic research tools under Grant AF–AFOSR 112–63 and Contract No. AF 49(638)–1271. The results of the research program noted herein were carried out under these contracts as well.

II. Facility and Models

A. Test Facility

The present experimental study was conducted in the Gas Dynamics Laboratory Hypersonic Nitrogen Tunnel, N-3. Only a brief description of the facility will be given, since full details are given by Vas and Koppenwallner (1964). The tunnel uses a high-pressure nitrogen supply and a four-stage steam ejector system common to the laboratory. The tunnel is designed to

FIG. 1. Hypersonic nitrogen tunnel *N*-3.

operate to 10,000 psia at 3000°K. The test gas, nitrogen, is heated by passing it down a spiral graphite resistance heater. The 20° included angle conical nozzle has a throat diameter of 0.0325 in. with an exit diameter of 6 or 8 in. In the present case, the smaller test section was employed. A centerbody conical diffusor and diverging diffusor were employed as well as a cooler to reduce the gas temperature prior to entering a vacuum manifold connected to the steam ejector. A photograph of the tunnel is shown in Fig. 1.

B. Cone Models

The present study is restricted to cones of 5°, 10°, and 15° half angle with a base diameter of 1.5 in. A photograph of some of the models is shown in Fig. 2. The cone models were designed to be either water or radiation cooled. For the cold wall tests (water cooled), the models were made from nickel electroformed on a lucite or aluminum mandrel and then ground down to size. The skin thickness was 0.020 in. The models normally had 14 pressure taps and 5 thermocouples. At one axial station, 4 pressure taps were located 90° apart and were used to align the model with the flow. The pressure taps were normally 0.024 I.D. at the model surface, connected to larger tubing between model and transducer in order to reduce the time lag in the measurement. The models were designed so that various diameter tips could be attached. The nose diameters used were 0.002, 0.038, 0.105, 0.165, and 0.225 in.

The hot models (radiation cooled) were constructed from a solid bar of stainless steel ending up with a cone shell of 0.020 in. The model was sealed at the tip to allow for various nose shapes. The pressure locations were identical to that on the cold model. Additional thermocouples were employed to determine the temperature gradient along the model.

C. Flat Plate Models

The flat plate experiments utilized two models constructed from stainless steel; one was run with a cold wall (water cooled), the other with a hot wall (radiation cooled). Both models were 3.5 in. wide, 6 in. long, and 0.5 in. thick with a leading edge wedge angle of 30°. The sharp leading edge was honed to a thickness of 0.0002 in. (estimated with a microscope). Tunnel conditions at the tip of the model were determined by an impact tube placed 0.63 in. below the leading edge. A photograph of the models is shown in Fig. 2.

Each model was fitted with 10 pressure taps along the centerline of the model, positioned from 0.27 to 5 in. from the leading edge, six of which were within 1.5 in. from the tip. Rectangular pressure taps with dimensions of 0.015 × 0.200 in. for the first four and 0.020 × 0.200 in. for the next eight were placed into the wall surface. At 1.5 in., two additional pressure taps were

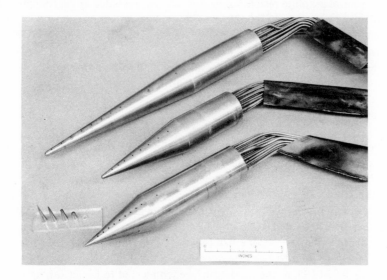

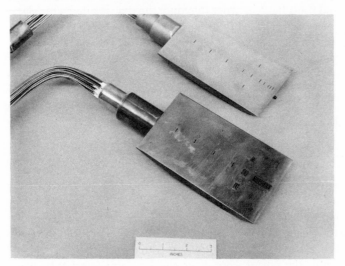

FIG. 2. Some typical cone models and flat plates.

placed at 0.75 in. on either side of the model centerline to indicate the size of the transverse wall pressure gradients. Chromel-alumel thermocouples were imbedded in the upper wall to permit continuous recording of the flat plate wall temperature.

In the case of the cooled model, a continuous stream of water was circulated to maintain the temperature of the exposed surface at about 300°K. The model contained an internal structure to maintain the upper surface flat in the face of the large pressure differential between the inner and outer surfaces of the model. Machining considerations involved with the placement of pressure taps required that the upper plate be no thicker than 0.1 in.

The hot model was not sealed, thus allowing the internal pressure to be approximately equal to the ambient pressure. Care was taken that no leaks existed on the measuring surface of the model. To allow the measuring surface to reach an equilibrium temperature as quickly as possible, this wall had a thickness of 0.017 in. Steel slugs containing the pressure taps and welded tubing were fitted into the thin plate. The resultant surface was flat to within a few thousandths of an inch.

III. Tunnel Conditions and Measurements

A. Tunnel Conditions

The measurements of the stagnation chamber conditions were outlined in detail in Vas and Koppenwallner (1964) and Vas and Harvey (1963). The high pressure in the chamber is measured by a Bourdon tube-type Heise gage. The gas stagnation temperature is indicated by the mass flow technique of Vas and Harvey (1963). The stagnation pressure varied from 2000 to 5000 psia and the stagnation temperature from 2000° to 2800°K. The test section pitot pressure was measured by a 0.5-psi absolute pressure transducer of the variable reluctance type. For frozen flow from the beginning of the nozzle, and including the effects of compressibility in the stagnation chamber, the conditions in the test section can be calculated. With the stagnation pressure and temperature range possible, the Mach number in the test section changes from 22 to 26, the static pressure from 7 to 15 μ, the free stream Reynolds number from 4000 to 16,000, and the free stream mean free path from 0.002 to 0.009 in., all owing to boundary layer variations.

B. Model Conditions

The static pressure on the models varied from about 50 to about 600 μ. For this pressure range, a 0.1-psi differential transducer of the variable reluctance type was employed (Pace). Fourteen of these transducers were used to measure the pressure on the model. A pressure of 1 μ or less was used on the reference side of the differential transducer. The output of the transducers was displayed on a Speedomax recorder and printer. Depending upon the model, the full scale reading on the recorder corresponded to about 150 μ Hg and upward. Normal reading accuracy in the range of 0 to 150 μ was about $\pm 2\,\mu$. The transducers are very sensitive to temperature change and were installed in an insulated box.

The model temperatures were recorded continuously on a Speedomax strip chart recorder. For the water cooled models, the full scale of the recorder was 0° to 80°C, using copper-constantan thermocouple wires. For the hot models, the full scale was 300° to 1300°K using chromel-alumel thermocouple wires. The accuracy of the temperature could be read to better than 1 % of the full scale value. Depending upon the model wall conditions, a calculation can be made to define a mean free path, which can have a value from 0.007 to 0.040 in. for the 5° cold model to 0.050 to 0.100 in. for the 5° hot model. The lower value on the 15° cold model is approximately 0.004 in.

C. Model and Flow Angularity

Some measurements were made in the tunnel to determine the flow angularity in the vicinity of the model location. These tests were performed with a 20° included angle wedge which had pressure taps on both surfaces. The wedge could be rotated from outside the tunnel. With this model, it was shown that the flow had an angularity of about 0.25° on the centerline of the tunnel. The flat plate model was mounted to correct for flow angularity. At one axial station on the cone models, four pressure taps were located so that the model could be aligned with the flow. For all the present set of tests, the model is essentially at zero angle of attack with respect to the flow (less than $\pm 0.2°$).

D. Outgassing of Tubes

Prior to the tests of a hot model, the tubing was thoroughly cleaned and the model baked in a vacuum oven to about 600°K. If this precaution were not taken, the model appeared to outgas in the tunnel during the test. For some cases, the model outgassed for about 40 minutes during the testing period. This trouble did not seem to occur for the water cooled models.

E. Model Temperature Gradients

For the water cooled model, no temperature gradients existed on the model skin. In the initial work done on the hot models, a temperature gradient did exist on the models. This was fairly large for the flat plate (50°K/in.) and smaller for the cones. The temperature on the plate would vary from 900°K near the front to about 700°K near the back. Later tests used lava insulators between the model and sting reducing the difference for the cone model to less than 10°K/in.

F. Thermal Transpiration Effect

For the cold model, since the pressure orifice at the model and at the point of measuring the pressure at the transducer are at the same temperature, no correction is necessary for the thermomolecular pressure effect. For the hot model with the tube Knudsen number about 0.3 and temperature ratio about 3, a correction factor in the pressure of about 25 % was obtained (Arney and Bailey, 1962).

IV. Results and Discussion

A. Cones

1. General Considerations. The pressure was measured on cones with 5°, 10°, and 15° half angles with nose bluntness of 0.002, 0.036, 0.105, 0.165, and 0.225 in. For the cold models, the wall temperature was 300°K. The hot models were radiation cooled (with some conduction losses to the model holder). The wall temperature was on the order of 900°K.

The basic data are presented as the measured pressure on the cone, p, nondimensionalized by the pitot pressure $p_{t,2}$ at the front of the cone versus the surface distance along the cone. For each model, as the stagnation pressure and temperature changed, a slight change in the free stream Mach number occurred. The free stream Mach number and Reynolds number are indicated for the different tunnel conditions for each set of data presented. The simplified Newtonian value " N " is usually indicated as well as the inviscid value as obtained from conical flow tables for $\gamma = 1.4$ (Sims, 1964). In some cases, a sliding scale is used. The pressure change due to viscous effects can be calculated by Probstein's method (1955) and the semigraphical method of Talbot et al. (1958). In the present paper, a comparison will be made only with Probstein's first order theory, where the pressure is a function of the viscous parameter $\bar{\chi}_{\infty}$.

Several theories are presently available to account for the bluntness effect of conical bodies at higher Reynolds numbers. In the present case, the parameters suggested by Cheng (1960) will be employed and his predicted values will be indicated.

2. Hot Cone. Some typical measurements on the 5° hot cone are shown in Fig. 3, for the sharpest and bluntest cone. With the sharp cone, for the lower Reynolds numbers, a pressure rise occurs at the front of the body followed by a drop in the pressure to a value higher than the inviscid value. The peak in the pressure distribution is about 3 to 4 in. from the front of the body. As the Reynolds number increases, the peak tends to move forward and the pressure decreases over the major length of the model. For the higher Reynolds numbers, the pressure level near the back of the model is slightly less than the inviscid value. In all cases, however, the pressure level is everywhere above the Newtonian value.

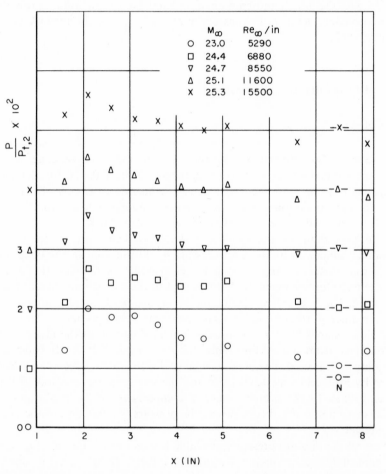

FIG. 3a. Pressure distribution on a 5° hot cone, over the Reynolds number range for $d = 0.002$ in.

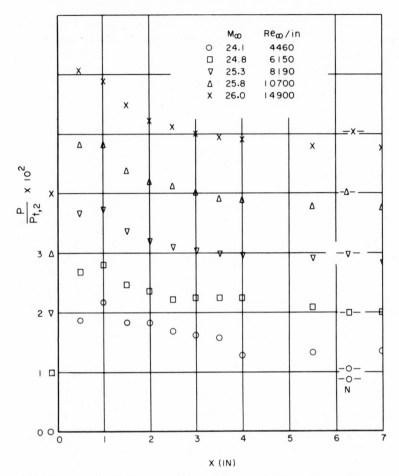

X (IN)

FIG. 3b. Pressure distribution on a 5° hot cone over the Reynolds number range for $d = 0.225$ in.

Some similar plots are shown for the blunt 5° cone with $d = 0.225$ in. For the low Reynolds number case, the pressure decays over the major portion of the model only, the first orifice recording a value less than the peak. The pressures are above the inviscid pressure level. As the Reynolds number increases the pressure on the rear portion of the model drops to below the inviscid value. For the highest Reynolds number case, the pressure decreases over the entire model.

The effect of varying the nose bluntness is shown for the lowest and highest free stream Reynolds numbers (Fig. 4). The bluntness effect at both the low- and high-free stream Reynolds number is definite but is greatly diminished at about 4 in. from the nose. At the lower free stream Reynolds numbers, the pressure level at the rear of the cone is higher than for the higher free stream Reynolds numbers. For the 5° cone, one might suspect that the viscous effect would be very large.

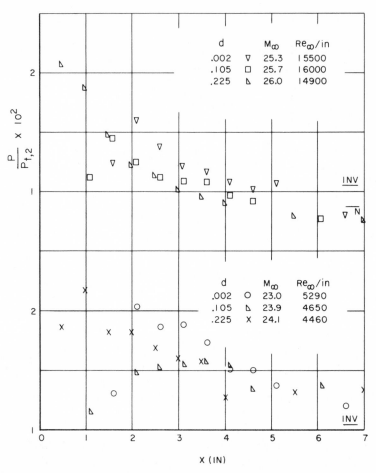

FIG. 4. Pressure distribution on a 5° hot cone for varying nose bluntness at low- and high-free stream Reynolds number.

A comparison is made between some of the present measurements and the prediction of Probstein (Fig. 5). Each set of data has a slope similar to that of the theory; however, the magnitude of the measured pressure is approximately $\frac{1}{2}$ that of the theory. For the cones with the smaller bluntness, a definite drop-off occurs at the higher values of $\bar{\chi}_\infty$ with a peak pressure at $\bar{\chi}_\infty \sim 80$.

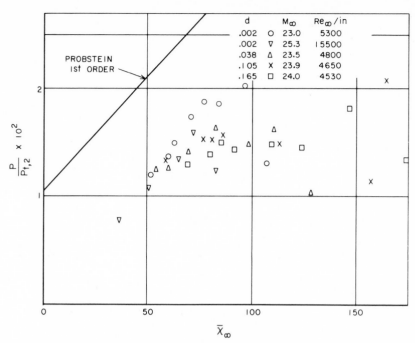

FIG. 5. Viscous correlation for the 5° hot cone.

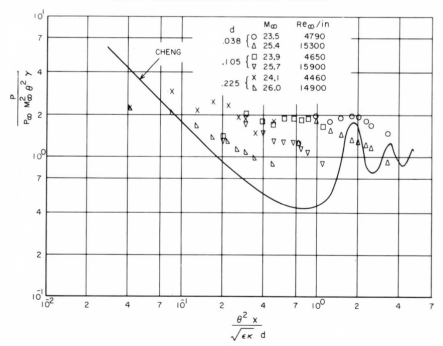

FIG. 6. Bluntness correlation for the 5° hot cone.

519

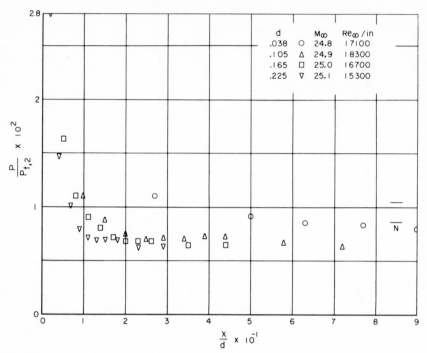

FIG. 7. Pressure on the 5° cold cone for the highest free stream Reynolds number.

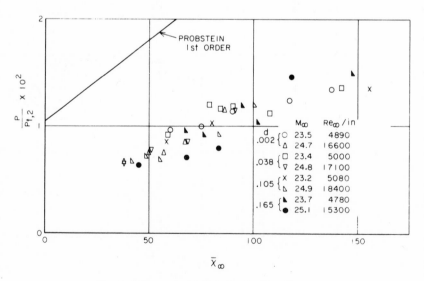

FIG. 8. Viscous correlation for the 5° cold cone.

For the larger values of d, the peak pressure tends to be larger at higher $\bar{\chi}_\infty$ primarily owing to the bluntness effect. An attempt to verify the bluntness parameter of Cheng is shown in Fig. 6. The correlation does not hold at all, very probably because the viscous effects are still quite large.

3. 5° Cold Cone. The basic data on the 5° cold cone will not be presented; only some comparisons will be made. If the flow over the model is essentially inviscid, the bluntness effect would be accounted for with an x/d parameter. For the 4 different nose diameters at the highest free stream conditions, the pressure is plotted against x/d in Fig. 7. Some reasonable agreement is noted. The pressure is plotted against the viscous parameter $\bar{\chi}_\infty$ in Fig. 8. The pressure measurements fall considerably below the theoretical prediction of Probstein (1955) and have a slope less than that of the hot wall case.

The data are also presented using Cheng's bluntness parameter in Fig. 9. Better correlation is noticed for the blunter bodies; however, when the nose diameter becomes smaller ($d = 0.038$ in.), the scatter increases.

The effect of the wall temperature is shown for a slender and blunt cone in Fig. 10 for low- and high-free stream Reynolds numbers. The data for the hot wall cone at the lower free stream Reynolds number is about 50% higher than

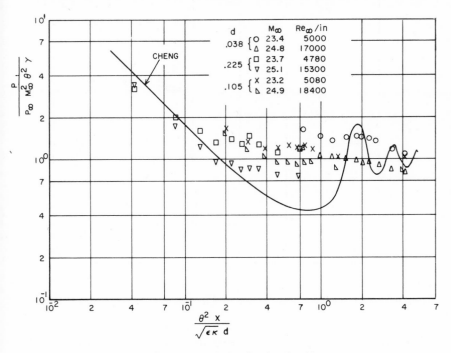

FIG. 9. Bluntness correlation for the 5° cold cone.

that for the corresponding cold slender cone. As the Reynolds number increases, the pressure levels tend to merge. Even for the blunt model, the free stream Reynolds number effect is considerable. For the high-Reynolds number case, the pressure levels approach each other near the rear of the model.

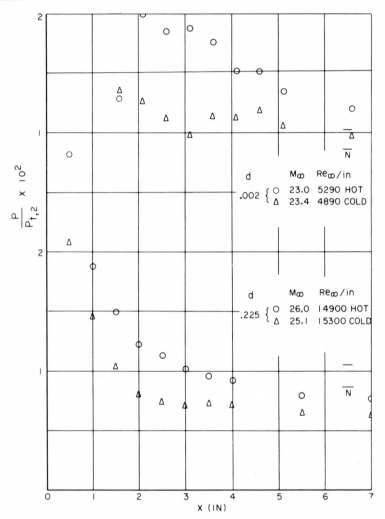

FIG. 10. Wall temperature effect on the 5° cone with varying bluntness and Reynolds number.

4. 10° Hot Cone. In general, the behavior of the pressure on the 10° hot cone is similar to that on the 5° hot cone. For small leading edge bluntness at low-free stream Reynolds number, the pressure is above the inviscid value; whereas for high-free stream Reynolds number, it is below it. For large bluntness, the pressure near the rear of the model at high Reynolds numbers definitely goes below the Newtonian pressure. The pressure near the tip is high as the effect of bluntness is felt. The effect of varying the leading edge bluntness at the lowest and highest free stream Reynolds number is shown in Fig. 11. For the high free stream Reynolds number, when the data are plotted against x/d, the variation of the pressure at any x/d is considerable. When the pressure is plotted against the viscous parameter, no trend in the data is obvious except that all the pressures are considerably below the predicted value.

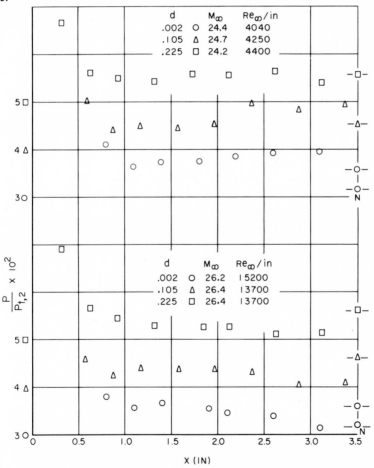

FIG. 11. Pressure distribution on a 10° hot cone for varying nose bluntness at low and high free stream Reynolds numbers.

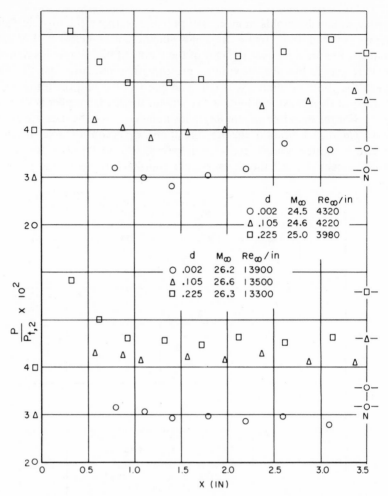

FIG. 12. Pressure distribution on a 10° cold cone for varying nose bluntness at low- and high-free stream Reynolds numbers.

5. 10° Cold Model. The effect of varying the leading edge bluntness at the lowest and highest free stream Reynolds number is shown in Fig. 12. For the low-free stream Reynolds number, the pressure over the major portion of the model is between the Newtonian and inviscid theories, with the pressure rising towards the back. For the high-free stream Reynolds number condition, the pressure is below the Newtonian value except for those points close to the tip for the large blunt nose. The bluntness effect is quite apparent. The pressure on the hot models is considerably higher than the pressure on the cold model. No correlation with the viscous parameter is at all apparent.

6. 15° Hot Cone. The pressure distributions for the 15° cone are somewhat different from those for the more slender cones. For the sharp cone, the pressure rises in the front for all the free stream Reynolds numbers. As the

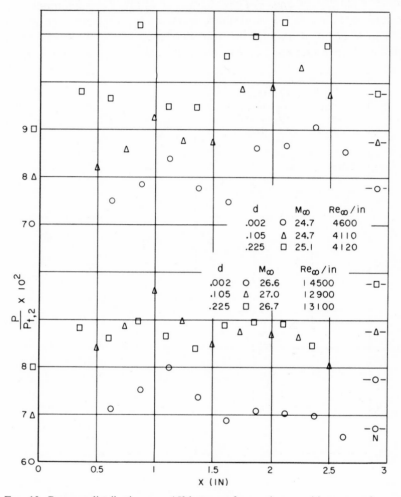

d		M_∞		Re_∞/in
.002	O	24.7		4600
.105	Δ	24.7		4110
.225	□	25.1		4120

d		M_∞		Re_∞/in
.002	O	26.6	1	4500
.105	Δ	27.0	1	2900
.225	□	26.7	1	3100

Fig. 13. Pressure distribution on a 15° hot cone for varying nose bluntness at low- and high-free stream Reynolds numbers.

bluntness increases, the pressure at the front tends to level off. For the sharp cone, over the Reynolds number range, the pressure falls between the inviscid and Newtonian values. For the blunter cones at low-Reynolds number the pressure lies between the Newtonian and inviscid values, and for high-Reynolds number it falls mainly below the Newtonian value. Some comparisons are shown in Fig. 13 with a sliding pressure scale. No correlation was observed either with the viscous or bluntness parameter.

7. 15° Cold Blunt Cone. For the sharp cone at low Reynolds number, the pressure continues to rise as distance increases from the tip. The pressure tends to level off at about 2 in. from the nose. As the Reynolds number increases the pressure rise becomes more gradual. At high-Reynolds number

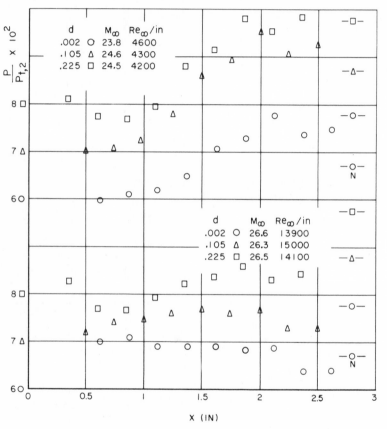

FIG. 14. Pressure distribution on a 15° cold cone for varying nose bluntness at low- and high-free stream Reynolds number.

the pressure decays along the entire model. The pressure level is usually between the Newtonian and inviscid values for low-Reynolds number and below the Newtonian value for high-Reynolds number. For the blunter noses, similar trends occur except for some small effect of the nose felt near the front of the body (Fig. 14). The data are not correlated by the viscous parameter

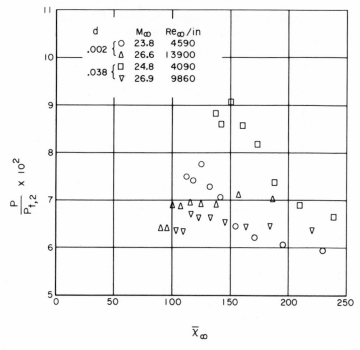

FIG. 15. Viscous correlation for the 15° cold cone.

although the pressures do tend to level off at high $\bar{\chi}_\infty$ (Fig. 15). The pressure on the hot model is higher than that on the cold model.

B. Flat Plate

The pressure distribution over a flat plate at zero angle of attack, with a sharp leading edge, and with a cold wall in high-Mach number, low-density flows have been thoroughly investigated in shock tunnel facilities (Vidal, et al., 1963; Wallace and Burke, 1963; Nagamatsu and Sheer, 1960). The chief advantage of this present work is that the Mach number is roughly the same for each test ($M_\infty \sim 25$) while the main variables are the free stream Reynolds number (5.4–14.0×10^3), and the wall to stagnation temperature ratio (0.11 and 0.4) on the flat plate surface.

Figure 16 presents the pressure data (hot wall and cold wall) in its simplest form with the wall pressure nondimensionalized by the impact pressure at the leading edge, plotted as a function of the position of the pressure orifice from the leading edge. The pressure at the rear of the model is observed to rise in the lowest Reynolds number case for the cold wall and for several of the cases for the hot wall. This may be due to the effect of the trailing edge on the boundary layer or to disturbances caused by the sting mounting. However, it is felt that the data obtained from the first 3 inches along the model surface are unaffected by downstream disturbances.

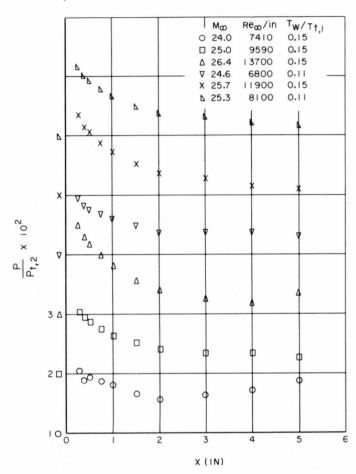

	M_∞	Re_∞/in	$T_w/T_{t,l}$
O	24.0	7410	0.15
□	25.0	9590	0.15
△	26.4	13700	0.15
▽	24.6	6800	0.11
X	25.7	11900	0.15
◭	25.3	8100	0.11

X (IN)

FIG. 16a. Pressure distribution on a sharp flat plate for varying Reynolds number, cold wall.

In Fig. 17, the wall pressure divided by the free stream pressure at the tip has been plotted as a function of the viscous interaction parameter $\bar{\chi}_\infty$ times a factor (from Cheng) to account for the variation of the wall and stagnation temperature. Several theories and proposed corrections have been included though no attempt will be made to justify any of them. The shaded portion of

Fig. 17 covers the range of the shock tunnel results previously cited and as compiled in Wallace and Burke (1963). As has been the result of all previous investigations in the $\bar{\chi}_\infty$ equal 50 to 300 range, the present pressure levels lie

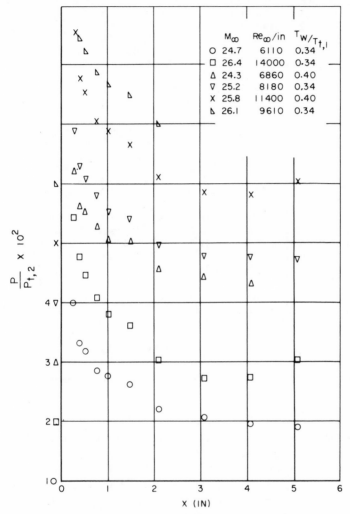

Fig. 16b. Pressure distribution on a sharp flat plate for varying Reynolds number, hot wall.

below those predicted by strong interaction theory (Cheng *et al.*, 1961). To account for the possibility that slip boundary conditions associated with an enthalpy and velocity jump at the wall near the leading edge are important, Aroesty's (1961) slip correction for an insulated wall has been applied to the

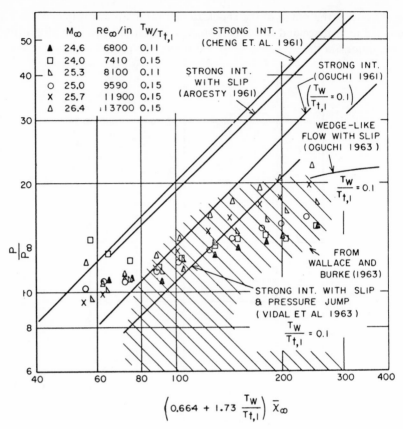

$$\left(0.664 + 1.73 \frac{T_w}{T_{t,1}}\right) \bar{X}_\infty$$

Fig. 17a. Pressure ratio on the flat plate as a function of the viscous parameter, cold wall.

strong interaction theory. Though this is an overcorrection for a noninsulated wall, its approximately 10 % reduction in the strong interaction level represents a significant undercorrection nonetheless.

It has been suggested by Vidal *et al.* (1963) that the classical slip boundary conditions must be accompanied by a pressure jump across the free molecule layer immediately above the plate surface. Though they have admitted certain inconsistencies in the approach taken to calculate the size of this pressure jump, the size of the correction is several times larger than the ordinary slip correction. This pressure jump correction to the strong interaction theory with slip, has been included in Fig. 17 using the same assumptions employed by Vidal *et al.* (1963). Of possible significance is the fact that this pressure correction curve runs through the present data equally well in both the cold and hot wall cases.

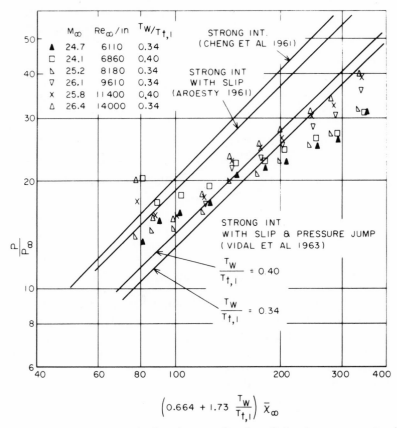

FIG. 17b. Pressure ratio on the flat plate as a function of the viscous parameter, hot wall.

Theories of Oguchi (1961, 1963) including his downstream strong inter-action limit and upstream wedgelike flow with slip are also indicated. Though the present data do not fall within the range of application of the latter theory, the tendency is for the data and theoretical curve to merge.

The primary indication of the present pressure data, all obtained at about the same free stream Mach number, is that the deviation from strong inter-action theory increases as the free stream Reynolds number is decreased, and decreases as the wall to stagnation temperature ratio is increased. In the latter case, even though slip effects at the surface will increase as the wall gets hotter, the increased viscous effects associated with a thicker boundary layer may tend to overshadow the slip effects.

Included in the Reynolds number effect on the pressure level is a somewhat different power law dependence than that contained in the viscous interaction

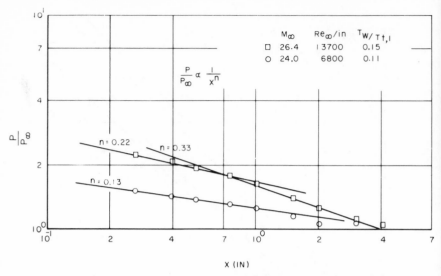

FIG. 18a. Pressure distribution on the cold flat plate, power law variation.

parameter $\bar{\chi}_\infty$ where $p/p_\infty \propto x^{-1/2}$. This effect has also been observed previously (Vidal *et al.*, 1963). Figure 18 indicates the power law to give the best fit for the highest and lowest Reynolds number in each of the cold and hot wall cases. The pressure on the hot wall, while having a level closer to strong interaction theory than does the cold wall, also indicates a power law closer to that of strong interaction theory.

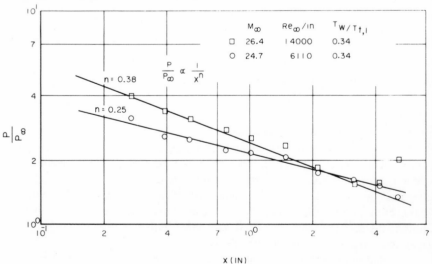

FIG. 18b. Pressure distribution on the hot flat plate, power law variation.

V. Concluding Remarks

Several experiments have been conducted in a Mach 25 continuous wind tunnel using nitrogen as the test gas. The free stream Reynolds number varied from 4000 to 16,000 and the mean free path from 0.002 to 0.009 in. Pressure measurements were made on sharp flat plates and sharp and blunted cones with cold wall ($\sim 300°$K) and hot wall ($\sim 900°$K) conditions. The mean free path using the hot wall conditions was calculated to be as high as 0.1 in.

The hot cone models give higher pressures than the cold models. The pressures measured on all models fall considerably below the theoretically predicted value of Probstein (1955). The pressure on the 5° hot cone reaches a peak value for the small bluntness cases at a $\bar{\chi}_\infty$ of about 80. However, the pressure on the cold model tends to rise even at values of $\bar{\chi}_\infty$ about 150. The pressure on the blunt 5° model does not agree with Cheng's theory for blunt slender cones. The pressures on the 10° cones could not be correlated using either the viscous or bluntness parameter.

The pressure distribution on the 15° models is considerably different from that for the more slender cases. The pressure tends to rise with distance from the tip: The effect of bluntness is negligible. The pressure level is not predicted by the viscous theory of Probstein.

The pressure distribution over the sharp flat plates was found to be considerably below that predicted by strong interaction theory and is consistent with shock tube data. Closer correlation is obtained, however, as the free stream Reynolds number and wall temperature are increased. As these conditions are reduced, the power law function of the surface pressure further deviates from that contained in the viscous interaction parameter $\bar{\chi}_\infty$.

List of Symbols

C Constant in the temperature-viscosity relationship
$$\mu/\mu_\infty = C(T/T_\infty)$$
d Nose diameter
k Nose drag coefficient
M_∞ Mach number at model tip
p Measured pressure on wall surface
p_∞ Free stream static pressure at model tip
$p_{t,1}$ Stagnation pressure
$p_{t,2}$ Pitot pressure at model tip

Re_∞ Reynolds number based on free stream conditions
$T_{t,1}$ Stagnation temperature
T_w Model wall temperature
x Surface distance from model tip
γ Ratio of specific heats
ε $(\gamma - 1)/(\gamma + 1)$
θ Cone half angle
$\bar{\chi}_\infty$ Hypersonic viscous parameter
$$M_\infty^3 C^{1/2}/(Re_{\infty,x})^{1/2}$$

REFERENCES

Arney, D. G., Jr., and Bailey, A. B. (1962). AEDC-TDR-62-188.

Aroesty, J. (1961). ARL Rept. 64.

Cheng, H. K. (1960). Cornell Aero. Lab. Inc. Rept. AF-1285-A-4.

Cheng, H. K., Hall, J. G., Golian, J. C., and Herztberg, A. (1961). *J. Aerospace Sci.* **28**, 353–381.

Nagamatsu, H. T., and Sheer, R. E., Jr. (1960). *ARS (Am. Rocket Soc.) J.* **5**, 454–462.

Probstein, R. F. (1955). ARL TR AF 279811.

Oguchi, H. (1961). *In* "Rarefied Gas Dynamics" (L. Talbot, ed.), pp. 501–524. Academic Press, New York.

Oguchi, H. (1963). *In* "Rarefied Gas Dynamics" (J. A. Laurmann, ed.), Vol. II, pp. 181–193. Academic Press, New York.

Sims, J. L. (1964 April). Private communication, Marshall Space Flight Center.

Talbot, L., Koga, T., and Sherman, P. M. (1958). NACA TN 4327.

Vas, I. E., and Harvey, J. K. (1963). Princeton Univ. Aero. Eng. Rept. 669.

Vas, I. E., and Koppenwallner, G. (1964) Princeton Univ. Aero. Eng. Rept. 690.

Vidal, R. J., Golian, J. C., and Bartz, J. (1963). AIAA Paper No. 63-435.

Wallace, J. E., and Burke, A. F. (1963). ASD-TDR-63-772 (Flat plate portion–Unclassified).

Experimental Study of Low Pressure Hypersonic Flow by Using an Electron Beam Densitometer

ISAMU WADA

National Aerospace Laboratory, Chohu, Tokyo, Japan

A double-diaphragm shock tunnel has been operated at low pressure conditions. An electron beam densitometer has been developed for flow measurements in the test section of the shock tunnel. A flat plate with a sharp leading edge is investigated in the present experiments in a hypersonic flow having a Mach number of 6.5 and Reynolds numbers of 16,000, 2000, and 1000 per centimeter. The pressure on the surface is obtained from the density measured by the densitometer. At large Reynolds numbers the induced surface pressure near the leading edge agrees with the strong and weak interaction theories. The experimental results at small Reynolds numbers indicate significantly smaller values than those predicted by the strong interaction theory and agree with the weak interaction theory. Finally, the pressure ratio downstream approaches the value predicted by the wedge-like solution. A flat-nosed cylinder in a hypersonic flow having a Mach number of 6.5 and a Reynolds number of 9500 based on the diameter of the cylinder is also investigated. The experimental result is compared with the blast wave theory. The density profile of the boundary layer on the surface is presented. Photographs of the flow around a cylinder are obtained by scanning the flow field with the electron beam.

I. Introduction

When ρ_{ata} represents the density of air at sea level, then the density is $10^{-2}\rho_{ata}$, $10^{-3}\rho_{ata}$, and $10^{-6}\rho_{ata}$ at altitudes of 30, 50, and 100 km, respectively. A double-diaphragm shock tunnel has been operated at low-pressure conditions in order to simulate the hypersonic flight of a rocket at high altitude. An electron beam densitometer has been developed for the measurement of the flow in the test section, instead of the Mach-Zehnder interferometer previously used (Wada, 1963a). The distribution of air density along the model surface is also measured by the densitometer. The pressure on the model surface can

FIG. 1. Hypersonic shock tunnel, electron beam densitometer mounted on the tunnel and Mach-Zehnder interferometer.

be calculated from the measured density because the wall temperature of the models is almost constant and equal to the initial temperature. [The induced surface pressure near the sharp leading edge of a flat plate model agrees with the strong and weak interaction theories and other experimental results. (Wada and Soga, 1963b)].

In the present experiment, the free-stream density at the test section ranges from $0.0047\rho_{ata}$ to $0.00028\rho_{ata}$. The distributions of density around models in a hypersonic flow having a Mach number of 6.5 and Reynolds numbers of 1.6×10^4, 2×10^3, and 1×10^3 per centimeter are determined by using the densitometer. The density of air at the model surface is below $0.003\rho_{ata}$.

Chuan and Waiter (1963) described experimental results for the induced surface pressure near the leading edge of the plate at Mach numbers of 6 and 8 in comparison with Oguchi's theory (1961) and strong interaction theory. The present experiment is designed to extend their results to larger hypersonic parameters at a Mach number of 6 and to investigate the downstream limit of wedge-like flow.

The distributions of density around a cylinder in hypersonic flow are determined by the same method at a Reynolds number of 9.5×10^3 based on the cylinder diameter.

A second densitometer designed for taking pictures of the flow is described in the Appendix.

II. Experimental Equipment

A. Hypersonic Shock Tunnel

A photograph of the hypersonic shock tunnel, the electron-beam densitometer and a Mach-Zehnder interferometer is shown in Fig. 1.

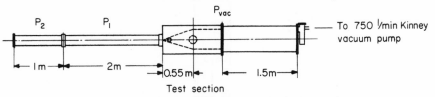

FIG. 2. Schematic diagram of hypersonic shock tunnel.

The hypersonic shock tunnel is shown in a schematic diagram in Fig. 2. The shock tunnel, which was studied by Tamaki and Kim (1956, 1957), consists of a high and a medium pressure channel and a vacuum chamber. The test section has a rectangular cross section of 30×6 cm and the throat of the nozzle has a section 0.4×6 cm. In the present case, the vacuum chamber can

TABLE I

OPERATING AND FREE-STREAM CONDITIONS

Initial pressure			Free stream		
High-pressure channel, P_2 (ata)	Low-pressure channel, P_1 (ata)	Vacuum chamber, P_{vac} (mm Hg)	$(\rho_\infty/\rho_{ata})_{mean}$	M	Re/cm
12	1	2.0		6.5	
6	1/2	1.0	0.0072	6.5	23,700
4	1/3	0.7	0.0047	6.5	16,000
1/2	1/24	0.08	0.00057	6.5	2,000
1/4	1/48	0.03	0.00028	6.5	1,000

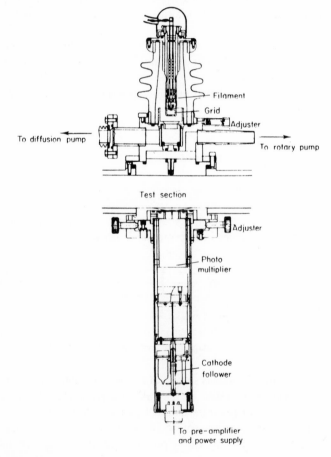

FIG. 3. Arrangement of electron beam densitometer mounted on the wall of test section.

be evacuated to a pressure of 20 μ Hg. Cellophane is used as the diaphragm material and a kind of gelatine (Oblate, G) is used for the second diaphragm for the experiments at low pressure. The free-stream density at the test section is shown in Table I. The establishment of the hypersonic flow in the test section is confirmed by the free-stream density measured by the densitometer.

B. Electron Beam Densitometer

The electron beam densitometer consists of an electron beam generator and the instrument for determining the beam intensity as shown in Fig. 3. The principle of this densitometer is known as an absorption method. The generator of the beam is made of an electron gun from an electron microscope. The platinum filament, covered with an oxide emitter, is mounted in the gun, which is evacuated to a pressure below 10^{-4} mm Hg. A differential pumping chamber is located between the filament chamber and the test section. A plastic phosphor scintillator, with a surface coating of sputtered aluminum, is used as a beam detector. The output of the photomultiplier measuring the scintillator output is connected to the preamplifier of a synchroscope. The calibration of the densitometer is shown in Fig. 4. In the case of lower pressures, a Faraday cage is available for the measurement of the beam intensity. The calibration with the Faraday cage is also shown in Fig. 4. A block diagram for the instrumentation is shown in Fig. 5.

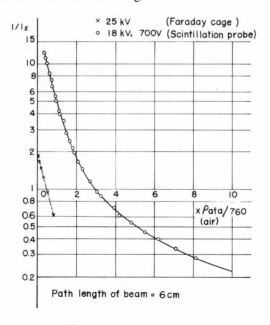

FIG. 4. Result of calibration of electron beam densitometer.

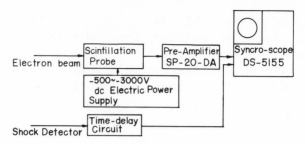

FIG. 5. Block diagram for the measurement of the intensity of electron beam.

III. Experimental Results

The operating and the free-stream conditions in the test section are shown in Table I. The experimental results confirm the establishment of hypersonic flow in the shock tunnel even at small Reynolds numbers.

A. Sharp Leading Edge Problem

An interferogram of the flow over the plate model is shown in Fig. 6. The shapes of shock wave and boundary layer over the plate at a Mach number of 6.5 and a Reynolds number of 16,000 per centimeter can be observed in this picture obtained by a Mach-Zehnder interferometer. However, it is difficult to determine the density of the undisturbed flow and that in the boundary layer. It is also impossible to get meaningful results with the interferometer in the case of small Reynolds numbers.

The variations of density with time at several points near the surface of the flat plate are measured by the electron beam densitometer. (Fig. 7). The density approaches a steady state value about 0.5 msec after the first shock. The time necessary for the establishment of steady-state conditions near the model is greater than that of the free stream. This seems to be the effect of the boundary layer growth on the plate. A typical density distribution along a direction perpendicular to the surface is shown in Fig. 8. Van Driest (1952) treats the temperature distribution across the boundary layer on a flat plate of constant temperature. When the wall-to-free-stream temperature ratio T_w/T_∞ is 5.25 and the Mach number is 6.5, the variation of temperature is considered small from the surface to a value for $(y/x)(\mathrm{Re}_x)^{1/2}$ of about 5 to 10. In the present experiments, the distance of the nearest measuring point to the surface was 0.2 mm, satisfying this criterion. The pressure can therefore be calculated when the wall temperature of bodies is assumed to be almost constant and to be equal to the initial temperature. Figure 9 shows the pressure distribution on the plate at a Reynolds number of 16,000 per centimeter. The nondimensional pressure ratio p/p_∞ on the plate is plotted against the hypersonic parameter, $x = M^3 c^{1/2}/(\mathrm{Re}_x)^{1/2}$, and is compared with other experimental as well as theoretical results (Hayes and Probstein, 1959) in Fig. 10. In this range of the hypersonic parameter the results agree with the weak and strong interaction theories for the insulated wall case.

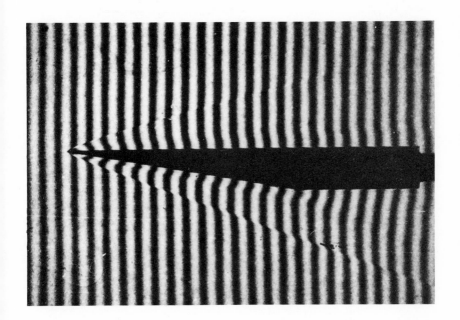

FIG. 6. Interferogram of the flow over a flat plate $M = 6.5$, Re/cm = 16,000.

The pressure distributions on the plate at Reynolds numbers of 16,000, 2000, and 1000 per centimeter are shown in Fig. 11. In the case of small Reynolds numbers, the induced pressure ratio is significantly smaller than the values predicted by the strong interaction theory, as presented by Chuan-Waiter's experiment at $M = 6$. Finally, the pressure ratio approaches the value predicted by the wedge-like solution at higher values for the interaction parameter.

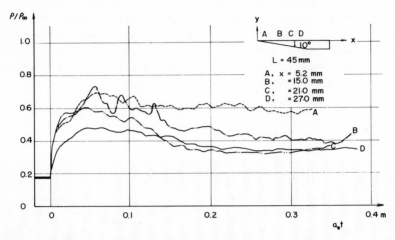

FIG. 7. Variation of density with time at several points ($a_* = 400$ m/sec, sonic velocity at nozzle throat).

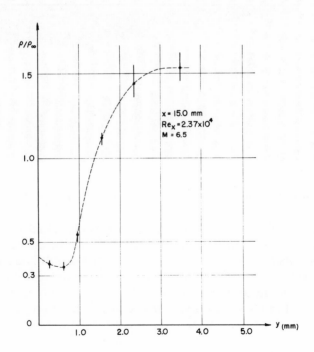

FIG. 8. Density profile of the boundary layer at $x = 15$ mm.

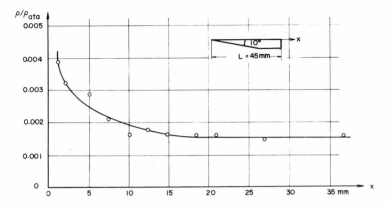

FIG. 9. Pressure distribution on a flat plate with a sharp leading edge.

B. Blunt-Nosed Cylinder

The shape of the bow wave and the pressure distribution on the surface of blunt-nosed bodies are described by the blast wave theory. The hypersonic flow field around bodies is treated by Seiff (1962) and his theory is compared with the experimental results. Distributions of the density across the

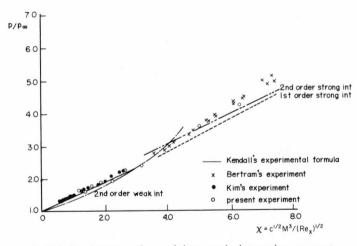

FIG. 10. Relation between p/p_∞ and hypersonic interaction parameter χ.

flow behind the bow wave of a flat-nosed cylinder are measured by using the electron-beam densitometer at values for x/d of 0.5, 1.0, 2.0, and 3.0, where d is the cylinder diameter and x is the distance along the axis as measured from the nose. Figure 12 shows the comparison between the present experimental

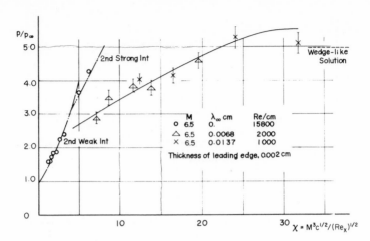

Fig. 11. Relation between p/p_∞ and χ at Re/cm = 16,000, 2000, and 1000.

result and the theory. The quantity r is the distance from the axis of the cylinder and the subscript star($_*$) refers to the value just behind the shock. The
solid black points show the estimated value of the density based on the initial
temperature of the surface and the pressure calculated with the blast wave
theory. These distributions agree with the results of the blast wave theory.

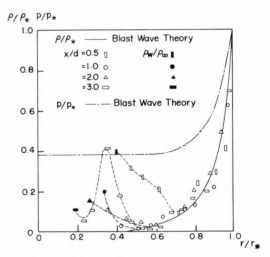

Fig. 12. Distributions of density around a flat-nosed cylinder.

However, the density distributions near the surface of the body do not agree
with theory because of the effect of the boundary layer on the cylinder as can
be seen from Fig. 12. At $x/d = 3.0$, it seems to be a shock.

Drag coefficient is calculated with Probstein's method (1956). The positions of the wall in Fig. 12 are different from those predicted by the theory, because the experimental values of r_* are greater than the theoretical results (Chernyi, 1961). Wilbey (1962) shows the distribution of pressure around a hemisphere-cylinder and compares the experimental result with the blast wave theory. The agreement between theory and experiment in his case is much better than the present result. Apparently the nose shape is an important factor.

IV. Conclusions

The present paper describes the possibility of experiments in hypersonic flow at low pressure by using a double-diaphragm shock tunnel and an electron beam densitometer.

The sharp leading edge problem of insulated and noninsulated flat plates has been studied theoretically and experimentally by many authors. At a Reynolds number of 16,000 per centimeter the induced surface pressure measured in the present experiments agrees with the strong and weak inter-action theories as shown in Fig. 10. In this case there appears to be no effect of heat transfer at the wall on the induced surface pressure, as is predicted by Li and Nagamatsu (1955).

The problem of the sharp leading edge in hypersonic flow at large Mach numbers and small Reynolds numbers was investigated by Nagamatsu and Sheer (1959). Comparison of the theory by Oguchi (1961) with these experimental results indicates good agreement. The present experiments show values between the weak interaction region and the wedge-like solution flow region at $M = 6.5$ and $T_w/T_0 = 0.60$. The values are smaller than those found by Chuan and Waiter (1963) at $M = 8$. At small hypersonic parameters, the present results approach their results at $M = 6$ and the values predicted by the weak interaction theory.

The flow past axisymmetric bodies at hypersonic speeds will be investigated by the present method and an electron beam fluorescence method in order to obtain the aerodynamic characteristics of a rocket. The experiments will in the future be extended to the case of hypersonic flow at lower pressures.

ACKNOWLEDGMENTS

The author would like to express his sincere thanks to Professor F. Tamaki, the University of Tokyo, for his valuable suggestion and discussion of this problem. He wishes to thank the late Dr. F. Nakanishi and Mr. I. Hiraki of the National Aerospace Laboratory, Japan, for their encouragement during the course of the experiments.

He is also indebted to Mr. K. Soga for his help in conducting the experiments and to Dr. Y. Kiuchi, Central Research Laboratory, Tokyo-Shibaura Electric Company, for preparing the new gun for the second electron beam densitometer.

Appendix

A second densitometer was especially made for taking pictures of the gas flow. The electron gun of a cathode-ray tube is mounted in a high-vacuum chamber and deflection plates to allow scanning by the beam are mounted in an inter-

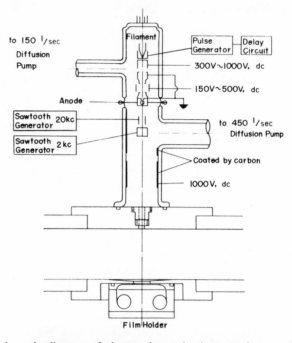

FIG. 13. Schematic diagram of electron beam densitometer for scanning.

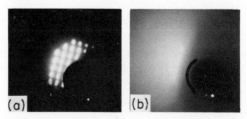

FIG. 14. Experimental result. (a) 11 keV, $\rho = 0.000066\rho_{ata}$ (still air); diameter of cylinder $= 0.4$ cm. (b) $M = 6.5$, $\rho = 0.00115\rho_{ata}$; position of surface of cylinder is marked.

mediate chamber. The inside wall of the intermediate chamber is coated by carbon (Aquadag) and this coating is connected to a 1000 V dc power supply to obtain a parallel electron beam. A thin molybdenum plate of 5 mm diameter having $200\,\mu$ diameter holes at $500\,\mu$ intervals is inserted as a window between the test section and the intermediate chamber. Fine grain positive film or electron-microscopic plate is used in a film holder. A schematic diagram of the densitometer is shown in Fig. 13. Photographs obtained with this device of the density near a cylinder without flow as well as for the case of the same cylinder in an $M = 6.5$ flow are shown in Fig. 14. The shock wave can be clearly seen in Fig. 14b.

REFERENCES

Chuan, R. L., and Waiter, S. A. (1963). *In* "Rarefied Gas Dynamics" (J. A. Laurmann, ed.), Vol. II, pp. 328–342. Academic Press, New York.

Chernyi, G. G. (1961). "Introduction to Hypersonic Flow." Academic Press, New York.

Hayes, W. D., and Probstein, R. F. (1959). "Hypersonic Flow Theory." Academic Press, New York.

Li, T. Y., and Nagamatsu, H. T. (1955). Purdue Eng. Ser., 128. pp. 273–287.

Nagamatsu, H. T., and Sheer, R. E., Jr. (1960). *ARS* (*Am. Rocket Soc.*) *J.* 30, 454–462.

Oguchi, H. (1961). *In* "Rarefied Gas Dynamics" (L. Talbot, ed.), pp. 328–342. Academic Press, New York.

Probstein, R. F. (1956). WADC TN 56-395.

Seiff, A., and Whiting, E. E. (1961). NASA TN D 1148.

Seiff, A. (1962). NASA SP 11, 269–282.

Tamaki, F. (1956). *J, Phys. Soc. Japan* 11, 803–804.

Tamaki, F., and Kim, C. S. (1957). *J. Phys. Soc. Japan* 12, 550–555.

Van Driest, E. R. (1952). NACA TN 2597.

Wada, I. (1963a). Natl. Aerospace Lab. Rept. TR–37T.

Wada, I., and Soga, K. (1963b) In *5th Intern. Symp. Space Tech. and Sci., Tokyo* (to be published).

Wilbey, P. G. (1962). *FFA Rept.* No. 92 (Flygtekniska Foersoeksanstalten, Meddelande).

Experimental Investigation of Low-Density Axial Flow through Short Tapered Ducts

T. ROGERS

The Marquardt Corporation, Van Nuys, California

AND

J. C. WILLIAMS, III

North Carolina State of the University of North Carolina at Raleigh, North Carolina

Measurements of wall static pressure and stream total pressure distributions were made in short two-dimensional axisymmetric ducts placed in a hypersonic low-density gas stream. It was found that, if the duct forms a convergent or constant area channel, a thick normal shock wave forms ahead of the duct, and the flow within the duct is subsonic. If the duct forms a slightly divergent channel, a shock-line transition[1] originates at the duct lip and extends downstream within the duct. The shape of this shock-like transition is defined from the impact pressure distributions within the duct.

The flow field downstream of the shock-like transition is characterized by: (1) large slip velocities at the wall, especially near the leading edge of the duct; (2) a fairly rapid static pressure increase over the first two-thirds of the length of the duct and a slight decrease in static pressure beyond this point; and (3) fully viscous flow throughout the duct. Owing to the large viscous losses in the duct, the average pressure recovery at the end of the duct is of the order of the pressure recovery through a normal shock wave at the free stream Mach number.

The skin friction found by momentum balance agreed fairly well with that found by suitably integrating the local skin friction obtained from velocity profiles. The skin friction coefficients obtained were greater than predicted.

[1] A descriptive term used by Chuan (1963) to describe the broad region of increasing pitot pressure from the free stream to the viscous region which has the characteristic of a shock wave in emanating from the leading edge in a straight line but across which the pressure transition is not constant and behind which the flow is fully viscous.

I. Introduction

Although external rarefied gas flows have been studied extensively in recent years, studies of internal hypersonic rarefied flows seem virtually nonexistent. The problem of effusive free molecular flow into ducts of any length seems adequately described by the Clausing (1932) theory. In the continuum regime flow in ducts and channels is adequately understood and is described reasonably well by either a quasi-one-dimensional approach or through the use of boundary layer theory. The intervening regimes of slip and transitional flow are, however, neither well understood nor adequately described either theoretically or experimentally. To the author's knowledge the only experimental study of such flows is that of Collins (1959) in which a study was made of the pressure recovery in a converging-diverging supersonic diffuser at Mach numbers up to 4 and at a static pressure of approximately 100μ. At higher Mach numbers and/or lower pressures there appears to be no further information available.

In view of the importance of low-density internal flows in propulsion system inlets and exhaust systems, in low-density hypersonic wind tunnel diffusers, and in flow measuring devices, the lack of information on such systems is surprising. This is especially true when it is realized that the effects of gas rarefaction in these devices may be manifest as very large viscous dissipation, in very strong interaction between shock wave systems and the viscous flow field, in slip at the wall, etc., at very low densities. All of these phenomena can seriously affect the performance of the devices mentioned above.

It is against this background that the studies to be described herein were initiated. The present paper presents the results of an experimental investigation of hypersonic rarefied gas flow in short ducts. No attempt was made to design an efficient inlet or diffuser; indeed, at this point it is impossible to determine what an efficient diffuser entails. Instead, the present experiments were designed to yield some physical insight into the manifold problems of low density internal hypersonic flow and to furnish a description of the flow field upon which theories may be developed.

II. Experimental Apparatus

A. Test Facility

The experiments to be described herein were conducted in the University of Southern California Engineering Center low density hypersonic wind tunnel. This wind tunnel employs a large helium cryopump to maintain flow through supersonic or hypersonic nozzles of the free jet type. The present tests were conducted slightly downstream of the exit plane of the large (12-in. diameter) nozzle. At this point there is a usable core of about $2\frac{1}{2}$ to 3 in. diameter in which the Mach number is approximately 9.38 and the static pressure is approximately 1μ. The free stream Knudsen number and Reynolds number, based on duct diameter, for the present test were approximately 0.075 and 650, respectively. Additional details on the design, construction and calibration of this wind tunnel were given by Chuan *et al.* (1960).

B. Models Tested

Two types of ducts were employed in the present tests: two-dimensional and axisymmetric ducts. The two-dimensional duct was used to determine the area ratio (inlet to exit area) required for the duct to " swallow " the shock-like transition and to determine the effect of area ratio on the static pressure distribution within the duct. The term " swallow " is used here to describe the condition in which the shock-like transition lies entirely within the duct as opposed to the condition where a strong thick normal shock wave lies ahead of the duct. The axisymmetric ducts were designed on the basis of information gained from the two-dimensional duct tests. Detailed studies were made of the flow field in the axisymmetric ducts.

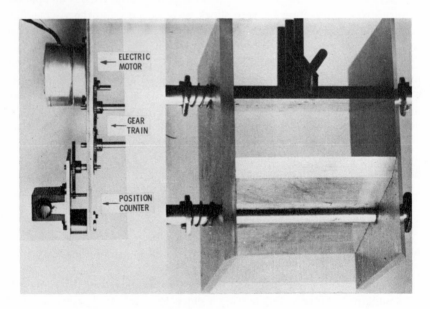

FIG. 1. Flat plate duct with sidewalls (actuating mechanism shown).

I. Rectangular Ducts

The two-dimensional duct consists basically of two steel flat plates designed so that each rotates about an axis through its midchord point. The shafts on which the plates rotate are geared together so that the leading edges of the plates can either converge or diverge together, thereby forming, respectively, a divergent, convergent, or a constant width channel. The midchord separation between the plates is constant at 1.5 in. To this basic configuration are added two steel side walls to prevent spanwise flow. The leading edges of the upper and lower plates and or both sidewalls are beveled on the outside to form sharp edges. Five static pressure taps are located at distances of 0.25, 0.75, 1.25, 2.0, and 2.75 in. from the leading edge of the upper plate.

The shafts on which the upper and lower plates are mounted are driven through a gear train by a small electric motor. A counter connected to the gear train indicates the relative orientation of the plates. Thus, the relative orientation of the plates can be controlled and measured from a remote location outside the wind tunnel shell. The two-dimensional duct in a closed (divergent channel) configuration is shown in Fig. 1.

2. Axisymmetric Ducts

Two axisymmetric ducts were constructed, their designs being based on the results of the two-dimensional duct tests. In each the internal contour was that of a frustum of a cone. The internal divergence half angles were $\frac{1}{2}$ and 2 degrees, respectively. Each axisymmetric duct was 3 in. long and had an internal diameter of 1.71 in. at the exit plane. The area ratios (inlet to exit area) were 1.06 and 1.30, respectively. The outside of each duct was cylindrical, and the leading edges were beveled on the outside to yield sharp leading edges. Both axisymmetric ducts were machined with great care from mild steel stock. Five pressure taps were machined into the wall of each duct at distances of 0.25, 0.75, 1.25, 2.0, and 2.75 in. from the leading edge so that wall static pressure distributions could be measured.

C. Pressure Measurements

The static pressure taps on either the two-dimensional or axisymmetric ducts were connected by short flexible tubing to five capacitance pressure transducers which were mounted just above the free jet nozzle within the wind tunnel pressure shell. The five transducers are all referenced to the static pressure within the tunnel pressure shell. This static pressure is measured on a McLeod gage. The signal from the pressure transducers is carried electrically through the tunnel shell and read on a digital voltmeter.

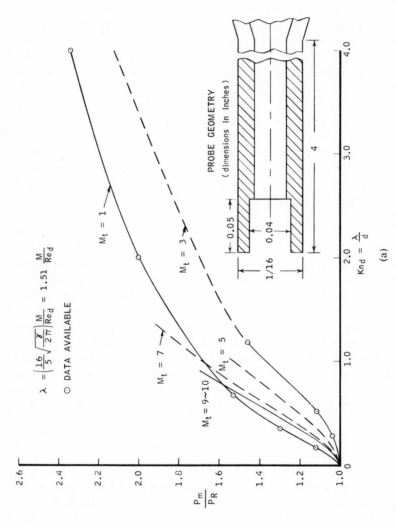

FIG. 2. (a, b) Impact pressure probe characteristics.

Impact pressure surveys were made using an open-ended pitot tube made of $\frac{1}{16}$ in. o.d., $\frac{1}{32}$ in. i.d. stainless steel tubing (see insert on Figure 2a). The impact pressure probe was connected directly to a differential pressure transducer which was referenced to the static pressure within the tunnel shell. The probe-transducer combination was mounted directly on the wind tunnel probe traversing mechanism. This traversing mechanism has 3 degrees of freedom so that complete impact pressure surveys within the ducts are possible. In the present tests, however, only 2 degrees of freedom were generally used because of the flow symmetry in the axisymmetric ducts. The output signal of the impact pressure transducer is carried through the tunnel pressure shell electrically and is used as the input to the abscissa of an x-y plotter. The y coordinate of the impact pressure probe within the duct is fed into the ordinate of the x-y plotter.

It is well known that the indication of an impact pressure probe used at low-Reynolds numbers must be corrected for viscous and free molecule effects on the probe. Early attempts to apply probe corrections extracted from the literature were unsatisfactory. The probe actually used in the tests described in this paper was recently calibrated in the same wind tunnel as part of an extensive study of viscous flow corrections to impact probes, the results of which are presented elsewhere in this symposium (Rogers *et al.*, 1964). The data made available for this probe are shown by solid lines on Fig. 2a. Interpolations of the data are shown dotted in the same figure. The subsonic probe characteristics assumed are shown in Fig. 2b. A convenient interpretation of the probe data, made possible by the fact that all the tests were run at the same total conditions of pressure and temperature, is shown in Fig. 3.

Finally, all pressure transducers used in the present tests were calibrated periodically during the test period to minimize the effects of drift.

III. Results

A. Results of Rectangular Duct Tests

The two-dimensional model was tested in the low-density wind tunnel at the following free stream conditions:

$$M_\infty = 8.74$$
$$p_\infty = 1.46\mu \text{ Hg}$$
$$\text{Re}_\infty = 790 \quad \text{\Big\} Based on plate separation at the mid-chord point}$$
$$\text{Kn} = 0.054 \quad (1.5 \text{ in.})$$

With these free stream conditions the angle of incidence of the plates was varied so that the plates formed either a convergent or a divergent duct and impact pressure surveys were made within the duct to determine whether

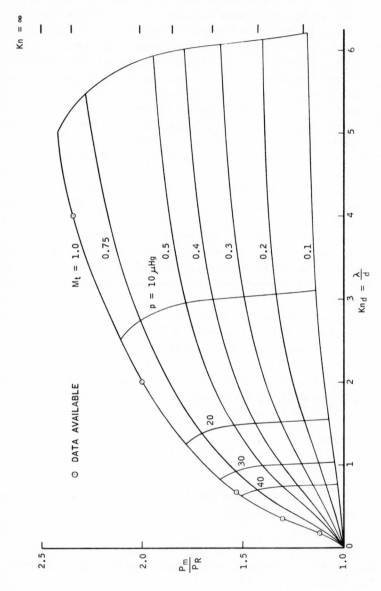

Fig. 2b.

there was a strong normal shock wave ahead of the duct or a shock-like
transition within the duct.

If a strong normal shock wave lies ahead of the duct, then the flow within
the duct is subsonic, and the total pressure varies smoothly from the wall to

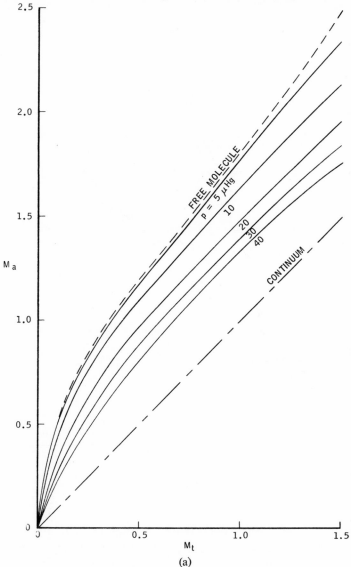

(a)

FIG. 3. (a, b) Probe characteristics—apparent versus true Mach number for test
conditions. Supply conditions: $P_s = 25$ mm Hg, $T_s = 530°$R, nitrogen gas.

the centerline of the duct. This variation arises from the entirely viscous nature of the flow within the duct. Furthermore, since the flow is subsonic, the local total pressure does not vary considerably from the local static pressure.

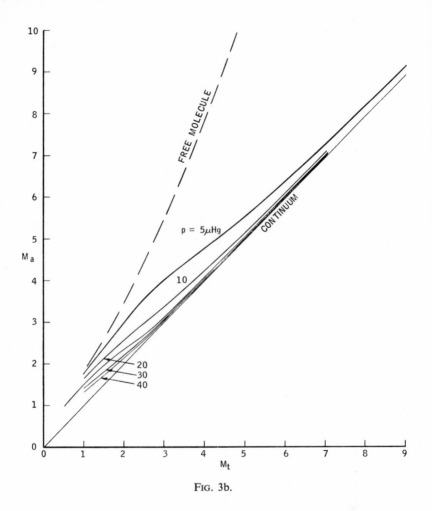

FIG. 3b.

If a shock-like transition (thick shock wave) occurs within the duct, extending downstream from the leading edge, then the impact probe can be traversed through it from wall to centerline or vice versa. Since the Mach number ahead of the shock-like transition is high, the dissipation through the probe shock wave will be large and the measured impact pressure will be low.

As the probe moves away from the centerline, it passes through the shock-like transition which originates at the lip. Once behind this transition, the probe measures a pressure which reflects both the dissipation in the shock-like transition and through the probe shock wave. This combined dissipation of the oblique shock-like transition and the probe normal shock wave at the lower Mach number is less than the dissipation through the normal shock wave on the probe when exposed to the free stream Mach number. Thus, the measured pressure rises as the probe moves from the centerline through the shock-like transition. As the probe moves closer to the wall, the pressure measured decreases as the result of dissipation in the viscous layer.

Therefore, if a shock-like transition exists within the duct, the impact pressure is low near the centerline, rises and passes through a broad peak defining the shock-like transition, and drops rapidly in the viscous region near the wall. This shock-like transition which exhibits characteristics of a shock wave by resulting in a rise in impact pressure and in emanating from the leading edge in a straight line (at least for some short distance), yet across which the pressure transition is not constant and behind which the flow is fully viscous was observed in their flat plate experiments by Chuan and Waiter (1963) who described it as a "shock-like transition."

The presence of a shock-like transition can be detected then from an impact pressure survey. The two-dimensional duct was tested at a number of incidence angles, and impact pressure surveys were made at each incidence angle. In this manner it was determined that the shock-like transition lies within the duct for all negative incidence angles greater than $\frac{1}{4}°$,i.e., for all area ratios (exit to inlet areas) greater than 1.009. Thus, with a very small wall divergence it was possible to swallow the shock-like transition in spite of the very thick viscous layers in the duct. Downstream of the shock-like transition the impact pressure decreases continuously as the probe moves from the centerline to the wall, indicating that viscous effects extend over the entire width of the channel.

Wall static pressure distributions in the two-dimensional duct are shown in Fig. 4 as a function of the axial distance along the duct for one case ($\alpha = 0$) where the normal shock wave lies ahead of the body and for several cases where the shock-like transition lies within the duct ($\alpha \geq \frac{1}{4}°$).

When the walls are parallel, a shock wave lies ahead of the duct and the flow in the duct is subsonic. The static pressure in the duct decreases indicating that, although the duct walls are parallel, the viscous layer creates such an effectively convergent channel that sonic and sometimes even supersonic flow was observed on the centerline at the exit plane.

When the wall divergence angle is greater than $\frac{1}{4}°$, the shock-like transition lies within the duct, and the flow downstream of this transition is supersonic. In spite of the fact that the duct walls form a divergent channel, the effect of the strong viscous effects is to produce again an effectively convergent channel. Hence, the pressure rises along the channel to a point approximately two-thirds the length of the channel and drops off slightly beyond this point. As illustrated by Fig. 4 increasing the wall divergence angle causes a decrease in the pressure rise along the channel, as might be expected.

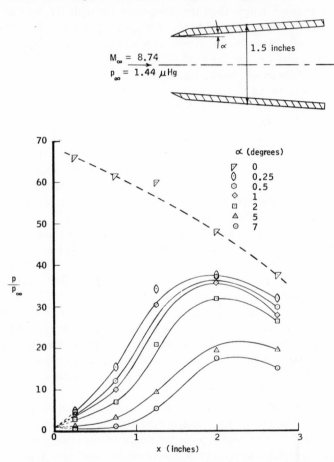

FIG. 4. Wall static pressure variation with plate inclination angle (rectangular duct with vertical sidewalls).

The pressure rise across the shock-like transition $\frac{1}{4}$ in. from the duct leading edge at $\alpha = \frac{1}{4}°$ is slightly lower than the pressure rise across the similar shock-like transition on a flat plate (Chuan and Waiter, 1963) as one might expect. The drop in static pressure near the exit of the duct is not clearly understood as yet, although one might postulate that it is caused by thinning of the viscous layer as a result of the expansion to low ambient pressure at the exit of the duct.

B. Results of Axisymmetric Duct Tests

The two axisymmetric ducts were tested in the low-density wind tunnel at the following free stream conditions:

$$8.91 \leq M_\infty \leq 9.38$$
$$1.27 \geq p_\infty \geq 0.9\mu \text{ Hg}$$
$$\left. \begin{array}{l} 0.058 \leq \text{Kn} \leq 0.075 \\ 680 \leq \text{Re} \leq 715 \end{array} \right\} \quad \text{Based on duct inlet diameter}$$

At these free stream conditions impact and static pressure distributions were measured in the ducts.

1. General Nature of the Flow—Shock-Like Transition. Typical impact pressure profiles at 0.5, 1.25, 2.0, and 2.75 inch from the leading edge in the axisymmetric duct with a 2° internal divergence are shown in Fig. 5. These impact pressures have not been corrected for the low-Reynolds number effects on the probe. The shock-like transition is clearly distinguished by the fairly broad peaks in the pressure profile. The location of this shock-like transition within the $\frac{1}{2}$° and 2° internal divergence duct, is shown in Fig. 6, where the location of the peak pressure is plotted on a scale drawing of the duct. The shock-like transition originates at the inlet lip and is initially straight and inclined to the axis between 25° and 28°. Downstream the slope decreases in the manner of a boundary layer. The inflection of the boundary curvature apparent near the axis may, or may not, be due to the presence of the impact probe itself. It is conceivable that in the absence of the probe the boundary between the isentropic free stream and the completely viscous flow downstream may be as shown dotted in Fig. 6.

It should be pointed out here that, although the flow in the $\frac{1}{2}$° internal divergence duct was stable once obtained, it could not be obtained without first running the wind tunnel at a higher supply pressure than the 25 mm Hg test pressure desired. Furthermore, once this stable flow was obtained it could be destroyed (the shock structure would disappear within the duct and the normal shock would appear ahead of the duct) by simply inserting the impact pressure probe up through the shock-like transition on the duct centerline to approximately 1 in. from the leading edge. Thus, it appears that the area ratio of the $\frac{1}{2}$° internal divergence duct (1.066) is very close to the critical area ratio below which a normal shock wave forms ahead of the duct.

Downstream of the shock-like transition the flow field is dominated by viscous effects as evidenced by the continuous variation in impact pressure

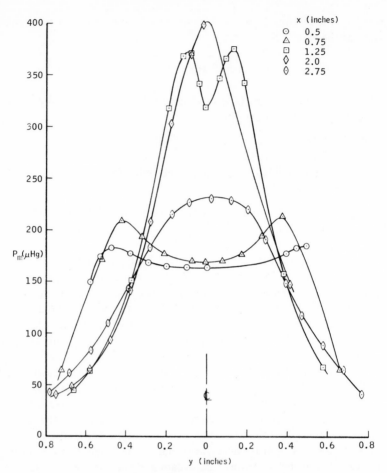

Fɪɢ. 5. Typical impact pressure profiles within axisymmetric duct (shock swallowed). Probe diameter, $\frac{1}{16}$ in.; duct divergence, $2°$; duct entrance diameters, 1.5 in.; $M_\infty = 8.91$; $p_\infty = 1.27 \, \mu$ Hg.

between the wall and the centerline (e.g., the profiles at $x = 2.0$ and 2.75 in. in Fig. 5).

The wall static pressure increases (as shown in Fig. 7) rapidly in the forward portion of the duct, reaches a peak at approximately two-thirds of the duct length and drops off slightly thereafter. These characteristics are the same as those observed in the two-dimensional duct when the walls formed a slightly divergent channel. The static pressure rise in all the diverging ducts indicates that, although the geometric area is increasing along the duct length, the viscous layer displacement effect produces an effectively convergent channel.

As in the two-dimensional case, the reason for the slight drop in pressure near the exit of the duct is not entirely clear at this time (see Section III, A). As expected, the static pressure level in the 2° internal divergence duct is slightly

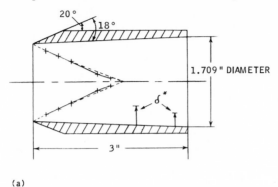

(a)

(b)

FIG. 6. Shock transition boundaries derived from impact pressure profiles. Axisymmetric duct: (a) 2° divergence, $M_\infty = 8.91$, $P_\infty = 25$ mm Hg; (b) 0.5° divergence, $M_\infty = 9.38$, $P_\infty = 25$ mm Hg.

lower than the pressure level in the $\frac{1}{2}°$ internal divergence duct. The Mach number effect shown is due entirely to the different free stream Mach number. The actual wall static pressures were not significantly different.

2. Velocity Profiles—Slip at the Wall. The impact pressure profiles obtained where possible in both axisymmetric ducts have been used to calculate velocity profiles for the flow in the ducts. In order to determine the velocity profile from the corrected total pressure profile, it was necessary to assume: (1) that the static pressure is constant across the region of purely viscous flow;

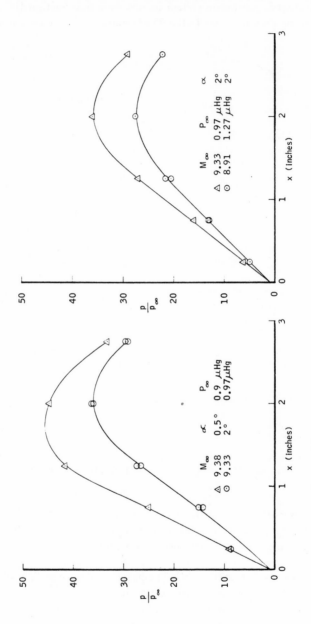

Fig. 7. Wall static pressure—axisymmetric ducts. (a) Effect of divergence, (b) effect of Mach number.

and (2) that the flow is isoenergetic. The first of these assumptions is probably justified. Theoretical estimates indicate that the pressure rise across the viscous layer in a two-dimensional channel is of the order of $4q_\infty/Re_\infty$. Thus, for the Reynolds numbers involved here the pressure difference between the wall and centerline of the channel (less than 1%) is but a small fraction of the dynamic pressure.

The second assumption is justified only if the wall is adiabatic and if the Prandtl number is unity. In the present tests the duct walls are adiabatic, but the gas involved (nitrogen) has a Prandtl number different from unity. Boundary layer experience indicates, however, that the assumption of a Prandtl number of unity for gases yields very good results, and it is expected that this will be the case here.

Velocity profiles and the corresponding Mach number profiles at several stations within the 2° internal divergence ducts are shown in Fig. 8. Near the leading edge velocity profiles were calculated only between the wall and shock-like transition since the assumption of constant static pressure is obviously not valid within the shock-like structure. It is clear from these velocity profiles that the viscous layer extends all the way from the wall to the shock-like transition. Downstream of the shock-like transition the flow is fully viscous as evidenced by the velocity varying continuously from the wall to the center-line of the channel.

Unfortunately, the impact pressure measurements were not made as close as possible to the wall in some of the present tests. The velocity at the wall was obtained by extrapolation of the calculated velocity profiles. In this extrapolation the first-order slip velocity $u_w = \lambda_w \, \partial u/\partial y)_w$ was used as a guide. The wall velocity (slip velocity) is shown in Fig. 9 for the 2° internal divergence duct. The mean free path at the wall, calculated from $\lambda = kT/\sqrt{2\pi\sigma^2 p}$ (Chapman, 1952) is also shown. The mean free path varies from about 0.12 in. at the first station within the duct (0.25 in. from the leading edge) to about a 0.05 in. minimum occuring 2 in. from the entry plane. The slip velocity, at the first station exceeds 2000 ft/sec or about 80% of free stream velocity, and drops off to a small (≈ 100 ft/sec) but not negligible value 2 in. from the entry plane. This decrease is, of course, related to the increase in static pressure (or decrease in mean free path). Both the slip velocity and mean free path increase slightly near the exit of the duct, owing to the slight decrease in static pressure in this region.

At present there is no theoretical analysis or experimental investigation of the viscous layer under the influence of a pressure gradient, with which these results can be compared. It is worth noting, however, that the slip velocities near the leading edge of the duct compare, reasonably well, with the slip velocities obtained by Chuan and Waiter (1962) near the leading edge of a flat plate as shown in Fig. 10.

It should be noted that the greatest difference between the present results for slip velocity and those of Chuan and Waiter occurs at the larger Reynolds numbers which, in the present case, occur downstream of the leading edge where the pressure is higher. One would expect smaller slip velocities in this region as a result of the reduced mean free path at the wall. Clearly, the mean

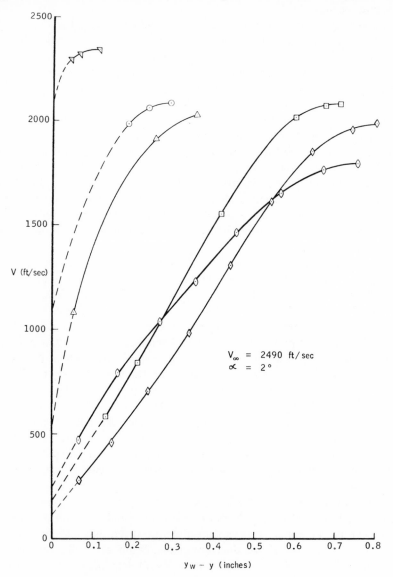

$V_\infty = 2490 \text{ ft/sec}$
$\alpha = 2°$

FIG. 8. (a) Velocity profiles in axisymmetric duct.

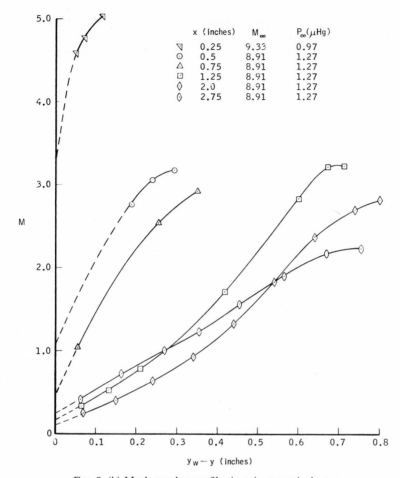

x (inches)	M_∞	$P_\infty(\mu Hg)$
◁ 0.25	9.33	0.97
○ 0.5	8.91	1.27
△ 0.75	8.91	1.27
▢ 1.25	8.91	1.27
◇ 2.0	8.91	1.27
◊ 2.75	8.91	1.27

FIG. 8. (b) Mach number profiles in axisymmetric duct.

free path is a better parameter to relate to slip velocity than the Reynolds number based on distance from the leading edge.

3. Skin Friction. From the slope of the velocity profile at the wall, the local skin friction coefficient has been calculated. Again no theory or experimental data is available with which to compare these results. The calculated skin friction coefficient is presented in Fig. 11, as a function of $(Re_\infty/M_\infty)^{1/2}$, where it is compared with the predicted free molecule and incompressible flow values. The values of skin friction are surprisingly large. This will be commented on later. These local skin friction coefficients have been integrated over the surface area of the duct and normalized to obtain the average skin friction coefficient. The average skin friction coefficient for the 2° internal divergence duct is 0.09. It is realized that this average skin friction coefficient depends upon the variation of skin friction near the leading edge, a region

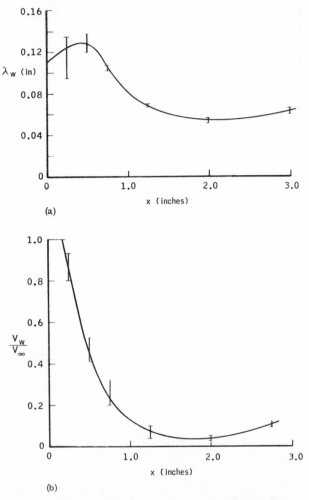

(a)

(b)

FIG. 9. (a) mean free path and (b) slip velocity at wall of axisymmetric duct with 2° divergence and 1.5-in. entrance diameter. $M_\infty = 8.91, p_\infty = 1.27\ \mu$ Hg.

where there is some doubt as to what the limiting value should be as the Reynolds number approaches zero. The free-molecule limit was used and any error due to this assumption is small. The result obtained will be compared later with the average skin friction obtained from a momentum balance.

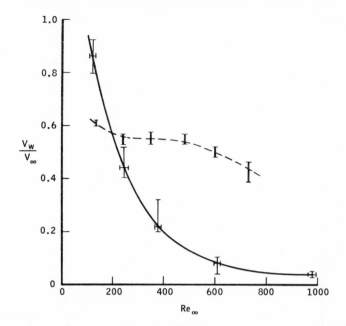

FIG. 10. Slip velocities in duct (entrance) flow and on flat plate compared. ——— axisymmetric duct, $P_s = 25$ mm Hg, $T_s = 530°$R; – – – – flat plate (Chuan, 1963), $P_s = 25$ mm Hg, $T_s = 530°$R; $8.5 < M_\infty < 9.5$.

4. Integrated Mass Flow. The assumption of isoenergetic flow may lead to some errors in the calculated velocity profiles. As a partial check on the errors resulting from this assumption, the mass flow distribution was computed and integrated; the calculated total mass flow was then compared with the free stream mass flow which is captured. The total mass flow can only be obtained downstream of the entire shock-like transition where it is then possible to

TABLE I

RATIO OF CALCULATED MASS FLOW TO
CAPTURED MASS FLOW
IN AXISYMMETRIC DUCTS

x (in.)	2° Internal divergence	$\frac{1}{2}°$ Internal divergence
2.0	0.95	*a*
2.75	0.95	0.97

a As shown in Fig. 6 the flow at $x = 2$ in. is not yet entirely viscous in this duct.

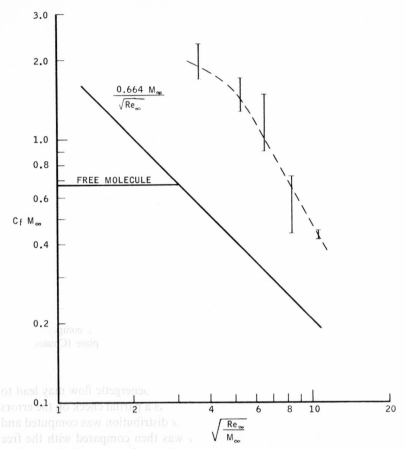

Fɪɢ. 11. Skin friction in axisymmetric ducts derived from velocity profiles: $8.91 \leqslant M_\infty \leqslant 9.33$.

calculate the velocity and density profiles across the entire duct. The comparison of the calculated and captured mass flow is shown in Table I.

The difference between the calculated mass flows and the actual mass flow does not exceed 5%. The calculation of the mass flow involves not only an integration but also depends upon the viscous correction of the impact probe measurements. In view of the several possible sources of error, the comparison is quite good. This would seem to indicate that the assumption of isoenergetic flow may not be too far from reality.

5. Total Pressure Recovery. An increase in entropy is a measure of the losses in a device. Since the total pressure drop and entropy rise in an adiabatic

system are related by

$$\ln(P_t/P_{t_\infty}) = -\Delta S/R, \tag{1}$$

it is desirable to maintain the total pressure drop in the device as small as possible.

In the short ducts under consideration the total pressure varies continuously across the duct, and it is necessary to average the total pressure in some manner in order to compare one duct with another. The proper method of averaging total pressure is open to question; however, Chuan (1961) has shown that the proper upper limit to the average total pressure is given by:

$$\frac{\bar{P}_t}{P_{t_\infty}} = \exp\left\{\frac{\displaystyle\int_A \rho u \, \ln(P_t/P_{t_\infty}) \, dA}{\displaystyle\int_A \rho u \, dA}\right\}. \tag{2}$$

The local total pressures in both axisymmetric ducts have been averaged in this manner. The results are shown in Table II. The average total pressure losses are of the order of the losses across a normal shock at the freestream Mach number in all cases. The total pressure shows a 36% loss between $x = 2.0$ and 2.75 in. which is the result entirely of viscous action.

TABLE II

FRACTION OF FREE STREAM NORMAL
SHOCK PRESSURE RECOVERY
OBTAINED IN AXISYMMETRIC DUCTS

x (in.)	2° Internal divergence	$\frac{1}{2}$° Internal divergence
2.0	1.15	—
2.75	0.74	0.84

6. Momentum Balance. A momentum balance was made for the flow in the axisymmetric ducts and average skin friction coefficients were thus obtained. These average skin friction coefficients were compared with average skin friction coefficients obtained from the integration of local values of the shearing stress. The comparison of the skin friction coefficients obtained in this way affords a rough check on both the assumptions made in obtaining the velocity profiles and on the extrapolation of the velocity profiles to the wall. Both the calculation of the average skin friction coefficient from a

momentum balance and the calculation of an average skin friction coefficient from local skin friction values involve integration, and it is realized that such integrations can cover a multitude of "sins." Nevertheless, it is felt that such a comparison reveals any gross errors in the measurements or the calculations.

The average skin friction coefficient determined from the momentum balance is given by

$$C_{f_{av}}\tfrac{1}{2}(\rho_\infty u_\infty{}^2)A_s = (p_\infty + \rho_\infty u_\infty{}^2)A - \left(pA + 2\pi \int_0^R \rho u^2 r \, dr\right)$$

$$+ 2\pi \tan \alpha \int_0^L p_w R \, dx \qquad (3)$$

where the average skin friction coefficient is defined by

$$C_{f_{av}}\tfrac{1}{2}(\rho_\infty u_\infty{}^2)A_s = \int_0^L 2\pi R \tau_w \, dx = 2\pi \int_0^L R\mu_w \frac{\partial u}{\partial y}\bigg)_w dx. \qquad (4)$$

The average skin friction can be computed in the first case using only the wall static pressure distribution and a total pressure distribution near the exit of the duct (together with the assumptions of constant static pressure across the viscous layer and isoenergetic flow). In the second case the average skin friction coefficient is computed from an integration of the local shear or more precisely the local wall velocity gradient. Average skin friction coefficients computed by these two methods are shown in Table III. The average skin friction values obtained from momentum balance and by summing local values differ by no more than 20% which lends support to the high local skin friction obtained from the velocity profiles. The authors at time of writing have no explanation for the high level of wall friction indicated which is approximately a factor of three higher than expected.[2]

In order to adjust the value downwards by a factor of three, in the momentum balance calculation the integrated downstream momentum would have to be increased by approximately 75%. This is clearly out of the question. Ignoring probe calibrations altogether the momentum would be increased less than 40% and of course continuity would be in error by 30%. Thus there is reasonable confidence in the momentum calculation.

On the other hand the first-order slip velocity relationship used in estimating the local skin friction is only correct in the order of magnitude and

[2] Since the symposium, Charwat's (1963) analysis has come to the authors' attention and his freemolecule limit $C_f = 2/M$ is in substantial agreement with the data obtained here. His condition that the velocity of the emitted molecules be low compared to the incident molecules which may be crucial could be met by less than full accommodation of the incident molecules at the wall.

permits the use of several rather than one mean free path as the slip coefficient. In this way the estimated friction might plausibly be reduced below
the free molecule and incompressible laminar flow values. This is hardly

TABLE III

AVERAGE SKIN FRICTION COEFFICIENTS

Axisymmetric duct	C_{fav} from momentum balance	C_{fav} from wall shear	Averaged from $x = 0$ to:
$\frac{1}{2}°$ internal divergence	0.078	—	2.75 inch
2° internal divergence	0.088	0.094	2.75 inch
2° internal divergence	0.099	0.083	2.0 inch

justifiable in light of the excellent continuity check and the friction value
deduced from momentum balance. Clearly further investigation is called for
in this area.

7. Displacement Thickness. The calculation of the displacement thickness of
the viscous layer within the channel is a fairly simple matter, since the mass
flow within the channel is constant. In this case the displacement thickness is
simply

$$\delta^* = R - (\dot{m}/\pi\rho_{\mathscr{C}}u_{\mathscr{C}})^{1/2}. \tag{5}$$

The displacement thickness has been calculated at the last two stations in the
axisymmetric ducts; the results of these calculations are shown in Fig. 6. There
is at this time, of course, no theory with which to compare these results.

TABLE IV

COMPARISON OF ACTUAL AND ESTIMATED DISPLACEMENT THICKNESS

x (in.)	Axisymmetric duct	δ^* (in.) (theor)	δ^* (in.) (exptl)
2.0	2° diverging	0.60	0.35
2.75	2° diverging	0.64	0.26
2.75	$\frac{1}{2}°$ diverging	0.69	0.33

Lacking any such theory, the results are compared with a displacement computed assuming that it is proportional to the distance from the leading edge
and inversely proportional to the local Reynolds number. The constant of
proportionality is taken from flat plate boundary layer theory using the local

centerline Mach number. The computed displacement thickness takes into account mass continuity. The results of this comparison are shown in Table IV.

The strong pressure gradients in the flow and the slip at the wall cause the displacement thickness to be approximately half that predicted by theory.

It should be noted that the displacement thickness seems to decrease near the exit plane of the duct. This decrease is no doubt related to the static pressure drop near the exit of the duct.

IV. Conclusions

Experimental studies of the flow in short two-dimensional and axisymmetric ducts in a hypersonic (Mach 9) rarefied (Kn $\approx$ 0.1) gas stream in the transition flow regime reveal that:

1. Constant area channels do not capture the supersonic stream but have normal shocks upstream of the entry plane and fully viscous flow throughout.

2. Channels with very slight divergence capture a stream tube of the same area as the entrance and an oblique shock-like transition is attached to the lip and extends downstream.

3. The initial slope of the shock-like transition is $27° \pm 2°$ and agrees with the slope on a flat plate observed by Chuan and Waiter (1963).

4. The wall static pressure increases downstream of the shock-like transition and reaches a peak at approximately one inch from the end of the duct.

5. Viscous effects dominate the flow field downstream of the shock-like transition. The viscous effects extend all the way from the wall to the centerline of the duct, so that there is no isentropic core. As a result the average total pressure decreases by approximately 35% in the short ($\frac{3}{4}$ in.) axial distance near the exit of the duct.

6. Slip velocities exist at the wall throughout the 3 in. long ducts and are as high as 80% of the undisturbed velocity about two mean free paths from the entrance.

7. Wall friction at least three times greater than might be expected was calculated from a momentum balance and from local velocity profiles. Further study of this is recommended.

8. Average total pressure recoveries in the short 3 in. long ducts are on the order of that across a normal shock at the free-stream Mach number ($M_\infty \approx 9$)

9. Displacement thicknesses measured in the fully viscous flow are less than but reasonably close to estimated values. The difference is probably due to the pressure gradient and slip at the wall, which is not accounted for in the estimation.

List of Symbols

A	Cross-section area	S	Entropy
A_s	Surface area	T	Temperature
C_f	Skin friction coefficient	u	x component of velocity
d	Diameter	x	Distance downstream of entrance plane along centerline
k	Boltzmann's constant		
Kn	Knudsen number	y	Radial distance in channels
L	Duct length	α	Divergence angle (of flat plates or axisymmetric duct walls)
$\dot{m}$	Mass flow in duct		
M	Mach number	$\delta*$	Viscous layer displacement thickness
M_a	Apparent Mach number—no correction made to impact pressure	λ	Mean free path
		μ	Absolute viscosity
M_t	True Mach number	ρ	Density
p	Static pressure	τ	Shearing stress at the wall
$\bar{P}$	Average total pressure [see Eq. (2)]	*Subscripts*	
P_m	Measured impact pressure	s	Refers to supply conditions
P_R	Actual continuum Rayleigh pressure	w	Refers to wall conditions
q	Dynamic pressure	∞	Refers to freestream conditions
R	Gas constant or radius of channel	t	Refers to total (or true in case of Mach number)
Re	Reynolds number		
Re_d	Reynolds number based on diameter	$\cancel{\mathltext{c}}$	Refers to centerline

ACKNOWLEDGMENTS

The experimental work reported herein was supported by Air Force Aero Propulsion Laboratory Research and Technology Division, Wright Patterson Air Force Base, Ohio. The authors wish to thank Dr. Chuan and John Wainwright (now of Celestial Research Company) who supplied the probe correction data and suggested the manner of its interpolation used in the paper. They would also like to thank Dr. E. T. Pitkin for helpful discussions and Mrs. Linda Gardner for the laborious data reduction and preparation of the figures.

REFERENCES

Chapman, S., and Cowling, T. E. (1952). "The Mathematical Theory of Non-Uniform Gases," p. 91. Cambridge Univ. Press, London and New York.

Charwat, A. F. (1963). "Theoretical Analysis of Near-Free-Molecule Hypersonic Flow at the Sharp Leading Edge of a Flat Plate." RAND Memo. RM-2553-PR.

Chuan, R. L. (1956). *J. Aeronaut. Sci.* **23**, 378.

Chuan, R. L., and Waiter, S. A. (1963). In "Rarefied Gas Dynamics" (J. A. Laurmann, ed.), Vol. II, pp. 328–342. Academic Press, New York.

Clausing, P. (1932). *Ann. Physik* **12**, 961.

Collins, A. M. (1959). "Low Density Supersonic Diffuser Performance." Univ. of Calif., Inst. Eng. Res., Berkeley, California, Tech. Rept. HE-150-164.

Rogers, K. W., Touryan, K. J., Wainwright, J. B., and Yang, H. T. (1965). Volume II of this Symposium, p. 151.

Research at the NPL on the Influence at Supersonic Speeds and Low Reynolds Numbers of Thick Laminar Boundary Layers

E. W. E. ROGERS AND C. J. BERRY

Aerodynamics Division, National Physical Laboratory, Teddington, Middlesex, England

This paper contains a brief description of the NPL low-density wind tunnel which has been operating at supersonic speeds and stream static pressures between 10 and 100μ for the past two years. The main part of the paper discusses briefly three recent experiments made in this tunnel in which the influence of thick laminar boundary layers was investigated. The viscous-induced pressures on two not-so-slender cones are shown to be well predicted by theory. Next the flow about two-dimensional circular cylinders is considered and it is shown that the effects of the surface boundary layer may be allowed for by means of a simple tangent-cylinder theory. Some evidence for the form of the surface-friction law for cylinders at low Reynolds numbers is presented. Finally, results from an investigation of boundary-layer flow along a flat plate having moveable steps normal to the stream are discussed. The upstream influence of the step and the resulting pressure rise seem to be determined mainly by the model geometry and not by local Reynolds number considerations. An attempt has been made to investigate the separation cavity upstream of the step.

I. Introduction

The National Physical Laboratory, at Teddington, England, has been concerned with aerodynamic research for some sixty years. During this period the range of interest has widened continuously, and at present the Aerodynamics Division is studying a broad spectrum of aerodynamic problems, from wind loading on buildings and bridges to the physics of shock-heated gases.

The Division's official interest in low-density aerodynamics began in 1958 when, under the direction of Dr. D. W. Holder, the design of the low-density tunnel began. The tunnel was subsequently constructed and erected, and commissioning trials started early in 1961. These were followed by a period in which operating experience was gained and suitable instrumentation developed. A modest start at research work was made in the summer of 1962. Some of the more recent investigations are the subject of the present paper.

Before describing results from the tunnel in which the influence of thick laminar boundary layers is dominant it is perhaps necessary to explain why this research field occupies an important part of the tunnel program. The Aerodynamics Division necessarily has close connections with the aircraft industry and its demand for fundamental aerodynamic data. There was a strong incentive therefore to use the low-density tunnel, for at least part of its time, to study the increasing influence of rarefied-gas effects on conventional air flows as the gas density or flow Reynolds number decreased. In this way the work of the tunnel could be integrated into the general research program of the Hypersonics Aerodynamics Group of the Division. The range of stream densities over which the tunnel operates was also very suitable for investigations in the near-continuum and transition-flow regimes.

This attitude to low-density aerodynamics is of course by no means novel and much valuable information has already been published. Nevertheless, the complex phenomena associated with thick boundary layers are as yet insufficiently understood, and it was felt that additional contributions to the subject would be of value. The influence of low-density boundary layers on body forces and surface pressures can be most marked, and occasionally unexpected. A full understanding can only come from a study of the interactions between the body surface, the viscous layer, and the external flow field. Basic to any investigation is a knowledge of the laminar boundary layer itself, and this must include the complicating effects of surface slip, transverse curvature, heat-transfer, and local separation. The importance of the boundary layer need not cease when the flow leaves the body surface and it is the intention of the NPL to study at some future date near-wake and vortex-wake flows.

In one sense the foregoing paragraph describes almost the whole of the aerodynamics of transition and near-continuum flows, or indeed any regime in which the boundary layer can be said to be well defined. The prime object, however, must be to relate the boundary-layer development to the body characteristics, and if possible to predict their manner of interaction. This is necessarily a long-term aim and at the NPL only a beginning has been made. As examples of the initial progress the results from three experiments will be described, all of which have been carried out since June 1963. First, however, a brief description of the tunnel will be given.

II. The NPL Low-Density Wind Tunnel

The design of the tunnel is conventional, the test flow being obtained by using three types of vacuum pumps in series. Initially five oil-diffusion pumps extract the air at low pressure from the large test chamber surrounding the nozzle exit. These discharge to five Roots'-type rotary pumps which in turn discharge to two rotary-piston pumps. The air is exhausted from these at a pressure just above the atmospheric value. The volume flow of the pumping system rises from about 14,000 liters/sec at 100 microns mercury (μ) static pressure in the working section to 24,000 liters/sec at 10 μ. These pressure levels represent the practical limits of the tunnel's working range.

At present the tunnel is operating at nominal Mach numbers of 2 and 4 using contoured nozzles with exit diameters of 7.2 and 4.8 in., respectively. An additional contoured nozzle for a Mach number of 6 is being constructed, as are a series of near-conical nozzles for Mach numbers up to 9. A small heater upstream of the nozzle section is used to raise the stream stagnation temperature above the atmospheric value; the maximum temperature available is 550°C.

For flow exploration the tunnel is equipped with a three-way traverse gear operated remotely from outside the test chamber; any part of the nozzle and test section may be explored. Up to the present only pitot tubes have been used because the characteristics of these in supersonic low-density flow are now fairly well defined. An afterglow flow-visualization system is available and this is similar to that developed at Berkeley. Argon afterglow has so far been most successful.

The tunnel is fitted with a force balance for the direct measurement of either lift or drag. Its design is similar in many respects to that used at Berkeley and described by Maslach and Latz (1960), but the force opposing the aerodynamic load on the model is obtained from a system of electric coils, changes in current then being used to return the balance arm to a null position. The balance has good sensitivity and reliability and can measure forces as low as 1 or 2 mg.

Up to the present the majority of investigations in the tunnel have been concerned with the measurement of pressures on the surface of a model. Such measurements require manometers of the highest possible accuracy for the range between 1 and 1000 μ. Early experience at the NPL suggested that a simple U-tube, filled with a low vapor-pressure oil and observed from outside the test chamber by means of a low-power traveling microscope did not give sufficient accuracy in the lower part of the pressure range. A manometer using thermistors was therefore developed and all results quoted in the present paper were obtained with this instrument. The model surface pressures are ducted in the normal way by means of hypodermic tubes within the model and plastic tubing outside the model to a bank of thermistors mounted just outside the test jet, but inside the test chamber. This bank is kept carefully at a controlled temperature by means of a water jacket; changes in thermistor temperature are certainly smaller than $\pm0.1\,°C$. In this way the responsiveness of the thermistors to small temperature variations can be almost eliminated. Each pressure hole on the model has its own thermistor, which then forms part of an individual bridge circuit. The pressure level is finally obtained in terms of a galvanometer reading. Fairly frequent calibration of the manometer against primary or secondary pressure standards is required to monitor the slow zero drift characteristics of some thermistors; in practice this does not prove arduous. The general accuracy and repeatability of the manometer depend on the required range; most readings tend to be between 10 and 100 μ, and here an accuracy better than ±0.5 μ can readily be obtained. A full description of the thermistor manometer has been given by Rogers et al. (1964).

III. Experiments on Boundary-Layer Effects

The development of a reliable and accurate pressure-plotting technique was considered sufficiently advanced early in 1963 to enable worthwhile experiments to be planned. The three investigations considered below were started between June 1963 and March 1964.

A. Circular Cones at Zero Incidence (Rogers et al., 1964)

As an initial exercise it was decided to investigate the magnitude of the viscous-induced pressure increment on the surface of not-so-slender cones placed at zero incidence in a stream of nominal Mach number 2. It was felt that such results would complement those made some years before by Talbot et al. (1958) in which slender cones were tested at a stream Mach number (M_0) near 4. For the NPL tests two semiapex angles (ϵ) were chosen, 15° and 30°. The stream Mach number varied between 1.95 and 2.24 as the test-section pressure changed. Based on the cone length (L) the test Reynolds number varied from 81 at a stream static pressure of 20 μ to 372 when the static pressure was 80 μ.

The cone surface pressure showed the expected longitudinal reduction from the high values near the apex associated with the rapidly growing boundary layer. This pressure variation could be predicted reasonably well in any given case by assuming a simple law for the displacement thickness growth along the cone surface, and then by further assuming that the pressure at any point on the cone and boundary-layer combination would be given by the

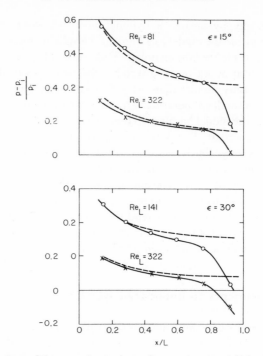

FIG. 1. Comparison of theory and experiment for cone pressures ($M_0 \approx 2$). Experiment, $-\bigcirc-$; tangent-cone theory, $-\,-\,-$.

equivalent cone in inviscid flow. An iteration procedure is needed to allow for the changes in flow conditions behind the shock from the apex; only three steps were normally required, however. This technique is very similar to that described by Talbot et al. (1958) for cones and by Aroesty (1958) for flat plates. The nature of the agreement between experiment and tangent-cone theory is illustrated in Fig. 1. The over-all pressure levels are well predicted but there is a tendency for the measured pressures to decrease a little more rapidly than theory suggests.

More approximately, the variation of inviscid surface pressure with changes in effective cone angle can be expressed as a power series in the angle. By retaining only the first term in this series the induced pressure becomes a simple linear function of $(Re_s)^{-1/2}$, where Re_s is the local Reynolds number based on the distance s from the cone apex. Figure 2 shows that the experimental results are in good agreement with this line, and lie between it and a curve which is obtained by including the second term in the power series.

The pressure hole situated at 0.92 of the cone length is strongly influenced by the flow over the cone shoulder into the base region. Somewhat surprisingly the pressures at this hole were virtually unchanged when a cylindrical afterbody of length equal to that of the cone was attached to the cone base. This result led to some speculation about the shape and extent of the base cavity and the magnitude of the expansion at the cone shoulder. The point was resolved by making traverses with a small pitot tube through the flow to the rear of the isolated cone. The flow expansion at the cone base

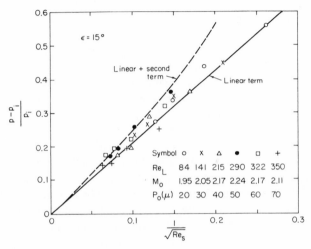

FIG. 2. Correlation of viscous-induced pressures on $15°$ cone ($M_0 \approx 2$).

could then be clearly discerned and seemed similar to that which occurs at far higher Reynolds numbers. The expansion fan could also be seen in subsequent argon flow-visualization tests. The presence of a cylindrical afterbody might be expected to alter this expansion to some extent and hence modify the cone surface pressures upstream of the shoulder. Experiment, however, had shown that no such interference was present. This apparent paradox can be resolved if the flow in the neighborhood of the shoulder is regarded as a free-interaction phenomenon. Changes in local surface pressure resulting from alterations in the flow expansion angle can then be shown to be small at positions which are not very close to the shoulder.

During these tests both cones were progressively truncated, the flat nose being normal to the cone axis and stream direction. The effects of these truncations were most marked for the more slender cone ($\epsilon = 15°$): a full discussion is contained in the report by Rogers et al. (1964).

Briefly this cone experiment showed the value of simple theories for predicting viscous-induced pressure increments on cones of moderate semi-vertex angles at rather low supersonic Mach numbers and the possible upstream effects of the base flow. The measured base pressures (down to 3μ) agreed well with those quoted by Kavenau (1956) thus giving some check on the performance of the thermistor manometer at very low pressures. The near-wake flow was found to be very similar to that which develops at much higher Mach numbers. Finally the effects of tip truncation were investigated and found to persist down to quite small values of the Reynolds number based on the tip diameter.

B. Circular Cylinder Tests

The cone tests described in the preceding section were followed by a short investigation in which the circumferential pressure distribution was measured on a number of circular cylinders spanning the tunnel stream. Again the test Mach numbers were near 2. Four models were used, with diameters (d) varying between 0.115 and 0.500 in. Over the operating pressure range of the tunnel these gave Reynolds numbers based on d between 5.4 and 134.

Away from the stagnation region, and upstream of the rear separation cavity, the effect of decreasing the test Reynolds number was to increase the ratio of the local pressure to that obtained at the stagnation position, i.e., the ratio $C_p(\theta)/C_p(0)$ increases. This effect could well be associated with the thick surface boundary layer. Accordingly a simple "tangent-cylinder" theory was developed. The basis of this was the circumferential pressure distribution measured at a Mach number of 1.85 by Ferri (1942). The Reynolds number in this test was about 10^5, and hence was taken to represent the "inviscid" pressure distribution for positions well upstream of the separation point. The ratio $C_p(\theta)/C_p(0)$ was assumed to depend only on the local slope of the edge of the boundary-layer displacement thickness and to have the same value as on the "inviscid" cylinder with identical surface slope. Thus in Fig. 3 the pressure ratio at B is the same as that at A in "inviscid" flow, because the slopes at A and A' are equal. The effect of this simple equivalence may be regarded as increasing the circumferential angle θ for a given pressure ratio as the boundary layer grows more rapidly. A simple method for predicting δ^*, the boundary-layer displacement thickness, is needed of course.

An example of the effectiveness of tangent-cylinder theory is presented in Fig. 3 for Re_d equal to 34, and θ varying between 40° and 100°.

The cylinder tests revealed that there were separate effects on the circumferential distribution associated with changes in the flow Mach number and model Reynolds number. At constant Re_d small changes in M_0 tended to increase the value of C_p everywhere including the stagnation and separated-flow regions. The shape of the distribution curve and in particular the pressure recovery aft of the separation point were virtually unchanged. In contrast, at constant stream Mach number, but varying Re_d, the pressure changed most near the nose of the model and over its rearward section. At Re_d down to about 30 there was ample evidence of an increase in pressure as θ approached

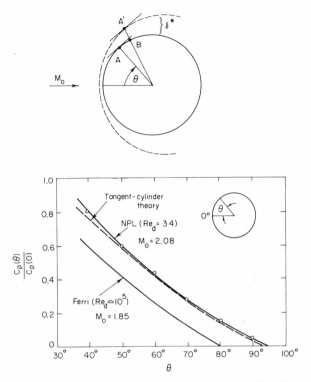

FIG. 3. Use of tangent-cylinder approximation near $M_0 = 2$.

180° (see also Tewfik and Giedt, 1959). Below this Reynolds number the pressure either remained constant for $\theta > 140°$, or at the lowest test Reynolds numbers decreased continuously and slowly until θ reached 180°. This marked change in pattern is presumably connected with movements in the separation position (which defied detection in the present tests) and in the momentum exchange within the thick laminar shear layers.

The variation in pressure at the forward stagnation position ($\theta = 0°$) could be correlated in terms of the parameter $M_0/(\text{Re}_d)^{1/2}$. When these results were plotted in terms of ϕ, where

$$\phi = \frac{C_p(0)_B - C_p(0)_c}{C_p(0)_{FM} - C_p(0)_c}, \qquad (1)$$

and where the suffices B, c, and FM refer to experimental, continuum and free-molecule values, respectively, they were found to be in good agreement with earlier data by Enkenhus (1957). The quantity ϕ tends rapidly to zero for $M_0/(\text{Re}_d)^{1/2} < 0.2$ and appears to approach unity when this parameter exceeds 2.

An investigation was made early in these tests of the effect of orifice size on the pressure reading, particularly near the forward stagnation point. It was found that hole diameters of 0.005 and 0.010 in. gave almost identical pressure readings for a stream static pressure of 30 μ. However, when the orifice diameter was reduced to 0.002 in., the measured pressure increased by nearly 10% and this increase was maintained at least for $0° \leqslant \theta \leqslant 60°$. It was concluded therefore that 0.005 in. was the smallest orifice size likely to give consistent results and this diameter (or greater) was used in the main tests. Enkenhus (1957) too found an increase in measured pressure when the orifice diameter decreased below a certain critical size, in his case 0.002 in. The stream Mach number (1.96) was identical in the two tests but Enkenhus' static pressure (20 μ) was less than for the NPL work. The difference in the critical hole size for the two sets of results may well be due to the different orifice geometry. Enkenhus' holes were pierced in foil and hence had a small depth compared with their diameter; the NPL holes were drilled in brass bushes and hence were "long" in terms of the orifice diameter.

As in the cone tests, pitot traverses were made behind the circular-cylinder models. The bow shock wave and trailing shockwave could be detected and their positions confirmed by subsequent flow-visualization tests. The pitot traverses also revealed the extent of the viscous wake. There was a strong resemblance between these traverse results and those obtained by McCarthy and Kubota (1964) for the flow behind a circular cylinder at a Mach number of 5.7 and comparatively low Reynolds number. From the flow-visualization photographs taken to supplement the traverse information, the bow-shock stand-off distance was measured, and found to increase from the well-known high Reynolds number value as the test Reynolds number decreased. At constant model size it seems that much of this increase may be attributed to growing shock thickness as the tunnel pressure falls.

One further deduction from these tests may be of interest. The circumferential pressure distributions were integrated to give the streamwise pressure force and hence the pressure-drag coefficient (C_{D_P}). When plotted against a Knudsen number based on free-stream conditions and cylinder diameter these results may be compared with the total drag coefficients (C_{D_T}) measured directly by Maslach and Schaaf (1962) and also Sreekanth (1961). This comparison is made in Fig. 4. The difference between the two curves is of course the surface-friction drag coefficient (C_{D_F}) and in the present case this is closely represented by

$$C_{D_F} = C_{D_T} - C_{D_P} = 1.7/(\mathrm{Re}_d)^{1/2}, \tag{2}$$

which, with some change in the value of the numerical constant, is similar to that deduced for circular cylinders in high-Reynolds-number continuum flow by laminar boundary-layer theory.

A full description of the work outlined in this section is contained in the report by Metcalf et al. (1964).

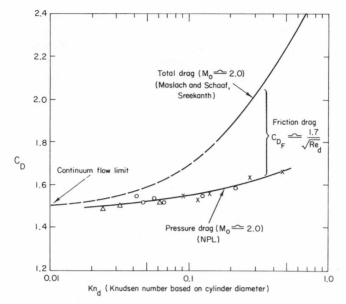

FIG. 4. Estimate of friction drag for circular cylinders near $M_0 = 2$.

C. Flat Plate Experiments

A somewhat more fundamental experiment than those described in Sections A and B has been under way since March 1964. A full analysis of the results has not been completed but several points of interest have so far emerged. A sharp-edged flat plate was made with 18 pressure holes centrally distributed along its 3 in. length. The plate was sufficiently wide to span a large part of the jet issuing from the nominal $M_0 = 2$ nozzle, but not so big as to partially block the flow and hence reduce the test Mach number. Steps of height between 0.1 and 0.9 in. could be traversed along the plate surface while the tunnel was running. The plate was at zero incidence with respect to the stream.

The tests were run at three static pressure levels; 30, 50, and 70μ, the unit Reynolds numbers then being 108, 200, and 252 per inch. For each step position the distribution of pressure along the plate was measured. The objects of the experiment were to investigate the influence of step height and position on the plate pressures, to examine the boundary-layer flow on the plate with and without the step in position and, if possible, to determine the shape and extent of the separated-flow cavity and the pressure rise to separation.

The pitot traverses made normal to the plate surface in the absence of a step showed the expected increase in pitot pressure through the boundary layer. The boundary layer is followed by a region where the probe pressure increases only slowly; this is presumably behind the slightly curved shock from the leading-edge zone. The pitot tube then passes through the shock itself and finally measures the pitot pressure of the undisturbed stream. The edge of the boundary layer at different stations along the plate may be

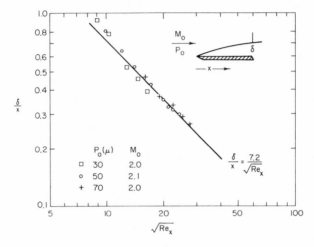

FIG. 5. Boundary-layer growth along flat plate (no step).

estimated from these traverses and Fig. 5 shows that away from the leading-edge region the boundary-layer growth is governed by a simple law of familiar form.

The rapid boundary-layer growth must induce a longitudinal pressure gradient on the plate surface. The magnitude of these induced pressures may be estimated with reasonable accuracy by an iterative tangent-wedge approach, similar in many ways to that developed for flat plates at $M_0 \approx 4$ by Aroesty (1958). For the NPL tests the ratio of the local plate pressure (p) to that of the undisturbed stream (p_0) correlates well when plotted against $M_0^3/(\mathrm{Re}_x)^{1/2}$ (see Fig. 6), though this is perhaps not the most suitable parameter for the rather low Mach number of the present tests. The trend as this parameter tends to zero is particularly well defined and on the right-hand side of Fig. 6 the NPL data is in agreement with that published by Aroesty.

With the step in position the surface pressures on the plate rise continuously up to the forward edge of the step. This is marked with an A in Fig. 7 where typical pressure distributions are presented at one step position and various step heights. The quantity $(\Delta p)_x$ denotes the increase in plate pressure at position x due to the presence of the step and hence is obtained by differencing two sets of results. At the step position and the stream static pressure of

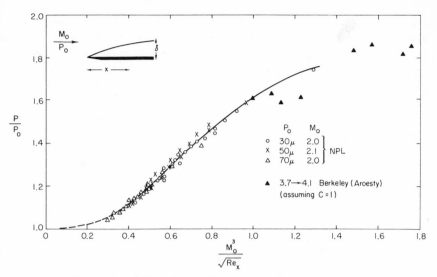

FIG. 6. Correlation of induced pressures on flat plate (no step).

Fig. 7, the boundary-layer thickness is about 0.9 in., the height of the largest step.

In no case was there any evidence of a region of constant pressure (the "plateau" discussed by Chapman *et al.*, 1958) downstream of the separation

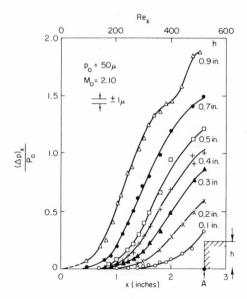

FIG. 7. Example of step-height influence on upstream pressures.

position. This seems to be a high-Reynolds-number phenomenon which develops when the interaction length is several times the local boundary-layer thickness. In Fig. 7 this interaction length is relatively small and only extends upstream by some 2 to 3 boundary-layer thicknesses for the tallest step. For this step there is a kink in the pressure distribution; at the lower stream pressure (30 μ) it is very slight but becomes extremely well defined when $p_0 = 70 \mu$. The cause of the kink is uncertain but it is thought to be associated with the reattachment pressure rise at the upper edge of the step. Because of this thick boundary layer, the influence of this can penetrate upstream and is superimposed on the pressure increment due to the separation cavity. Only for high static pressures and large steps do the viscous effects fail to "smooth" the resultant curve and a kink results.

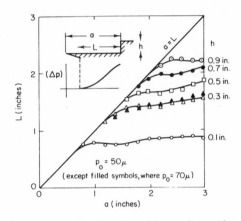

FIG. 8. Influence of step height and position on interaction distance.

It is clear from Fig. 7 that both the interaction length and the magnitude of the pressure rise depend on the geometry of the obstacle causing the disturbance. Thus the interaction is not of the "free" type and this may well be characteristic of steps which are similar in size to the boundary-layer thickness. The variation of the interaction distance L with step height and position relative to the leading edge is indicated in Fig. 8. L is seen to be largely independent of step position (at least until the beginning of the interaction approaches the leading edge), but to depend strongly on step height. In fact L is very closely proportional to $h^{1/2}$. It follows that L is not much influenced by boundary-layer thickness (or local Reynolds number) at the beginning of the interaction, as would be the case if it were of the "free" type. Further evidence for this lack of influence of Reynolds number is given by the solid symbols in Fig. 8 which are for a higher stream pressure.

Because no "plateau" pressure is developed at these low Reynolds numbers,

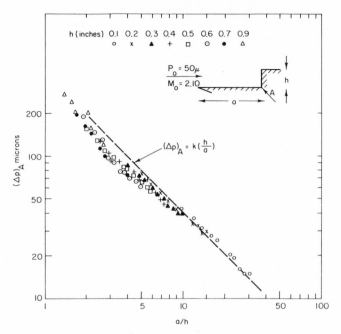

FIG. 9. Correlation of corner pressure-increment with model geometry.

the maximum pressure increment at the step position $(\Delta p)_A$ is of interest. It was found that $(\Delta p)_A$ depends strongly on the ratio of the step position measured from the leading edge (a) to the step height (h). A typical correlation at a stream static pressure of 50 μ is presented in Fig. 9. Equally good results were obtained at the other two pressure levels; indeed all three sets of results collapse into a single band if plotted in the nondimensional form $(\Delta p)_A/p_0$. The results of Fig. 9 do show some influence of step height particularly near $a/h = 3$, but this variation is small compared with that induced by changes in a/h. Once again then there is evidence of a geometric significance in the results and an absence of strong trends dependent on unit Reynolds number and local boundary-layer thickness. In particular there is no correlation with $\mathrm{Re}_B{}^{-1/4}$, where Re_B is the local Reynolds number at the beginning of the inter-action. Any one set of results at constant step height in Fig. 9 represents a large change in Re_B or the ratio of local boundary-layer thickness to step height. An explanation for this correlation can probably be found in the boundary-layer profiles, where a constant pitot pressure is approximately obtained along lines of constant x/y. Thus as a given step moves along the plate surface it responds to pressures related to x/y (i.e., a/h). If the ratio a/h is fixed, the relevant local total pressure and hence maximum pressure rise due to the step is unchanged.

It thus appears that the length of the pressure interaction is proportional to $h^{1/2}$, while the maximum pressure ratio $(\Delta p)_A/p_0$ is mainly dependent on a/h and may approximately be regarded as being proportional to h/a. By noting that the general shape of the pressure increment curve is not greatly altered by changes in h (Fig. 7) or step position (provided the step is not too close to the leading edge) the whole pressure curve can be predicted with good accuracy for any test condition. From an empirical viewpoint this is satisfactory; a fuller understanding of the basic mechanism is needed however.

As was remarked earlier one of the objectives of the present investigation was to determine the extent and nature of the separated flow region ahead of the step. Though considerable data on this matter exists at high Reynolds numbers, more knowledge of the influence of thick laminar boundary layers would be most valuable.

So far in the NPL experiments there has been only a limited success from simple attempts to determine where separation starts on the plate or cylinder. The separation cavity on the plate could not be detected using argon afterglow flow visualization or by working with conventional optical techniques at their most sensitive. Attempts to observe the motions of light liquid films or dust bands moving under the combined influence of viscous traction and buoyancy forces were rather unsuccessful, though this has proved a valuable technique in conventional supersonic flows. In view of the importance of detecting separation in low-density aerodynamic phenomena, work is in hand to develop more sophisticated methods including the use of thin, bonded, electrically conducting surface films. Such developments tend to be rather long-term ones however and in the present tests it seemed that some information (albeit crude) on the separation cavity might come from traverses made with a fairly small pitot tube (0.048 in. o.d.).

The simplest results were obtained by traversing a backward-facing pitot tube along the plate surface whilst firmly in contact with it. It may then be argued that this probe will read less than the local static pressure when the flow is attached (i.e., the probe orifice is then in a kind of base flow), and will record a greater pressure than local static when reverse flow takes place inside the separation cavity. The onset of separation thus corresponds to the position where the probe reading and local static pressure are equal. This simple criterion is modified when the finite size of the probe, and its geometry, are allowed for, and when possible velocity gradients normal to the plate surface are considered. Tests made in this way at three step heights (0.3, 0.5 and 0.7 in.) and three stream pressures appeared to be reasonably consistent and showed that the " separation point " moved steadily away from the step as the height of this increased. For a given step height the separation was smallest in extent at the lowest stream pressure (i.e., thickest boundary layer) and increased in length as the static pressure rose. The angle between the separation point and the upper edge of the step (a rough guide to the upper boundary of the cavity) was about 20° at $p_0 = 70$ μ but increased to over 30° when p_0 was 30 μ. This trend with decreasing test Reynolds number is similar to that demonstrated theoretically by Abbott *et al.* (1963) and the actual value of angles in the NPL tests are not inconsistent with this higher Reynolds number data.

In a few cases when the step was present pitot traverses were made upwards from the plate surface. These results could be compared directly with corresponding traverses made when the step was not fitted. For the 0.5 in. high step, placed 3 in. from the leading edge, these new traverses were almost identical at positions between $x = \frac{1}{2}$ to $1\frac{1}{2}$ in. with those for the plate without step. Small changes in the shape of the curve could be detected at $x = 2$ in. and appreciable differences at larger values of x. The surface pressure ahead

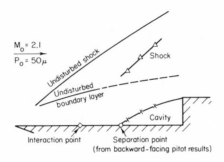

FIG. 10. Boundary of separation cavity for $a = 3.0$ in. From backward pitot, O; from pitot transverse, ×.

of the step begins to depart from the flat plate value near $x = 1.1$ in. which is well upstream of the last station for which no change in boundary-layer profile could be detected. Traverses made with the backward-facing pitot suggested a separation point near $x = 1.9$ in. and the distortion of the vertical traverse curves at $x = 2.0$ in. was sufficiently well defined to provide an estimate of the upper boundary of the separation cavity. This position, and those deduced at two stations closer to the step are shown in Fig. 10, and together with the separation point and the upper-edge of the step seem to define the cavity reasonably well. Thus the results from the vertical traverses appear to lend some confidence to the interpretation of the backward-facing pitot data.

The vertical traverses made with the step in position contained a marked slope change some distance from the plate surface and this may be attributed to the external compression wave caused by the thickening boundary-layer upstream of separation. The position of this shock is drawn on Fig. 10.

Once the separation point is known, the influence of the various test parameters on the pressure rise to separation may be considered. Perhaps the most striking correlation is obtained if this pressure rise is measured from the stream value (i.e., $p_B - p_0$) rather than above the local flat-plate value with no step. Made nondimensional by dividing by p_0, this quantity is independent of step height but falls towards the high-Reynolds-number value as the stream static pressure increases. More work is needed before the significance of this result is fully appreciated. There is little evidence from the present results of a strong correlation in terms of local Reynolds number at separation but the general level of separation pressure ratios in the low-density flow are in accord with an extrapolation of earlier data at $\mathrm{Re}_B \approx 10^6$ to $\mathrm{Re}_B \approx 10^2$ using a $\mathrm{Re}_B^{-1/4}$ law.

IV. Concluding Remarks

The main aim of this paper is to present results from recent NPL research at supersonic speeds and low Reynolds numbers which appear to contribute toward an understanding of the influence of the thick laminar boundary layer. In some cases the work discussed is an amplification and extension of earlier results by other authors; for the flat plate experiment a full analysis of the data has not yet been completed. Nevertheless it is felt that these results may be of interest to other research workers in this field, partly because of the new information they contain and partly because they give an indication of one of the main trends in the NPL research program. In the near future this type of work will be conducted at much higher stream Mach numbers, and more detailed studies will be made in areas which have so far been explored in a rather tentative manner. Improvements in experimental techniques should allow some slip effects to be investigated and a start made on skin friction and heat-transfer measurements. The need for good experimental data in the low-density continuum and transition-flow regimes is pressing, and the NPL hope to make a modest contribution toward filling this need.

ACKNOWLEDGMENTS

The authors wish to acknowledge the valuable assistance received from Miss B. M. Davis in both the experimental work and in the subsequent analysis. Mr. S. C. Metcalf was responsible for supervising the experiment on circular-cylinder flow.

This paper is published by permission of the Director of the National Physical Laboratory and the work described forms part of the research program for the Aerodynamics Division.

List of Symbols

a Distance of step from leading edge of plate

C_D Drag coefficient

C_p Pressure coefficient

d Circular cylinder diameter

h Step height

k Numerical constant

Kn   Knudsen number

L Cone length; also interaction length on flat plate

M Mach number

(Δp) Pressure increase above flat-plate value

p Local surface pressure

Re   Reynolds number

x Distance from leading edge of plate

y Distance normal to plate surface

δ Boundary-layer thickness

δ^* Boundary-layer displacement thickness

ε Cone semivertex angle

θ Circumferential angle on cylinder, measured from forward stagnation point

μ Pressure of one micron mercury

ϕ Pressure parameter defined in Section III, B

Subscripts

A At step position

B At separation position

d Based on cylinder diameter

F Associated with the surface friction

i Value in inviscid flow

L Based on cone length

o Free-stream value

p Associated with the surface pressures

s Along cone surface from apex

T Total

x At position x

REFERENCES

Abbott, D. E., Holt, M., and Nielsen, J. N. (1963). AIAA. summer meeting, June 1963, Paper 63–172.

Aroesty, J. (1958). Univ. Calif. Inst. Eng. Res. Tech. Rept. HE-150-157.

Chapman, D. R., Kuehn, D. M., and Larson, H. K. (1958), NACA Rept. 1356.

Enkenhus, K. R. (1957). UTIA Rept. No. 43.

Ferri, A. (1942). Atti Guidonia Rept. Nos. 67, 68, and 69 (or see " Modern Developments in Fluid Dynamics—High Speed Flow," Vol. II. Oxford Univ. Press, London and New York, 1953).

Kavenau, L. L. (1956). *J. Aeronaut. Sci.* **23**, 193.

Maslach, G. J., and Latz, R. N. (1960). *In* "Advances in Vacuum Science and Technology," Vol. 2, p. 809. Macmillan (Pergamon Press), New York.

Maslach, G. J., and Schaaf, S. A. (1962). Univ. Calif. Inst. Eng. Res. Tech. Rept. HE-150-194.

McCarthy, J. F., and Kubota, T. (1964). AIAA J. **2**, 629.

Metcalf, S. C., Berry, C. J., and Davis, B. M. (1964). NPL Aero Rept. 1097.

Rogers, E. W. E., Berry, C. J., and Davis, B. M. (1964). NPL Aero Rept. 1095.

Sreekanth, A. K. (1961). UTIA Rept. No. 74.

Talbot, L., Koga, T., and Sherman, P. M. (1958). NACA T.N. 4327.

Tewfik, O. K., and Giedt, W. H. (1959). Univ. Calif. Inst. Eng. Res. Tech. Rept. HE-150-162.

Investigations of the Flow Field near the Leading Edge of a Heated Flat Plate in a Mach 0.5 Air Flow

S. A. GORDON[1]

Institute of Aerospace Studies, University of Toronto, Toronto, Ontario, Canada

The flow field near the leading edge of heated flat plates was investigated in a Mach number 0.5 flow of air. The model had a chord of 2 in. and the free-stream Knudsen number based on the chord was 0.05. Experiments were performed with room temperature, 100° and 200°C plate wall temperatures. Measurements were made with a pair of free-molecular pressure probes for the determination of speed ratio, and with a free-molecular equilibrium temperature probe. The characteristics of the flow field are presented in the form of graphs showing lines of constant speed ratio, static, and total temperatures. A comparison is made between the simple Maxwell slip and temperature jump conditions and the experimental data.

I. Objectives

While much of the basic theory of low-density flow dates back to Maxwell, Smoluchowski and Knudsen, remarkably little of the theory has been tested experimentally in a satisfactory manner. In particular, many of the details of the interaction of a flowing stream of low-density gas with a solid surface are still a matter of conjecture. The reason for this is not hard to find, since the experimental difficulties are formidable and until recently the facilities for performing the necessary tests have not been available. These experiments are further hampered by the underdeveloped state of experimental techniques.

The investigations reported here are primarily experimental and were undertaken to explore the interesting problem of heat transfer in upper altitude flight. Because of the large number of experimental and theoretical problems involved the experiment had to be greatly simplified, so that in the end it

---

[1] *Present address*: AeroChem Research Laboratories, Inc., Princeton, New Jersey.

reduced to the more classical problem of a subsonic flow in the immediate vicinity of the leading edge of a flat plate in which relatively large temperature differences are involved. Even without heat transfer this problem is of considerable interest since it concerns the type of flow that will occur at the leading edge of a flat plate in continuum flow, in the low Reynolds number region where the Blasius boundary-layer solution breaks down. In these experiments the heat transfer was from the plate to the flow rather than the reverse situation more commonly ascribed to high altitude flight, i.e., heat transfer to a cold surface. However, the temperature differences were relatively large, being of the magnitude of the static temperature of the gas. In effect, low densities were used to scale up the mean free path, so that the region of interest in the experiment occupied only twenty or so mean free paths.

These investigations, in some ways, can be considered an extension of work carried out at the Institute of Aerospace Studies by Harris (1958), although different instrumentation and experimental conditions were used. Harris experienced difficulty in getting quantitative measurements in terms of the speed ratio, S [where S is defined as $U/(2RT)^{1/2} = (\gamma/2)^{1/2}M$ where U is mass velocity, T is temperature, R is the gas content, γ is the ratio of specific heats, M is Mach number], but he was able to demonstrate the presence of something akin to a displacement thickness, one mean free path ahead of a flat plate in a low-density flow. The Knudsen number of the plate, Kn, defined as λ/L, where λ is the mean free path and L is a characteristic length (in this case, plate chord), was approximately 0.2 in his experiment. Experimental and theoretical difficulties tended to obscure the impact of these findings, however. Dewey (1961), investigating the hypersonic wake of a cylindrical body, was able to overcome some of these problems and obtain measurements of temperature, mass flow and velocity defect by use of a hot-wire probe in free-molecular flow.

II. Experimental Procedures

A. Model

The present experiments involved measurements extending over as large a number of mean free paths as possible and yet required the use of free-molecular-flow pressure probes. Since the jet properties were reasonably uniform for only about one nozzle radius downstream of the nozzle exit plane, the design of the experiment required a careful choice of test pressure and the use of small probes. In fact, the experiment was feasible only because it had been possible to develop tiny pressure gages for use in these probes which still retained an excellent sensitivity (Gordon, 1963). By operating the pressure probes at a rather low Knudsen number of 4 (and thus introducing a small but predictable departure from the theoretical free-molecular-flow response; Lafrance, 1963), it was possible to have the model operate in the uniform region of the jet with a pressure high enough to allow for a model with a Knudsen number of 0.05 (based on plate chord).

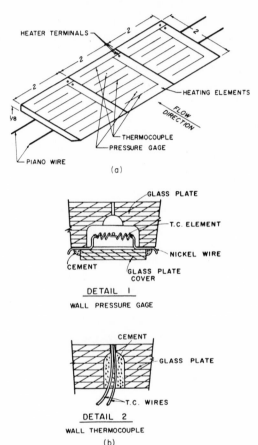

FIG. 1. (a) Schematic of flat plate model. All dimensions in inches. (b) Detail drawing of fully instrumented plate.

As shown in Fig. 1, the model was constructed of three $\frac{1}{8}$ in. thick glass plates. The leading edge of each plate was sharpened to 0.005 in. and the upper surface was coated with an electrically conducting film which acted as a heater. This film was deposited in a grid pattern, so that when connected to a suitable electrical input it supplied heat to the plate at a uniform rate per unit area.

On the centerline of the model three equally spaced chromel-alumel thermo-couples were embedded with their junctions flush with the upper surface. In addition, two small pressure gauges of the thermal-conductivity type (Gordon, 1963) were embedded in the wall with pressure taps extending through the upper surface. These taps were positioned on the model centerline, symmetrically positioned between the three thermocouples. Their internal volume was less than 0.1 cc. The chord of the completed model was 2 in., or about twenty mean free paths.

All electrical leads were brought in along the lower surface, which was eventually coated with a flexible cement to give a smooth surface free from sharp protusions. The upper surface was smooth, flat and completely un-obstructed. The entire model was supported on two taut piano wires which were strung between two arms of an adjustable holder. The 6-in. span of the model extended across the jet issuing from the 5.5-in. diameter subsonic nozzle, so that the holder was completely outside the flow. The centerline of the model, along which the thermojunctions and pressure taps were arranged, was set to coincide exactly with the axis of the nozzle. The leading edge of the model was set 1 inch (ten mean free paths) back of the nozzle exit plane.

The UTIAS low density tunnel and subsonic nozzle have been described in detail by Enkenhus (1957). This tunnel is of the free-jet, single-pass type and may be operated continuously within its rated characteristics. The probes themselves were so mounted that they could be positioned anywhere in the flow region above the flat plate, up to the nozzle exit plane. However, it was not possible to probe the region below the plane of the plate.

B. Pressure Probes

The free-molecular-flow pressure probe, as developed at UTIAS by Patterson and his students (Patterson, 1956; Harris and Patterson, 1958), was used to measure the molecular speed-ratio. A particular form of the long-tube impact probe was developed especially for these experiments. Because this probe senses number-flux rather than momentum-flux, one generally obtains measurements proportional to $p/T^{1/2}$ rather than p. (Here p is the static pressure and T the static temperature of the gas.) Since T is not normally known explicitly, this usually presents a problem in the interpretation of the data. However, it is easily shown (Gordon, 1964) that important simplifications result if a static pressure probe (i.e., one whose opening faces exactly perpendicular to the flow direction), and a long-tube impact probe (opening facing into the flow) are operated in a flow-region where the flow conditions are uniform. In particular, if the sensing heads of these two probes are kept at identical temperatures, the ratio of the two sensing-head pressures can be used to determine speed ratio, independent of the static temperature of the flow.

Using models of the previously mentioned small thermal-conductivity pressure gage, a molecular-speed-ratio probe was constructed (Fig. 2). The two parallel probe tips were made of 0.025 in. o.d. hypodermic tubing with an 0.022-in. internal bore and were spaced 0.100 in. apart. The 0.012-in. opening in the wall of the static probe faced away from the impact probe and was positioned exactly level with the open end of the latter. The two gage

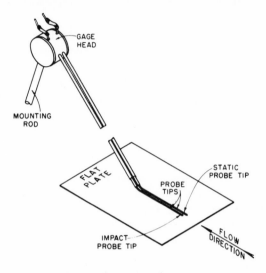

Fig. 2. Pressure probes.

heads were constructed in a single block of metal so that envelope temperatures were identical. Since the sensing elements were also run at identical temperatures, the probe fulfilled the requirements of the theory and therefore the ratio of the measured pressures gave molecular speed ratios without requiring the determination of the static temperature.

C. Temperature Probe

The equilibrium temperature probe, as developed by Stalder *et al.* (1950) and Bell and Schaaf (1953), has been used to determine flow properties in adiabatic flows (e.g., Laurmann, 1954). Since its output is a function of both the local static temperatures of the flow and the speed ratio, it can also be used to determine the local temperature, if the local speed ratio is known. In these experiments a thermocouple was used as the temperature-sensing element of the probe. By placing a reference junction in the stagnation chamber of the tunnel, a difference signal could be obtained which was almost entirely independent of ambient fluctuations in the reservoir temperature of the tunnel.

While this resulted in a very sensitive and convenient instrument for probing adiabatic flows, it was shown experimentally that even very small departures from adiabatic conditions could result in large errors in the apparent speed ratio. Consequently, one could not make reliable speed ratio measurements in the boundary layer with this instrument. However, if speed ratios were known it could be used to obtain very accurate and precise values for static temperature or total temperature. Because the speed ratios were relatively low, the differences between equilibrium temperature and static temperature in these experiments were of the order of several degrees, at most. As a result, the temperature measurements have a relatively higher accuracy than the speed ratio measurements. In fact, the speed ratio corrections were small enough so that in the heated plate experiments the two types of measurements could often be considered as essentially independent measurements.

D. Experimental Conditions

The experiments were conducted in air, at a test-section static pressure of 20 mtorr and a free-stream Mach number of 0.5, giving a free-stream mean free path of about 0.10 in. Flow measurements were made for (1) an adiabatic plate, (2) a plate temperature of about 100°C, and (3) a plate temperature of about 200°C.

Thus, while the temperatures were never high enough to cause serious problems with the materials of construction, the temperature differences were a very significant fraction of the free-stream temperature and therefore a region was explored where the theory is not too well established. Careful calibration was resorted to and elaborate measures were taken to check the accuracy of all the measurements.

Measurements were obtained at a large number of points above the nozzle axis at five stations downstream of the nozzle axis. They were taken with both the pressure probes and the equilibrium temperature probe, and the data were reduced to determine the free-molecular speed ratios and total and static temperature at each point. Power input to the plate, plate static pressure and plate wall temperature were determined at frequent time intervals, while the tunnel performance was monitored by a variety of means (Gordon, 1964). The data were eventually replotted to show lines of constant speed ratio, constant total temperature or constant static temperature in the region above and ahead of the flat plate. It should be pointed out that this replotting involved a certain amount of interpolation between stations so that the accuracy of the data is greater at those points where the measurements were made than in the intermediate regions. The stations for measurement were (1) at the nozzle exit, (2) 0.5 in. downstream of the nozzle, (3) at the leading edge, (4) at the mid point of the plate and (5) at the trailing edge.

E. Accuracy

A careful examination, both theoretical and experimental, was made of the accuracy and reliability of the present measurements. In developing the theory of probe response it was necessary to assume Maxwellian distributions, accommodation coefficients of unity, two-stream distribution functions and other such simplifications in order to make the mathematics manageable. Experimentally, it is by no means certain that these assumed conditions are accurate representations of the actual conditions and the effects of departures from the ideal were not always possible to determine. While it was possible to show that departures from Maxwellian distributions were probably not causing serious errors, the effect of failure of the other assumptions remains a source of some uncertainty. The measurements were quite precise however, although drift in the tunnel conditions reduced the reproducibility of the measurements somewhat. It is felt that an over-all accuracy of 5% in speed ratio measurements could be claimed (at the higher speed ratios), while the temperature measurements were probably correct to a few tenths of a degree.

The reduced accuracy at lower speed ratios was simply due to the fact that differences between static and impact pressure were reduced to the point where inherent inaccuracies of the probes become important. However, these regions of low speed ratio occurred toward the trailing edge of the model and were of somewhat less interest.

A numerical calculation was made of the probable probe response in the immediate neighborhood of the flat plate, assuming that the incoming and outgoing streams could be represented by Maxwellian distributions. When measured gradients and accommodation coefficients were used it became apparent that no significant error was introduced by ignoring either the gradient or the two-stream effect in either type of probe and that it was therefore meaningful to use the values obtained from a simple interpretation of the probe measurements as being the true local values.

The flow was also carefully probed to determine if any significant departures from two-dimensional flow occurred on the model. Because of a failure of the outer heating elements during the experiment, there was some reason to fear such effects, but in fact, they were smaller than expected. However, the transverse temperature gradients for the 200°C plate were large enough to raise some doubts as to the reliability of these results. The general pattern of the measurements did not alter even for the 200°C case so that the results are probably substantially correct. Nonetheless, the 200°C data are somewhat less reliable than those of the other runs and are treated here mostly as corroborating evidence.

In making measurements with the pressure probes a curious pattern of discrepancies was observed, which was eventually interpreted as being caused by changes in gage-head envelope temperature, as the probes were moved inside the test section into regions of greater or smaller heat transfer. Because no evidence for a significant variation in static pressure could be observed over the flat plate in a variety of subsidiary experiments, it was eventually assumed that any apparent differences between static pressure probe measurements and those measured at the flat plate wall-tap (Fig. 1) were due to changes in the probe gage-head temperature. Since the impact probe gage-head temperature varied in exactly the same way as that for the static probe it was possible to correct its readings accordingly. These corrections were never large, but they managed to completely remove the observed discrepancies. Since the low speed ratio measurements were particularly sensitive to any small errors in pressure measurement, this disappearance of discrepancies was considered to be a very stringent test of probe accuracy. However, to make these corrections it was necessary to assume a constant static pressure throughout the flow field. Since elsewhere the absence of any significant change in static pressure ahead of the leading edge is cited as proof of the assertion that the decrease in speed ratio was a true boundary layer effect, it should be clearly stated that in the adiabatic plate experiments, even before the corrections were made, the discrepancies were very small indeed, and of such a nature that they would require a speeding up of the flow rather than a slowing down. Even in the case of the 200°C plate the discrepancies were not large enough to alter any of the conclusions arrived at. (In any further experiments it would be advisable to control the gage-head temperature in order to remove this slight source of error, however.)

III. Discussion of Results

A. Plate Temperature

Plots of plate temperature against distance from the leading edge of the plate for the 100°C plate (Fig. 3) and the 200°C plate (Fig. 4) are substantially

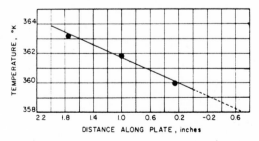

FIG. 3. Actual wall temperatures on 100°C flat plate.

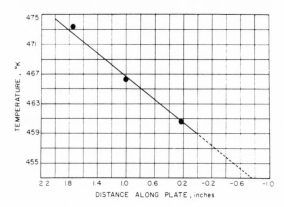

Fig. 4. Actual wall temperatures on 200°C flat plate.

linear. Since the heat input per unit area was constant, this suggests a linearly increasing thickness for the thermal boundary layer, somewhat analogous to that sometimes assumed for the viscous boundary layer (Harris, 1958 and Dewey, 1961). However, an examination of the maps of the flow field and temperature field above and ahead of the leading edge (Figs. 5–11) indicates that this is an oversimplification. One feature common to all these data is the existence of a leading-edge effect several mean free paths upstream of the leading edge. Since the interpretation of the boundary layer thickness in terms of a linear rate of growth does not take this into account it cannot be entirely correct.

This appearance of the boundary layer upstream of the leading edge is a constant feature of all data taken in these experiments. Since there was no

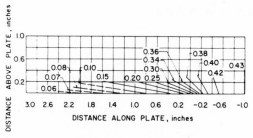

Fig. 5. Lines of constant speed ratio above the adiabatic plate. (*Note*: For Figs. 5–11, the nozzle exit is at −1.0, the leading edge at 0.0, and the trailing edge at 2.0.)

increase in static pressure that could be correlated with this decrease in molecular speed ratio, it seems necessary to assume that it is truly a boundary layer (i.e., dissipative) effect. Because kinetic theory in fact requires that a certain fraction of the molecules reflected from the leading edge should travel several mean free paths upstream and thus reduce the average molecular

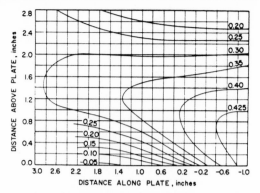

FIG. 6. Lines of constant speed ratio above 100°C flat plate.

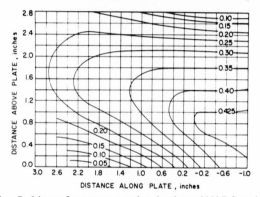

FIG. 7. Lines of constant speed ratio above 200°C flat plate.

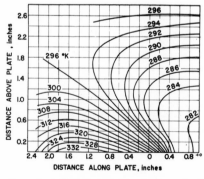

FIG. 8. Lines of constant static temperatures above the 100°C flat plate.

speed ratio at these points, the results seem quite reasonable, although little emphasis has been placed on this phenomenon in the general theory of low density flows.

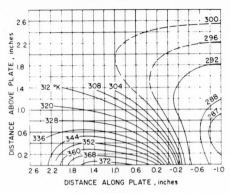

Fig. 9. Lines of constant static temperatures above the 200°C flat plate.

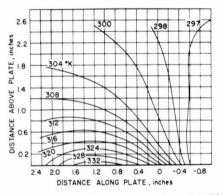

Fig. 10. Lines of constant total temperatures above the 100°C flat plate.

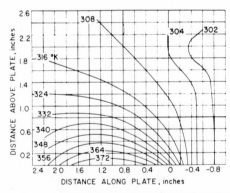

Fig. 11. Lines of constant total temperatures above the 200°C flat plate.

These same figures show several other interesting features. In particular, it will be observed that a thick boundary layer has grown out from the nozzle wall and rather quickly merged with that produced on the flat plate (Figs. 6–9).

This merging of the boundary layers indicates a region in which an undisturbed free-stream ceases to exist and beyond which the measurements become less reliable. Velocity slip and temperature jump at the plate wall are clearly shown, as is the rather rapid growth of the boundary layer.

B. Maxwell Slip Conditions

Maxwell (1879), in a consideration of the interaction of a gas stream with an infinite wall parallel to the flow, postulated the existence of a relationship between the slip velocity at the wall and the rate of change of velocity perpendicular to the wall. If slip velocity is designated by U_s the relationship in its simplest form (e.g., Street, 1957) is usually given as

$$U_s = (2 - \sigma)\sigma^{-1}\lambda(\partial U/\partial y)_0, \tag{1}$$

where σ is the accommodation coefficient for tangential momentum, λ is the mean free path and $(\partial U/\partial y)_0$ is the rate of change of tangential velocity in a direction normal to the wall, as evaluated at the wall. This relationship, because of its simplicity and its essential reasonableness, has been extensively used as a boundary condition for slip flow and is frequently applied to leading edge flows as well. Near the leading edge, the flow loses its one-dimensional character however, and the logic of the derivation loses some of its force. It seemed worthwhile to test this relationship using the experimental data gathered here. Strictly speaking, the slip velocity is not defined for any region ahead of the leading edge, but for these experiments it is a simple matter to redefine $(\partial U/\partial y)_0$ so that the derivative is now evaluated on the infinite plane within which the surface of the flat plate lies. As the flow has lost its one-dimensional character the possibility also arises that one should perhaps use the expression $(\partial U/\partial n)_0$ where now the derivative is evaluated in the direction of most rapid change, which no longer need coincide with the normal to the plate. In fact, in the tests to be described here, both derivatives were tested,

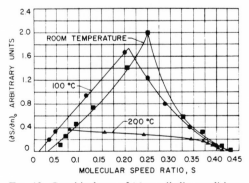

FIG. 12. Graphical test of Maxwell slip conditions.

with little significant difference in results. The derivatives in the direction of greatest change are reported here. In Fig. 12 the slip speed ratio is plotted against the rate of change of the tangential speed ratio at the wall, i.e., S_s vs. $(\partial s/\partial n)_0$ which, except for a numerical factor, is equivalent to plotting U_s vs. $(\partial U/\partial n)_0$. If the Maxwell slip conditions are a good empirical fit to the experimental values the results should lie on a straight line through the origin. The most notable feature of this plot is the presence of a cusp very close to the leading edge. Ahead of this the Maxwell slip conditions are obviously contrary to reality, while back of the cusp the fit is, at best, somewhat doubtful, although not seriously in error. The distinct cusp is obviously related to a change in the mechanism of boundary-layer formation, brought about by the physical presence of the solid boundary. From these considerations one may conclude that it is not realistic to apply the Maxwell slip conditions near the leading edge unless some other means is utilized to take care of the observed upstream effect.

C. Temperature Jump Conditions

The standard expression for temperature jump at a boundary wall has been obtained in a manner quite analogous to the Maxwell slip conditions (Schaaf and Chambre, 1958). This temperature jump, ΔT can be related to the normal derivative of temperature at the boundary by the expression

$$\Delta T = (2 - \alpha)\alpha^{-1}\lambda \operatorname{Pr}^{-1} 2\gamma(\gamma + 1)^{-1}(\partial T/\partial y)_0 \tag{2}$$

where α is the thermal accommodation coefficient, γ is the ratio of specific heats, Pr is the Prandtl number, while λ, as before, is the mean free path. When the appropriate data are treated in a fashion similar to the Maxwell slip data very similar results are obtained (Fig. 13). In fact, the close correspondence of the two graphs is a gratifying confirmation of the essential

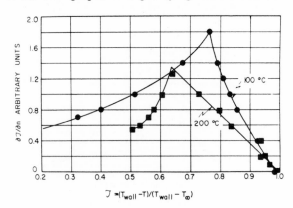

FIG. 13. Graphical test of temperature jump conditions.

correctness of the data used. It may be concluded that the temperature jump conditions may not properly be applied to leading-edge flows unless some other means is utilized to take care of the upstream effect. Downstream of the leading edge the temperature jump conditions are not far wrong, although there is some indication that they are not entirely correct.

D. Accommodation Coefficients

It is also possible to analyze the data obtained in terms of the various accommodation coefficients involved in the surface interaction. However, because the accommodation coefficients are defined in terms of incoming and outgoing streams of particles, while the measured values represent the average of the contributions of both types of particles there is an inescapable ambiguity in interpreting the data. In these cases, Maxwell's assumptions are used, namely:

$$\zeta_{av} = \zeta_{in} + \zeta_{out}, \tag{3}$$

$$\zeta_{in} = \zeta_{av(\lambda)}, \tag{4}$$

where ζ is taken to be the variable of interest (velocity, temperature, etc.) and the subscripts "av," "in," and "out" refer to average quantities, incoming stream quantities and outgoing stream quantities, respectively. $\zeta_{av(\lambda)}$ represents the value of ζ_{av} as determined exactly one mean free path away from the point in question, in the direction of the greatest rate of change toward the free-stream value.

A standard definition of accommodation coefficient is assumed, i.e.,

$$\alpha_{\zeta} = (\zeta_{in} - \zeta_{out})/(\zeta_{in} - \zeta_{wall}), \tag{5}$$

where the subscript "wall" refers to conditions at the wall. Making the preceding assumptions, accommodation coefficients were determined at the leading edge where the data was presumed to be particularly accurate. These values are given in Table I.

It will be seen that in Table I the accommodation coefficients are rather low compared to published values on "engineering" or "dirty" surfaces as given by Hartnett (1960). An examination of an earlier measurement by Laurmann (1954) on the flow of Mach 2 air over a flat plate turns up corroborating evidence. In this report Laurmann used an equilibrium temperature probe but did not interpret the results in terms of actual speed ratio. In view of our further experience with this device, it seems permissible to carry the data somewhat further than he did. When actual speed ratios are calculated and the data at the leading edge interpreted as in this work, a value may be calculated for the tangential accommodation coefficient which is about the same as obtained here, making due allowance for the reduced accuracy of the

TABLE I

EXPERIMENTAL VALUES OF VARIOUS ACCOMMODATION COEFFICIENTS[a]

	α_S	α_U	α_{T_0}	α_T
Room temp. plate	0.61	0.61		
100°C plate	0.53	0.51	0.34	0.38
200°C plate	0.14	0.10	0.22	0.23

[a] Accommodation coefficient defined as follows:

$$\alpha = (\zeta_{in} - \zeta_{out})/(\zeta_{in} - \zeta_{wall}).$$

results. This seems to indicate that the low accommodation coefficients are not just due to our particular experimental conditions but demand a more fundamental explanation.

As an alternative test, assuming the Maxwell slip conditions to be correct (and knowing the mean free path), it is possible to calculate the tangential momentum accommodation coefficient α_U (or σ) from Eq. (1). As might be expected from the presence of the cusp in Figs. 12 and 13, the value changes drastically in the neighborhood of the leading edge, but near mid-plate it assumes a fairly constant value of $\sigma \approx 0.71$ for the room temperature plate and 0.91 for the 100°C case. The thermal accommodation coefficient as determined by the temperature jump equation, Eq. (2), is $\alpha = 0.49$ for the 100°C plate. The data for the 200°C plate are considered less reliable, but give $\sigma = 0.36$ and $\alpha = 0.34$. Thus, it can be seen that in both types of calculations the accommodation coefficients appear to be surprisingly low, particularly at the leading edge. It is reassuring that the Maxwell slip condition calculations and the temperature jump calculations give values of at least the correct order of magnitude when one considers the number of assumptions that have been made and the possibility of serious error.

The fact that both these experiments and Laurmann's earlier data give very similar results suggests that a discrepancy may exist in the theory itself. Thus, it may well be that no single accommodation coefficient exists for a particular surface, but that it is rather a function of geometry, speed ratio, temperature or a variety of other possible variables. However, there was a great difference between the nature of the polished metal surface used by Laurmann and the mixture of silver and plastic binder applied on a glass substrate that constituted the surface in these experiments, which suggests that the type of surface was not particularly important. On the face of it, the feature most common to these two studies was the requirement that considerable energy had to be transferred on each collision in order to produce a high degree of accommodation.

F. Theoretical Solutions

The experimental values of slip velocity over an adiabatic flat plate are plotted in Fig. 14 along with representative theoretical values by Yang and Lees (1956) and Mirels (1952). The solution to the Rayleigh problem of an infinite flat plate started impulsively from rest can be converted to an expression for flow over the leading edge of a flat plate by the substitution $x = Ukt$ where x is distance from the leading edge, U is free-stream velocity, t is time,

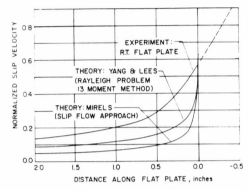

FIG. 14. Experimental and theoretical slip velocities along the flat plate.

and k a constant near unity. Since it contains the fewest assumptions about the nature of the phenomenon involved, it is unfortunate that this model cannot possibly predict a boundary layer upstream of the leading edge. Other types of solutions tend to require the assumption of the Maxwell slip condition as a boundary condition, or else some equally unproved assumption. Since the Rayleigh model might be expected to give some sort of picture of the functional dependence of the flow properties back of the leading edge, even if it gives the wrong picture ahead of the leading edge, an approximate kinetic-theory solution of the Rayleigh problem was attempted. The details of this solution are given elsewhere (Gordon, 1964), but it involves a solution using the Krook approximation to the Boltzmann equation for a plate set impulsively in motion and simultaneously raised in temperature by a step function. While an additional severe approximation had to be made, the method allowed about the greatest degree of complication that would yield a straight-forward, explicit solution. Since the analogy itself is inexact, no greater degree of complexity seemed justified. One main result of this theory was the prediction that the slip speed ratio and temperature jump would both decrease exponentially with distance downstream of the leading edge of the plate. Because of this prediction the logarithms of the slip speed ratio and of temperature jump were plotted against distance from the nozzle exit as shown in

Figs. 15 and 16. These plots have the added virtue of delineating three distinct regions of the flow, namely, a region ahead of the leading edge, a region of nearly exponential change and then a trailing edge region extending almost to the mid point of the model. Between the leading edge and the midpoint

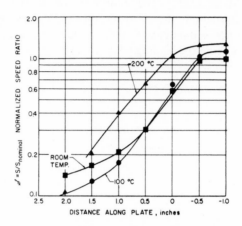

Fig. 15. Test for exponential decay of slip speed ratio.

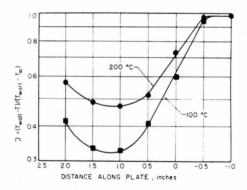

Fig. 16. Test for exponential decay of temperature jump ratio.

of the model, where trailing edge effects begin to appear, the data appears to fit an exponential decay prediction somewhat better than the Maxwell slip conditions or the temperature jump conditions. While the evidence is not conclusive, it does appear probable that the Maxwell slip conditions and temperature jump conditions are only an approximation to the true boundary conditions immediately back of the leading edge. The evidence brought forward here is not very reliable, but the data tend to fit the slip and jump conditions better as one goes further back from the leading edge.

IV. Concluding Remarks

The data appear to indicate that the simple Maxwell slip conditions and the temperature jump conditions may not be applied in free-molecule or transition flows unless some provision is made for the influence of the boundary layer upstream of the leading edge. On the other hand, these same boundary conditions predict accommodation coefficients of the right order of magnitude, as little as five mean free paths back of the leading edge, so that they probably do not introduce large errors. In this five mean free path region the slip velocity and temperature jump give some evidence of decreasing exponentially with distance rather than following the Maxwell slip conditions or temperature jump conditions as the case may be.

It does seem certain that the indiscriminate use of the simple Maxwell slip conditions or the temperature jump conditions as boundary conditions in theoretical solutions might lead to erroneous conclusions where the contributions of the first five mean free path lengths of the plate are a significant fraction of the total effect. As this leading edge contribution to the total effect becomes smaller, the error introduced by these assumptions ought to decrease.

As far as accommodation coefficients are concerned there seems to be a discrepancy between these results and other values reported in the literature. Laurmann's previously published study seems to confirm the measurements reported here. It is not apparent why these values are so low, but our understanding of the theory may well be at fault. However, previous measurements of accommodation coefficients have not generally been for such a high-speed flow of a gas nor for a case where such large temperature gradients may occur. It may be that accommodation coefficients are naturally low under these conditions.

The experiments reported here are capable of considerable refinement, so that more detailed information could be obtained using this technique. On the other hand the accuracy of these measurements was adequate for the conclusions arrived at in this paper. The results point out the necessity for checking many of the fundamental assumptions that have been used for many years in theoretical treatments of the flow of low densities gases.

REFERENCES

Bell, S., and Schaaf, S. A. (1953). *ARS. (Am. Rocket Soc.) J.* **23**, 314.
Dewey, C. F., Jr. (1961). *ARS. (Am. Rocket Soc.). J.* **31**, 1709.
Enkenhus, K. R. (1957). Univ. of Toronto, Inst. Aerophys., Rept. No. 44.
Gordon, S. A. (1963). *In* "Transactions, Tenth National Vacuum Symposium American Vacuum Society" (G. Bancroft, ed.), p. 238. Macmillan, New York.

Gordon, S. A. (1964). Univ. of Toronto, Inst. Aerospace Studies, Rept. No. 92.

Harnett, J. P. (1960). *In* "Rarefied Gas Dynamics" (L. Talbot, ed.), p. 1. Academic Press, New York.

Harris, E. L. (1958). Univ. of Toronto, Inst. Aerophys., Rept. No. 53.

Harris, E. L., and Patterson, G. N. (1958). Univ. of Toronto, Inst. Aerophys. Rept. 52.

LaFrance, J. C. (1963). Univ. of Toronto, Inst. Aerophys., Tech. Note No. 67.

Laurmann, J. A. (1954). California Univ. Inst. Eng. Res. HE-150-156.

Maxwell, J. C. (1879). *Phil. Trans. Roy. Soc.* Part I, **170**, 231-256.

Mirels, H. (1952). NACA TN 2609.

Patterson, G. N. (1956). Univ. of Toronto, Inst. Aerophys., Rept. No. 41.

Schaaf, S. A., and Chambre, P. L. (1958). *In* "Fundamentals of Gas Dynamics" (H. W. Emmons, ed.), p. 719. Princeton Univ. Press, Princeton, New Jersey.

Stalder, J. R., Goodwin, G., and Creager, M. O. (1958). NACA Rept. 1032, also NACA TN 2244.

Street, R. E. (1957). NACA RM 57A30.

Yang, H. T., and Lees, L. (1956). *J. Math. and Phys.* **35**, No. 3.

The Aerodynamic Drag Torque on a Rotating Sphere in the Transition Regime

R. G. LORD[1] AND P. J. HARBOUR[2]

Physics and Chemistry of Solids, Cavendish Laboratory, University of Cambridge, Cambridge, England

An experimental and theoretical study has been made of the problem of an isolated sphere rotating in an otherwise stationary gas. The aerodynamic drag torque experienced by a magnetically suspended test sphere (Beams, 1947; Bowden and Lord, 1963) has been measured over the entire range of Knudsen number from continuum to free molecule flow in air, krypton, and di-ido-methane. Some early results in air have already been published (Lord, 1964). The highest Mach numbers (based on equatorial speed) which have been achieved in permanent gases are approximately 1.5, but by using di-ido-methane, a heavy vapor, the range of the experiments has so far been extended to up about Mach. 2.5. A method of correlating the data under a single parameter has now been developed following Sherman (1963) and an approximate interpolation formula between continuum and free molecule flow has been derived which is in good agreement with experiment.

I. Introduction

Theoretical analysis of transition regime flow problems has proved to be extremely difficult and so far investigations have been restricted to problems of exceptionally simple geometry. Consequently, there is still a great demand for experimental data, both for its intrinsic usefulness and its capability to act as a guide for further development of the theory.

The aim of the work described here was to provide such data for one reasonably simple transition flow problem, namely that of the drag torque experienced by an isolated sphere rotating in an otherwise stationary gas. The range of the experiments was sufficient to span the whole of the transition regime, from continuum to free molecule flow, up to supersonic speeds.

[1] *Present address*: Division of Aeronautical Sciences, University of California, Berkeley, California.

[2] *Present address*: Department of Aerospace and Mechanical Sciences, Gas Dynamics Laboratory, Princeton University. Princeton, New Jersey.

II. Experimental Equipment

A. The Suspension System

The sphere, a polished steel ball, was suspended freely beneath an electro-magnet, the position of equilibrium (normally unstable) being stabilized by means of a photoelectric servomechanism, illustrated schematically in Fig. 1.

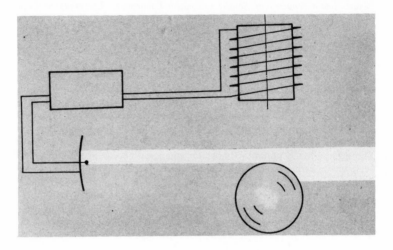

FIG. 1. The magnetic suspension system.

Lateral stability was achieved by means of a device described previously (Bowden and Lord, 1963). Figure 2 shows a photograph of a suspended rotor. The sphere was enclosed in a glass vacuum chamber (not shown in Fig. 2) and could be rotated about a vertical axis by means of an induction drive provided by four symmetrically disposed horizontal coils. The frequency of rotation was measured in the following way: a photomultiplier was arranged to pick up light from the lamp in the suspension servosystem after reflection from the top of the rotor, and the intensity of this light was modulated by means of a small scratch on the rotor surface. The output of the photomultiplier was then compared with that of an accurate signal generator on an oscilloscope.

The resistance to rotation of the sphere caused by electromagnetic inter-actions with the suspension field was exceedingly small—negligible compared to aerodynamic drag at pressures greater than 10^{-5} Torr. It was possible, therefore, to measure the aerodynamic drag by observing the angular decelera-tion of the sphere while coasting (i.e., with the driving field off).

Fig. 2. Photograph of suspended rotor showing lateral stabilizer and driving coils.

B. Vacuum System

1. Permanent Gases. The sphere used in this work was $\frac{1}{4}$ in. in diameter, and was suspended inside a glass chamber of diameter $1\frac{1}{4}$ in., so that the error in assuming the sphere to be completely isolated was very small (less than 0.5 %). The pressures at which experiments were performed (10^{-3} to 1 Torr) were high enough for the system to be used statically and were set by evacuating the system to 10^{-5} Torr and then isolating the pumps and admitting dry gas via a metering valve. A McLeod gage was used for pressure measurement (estimated accuracy $\pm 1\%$ at 1 Torr to $\pm 5\%$ at 10^{-3} Torr).

2. Vapor. In order to extend the range of the experiments to higher Mach numbers, drag measurements were also made in di-ido-methane (CH_2I_2) which is a heavy vapor having a sonic speed approximately one third that of air. Since a McLeod gage cannot be used to measure the pressure of a condensable vapor, a different technique was adopted for these experiments.

Two spheres were suspended independently but in the same vacuum chamber and one of these, rotating at low speed (corresponding to $M < 0.1$) was used as a pressure gage in conjunction with the results obtained at low Mach numbers in permanent gases. The second sphere was used as a test sphere and rotated at high speed. In order to obtain measurements in continuum flow where the low Mach number drag is independent of pressure it was necessary to make the radius of the test sphere about ten times that of the reference sphere. Measurements could then be made at Knudsen numbers as low as 10^{-2}, since the reference sphere was in slip flow at Kn $\approx 10^{-1}$ where the drag is still reasonably pressure dependent. This procedure makes possible a threefold increase in Mach number with only a slight loss in experimental accuracy.

III. Results

The results of drag measurements at several different Mach numbers in air and krypton are shown in Figs. 3a and 3b. They are presented in terms of the

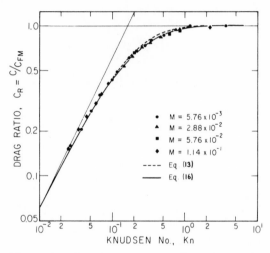

FIG. 3a. Transition regime drag torque on a rotating sphere at low Mach numbers. Data for air.

drag ratio $C_R = C/C_{fm}$ where C = measured drag torque, and C_{fm} = calculated free molecule value for diffuse reflection, $[=(2\pi/3)\rho\bar{c}a^4\Omega]$. The variation of C_R with Knudsen number Kn based on sphere radius is shown on a double logarithmic plot. The results for both gases tend to the value 1 at high values of Kn, which suggests that the molecules are reflected diffusely from the rotor surface ($\sigma = 1$) in each case.

The results at low Mach numbers (Fig. 3a) lie on a single curve (within the experimental error), but those at higher Mach numbers (Fig. 3b) show deviations at low Knudsen numbers. The reason for this is that the continuum

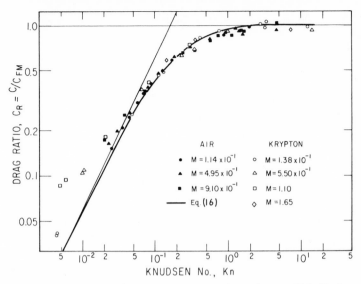

FIG. 3b. Transition regime drag torque on a rotating sphere at high Mach numbers. Data for air and krypton.

drag ratio, C_{cont}/C_{fm}, is in general dependent on M (or more properly, Re) as well as Kn, except at low Reynolds numbers where (Lamb, 1924)

$$C_{cont} = C_c = 8\pi\eta a^3\Omega, \qquad (1)$$

so that

$$C_c/C_{fm} = 6 \text{ Kn}. \qquad (2)$$

This line is plotted on Fig. 3 and agrees very well with the low Mach number results in the continuum regime.

Sherman (1963) has suggested that subsonic drag data may be correlated by plotting the measured drag ratio C_R against the continuum drag ratio C_{cont}/C_{fm} instead of Kn, but in order to do this it is necessary to know how C_{cont}/C_{fm} varies with Kn and Re. At high Reynolds number (boundary layer regime)

$$C_{cont} = C_{bl} = 3.50(\eta\rho)^{1/2}a^4\Omega^{3/2} \qquad \text{(Bowden and Lord, 1963),} \qquad (3)$$

so that

$$C_{cont}/C_{fm} = C_{bl}/C_{fm} = 0.835 \text{ Kn(Re)}^{1/2}, \qquad (4)$$

but a difficulty arises with intermediate values of Re for which the continuum problem has not been solved. In order to resolve this problem measurements were made of the continuum drag torque over a range of Reynolds number from 10^{-2} to 100. It was found that the results were well represented by the formula

$$C_{cont} = [C_c{}^2 + C_{bl}^2]^{1/2},\tag{5}$$

which yields

$$C_{cont}/C_{fm} = 6\ \text{Kn}[1 + 1.94 \times 10^{-2}\ \text{Re}]^{1/2}.\tag{6}$$

The results in Fig. 3b have therefore been replotted against the modified rarefaction parameter.

$$\text{Kn}' = \text{Kn}[1 + 1.94 \times 10^{-2}\ \text{Re}]^{1/2}.\tag{7}$$

The result is shown in Fig. 4, and it can be seen that the Mach number dependence has now been completely suppressed.

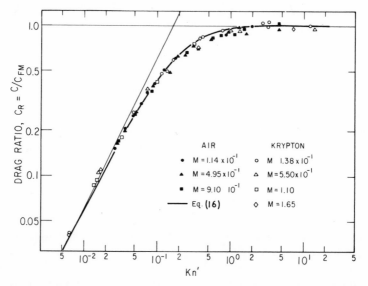

FIG. 4. Data for air and krypton at high Mach numbers plotted against Kn′ (Eq. 7).

The experimental results for di-ido-methane are shown in Figs. 5a and 5b.

IV. Theoretical

In the absence of any rigorous theoretical treatment of the transition regime flow around a rotating sphere it was considered worthwhile to construct a simple interpolation between the slip and free molecule solutions to the problem, in order to provide a comparison with the experimental results. This was done on the basis of the following simple physical model of the flow at low Reynolds numbers.

In the continuum solution (Lamb, 1924) the gas in a thin spherical shell of radius r (concentric with the sphere) rotates uniformly with angular velocity ω where the variation of ω with r is determined by the Navier-Stokes equations. It is found that

$$\omega = a^3\Omega/r^3. \qquad (8)$$

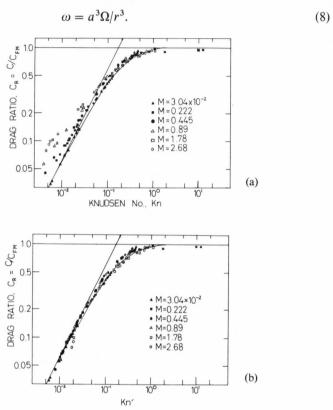

FIG. 5. Data for di-ido-methane; (a) plotted against Kn; (b) plotted against Kn′.

In the transition regime it was assumed that outside a sphere of radius $a + \lambda$ the continuum equations are still valid but for $a < r < a + \lambda$ the flow is essentially free molecular. The magnitude of the angular velocity at radius $a + \lambda$ was determined from the condition that the total radial flux of angular momentum was the same in the two regions. Now the flux of angular momentum from the sphere in the free molecule region is

$$C = (2\pi/3)\sigma\bar{\rho}\bar{c}a^4[\Omega - \omega(a + \lambda)], \qquad (9)$$

and in the continuum region

$$C = 8\pi\eta a^3\omega_0 = 4\pi\rho\bar{c}\lambda a^3\omega_0, \tag{10}$$

where now

$$\omega(r) = a^3\omega_0/r^3. \tag{11}$$

In the above equations ω_0 is the angular velocity of the gas at the surface of the sphere. Because of slip this is not equal to the angular velocity of the sphere itself.

From Eqs. (9)–(11) we find

$$1/C_R = C_{fm}/C = (1/\sigma) + \{1/[6\text{ Kn}(1 + \text{Kn})^3]\}, \tag{12}$$

or alternatively,

$$C_R = \frac{6\text{ Kn}(1 + \text{Kn})^3}{1 + (6\text{ Kn}/\sigma)(1 + \text{Kn})^3}. \tag{13}$$

It can easily be verified that this formula reduces to 6 Kn, 6 Kn/$\{1 + 3$ Kn$\cdot$ $[(2 - \sigma)/\sigma]\}$, and σ in the continuum, slip, and free molecule limits, respectively, and that these are in fact the correct limits for this problem. Although Eq. (13) is strictly limited to creep flow conditions, it may be applied to flows of larger Re merely by replacing Kn by Kn'.

Equation (13) is represented by the broken curve in Fig. 3a. Agreement between it and the experimental results is excellent in the continuum, slip, and free molecule regimes, but there appears to be a discrepancy of about 5% in the transition regime. This, however, is not really surprising considering the approximate nature of the theory. A slightly more detailed model has now been developed by one of the authors (Harbour, 1963), which takes into account the distribution of free paths of the gas molecules. That is, instead of assuming that each molecule striking the sphere had its last collision at radius $a + \lambda$, we now assume that a fraction,

$$\lambda^{-1} \exp -[(r - a)/\lambda]\, dr,$$

had their last collisions at a radius between r and $r + dr$. The drag torque exerted on the sphere by such molecules is

$$dC = (2\pi/3)\sigma\rho\bar{c}a^4[\Omega - \omega(r)] \exp -[(r - a)/\lambda](dr/\lambda), \tag{14}$$

so that the total drag is

$$C = (2\pi/3)\sigma\rho\bar{c}a^4 \int_a^\infty [\Omega - \omega(r)] \exp -[(r - a)/\lambda](dr/\lambda). \tag{15}$$

Equation (15) now replaces Eq. (9). The continuum equations (10) and (11) remain unchanged.

From Eqs. (15), (10), and (11) we find

$$1/C_R = (1/\sigma) + (1/6\ \mathrm{Kn}^4)\exp(1/\mathrm{Kn})E_3(1/\mathrm{Kn}), \qquad (16)$$

where

$$E_3(x) = \int_x^\infty [\exp(-t)/t^3]\,dt. \qquad (17)$$

Equation (16) is also plotted in Fig. 3a, and is seen to be in somewhat better agreement with experiment in the transition regime. It is therefore shown in Figs. 3b, 4 and 5 also.

V. Conclusions

The aerodynamic drag torque on a rotating sphere has been determined over a large range of variables including the whole of the subsonic transition regime. In this range the drag ratio $C_R = C/C_{fm}$ was found to be a function of a single parameter Kn' defined as

$$\mathrm{Kn}' = \mathrm{Kn}(1 + 1.94 \times 10^{-2}\ \mathrm{Re})^{1/2},$$

and the variation of C_R with Kn' is well represented by Eq. (16) (with Kn replaced by Kn').

One interesting result of the form of Eq. (6) is that the effect of inertia of the gas on the drag torque does not become appreciable until surprisingly high Reynolds numbers. For instance, when $\mathrm{Re} = 10$ (a value usually considered to be well above the limit for creep flow) the drag torque differs from its creep flow value by only 10%.

The small magnitude of the inertia effects was noted previously (Lord, 1964), but was thought to be connected with a theoretical result of Bickley (1938) that the secondary flow around a rotating sphere (obtained by taking into account first order terms in Re) has no effect on the drag torque. This result, however, does not appear to be consistent with the present experiments which show a definite, though small, first order trend with Reynolds number.

ACKNOWLEDGEMENT

The authors wish to thank Dr. F. P. Bowden for his help and guidance in this work.

List of Symbols

a Radius of sphere

C Drag torque

C_R Drag ratio C/C_{fm}

c Velocity of sound

$\bar{c}$ Mean thermal speed of gas molecules

Kn   Knudsen number λ/a

M Mach number $a\Omega/c$

Re   Reynolds number $a^2\Omega\rho/\eta$

λ Mean free path (defined by $\eta = \tfrac{1}{2}\rho\bar{c}\lambda$)

η Viscosity

ρ Density

σ Tangential momentum transfer coefficient

Ω Angular velocity of sphere

REFERENCES

Beams, J. W. (1947). *J. Wash. Acad. Soc.* **37**, 221.

Bickley, W. G. (1938). *Phil. Mag.* **25**, 746.

Bowden, F. P., and Lord, R. G. (1963). *Proc. Roy. Soc.* (*London*) **A271**, 143.

Harbour, P. J. (1963). Ph.D. Thesis, Univ. of Cambridge.

Lamb, H. (1924). "Hydrodynamics," p. 557. Cambridge Univ. Press, London and New York.

Lord, R. G. (1964). *Proc. Roy. Soc.* (*London*) **A279**, 39.

Sherman, F. S. (1963). *In* "Rarefied Gas Dynamics" (J. A. Laurmann, ed.), Vol. II, p. 228. Academic Press, New York.

Some Experiments on the Flow of a Rarefied Gas through a Circular Orifice

A. K. SREEKANTH

Boeing Scientific Research Laboratories, Seattle, Washington

The mass flow of nitrogen gas through a circular orifice was measured at five Knudsen number values between 0.13 and 1.78 for a range of upstream to downstream pressure ratios from 1 to 18. The Knudsen number in this case is defined as the ratio of upstream mean free path to the diameter of the orifice. For extremely low-pressure ratios across the orifice the present results show a very smooth transition from the continuum flow theoretical value, at very low Knudsen numbers, to the free molecule flow limit. Using a free molecule flow pressure probe, some pressure measurements were taken to study the structure of the jet downstream of the orifice.

I. Introduction

Both theoretical and experimental investigations have been carried out in the past on the flow of a rarefied gas through a circular orifice by Willis (1960), Narasimha (1961) and Liepmann (1960). All these studies consider only very high pressure ratios across the orifice. The present experimental work was undertaken to extend this data to very low and moderate pressure ratios to get a complete picture of mass flow through the orifice at all pressure ratios in the transition regime.

II. Experimental Arrangement and Measurements

A. Apparatus

All the experiments were conducted in the Boeing Scientific Research Laboratories continuous flow, low density gas dynamic facility. It consists of

621

a large stainless steel vacuum tank, 44 in. in diameter and 106 in. long. An orifice plate separates the tank into upstream and downstream chambers. Nitrogen gas at room temperature is admitted through a mass flow transducer and a throttle valve into the upstream chamber. Downstream pressure

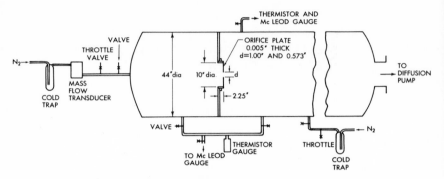

FIG. 1. Experimental apparatus.

is controlled by a large oil diffusion pump and an adjustable leak (Fig. 1). The pressures in the two chambers are measured and monitored by a set of thermistor gages calibrated against a precision McLeod gage.

B. Mass Flow Transducer

Commercially available Hastings Raydist mass flow transducers with slight modifications were used to measure the net mass flow. Two sets of transducers, one having a range of 0 to 20 standard cc/min and the other 0 to 100 standard cc/min, were used. The mass flow meter consists of an electrically heated tube and an arrangement of thermocouples to measure the differential cooling caused by a gas passing through the tube. Thermoelectric elements generate a dc voltage proportional to the rate of mass flow of gas through the tube. The dc output was measured by a precision millivolt meter. The mass flow transducers were calibrated both before and after the experiments against a precision primary standard Porter low flow calibrator. It was estimated that the mass flow measurements were accurate to $\pm 2\%$ and the repeatability better than $\pm 1\%$.

C. Orifice Plate

The orifice plate consisted of a circular hole drilled into a 0.005 in. thick copper sheet soldered to a brass ring 12 in. in diameter. This ring, in turn, was fitted with O-ring seals into the dividing wall in the tank. Two such plates, one with an orifice diameter of 1.00 in. and the other with an orifice diameter of 0.573 in., were used. The 0.573 in. diameter orifice plate was used only for the Kn = 1.67 experiment. For all other experiments the 1.00 in. diameter orifice plate was used.

D. Pressure Probe

An orifice on the side of a hypodermic tubing was used as a pressure probe. The dimensions of the probe were such that the Knudsen number based on the probe diameter was always greater than 5, thereby assuring that the flow with respect to the probe was free molecular. Pressure readings at any angular position of the probe orifice with respect to the flow direction can be obtained by rotating the probe remotely. The probe pressures were measured by a thermistor gage.

E. Outgassing and Leaks

The outgassing or the leak rate at the pressure levels at which these experiments were conducted was extremely small (2.8 μ liters/hr) and could have had no significant effect on the measurements.

III. Experimental Results and Discussion

A. Mass Flow Measurements

The results of the mass flow measurements are shown in Figs. 2 to 5. Figures 2 and 3 give the measured mass flow in standard cc/min as a function of the pressure ratio across the orifice for various Knudsen number values. The Knudsen number in this case is the ratio of the mean free path upstream of the orifice to the diameter of the orifice (the upstream pressure was kept constant for each of the Knudsen numbers and only the downstream pressure was varied to obtain different pressure ratios). Figure 4 is a plot of the non-dimensionalized mass flow, i.e., the actual mass flow divided by the theoretical free molecule flow value at these pressures versus the pressure ratio. The same figure shows the results of Liepmann which were obtained at pressure ratios greater than 10^3 at these Knudsen numbers. It is pointed out that there is considerable scatter in Liepmann's data, and hence the limits marked for high pressure ratios may not be too accurate. Referring to Fig. 2, it is seen that the mass flow increases rapidly with pressure ratio up to 8 and reaches the asymptotic, infinite pressure ratio value at pressure ratios greater than 20. If one assumes that the flow is still close to continuum at a Knudsen number of 0.13,

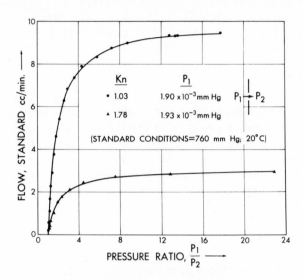

FIG. 2. Mass flow vs. pressure ratio.

the lowest value at which the experiments were conducted, then the measurements substantiate the fact that the pressure ratios required to obtain maximum mass flows are very much higher than for a conventional smooth nozzle as pointed out previously by Liepmann.

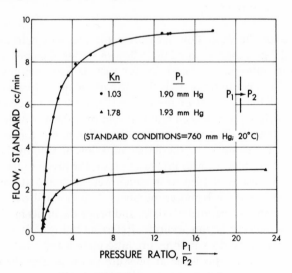

FIG. 3. Mass flow vs. pressure ratio.

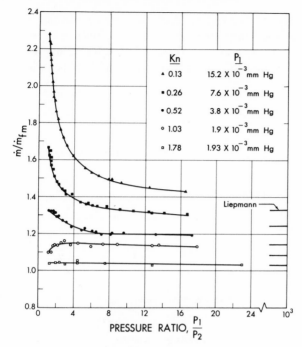

FIG. 4. Nondimensionalized mass flow vs. pressure ratio.

Lack of any theoretical analyses of flow through tubes or orifices at moderate pressure ratios in the transition or near free molecular flow regimes prevents comparisons of the present data with theory at these pressure ratios. It was found that the measured mass flows were linearly proportional to the pressure difference across the orifice for pressure ratios very close to one.

The following relation is obtained by Wuest (1954), who solved the Navier-Stokes equation neglecting the inertia terms for the flow of a continuum gas through a circular orifice (for very low Reynolds numbers and consequently for very low pressure ratios $p_1/p_2 \approx 1$)

$$(Q/\Delta p)(\mu/\pi D^3) = 1/50.4,$$

where

Q = Volumetric flow through the orifice,
Δp = Pressure drop across the orifice,
μ = Viscosity of the gas,
D = Diameter of the orifice.

For the case of free molecule flow, the nondimensionalized quantity $(Q/\Delta p)/(\mu/\pi D^3)$ turns out to be a function of the Knudsen number and the relation is $(Q/\Delta p)(\mu/\pi D^3) = (5/64)\text{Kn}$.

Figure 5 gives the plot of $(Q/\Delta p)/(\mu/\pi D^3)$ as a function of the Knudsen number for very low pressure ratios across the orifice $(p_1/p_2 \leqslant 1.2)$. A smooth transition from the constant continuum flow value at low Knudsen numbers to a linear function of Kn in free molecule flow is evident from these measurements.

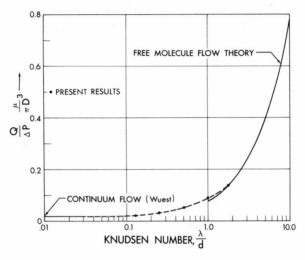

FIG. 5. Parameter $(Q/\Delta p)/(\mu/\pi D^3)$ vs. Knudsen number for very small pressure ratios.

B. Pressure Measurements

To study the feasibility of utilizing the expanded jet from an orifice at low densities for aerodynamic testing purposes and also to study the jet structure, some pressure measurements were taken using a free molecule flow pressure probe downstream of the orifice along both the orifice center line and across it. If the flow downstream of the orifice is Maxwellian (Maxwellian velocity distribution superimposed on the local mass velocity), then the measurement of pressures at a point at two different angular positions of the probe with respect to the mean flow direction should be sufficient to calculate the local speed ratio (ratio of mass velocity to the most probable molecular speed) (Patterson, 1959). Pressure readings were taken at various angular positions of the probe varying from 0° to 360°. From the measured pressures at 0° and 90° (0° corresponding to the probe orifice facing the flow direction), the speed ratio was calculated assuming that the flow is Maxwellian. Once the speed ratio was determined the pressure distribution around the probe was calculated for all the angular positions and compared with the measured values. Comparison between measured and calculated values should provide some indication of the departure of the flow from the assumed Maxwellian distribution. Figure 6 gives a typical plot of the measured and calculated pressure distribution around the probe. It should be remembered that the measured and theoretical values are matched at $0°$ and $90°$. The data shows that close

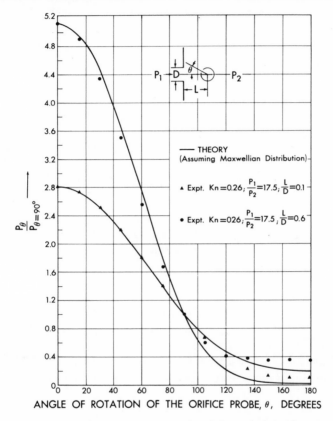

FIG. 6. Comparison between the measured and theoretical probe pressures.

to the orifice the measured pressure was lower than the theoretical values for probe angles greater than $90°$. As the probe is moved downstream the theoretical pressure distribution becomes less than the measured values for probe angles greater than $90°$. It was also observed that the departure from the theoretical values increases as the pressure ratio is decreased for the same upstream pressure. Since the departure from the theoretical values is not too great, the calculated speed ratio is close enough to the actual value at that point. Figure 7 is a plot of the variation of the speed ratio downstream of the orifice along the center line at two Knudsen number values, viz,. 0.26 and 0.52, for pressure ratios of around 18. On the same figure is shown the theoretically predicted speed ratio variation as calculated by Owen and Thornhill (1948) for the case of a gas expanding into vacuum through a circular orifice. The gradual decrease in the measured speed ratio may be due to the existence of a thick diffusive shock. The shock location from the exit plane is less than that predicted by the inviscid continuum theory (Adamson and Nicholls, 1959).

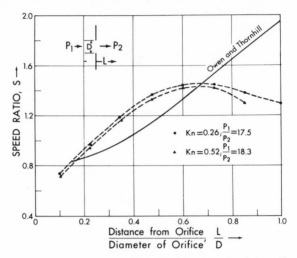

FIG. 7. Variation of the speed ratio along the axis of the orifice.

The departure of the axial variation of the speed ratio from the theory is most probably due to rarefaction and viscous effects. Figure 8 is a plot of the variation of the speed ratio across the jet at various downstream distances. The numbers in brackets at each point in the graph give the inclination of the streamlines at that point with respect to the orifice center line.

IV. Conclusions

The mass flow measurements show a smooth transition from the continuum flow theoretical value to the free molecule flow limit for very small pressure ratios across the orifice. Curves are presented of the mass flows at low and moderate pressure ratios in the transition regime. Pressure ratios greater than 20 are required before the mass flow becomes independent of the pressure ratio for the same upstream conditions. At a Knudsen number of about 1.8, the measured mass flows are within 4% of the free molecule flow values, thereby indicating that free molecule flow conditions prevail at a Knudsen number of about 2. Pressure measurements at Knudsen numbers of 0.26 and 0.52 indicate that the flow downstream of the orifice is not uniform for any appreciable distance. The strong gradients and the curvature of streamline precludes the possibility of successfully using the jet downstream of the orifice for aerodynamic testing purposes at these Knudsen numbers. Lack of

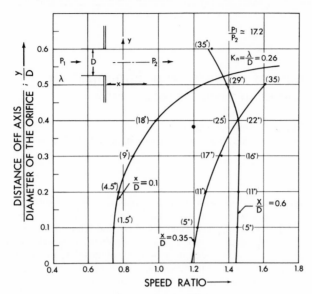

FIG. 8. Variation of the speed ratio across the jet.

theoretical work in the transition regime for the flow through an orifice at these pressure ratios prevents the comparison of the present data with any theory. It is hoped that the availability of more experimental data in the transition regime may help in the formulation of new theories to explain the complicated flow phenomena.

REFERENCES

Adamson, T. C., and Nicholls, J. A. (1959). *J. Aerospace Sci.* **26**, 16.

Liepmann, H. W. (1960). *J. Fluid Mech.* **10**, 65.

Narasimha, R. (1961). *J. Fluid Mech.* **10**, 371.

Owen, P. L., and Thornhill, C. K. (1948). ARC R and M 2616, Great Britain.

Patterson, G. N. (1959). UTIA Rept. 41 (revised).

Willis, D. R. (1960). Division of Gas Dynamics, Roy. Inst. Technol., Stockholm, Tech. Note 3.

Wuest, V. W. (1954). *Ing. Arch.* **22**, 357.

Free Molecule and Internal Flow

Some Problems of Nose Drag Minimization for Bodies in Free Molecule Flow

VSEVOLOD P. SHIDLOVSKY [1]

Institute of Mechanics, Academy of Science of the USSR, Moscow, USSR

This paper is concerned with the determination of the optimum nose form of an axisymmetrical body in free-molecule flow with arbitrary diffuse reflection coefficient and arbitrary Mach numbers and temperature ratios. It is shown that in the general case the problem is reduced to the calculation of an ordinary integral, and the asymptotic behavior of the solutions is investigated. The effect of each of the three main parameters on the form of the integral curves is analysed separately. The question of the more precise formulation of the problem with due regard for the contribution to the total drag by the flat tip of a body is considered.

I. Introduction

The variational problem of the determination of the nose form of an axisymmetrical body to yield minimum drag in free-molecule flow was considered by several authors. One of the first papers devoted to the question was an article by Carter (1957), where the case of hypersonic flow was investigated for two extreme forms of molecular reflection from the surface: (a) specular reflection, or (b) diffuse reflection. As Dennis (1958) has pointed out, the hypothesis of specular reflection leads to the same form of the optimum surface for hypersonic free-molecule flow as is found for Newtonian theory. The same extreme cases of hypersonic flow were considered by Tan (1958a,b), who investigated also the asymptotic behavior of the optimum curves for large distances from the tip and on the basis of the calculations came to the conclusion that the optimum curve for diffuse reflection is more gently sloping than that for specular reflection.

The papers cited hardly take into consideration two important flow

[1] *Present address:* Computing Center, Academy of Science of the USSR, Moscow, USSR.

parameters—the Mach number and the surface-to-mean-flow temperature ratio. An attempt to consider the influence of these factors is made in a paper by Tan (1959), where the case of diffuse reflection of the molecules was investigated and some calculations were made both for hypersonic flow and for flow with very small Mach numbers; but even in that paper only a rather limited analysis of the possible flow varieties is made. This problem is studied below in more complete detail.

II. Formulation of the Problem and Its Solution

In the theory of free-molecule flow (see, for example, Schaaf and Chambré, 1957) the forces acting on a unit surface element in a flow of velocity V (Fig. 1), are expressed in the form

$$p = \frac{\rho_\infty V^2}{2} \left\{ \frac{1}{\pi^{1/2}B} \left[(2 - \theta) \sin \beta + \frac{\theta}{2B} \left(\pi \frac{T_w}{T_\infty} \right)^{1/2} \right] \exp(-B^2 \sin^2 \beta) \right.$$

$$+ \left[(2 - \theta) \left(\sin^2 \beta + \frac{1}{2B^2} \right) + \frac{\theta}{2B} \left(\pi \frac{T_w}{T_\infty} \right)^{1/2} \right] [1 + \mathrm{erf}(B \sin \beta)],$$

(1)

$$\tau = \frac{\rho_\infty V^2}{2} \theta \cos \beta \left\{ \frac{1}{\pi^{1/2}B} \exp(-B^2 \sin^2 \beta) + \sin \beta [1 + \mathrm{erf}(B \sin \beta)] \right\},$$

where p is the normal pressure, τ the tangential stress, ρ_∞ and T_∞ the density and temperature of the mean flow, T_w the temperature of the surface, $B = V/(2RT_\infty)^{1/2} = (\kappa/2)^{1/2} M_\infty$ the modified Mach number, R the gas

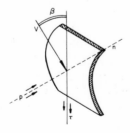

FIG. 1. A surface element in free-molecule flow.

constant, κ the specific heat ratio, and $\mathrm{erf}(w)$ the error function. The symbol θ denotes the so-called coefficient of diffuse reflection of molecules from the surface; the value $\theta = 0$ corresponds to specular reflection and the value $\theta = 1$ to purely diffuse reflection.

If we consider an axisymmetric body (Fig. 2) in a uniform flow directed along the axis of symmetry, then it is easy to ascertain that the elementary drag force dX will be determined as

$$dX = (p \sin \beta + \tau \cos \beta) \, dS.$$

Designating, furthermore,

$$y' \equiv dy/dx = \tan \beta, \qquad dS = 2\pi y (1 + y'^2)^{1/2} \, dx,$$

we shall obtain the expression for the total drag force of the body located in the interval $x_0 \leqslant x \leqslant x_1$ in the form

$$X = \int_{x_0}^{x_1} F(y, y') \, dx = \pi \rho_\infty V^2 \int_{x_0}^{x_1} \varphi(y') y \, dx, \tag{2}$$

where $\varphi(y')$ is a given function, containing three parameters: θ, B, and $\chi = (\pi T_w/T_\infty)^{1/2}$.

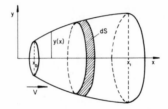

FIG. 2. Coordinate system for the case of an axisymmetric body.

Let us formulate the following variational problem: determine the function $y(x)$, minimizing the drag force X which is expressed by Eq.(2), with the given values of the parameters and with an end condition $y(x_1) = y_1$ (the mid-section radius). In order to solve this problem it is necessary that the function $F(y, y')$ satisfy Euler's equation

$$\frac{d}{dx}\left(\frac{\partial F}{\partial y'}\right) - \frac{\partial F}{\partial y} = 0. \tag{3}$$

As is known from the fundamentals of the calculus of variations (see, for example, Gel'fand and Fomin, 1961), in the case of no direct dependence of the function on the variable x, the first integral of Euler's equation is used,

$$F - y' \, \partial F/\partial y' = C_0,$$

or in a more convenient form for us,

$$y(\varphi - y' \, d\varphi/dy') = C. \tag{4}$$

It is interesting to note that the term in parentheses on the left-hand side of

Eq. (4) is nondimensional, so that the constant C has the dimension of length and may be considered as a characteristic scale.

After introducing the abbreviation

$$\phi(y') = \varphi - y' \, d\varphi/dy', \tag{5}$$

one can obtain a parametric representation of the dependence $y(x)$ in the form

$$y = \frac{C}{\phi(y')}, \qquad x = -C \int \frac{\phi'(y')}{y' \phi^2(y')} \, dy' + C_1. \tag{6}$$

Thus the determination of the form of a minimum drag body is reduced to the calculation of the integral occurring on the right-hand side of the second of Eqs. (6). We have at our disposal two constants, C and C_1, which are needed to satisfy the boundary conditions. As was mentioned previously, quantity C may be regarded here as a scale factor and by means of the quantity C_1 the position of the origin of the variable x is determined.

III. Asymptotic Behavior of the Solution

Considering Eq. (4) we can see that if the generatrix of the sought optimum body shape intersects the x-axis, then the condition $C = 0$ should be fulfilled. In other words, the aforementioned body in that case is nothing more than a cone, the slope of its generatrix, y_c', being equal to the root of the algebraic equation

$$\phi(y') = 0. \tag{7}$$

On the other hand, even in the case $C \neq 0$ it is evident from Eq. (4) that for large values of y the derivative y' will asymptotically approach the quantity y_c'. Thus in any case it is necessary to analyse the behavior of the roots of Eq. (7), which may be written in the following detailed form:

$$\frac{y'^2}{(1 + y'^2)^{3/2}} \left\{ \frac{1}{\pi^{1/2}B} \left[4(1 - \theta) - \frac{\theta}{y'^2} \right] \exp\left(-B^2 \frac{y'^2}{1 + y'^2} \right) \right.$$
$$\left. + \left[4(1 - \theta) \frac{y'}{(1 + y'^2)^{1/2}} + \frac{\theta\chi}{2B} \right] \left[1 + \mathrm{erf}\left(B \frac{y'}{(1 + y'^2)^{1/2}} \right) \right] \right\} = 0. \tag{8}$$

In the case $\theta = 0$ (specular reflection from the surface) the only nonnegative root of Eq. (8) will be $y_c' = 0$. Picking out the main part of the function $\phi(y')$ in the vicinity of the zero point and disregarding an unessential constant factor, we obtain

$$\phi(y') \approx y'^2 \left(\frac{1}{\pi^{1/2}B} + y' \right). \tag{9}$$

With the additional condition $B \to \infty$ it is easy to see from Eq. (9) that far from the tip, that is for large enough y, an approximate law of proportionality will be satisfied in the form

$$y \sim x^{3/4},$$

which means that the body contour approaches asymptotically to the form corresponding to Newtonian theory. But with any finite (even rather large) value of B the asymptotic behavior of the curve will correspond to another law, namely

$$y \sim x^{2/3}.$$

However, the case $\theta = 0$ is purely hypothetical and does not appear to be realized in practice. According to existing experimental data this parameter varies in the interval $0.7 \leqslant \theta \leqslant 1$ and depends on may factors, primarily on the nature of the surface and its quality (the degree of roughness, etc.). Considering Eq. (8) with the assumption $\theta > 0$, we shall see that this equation is sure to have a root $y_c' = \text{const} > 0$; as will be shown later, it is this root that has physical significance. Thus the asymptotic behavior of the optimum contour curve for this case differs from the asymptotic behavior for specular reflection: instead of a power dependence at large distance from the tip we shall have simply

$$y \approx y_0 + y_c' x \qquad (y_0 = \text{const}). \tag{10}$$

Hence the optimum surface will asymptotically approach a conical surface.

As may be seen from the analysis of the roots of Eq. (8), the quantity y_c' essentially depends on the three main parameters of the problem, θ, B and χ. At infinitely large values of the number B one has again $y_c' \to 0$ and the asymptotic behavior of the contour corresponds to that according to Newtonian theory; but practically, setting $\theta \approx 1$ and $T_w \approx T_\infty$ we come to such an asymptotic form only for $B \gtrsim 20$.

Considering the opposite case, when the number B is very small, one can obtain an approximate expression

$$y_c' \approx \left[\frac{2\theta}{8(1 - \theta) + \theta \pi^{1/2} \chi} \right]^{1/2}, \tag{11}$$

which quite clearly indicates the influence of the diffuse reflection coefficient and the temperature ratio on the value of y_c'. In particular, for the theoretical case of a very hot surface, when $\chi \to \infty$ then $y_c' \to 0$. Another, also unrealistic, case arises when $\theta = 1$ and $\chi = 0$; from Eq. (11) it is evident that in this case $y_c' = \infty$.

In Fig. 3 are represented the curves for y_c' in the interval $0 \leqslant B \leqslant 5$ with $\theta = 1$ (diffuse reflection) and with three different values of the temperature

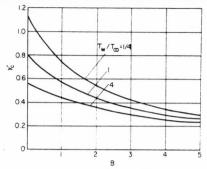

FIG. 3. Variation of the quantity y_c' with modified Mach number B at $\theta = 1$.

ratio $T_w/T_\infty = \chi^2/\pi$. Furthermore, in Table I the data are given showing the influence of the diffuse reflection coefficient on the quantity y_c' at $B = 0$ and $B = 5$, with $T_w/T_\infty = 1$.

TABLE I

DEPENDENCE OF y_c' ON THE COEFFICIENT OF
DIFFUSE REFLECTION θ
$(T_w/T_\infty = 1)$

θ	$B = 0$	$B = 5$
	y_c'	y_c'
0.6	0.4858	0.1922
0.8	0.6237	0.2229
1.0	0.7979	0.2643

IV. Determination of the Maximum Slope of the Optimum Curve

If the function $y(x)$ is chosen to satisfy Euler's equation [Eq. (3)], then only an extremal value of the drag force from Eq. (2) is ensured for the given parameters. In order to obtain the minimum drag by means of this function, it is necessary to satisfy yet another condition—that of Legendre (Gel'fand and Fomin, 1961)

$$\partial^2 F/\partial y'^2 \geqslant 0,$$

or

$$d^2\varphi/dy'^2 \geqslant 0. \qquad (12)$$

Investigating the properties of the function $\varphi''(y') \equiv d^2\varphi/dy'^2$ one may notice that if the argument increases from y_c' up to some critical value y_0', this function will monotonically decrease to zero. Further increase of y' would lead to the violation of the condition Eq. (12), so that that part of the integral curve where $y' > y_0'$ will have no meaning. We designate here by y_0' the root of the equation $\varphi''(y') = 0$, or, in detail,

$$\frac{1}{\pi^{1/2}B}\left[\frac{2B^2 y'}{(1 + y'^2)^3}\left(\frac{\theta\chi}{2B} - \frac{\theta y'}{(1 + y'^2)^{1/2}}\right) + \frac{20B^2 + 8 - 5\theta - 4(1 - \theta)y'^2}{(1 + y'^2)}\right]$$

$$\times \exp\left(-\frac{B^2 y'^2}{1 + y'^2}\right) + \left[\frac{4(1 - \theta)y'}{(1 + y'^2)^3}(3 - y'^2) + \frac{1}{(1 + y'^2)^{5/2}}\frac{\theta\chi}{2B}(2 - y'^2)\right]$$

$$\times \left[1 + \operatorname{erf}\left(\frac{By'}{(1 + y'^2)^{1/2}}\right)\right] = 0. \tag{13}$$

The fact of the existence of a limit value y_0' was noted already by Carter (1957). As we have noted in the Introduction, this author considered the case $B \gg 1$, when the first term of Eq. (13) could be neglected. In that case instead of Eq. (13) one should solve the equation

$$4(1 - \theta)\frac{y'}{(1 + y'^2)^{1/2}}(3 - y'^2) + \frac{\theta\chi}{2B}(2 - y'^2) = 0. \tag{14}$$

The second term of Eq. (14) should not be neglected because the quantity $1 - \theta$ may be of the same order as B^{-1}. Hence one can immediately obtain Carter's results:

$$\text{at } \theta = 0 \quad y_0' = \sqrt{3}, \qquad \text{at } \theta = 1 \quad y_0' = \sqrt{2}.$$

At $0 < \theta < 1$ in the hypersonic regime we shall have $\sqrt{3} > y_0' > \sqrt{2}$.

If the number B is small, $B^2 \ll 1$, then Eq. (13) may be simplified again to take the form

$$8 - 5\theta + \theta\pi^{1/2}\chi - [4(1 - \theta) + \tfrac{1}{2}\theta\pi^{1/2}\chi]y'^2 = 0. \tag{15}$$

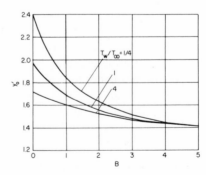

FIG. 4. Variation of the quantity y_0' with modified Mach number B at $\theta = 1$.

In all cases where the modified Mach number B is of the order of unity, one cannot use the simplified equations like Eq. (14) and Eq. (15) and the quantity y_0' should be found directly from Eq. (13).

TABLE II

DEPENDENCE OF y_0' ON THE COEFFICIENT OF
DIFFUSE REFLECTION θ, $(T_w/T_\infty = 1)$

θ	$B = 0$	$B = 5$
	y_0'	y_0'
0.6	1.6456	1.7081
0.8	1.7796	1.6753
1.0	1.9774	1.4142

In Fig. 4 the curves for the maximum slope y_0' are shown under the same conditions as the curves of Fig. 3. The character of the influence of the coefficient θ is evident from Table II. In particular it is seen from this table that an increase of the number B leads to a qualitative change of the dependence $y_0'(\theta)$.

V. Construction of the Optimum Contour

Having those data which were discussed in Sections III and IV one can go on to the construction of the optimum contour. Provided that Eq. (8) has a nonzero root, two possibilities arise. First, for the surface sought one could choose a cone, with an angle which corresponds to the quantity y_c'. As was pointed out previously, Euler's equation will be satisfied with such a solution; furthermore, Legendre's condition will be satisfied, too, because it is possible to show that the relation $\varphi''(y_c') \geqslant 0$ is always satisfied.

But if for some reason we must choose another surface than a conical one, we can use the second possibility, that is the solution in the form of Eqs. (6). The scale factor C is then to be chosen in such a way that at $y' = y_0'$, the condition $y \ll 1$ will be fulfilled, for example, $y_0 \equiv y(y_0') = 0.05$. The integral curve is subsequently constructed up to that point where $y = 1$, and the point $y = y_0$ is connected with the body axis in some arbitrary way. In so doing we assume that the contribution to the total drag due to this "nonoptimum" nose section is negligibly small.

In Fig. 5 are seen the optimum contours constructed by this method at $\theta = 1$, $T_w = T_\infty$ for three values of the number B. In Fig. 6 the optimum contours are shown for various temperature ratios, T_w/T_∞, and in Fig. 7 they are given for various values of the diffuse reflection coefficient, θ. It is

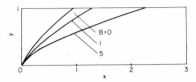

FIG. 5. Optimum contours ($\theta = 1$, $T_w/T_\infty = 1$).

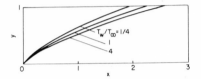

FIG. 6. Optimum contours ($\theta = 1$, $B = 5$).

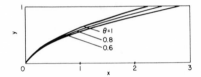

FIG. 7. Optimum contours ($B = 5$, $T_w/T_\infty = 1$).

evident that the increase of Mach number, the surface temperature and the decrease of the coefficient θ lead to very similar results, namely to more gentle and more stretched contours.

Thus for each set of values for the three main parameters two contours ensure the minimization of drag: (1) a straight line making an angle $\alpha = \tan^{-1} y_c'$ with the x-axis, (2) a curve constructed by the method described in this Section. It is interesting to compare the differences in the drag of the two corresponding optimum bodies. From the calculations made for $B = 5$, $\theta = 1$ and $T_w/T_\infty = 1$, it is seen that the drag of a body with a curvilinear generatrix is approximately 3 % less than the cone drag. However, it is necessary to take into account the fact that one should add the resistance of the tip to the drag of the curved body, and then the total drag will be somewhat larger than that for a cone. On the other hand, with equal base radii, the curved body has a smaller fineness ratio compared with that of a cone, which fact may be of importance for the constructor.

Tan (1959) has proposed a modified formulation of the same variational problem taking into account the contribution of the tip of the body to the total drag. This contribution is represented by the drag of a round flat plate with radius y_0. Then the total drag may be expressed in the form

$$X_s = \pi \rho_\infty V^2 \left[\tfrac{1}{2} y_0{}^2 K(\theta, B, \chi) + \int_{x_0}^{x_1} \varphi(y')y \, dx \right], \tag{16}$$

where

$$K(\theta, B, \chi) = \left(\frac{2 - \theta}{\pi^{1/2} B} + \frac{\theta \chi}{2\pi^{1/2} B^2} \right) \exp(-B^2)$$

$$+ \left[(2 - \theta)\left(1 + \frac{1}{2B^2} \right) + \frac{\theta \chi}{2B} \right](1 + \operatorname{erf} B). \tag{17}$$

If the radius y_0 is not fixed in advance, the problem of the minimization of the force X_s may be reduced to the solution of Euler's equation described in Section II, the only difference being that the end condition at $x = x_0$ is now written in the form

$$y_0(K - d\varphi/dy')\delta y_0 = 0,$$

or

$$\varphi'(y_0') - K = 0. \tag{18}$$

The quantity y_0' to be found from Eq. (18) should be equal or less than the root of the equation $\varphi''(y_0') = 0$. Provided this condition is satisfied the further operations are similar to those described in Section III with the only difference that there is no constraining condition $y(x_0) \ll y(x_1)$. Thus such a generalized approach may be useful when, for example, the fineness ratio of the body is fixed by engineering considerations.

VI. Concluding Remarks

In this paper we have set forth a method for constructing the contour of an axisymmetric nose with minimum drag in free-molecule flow for arbitrary values of the three main characteristic parameters. The nature of the influence of these parameters on the optimum contour is demonstrated and it is ascertained that the hypothetical case of a specularly reflecting surface considered previously by some authors is a singular case and cannot serve as a basis for generalization. It is ascertained also that the only pointed body of minimum drag is a cone with the angle at its vertex depending on the aforementioned parameters; this angle is not equal to zero for a finite Mach number and for nonspecular reflection of the molecules from the surface. It is found out, however, that a properly shaped blunt body has a drag which is not much larger than the drag of a cone and has, at the same time, a smaller fineness ratio and smaller volume; thus the choice of the kind of optimum body may well depend on additional engineering considerations.

ACKNOWLEDGMENT

The author wishes to thank A. A. Nickolsky and Ju. D. Shmyglevsky for their helpful discussion of the problems considered in this paper, and I. M. Couz'mina, who conducted the programming work and directed the calculations.

REFERENCES

Carter, W. (1957). *J. Aeron. Sci.* **24**, 527.

Dennis, D. (1958). *J. Aeron. Sci.* **25**, 216.

Gel'fand, I. M., and Fomin, S. V. (1961). "Calculus of Variations" (in Russian). Fizmatgiz, Moscow.

Schaaf, S. A., and Chambré, P. (1957). *In* "High-Speed Aerodynamics and Jet Propulsion" (H. W. Emmons, ed.), Vol. III, pp. 687–739. Princeton Univ. Press, Princeton, New Jersey.

Tan, H. S. (1958a). *J. Aeron. Sci.* **25**, 56.

Tan, H. S. (1958b). *J. Aeron. Sci.* **25**, 263.

Tan, H. S. (1959). *J. Aeron. Sci.* **26**, 360.

Free-Molecule Flow through Conical Tubes[1]

S. J. TOWNSEND, G. N. PATTERSON, AND S. R. M. SINCLAIR

Institute for Aerospace Studies, University of Toronto
Toronto, Canada

The transport of mass, axial momentum, and energy through axially symmetric tubes in free-molecule flow is considered. The dependence upon wall temperature of the axial momentum and energy flows in the exit plane is outlined. The resultant transport equations are presented along with representative numerical solutions. Extensions of these flow distributions to the case of arbitrary speed ratio can be carried out. The problem of an optimum free-molecule "scoop" for orbital vehicles is also considered. Optimum wall angles for convergent cones can be found, resulting in maximum mass flow passed by the scoop.

The paper is essentially in three parts. Section I concerns the mass, axial momentum, and energy flow through tubes with both constant and variable temperature profiles along the wall. The results are limited to conical tubes at rest in a Maxwellian gas, although tubes having curved walls that do not "shadow" internal surfaces can be easily treated as an extension. Section II gives a solution for the mass flow passed by conical tubes in flows of arbitrary speed ratio. Section III extends the concepts of Section I to flows of arbitrary speed ratio.

I. Radial Variation of Flow Properties in the Exit Plane of a Stationary Conical Tube

The detailed specification of the flow properties at any point within an internal flow system of known geometry depends upon two boundary conditions: first, the distribution function at the inlet for those molecules entering the tube, and second, the wall temperature. The number flux of molecules on the wall can be found from the inlet conditions and tube geometry through Clausing's integral equation. The number flux striking the wall and the wall temperature together specify the distribution function along the wall. The assumptions inherent in the above approach are as follows: (1) the flow is

---

[1] This work was supported by Air Force Office of Scientific Research Grant #276-64.

sufficiently rarefied that intermolecular collisions within the tube are infrequent compared with multiple collisions with the wall; (2) there is no accumulation or ablation at the wall; (3) those molecules striking the wall undergo perfect accommodation resulting in a Maxwellian distribution function for the reflected molecules. The inlet and wall boundary conditions allow the complete determination of the transport properties of the tube. In case there is a back flux from the exit into the tube, the method of superposition of free molecule streams can be used.

The geometry of the conical tube is shown in Fig. 1. The quantities X, the

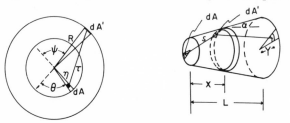

FIG. 1. Tube geometry and calculation of $\zeta_1(X, \alpha)$.

partial distance along the tube axis from the inlet, L, the tube length, R, the tube radius at position X, R_0, the outlet radius, and Y, the fractional radius in the exit plane, have all been nondimensionalized by the inlet radius. The quantity Y is replaced by $Y' = Y/R_0$ as the abcissa for presentation of the results. The semivertex angle of the cone, α, is defined to be positive for divergent cones and negative for convergent cones by the definition $R = 1 + X \tan \alpha$. All number flux quantities have been non-dimensionalized by the number of molecules crossing the inlet area in unit time, $N_i = nc_m \pi r_i^2 / 2\pi^{1/2}$.

A. Mass Transport

The number of molecules per unit time passing through unit area of the outlet at radius Y is given according to Patterson (1964) by

$$N_e(Y, L, \alpha) = N_{cc}(Y, L) + \int_{x=0}^{L} P(X, Y, L, \alpha)\zeta(X, L, \alpha) \, dX, \qquad (1)$$

where $\zeta(X, L, \alpha)$ is the number flux per unit tube length of molecules coming from the wall surface. It is given by Clausing's integral equation

$$\zeta(X, L, \alpha) \, dX = \zeta_1(X, \alpha) \, dX + \int_{X'=0}^{L} K(X, X', \alpha) \, dX \, \zeta(X', L, \alpha) \, dX' \quad (2)$$

The quantity $N_{cc}(Y, L)$ in Eq. (1) is the number flux coming directly from the inlet and passing through unit area of the outlet at Y; it represents the orifice effect of the inlet. $P(X, Y, L, \alpha)$ is the probability of a molecule leaving the wall at X and passing directly through unit area of the outlet at radius Y. By a process of integrating the Maxwellian distribution function over differential elements of area, N_{cc} can be shown to be

$$N_{cc}(Y, L) = \frac{1}{2\pi} \left\{ 1 - \frac{L^2 + Y^2 - 1}{[(L^2 + Y^2 + 1)^2 - 4Y^2]^{1/2}} \right\}, \tag{3}$$

and P can be shown to be

$$P(X, Y, L, \alpha) = \frac{(L - X) \cos \alpha}{\pi} \left\{ \frac{R_0[(L - X)^2 + R^2 + Y^2] - 2RY^2}{[\{(L - X)^2 + R^2 + Y^2\}^2 - 4R^2 Y^2]^{3/2}} \right\}. \tag{4}$$

The function K can be calculated from the tube geometry and the integral equation can be solved numerically by a process of iteration. K can be shown to be

$$K(X, X', \alpha) \, dX = \frac{\cos \alpha}{2R'} \left\{ 1 - \frac{|X - X'|[(X - X')^2 + 6RR' \cos^2 \alpha]}{[(X - X')^2 + 4RR' \cos^2 \alpha]^{3/2}} \right\} dX. \tag{5}$$

The function $\zeta_1(X, \alpha) \, dX$ is now calculated. The function $\zeta_1(X, \alpha)$ represents the number flux per unit tube length of molecules that strike an annulus dX wide at X, having come directly from the inlet. The number of molecules per unit time leaving dA in the entrance plane and striking dA' on the wall is

$$\frac{N \, dA \cos \varphi \cos \varphi'}{\pi \quad s^2} \, dA', \tag{6}$$

where N is the number flux per unit area crossing dA from the Maxwellian gas at the inlet.

From the geometry shown in Fig. 1, the angles φ and φ' defining the normals to the elements of area dA and dA' are

$$\cos \varphi = \frac{X}{s}, \qquad \cos \varphi' = (R + \eta \cos \psi) \frac{\cos \alpha}{s} - X \frac{\sin \alpha}{s}. \tag{7}$$

Also, $dA = \eta \, d\eta \, d\theta$, $dA' = dX \, R \, d\psi / \cos \alpha$ and $s^2 = X^2 + \tau^2 = X^2 + \eta^2 + R^2 + 2\eta R \cos \psi$. The number of molecules per unit time crossing the entrance area and striking the annulus at dX is then

$$\zeta_1(X, \alpha) \, dX =$$

$$= \frac{NRX \, dX}{\pi} \int_{\theta=0}^{2\pi} \int_{\eta=0}^{1} \int_{\psi=0}^{2\pi} \frac{(R + \eta \cos \psi) - X \tan \alpha}{[X^2 + R^2 + \eta^2 + 2\eta R \cos \psi]^2} \, d\psi \, \eta d\eta \, d\theta, \tag{8}$$

or

$$\zeta_1(X, \alpha) \, dX =$$

$$= \left\{ \frac{(X^2 + R^2 + 1) \cos^2 \alpha + R \tan \alpha (X + 2 \tan \alpha \cos^2 \alpha)}{[X^2 + 4R \cos^2 \alpha]^{1/2}} - (X + R \tan \alpha) \right\} dX. \tag{9}$$

Solutions of Eq. (1) have been obtained numerically for various cases of tube geometry. The results are shown in Fig. 2 for a typical case, $L = 2.0$.

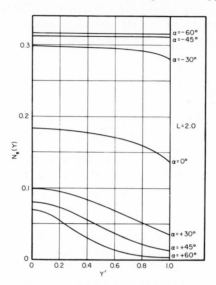

FIG. 2. Mass flux per unit area.

The most noticeable features are the approach to orifice flow as the tube diverges widely, and the approach to a flat mass flux profile as the tube converges sharply. In the latter case, of course, the exit plane flow is starting to assume the uniform properties of the inlet gas as the effect of the walls diminishes. The radial distributions are in agreement with those of Richley and Reynolds (1964). The total mass flow obtained by integrating under the curves shown here also agrees with the results of Richley and Reynolds (1964) and Sparrow and Jonsson (1963).

B. Axial Momentum Transport

The rate of axial momentum flow through unit area of the exit plane at radius Y is given by

$$M_e(Y, L, \alpha) = M_{cc}(Y, L) + \int_{X=0}^{L} [T(X)]^{1/2} M_w(X, Y, L, \alpha)\zeta(X, L, \alpha)\, dX, \quad (10)$$

where $M_{cc}(Y,L)$, the axial momentum per unit outlet area that is carried by molecules that do not undergo boundary collisions, is given by

$$M_{cc}(Y, L) = L^3 \int_{\psi=0}^{2\pi} \int_{\sigma=0}^{1} \frac{\sigma\, d\sigma\, d\psi}{[L^2 + \sigma^2 + Y^2 + 2\sigma Y \cos\psi]^{5/2}}, \quad (11)$$

and

$$M_w(X, Y, L, \alpha)$$

$$= \frac{3 \cos \alpha}{2\pi^2} \int_{\psi = 0}^{\pi} (L - X)^2 \frac{(R_0 + Y \cos \psi) \, d\psi}{[(L - X)^2 + R^2 + Y^2 + 2RY \cos \psi]^{5/2}} \, . \qquad (12)$$

All axial momentum flux quantities have been nondimensionalized by the total axial momentum crossing the inlet area. $T(X)$ has been nondimensionalized by the inlet temperature, T_i.

Solutions of Eq. (10) have been obtained numerically for various temperature profiles along the wall, and various tube geometries. Typical results are shown in Fig. 3. The effect of a temperature profile increasing toward the exit plane is to raise and flatten the axial momentum profile in the exit plane.

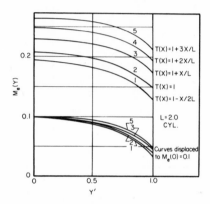

FIG. 3. Axial momentum flux per unit area.

Integration under the exit plane and inlet plane curves in order to obtain total axial momentum quantities indicates that for tubes of any length and wall angle, a particular temperature profile can be chosen to yield a net thrust or drag on the internal system.

C. Energy Transport

The rate of energy transport through unit area of the exit plane at radius Y is given by

$$E_e(Y, L, \alpha) = E_{cc}(Y, L) + \int_{X = 0}^{L} T(X)E_w(X, Y, L, \alpha)\zeta(X, L, \alpha) \, dX. \qquad (13)$$

The energy flow bears a simple scalar relation to the mass flow and accordingly $E_{cc}(Y, L) = N_{cc}(Y, L)$ and $E_w(X, Y, L, \alpha) = P(X, Y, L, \alpha)$, when Eq. (13) has been nondimensionalized by the total kinetic energy crossing the inlet area. Numerical solutions of Eq. (13) for various wall temperature profiles are shown in Figs. 4 and 5. Various temperature profiles have little effect on the shape of the energy profile for diverging cones, but have a stronger effect on converging cones.

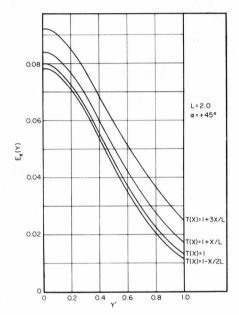

FIG. 4. Energy flux per unit area.

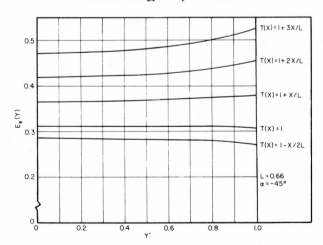

FIG. 5. Energy flux per unit area.

II. Mass Flow Passed by a Moving Conical Tube

A slightly different technique has been employed to calculate the mass flow passed by a scooping conical tube. Instead of the total number flux along the wall, the first-collision flux was calculated. The random motion of the free stream was assumed to be Maxwellian. All molecules passed by the exit plane were assumed to be captured and not returned. Where this is not so, the equations from Section I can be used to calculate the back leakage from the scooping inlet according to Sinclair (to be published).

The number of molecules that pass through the tube is given by

$$N(\alpha, L, S) = N_0(\alpha, L, S) + \int_{X=0}^{L} W(\alpha, X, L)\zeta_1(\alpha, X, S) \, dX, \qquad (14)$$

where N_0 is the number of molecules per unit time passing directly through the tube without encountering the wall, $\zeta_1 \, dX$ is the number of molecules per unit time which strike an annulus dX wide at X after coming directly from the inlet, W is the probability of a molecule at X eventually exiting after any number of additional wall encounters. W can be found from the integral equation

$$W(\alpha, X, L) = P(\alpha, X, L) + \int_{X'=0}^{L} K(X', X, \alpha)W(\alpha, X', L) \, dX', \qquad (15)$$

where P in Eq. (4) has been integrated over Y and θ in the exit plane, and $K \, dX'$ is given by Eq. (5) with X and X' interchanged. ζ_1 can be calculated by differentiating the "collisionless" flux at X,

$$\zeta_1(\alpha, X, S) = -\frac{\partial}{\partial X} N_0(\alpha, X, S). \qquad (16)$$

However, since ζ_1 is part of the integrand to be integrated over X, the exact equation, Eq. (14), can be represented by the numerical finite-interval approximation

$$N(\alpha, L, S) = N_0(\alpha, L, S) + \sum \overline{W}(\alpha, X, L)\Delta N_0(\alpha, X, S), \qquad (17)$$

where

$$\Delta N_0(\alpha, X, S) = N_0(\alpha, X, S) - N_0(\alpha, X + \Delta X, S),$$

$$\overline{W}(\alpha, X, L) = \frac{W(\alpha, X, L) + W(\alpha, X + \Delta X, L)}{2}.$$

Now the function $N_0(\alpha, X, S)$ is calculated. Consider the flow in a polar coordinate frame of reference. The macroscopic stream velocity, $\mathbf{U}$ is directed along the x_1 axis, $\mathbf{c}$ is the random velocity vector, and $\mathbf{V}$ is the total velocity vector. Hence, we have

$$V_1 = U + c_1 = V \cos \phi,$$

$$V_2 = \qquad c_2 = V \sin \phi \cos \theta,$$

$$V_3 = \qquad c_3 = V \sin \phi \sin \theta,$$

where V_1, V_2, V_3, c_1, c_2, c_3 are the components of $\mathbf{V}$ and $\mathbf{c}$. By definition

$$c^2 = U^2 + V^2 - 2UV \cos \varphi,$$

and when all speeds are nondimensionalized with respect to c_m, we have

$$C^2 = S^2 + \Lambda^2 - 2S\Lambda \cos \varphi$$

where S is the speed ratio. The element of volume in velocity space is $V^2 \sin \varphi \, d\varphi \, d\theta \, dV$ and the number of molecules per unit volume of physical space in the gas in front of the tube in the velocity element V to $V + dV$, φ to $\varphi + d\varphi$, θ to $\theta + d\theta$ is $nfV^2 \sin \varphi \, d\varphi \, d\theta \, dV$. The number of molecules of this class which cross unit area perpendicular to the beam in unit time is

$$VnfV^2 \sin \varphi \, d\varphi \, d\theta \, dV$$

$$= n\pi^{-3/2} c_m \exp(-\Lambda^2 + 2S\Lambda \cos \varphi - S^2)\Lambda^3 \, d\Lambda \sin \varphi \, d\varphi \, d\theta. \quad (18)$$

This expression can be integrated analytically over the two variables Λ and θ. Symmetry in the azimuthal angle θ, for zero angle of attack, renders this integration simple. The integration of Λ over the range $-S \cos \varphi < \Lambda < \infty$ involves standard integrals. The result, Beam(S, φ), is the number of molecules in the beam $d\varphi$ about φ which cross unit area perpendicular to the beam in unit time.

$$\text{Beam}(S, \varphi) = \frac{nc_m}{\pi^{1/2}} \exp(-S^2 \sin^2 \varphi)[(1 + S \cos \varphi) \exp(-S^2 \cos^2 \varphi)$$

$$\qquad (19)$$

$$+ S\pi^{1/2} \cos \varphi(1 + \text{erf}(S \cos \varphi))(3/2 + S^2 \cos^2 \varphi)] \sin \varphi \, d\varphi.$$

The foregoing approach making use of elemental beams follows the method described by Hughes and deLeeuw (1964).

It remains to find the area of the inlet, projected perpendicular to the beam, through which the beam at angle φ can see past X. This is a simple geometrical calculation (see Fig. 6). For $\varphi \leqslant \alpha$

$$A_1(\varphi) = \pi r_0^2 \cos \varphi, \qquad (20)$$

and for $\varphi > \alpha$

$$A_2(\varphi) = \{r_i^2 \tan^{-1}(d/z) - zd + \pi r_0^2 - [r_0^2 \tan^{-1}(d/y) - yd]\} \cos \varphi, \quad (21)$$

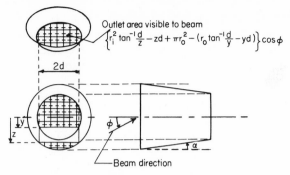

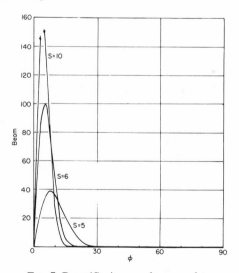

FIG. 6. Geometry of outlet area.

where $2d$ is the maximum width of the beam passing through the circle at X. Therefore,

$$N_0(\alpha, X, S) = \int_0^\alpha A_1(\varphi)\, \text{Beam}(S, \varphi)\, d\varphi + \int_\alpha^{\varphi_1} A_2(\varphi)\, \text{Beam}(S, \varphi)\, d\varphi, \quad (22)$$

where φ_1 is the cutoff angle. For $\varphi > \varphi_1$ the beam cannot see past the circle at X. It was found that $\text{Beam}(S, \varphi)$ drops off very rapidly from its maximum for large values of S, allowing the range of φ to be diminished in the integration of Eq. (22) (see Fig. 7).

FIG. 7. $\text{Beam}(S, \varphi)$ versus beam angle φ.

The case of infinite speed ratio has a particularly simple solution once values of $W(\alpha, X, L)$ have been determined. It was expected that this case would be a reasonable approximation in the speed ratio range of orbital vehicles in the free molecule regime (i.e., $6 < S < 9$). The approximation was shown to be quite good for short tubes for speed ratios as low as $S = 5$.

The approximation $S = \infty$ means that the molecules have no random motion and travel in a direct path ($\varphi = 0$) with velocity U to their first wall encounter. Hence,

$$\zeta_1(\alpha, X, \infty) = nU2\pi R \tan \alpha, \tag{23}$$

$$N(\alpha, L, \infty) = nU\pi R_0^2 + \int_0^L nU2\pi R \tan \alpha \, W(\alpha, X', L) \, dX'. \tag{24}$$

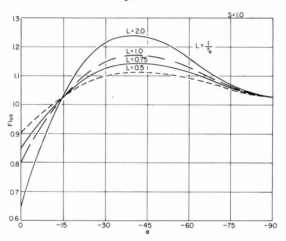

FIG. 8. Exit mass flux variation with cone angle, $S = 1$.

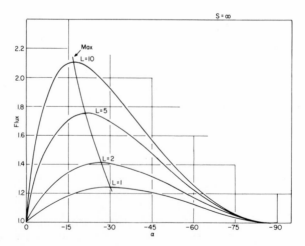

FIG. 9. Exit mass flux variation with cone angle, $S = \infty$.

Solutions of Eqs. (17) and (24) were obtained for tubes with lengths ranging from $L = 0.5$ to $L = 10$ and wall angles ranging from $\alpha = 0°$ to $\alpha = -90°$. Results are shown in Figs. 8 and 9 for speed ratios of $S = 1$ and $S = \infty$. For the particular application of these conical tubes to scooping of rarefieɩ gases (e.g., free-molecular orbital vehicle propellant accumulators), the maxima of these curves are of interest. For speed ratios of $S = 5$, 10, and infinity a narrow range of values of α about the flux maximum was considered. In comparing the finite and infinite speed ratio cases, it was found that for $L = 10$, $S = \infty$ the maximum occurred at $\alpha = -17°$. This value was 1.6% higher than that calculated for $S = 5$, $\alpha = -17°$. The maximum of the $S = 5$ curve occurred at $-19°$.

III. Radial Variation of Flow Properties in the Exit Plane of a Moving Conical Tube

As an extension of Sections I and II, the mass, axial momentum and energy flow distributions in the exit plane are now easily calculable for arbitrary speed ratio. The value of ζ_1 from Eq. (16) for the speed ratio case can be substituted into Eq. (2) in order to find the equilibrium flux distribution along the wall. Similarly, N_{cc} from Eq. (1) can be replaced by an N_{cc} based on speed ratio. The radial variation of this new $N_{cc}(Y, L, S)$ can be derived from Eq. (22) for $X = L$ by using a differential radii technique in Eq. (21) instead of the tube outlet radius, r_0. Detailed calculations based on this approach are near completion.

IV. Conclusion

The object has been to calculate the mass, axial momentum and energy transport properties of axially symmetric tubes. The transport equations have been presented along with representative numerical solutions. The dependence of the axial momentum and energy flow distributions in the exit plane upon wall temperature has been outlined.

The extension of all these flow distributions to arbitrary speed ratio can be easily accomplished.

The problem of an optimum free-molecular "scoop" for orbital vehicles has also been considered. Optimum wall angles for convergent cones can be found for the case of complete absorption of all molecules passing the exit plane.

ACKNOWLEDGMENT

We would like to acknowledge the cooperation given by The Institute of Computer Science, University of Toronto whose IBM 7090 digital computer was used for the numerical computation.

REFERENCES

Hughes, P. C., and de Leeuw, J. H. (1965). This Volume.

Patterson, G. N. (1964). Univ. of Toronto, Institute for Aerospace Studies. Review No. 18 (also available as Aerospace Research Lab. (OAR, USAF) Rept. ARL 64–60).

Richley, E. A., and Reynolds, T. W. (1964). NASA TN D-2330.

Sinclair, S. R. M. (1964). Univ. of Toronto, Institute for Aerospace Studies. Tech. Note No. 76.

Sparrow, E. M., and Jonsson, V. K. (1963). *AIAA J.* **1**, 1081.

Theory for the Free Molecule Impact
Probe at an Angle of Attack[1]

P. C. HUGHES and J. H. DE LEEUW

Institute for Aerospace Studies, University of Toronto, Toronto, Canada

A theoretical analysis of the behavior of the free molecular impact pressure probe at an arbitrary angle of attack is presented. The solution is formulated in terms of three parameters which represent the tube geometry, the free stream gas velocity, and the angle of attack. A drifting Maxwellian motion of the gas particles at infinity and a perfectly diffuse law for the reflection of particles from the internal tube wall are assumed. Calculations were made for angles of attack up to 90°, for speed ratios from zero to infinity, and tube geometries ranging from an orifice to an infinitely long tube.

I. Introduction

The properties of free molecular impact probes are of interest because such probes can be used for the mapping of low density flow fields in the laboratory and these properties can also be used to make quantitative predictions on the effect of connecting tubes to rocket borne instruments like pressure gages or mass spectrometers.

This report is concerned with the response of an impact tube pressure probe to a gas flow which is sufficiently rarefied that the flow around the probe and in its interior is free-molecular. This means that individual particles do not collide with each other on the average in the vicinity of the probe but only collide with the tube wall. The reflection from the tube wall is assumed to be perfectly diffuse in this paper.

The problem of the free molecular impact probe at zero angle of attack has been considered previously by Pond (1962) and de Leeuw and Rothe (1963). The methods in these papers resulted in cumbersome computations

[1] This work was supported by the USAF Cambridge Research under Contract No. 19(628)-363.

and the use of similar methods to treat the case of a probe at angle of attack would have led to a prohibitive amount of numerical work. The theoretical approach to the problem in this paper is based on a different point of view and leads to a negligible computational effort for the zero angle of attack case and to an acceptable level of effort for the case of probes at angle of attack.

II. Theory

Consider a circular cylindrical pressure probe which has a diameter/length ratio " D " and which is connected to a large gage volume (Fig. 1). The

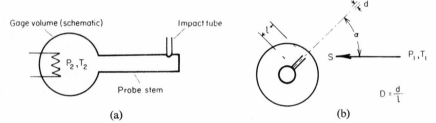

FIG. 1. Schematic of probe. (a) View looking into free stream. (b) View looking down probe stem.

flow is incident at an angle α to the cylinder axis and it has a speed ratio " S." ($S = u/c_m$, the ratio of mean speed to the most probable random velocity.) It is clear that of the molecules which enter the tube, some will travel directly to the gage volume without colliding with the walls while of the remaining ones which do collide with the walls only some will eventually (after one or more collisions with the wall) pass into the gage volume. The same is true for the molecules which enter the tube from the gage and leave it through the entrance. Since free molecular conditions are assumed, these two streams of molecules in opposite directions do not interfere with each other and can be calculated independently.

The theory is based on the work by Clausing (1932) on the free molecular flow through cylindrical tubes. He showed that in such tubes, when ideal diffuse reflection off the walls is valid, the probability that a molecule leaving the wall at a position $X = x/l$ will ultimately reach the outlet of the tube, ($X = 1$) is in very good approximation given by a linear function of position

$$w(X, D) = a(D) + [1 - 2a(D)]X,$$

where " a " is a function of D.

In a previous analysis by Harris and Patterson (1958) it was observed that the number of particles which succeed in passing through the tube can be written as

$$N = N_{cc}(S, D) + \int_0^1 N_{cr}(S, X)w(X, D)\,dX, \tag{1}$$

where N_{cc} is the number of molecules passing straight through the tube without colliding with the walls and $N_{cr}\,dX$ is the number of molecules entering the tube that have their first collision with the wall between X and $X + dX$.

The functions N_{cc} and N_{cr} are integrals of the velocity distribution function and take into account particles arriving from all directions. They will therefore depend on the speed ratio and the angle of attack as well as the tube geometry. In particular, these functions will be different for the molecules entering the probe from the flow and those coming from the gage volume where the distribution function may be assumed Maxwellian with zero mean velocity because the gage volume diameter is assumed to be much larger than the tube diameter. When the probe and gage volume reach equilibrium the flows into and out of the gage volume must be equal and this can, in general, only occur if the pressure in the gage is different from that in the flow.

It will be shown that the solution of this problem can be expressed in the form

$$(P_2/P_1)(T_1/T_2)^{1/2} = R(S, D, \alpha),$$

where $(P_2/P_1)(T_1/T_2)^{1/2}$ is called the "probe pressure ratio," and P_2, T_2, P_1, and T_1 refer to the pressure and temperature in the gage volume and the free stream, respectively.

Before developing the general theory of this report, the previous analyses for special restricted cases are briefly outlined in this section. One case of interest, namely when the tube length shrinks to zero, is referred to as the orifice probe case for which the theory is given, for instance, by Patterson (1956). In this special case the problem is greatly simplified because all molecules that enter the orifice, i.e., a tube of zero length, will pass into the gage volume, and the results can be expressed in the form

$$R(S, \infty, \alpha) = \chi(S \cos \alpha), \tag{2}$$

where

$$\chi(u) = \exp(-u^2) + \pi^{1/2}u(1 + \text{erf } u),$$

and

$$\text{erf } u = (2/\pi^{1/2}) \int_0^u \exp(-t^2)\,dt.$$

A significant feature of this relation is that when the orifice is at an angle of attack to the flow, the probe registers a pressure which corresponds to the component of the speed ratio normal to the orifice area. Unfortunately, this simple dependence on α does not remain valid for finite tube lengths.

Harris and Patterson (1958) derived the following relations for tubes of arbitrary length at zero angle of attack.

$$R(S, D, 0) = \frac{\mathscr{W}(S, D)}{\mathscr{W}(0, D)},\tag{3}$$

where

$$\mathscr{W}(S, D) = a(D)[2\chi(S) - \exp(-S^2)\psi(D) - (4S/\pi^{1/2})\eta(S, D)]$$

$$+ [1 - 2a(D)][\chi(S) - \exp(-S^2)\zeta(D) - (4S/\pi^{1/2})\mu(S, D)],\tag{4}$$

in which

$$\left.\begin{aligned}
&\psi(D) = (2/D^2)[(1 + D^2)^{1/2} - 1],\\
&\zeta(D) = (2/3D^2)\{(1 + D^2)^{3/2} - D^3 - 1\},\\
&\eta(S, D) = (1/D)\int_0^1 dY \times\\
&\qquad\times \int_0^{\tan^{-1}D(1 - Y^2)^{1/2}} [1 + \mathrm{erf}(S\cos\phi)]\cos\phi\exp(-S^2\sin^2\phi)\,d\phi,\\
&\mu(S, D) = \int_0^1 \eta(S, D/X)\,dX,
\end{aligned}\right\}\tag{5}$$

and where $a(D)$ is a function developed by Clausing (1932).

The solution is seen to take the form of a triple integration from which actual values must be obtained numerically. In fact a complete solution of Eqs. (4) and (5) has been obtained by Pond (1962) and independently by de Leeuw and Rothe (1963). The numerical work was formidable and made the extension of similar calculation schemes to treat the case of a probe at angle of attack unattractive.

In this paper the problem of determining the flux of molecules from a drifting Maxwellian gas that passes through a cylindrical tube is analysed from a new point of view. In contrast to the formulation in Eq. (1) which requires the calculation of the flux of molecules striking each element of the tube wall from all directions, it is found expedient to calculate first the response of the tube to a unidirectional beam of molecules. The final probe response is then obtained by integrating over all such "beams" of molecules that together make up the external flow. It will be shown that a relation may be derived for $R(S, D, \alpha)$ which involves, at most, a double integration and that this relation further simplifies to a single integration for two particular cases of the probe angle of attack, namely, at $\alpha = 0°$ and $\alpha = 90°$. The approach taken in this report is outlined qualitatively in the remainder of this section.

Consider first the response of a cylindrical impact tube to a beam of molecules all of which have their velocity vectors at the same azimuthal angle and inclined at the same angle to the tube axis, the angle ϕ. It is evident from the discussion in the introduction that not all the molecules which enter the tube will enter the gage volume. It is to be expected that the fraction which reach the gage volume (either by passing directly through the tube or after one or more collisions with the tube surface) will be large for small values of ϕ and large values of D. Accordingly a quantity $K(\phi, D)$ will be defined as

$$K(\phi, D) \equiv \frac{\text{number of molecules per second which enter the gage volume per unit area of tube outlet}}{\text{number of molecules per second which enter the tube from a beam which makes an angle } \phi \text{ with the tube axis, per unit area of tube inlet}} \tag{6}$$

The value of K will lie between 0 and 1; it will decrease with ϕ and increase with D.

Let us now examine a drifting Maxwellian gas which moves with a speed ratio S at an angle of attack α to the tube axis, and determine the flux of molecules which strike a surface perpendicular to the tube axis at an angle (with the normal to the surface) between ϕ and $\phi + d\phi$. This flux will be represented by the quantity $F(\phi, S, \alpha)$ which is defined as

$$\frac{n C_m F(\phi, S, \alpha)\, d\phi}{\pi^{1/2}} \equiv \begin{cases} \text{number of molecules per second with angle between} \\ \phi \text{ and } \phi + d\phi \text{ passing through a unit area normal to} \\ \text{the tube axis. The source of molecules is a Max-} \\ \text{wellian gas having a speed ratio } S \text{ which makes an} \\ \text{angle } \alpha \text{ with the tube axis.} \end{cases} \tag{7}$$

A. Response of a Cylindrical Tube to a Molecular Beam, $K(\phi, D)$

Consider now the response of a cylindrical tube (diameter/length ratio D) to a beam of molecules all of which have a velocity U, which is inclined to the tube axis at an angle ϕ. We define an x-y-z coordinate system in the following way (Fig. 2). The center of the inlet of the tube will be taken as the origin and the distance down the tube will be denoted by x. Let the flow direction be parallel to the x-y plane. Furthermore, let β denote the angle between the normal to an element of tube surface and the x-y plane. The number of molecules which fall per second on the infinitesimal area of tube surface can be written as

$$\text{flux} = n_b U r\, d\beta\, dx \sin \phi \cos \beta, \tag{8}$$

where n_b is the number density in the beam. The total flux of molecules hitting the inside of the tube between x and $x + dx$ can be found by integrating Eq. (8) with respect to β.

Let the lower limit for β be denoted by $\beta_1(x)$. A study of Fig. 3 shows that

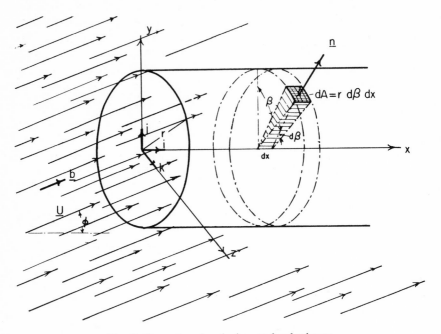

FIG. 2. Geometry of probe in a molecular beam.

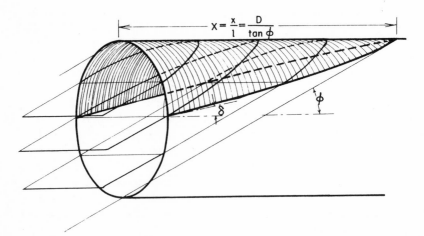

FIG. 3. Region of probe struck by beam molecules incident at a angle ϕ.

the region of the tube upon which molecules may fall is bounded by a plane which makes an angle δ with the x-z plane. Geometrically, $\tan \delta = \frac{1}{2} \tan \phi$, so since $y = (\tan \delta)x = \frac{1}{2}(\tan \phi)x$ and since y is also given by $y = r \cos \beta$ we have

$$\cos \beta_1(x) = (X/D) \tan \phi, \tag{9}$$

where $X = x/l$ and $D = 2r/l$.

The number of molecules per second falling on the tube between X and $X + dX$ is then found after integration to be

$$\text{flux falling between } X \text{ and } X + dX = \frac{4r^2 n_b U}{D} \sin \phi \, [1 - (X/D)^2 \tan^2 \phi]^{1/2} \, dX$$

$$= \frac{4r^2 n_b U}{D} \sin \phi \, (1 - X^2 T^2)^{1/2} \, dX, \tag{10}$$

where

$$T = T(\phi, D) = (\tan \phi)/D. \tag{11}$$

To find the flux of molecules into the gage volume the flux of molecules falling on dX at X, as given by Eq. (10), will be multiplied by the probability $w(X, D)$ that a molecule leaving X will eventually reach the gage volume, and then this product will be integrated over X. Clausing (1932) showed that the function $w(X, D)$ is given in very good approximation by a linear relation in X,

$$w(X, D) = a(D) + [1 - 2a(D)]X \tag{12}$$

where $a(D)$ is plotted in Fig. 4.

With regard to integrating over X, it is clear that two cases are possible.

Case I. $T > 1$. In this case it is not possible for any molecule to pass straight into the gage volume without collisions with the tube wall. For this case, it is found that the number of molecules per second reaching the gage volume, $N_b(\phi, D)$ is given by

$$N_b(\phi, D) = \frac{4r^2 n_b U}{D} \sin \phi \int_0^{1/T} (1 - X^2 T^2)^{1/2}[a + (1 - 2a)X] \, dX. \tag{13}$$

Case II. $T < 1$. In this case a certain fraction of the incoming molecules travel straight into the gage volume. To calculate $N_b(\phi, D)$ for this case, the length of the tube is conceptually extended to $X = 1/T$ and the probability of a molecule entering the gage volume after colliding with the tube at $1 < X \leqslant 1/T$ is regarded as unity. From this line of reasoning the following relation is obtained for $T < 1$:

$$N_b(\phi, D) = \frac{4r^2 n_b U}{D} \sin \phi \left\{ \int_0^1 (1 - X^2 T^2)^{1/2} [a + (1 - 2a)X] \, dX \right.$$

$$\left. + \int_1^{1/T} (1 - X^2 T^2)^{1/2} \, dX \right\}. \tag{14}$$

Fortunately the integrals involved in Eqs. (13) and (14) are readily evaluated and one obtains

$$N_b(\phi, D) = 4r^2 n_b U \cos \phi \left[a \frac{\pi}{4} + \frac{1 - 2a}{3T} \right], \qquad T > 1; \tag{15}$$

$$N_b(\phi, D) = 4r^2 n_b U \cos \phi \left[\frac{\pi}{4} + \frac{1 - 2a}{3T} \{1 - (1 - T^2)^{3/2}\} \right.$$

$$\left. - \frac{1 - a}{2} (T(1 - T^2)^{1/2} + \sin^{-1} T) \right], \qquad T < 1. \tag{16}$$

From the definition of $K(\phi, D)$, Eq. (6), it is possible to form $K(\phi, D)$ from $N_b(\phi, D)$ as follows:

$$K(\phi, D) = \frac{N_b(\phi, D)}{n_b U(\pi r^2) \cos \phi}. \tag{17}$$

Hence the following expressions have been derived for $K(\phi, D)$:

$$K_1(\phi, D) = a + \frac{4(1 - 2a)}{3\pi T}, \qquad T > 1;$$

$$K_2(\phi, D) = 1 + \frac{4(1 - 2a)}{3\pi T} \{1 - (1 - T^2)^{3/2}\} \tag{18}$$

$$- \frac{2(1 - a)}{\pi} (T(1 - T^2)^{1/2} + \sin^{-1} T), \qquad T < 1.$$

It should be carefully noted that the usefulness of $K(\phi, D)$ is more general than might be immediately apparent from the above derivation. It was found convenient in the above to assume that all molecules entered at the same azimuthal angle, and that all molecules had an identical speed U. However it is evident that a molecule may enter from any azimuthal angle whatever, as long as its trajectory makes an angle ϕ with the tube axis. Furthermore, the concept of the K function involves the direction of motion of a beam of molecules, not its speed. As a consequence, the incoming molecules may have any velocity whatever, subject only to the constraint that the number of molecules per unit volume in any speed class (i.e., those molecules which have speeds between ε and $\varepsilon + d\varepsilon$) is independent of position in the free stream, and that their velocity vectors make an angle ϕ with the tube axis.

B. Drifting Maxwellian Beam Flux Density, $F(\phi, S, \alpha)$

It can be seen from the discussion in the previous section that the flux of molecules through the impact tube will be known if the molecular flux entering the inlet at an angle ϕ with the tube axis can be determined for all values of ϕ in the range $0 \leqslant \phi \leqslant \pi/2$. The detailed derivation of this quantity, which is proportional to $F(\phi, S, \alpha)$, has been given by Hughes (1965). The derivation is essentially straightforward and the final expression is

$$\text{flux in } \phi \text{ direction per unit area normal to inlet} = \frac{nC_m}{\pi^{1/2}} F(\phi, S, \alpha)\, d\phi, \quad (19)$$

where

$$F(\phi, S, \alpha) = \pi^{-1} \sin \phi \cos \phi \int_0^\pi \{(1 + S^2 \cos^2 \Omega) \exp(-S^2)$$

$$+ \pi^{1/2} S \cos \Omega \exp(-S^2 \sin^2 \Omega)(\tfrac{3}{2} + S^2 \cos^2 \Omega)$$

$$\times (1 + \text{erf } S \cos \Omega)\}\, d\theta, \quad (20)$$

and where

$$\cos \Omega = \cos \alpha \cos \phi + \sin \alpha \sin \phi \cos \theta. \quad (21)$$

The right-hand side of Eq. (20) may be partly integrated to yield

$$F(\phi, S, \alpha) = \sin \phi \cos \phi (1 + S^2 \cos^2 \alpha \cos^2 \phi - \tfrac{1}{2} S^2 \sin^2 \alpha \sin^2 \phi) \exp(-S^2)$$

$$+ \pi^{-1/2} \sin \phi \cos \phi \int_0^\pi S \cos \Omega \exp(-S^2 \sin^2 \Omega)$$

$$\times (\tfrac{3}{2} + S^2 \cos^2 \Omega)(1 + \text{erf } S \cos \Omega)\, d\theta. \quad (22)$$

Unfortunately, attempts to evaluate the remaining integrals have met with no success except for two particular cases which are now discussed.

When attention is restricted to the impact tube at zero angle of attack, $\cos \Omega$ reduces to $\cos \phi$ and the integral in Eq. (20) becomes trivial. At zero angle of attack, then, one obtains

$$F(\phi, S, 0) = \sin \phi \cos \phi [(1 + S^2 \cos^2 \phi) \exp(-S^2)$$

$$+ \pi^{1/2} S \cos \phi \exp(-S^2 \sin^2 \phi)(\tfrac{3}{2} + S^2 \cos^2 \phi)(1 + \text{erf } S \cos \phi)]. \quad (23)$$

For the situation where the impact tube is perpendicular to the flow direction, the integral in Eq. (20) can also be evaluated:

$$F(\phi, S, 90°) = \sin \phi \cos \phi \exp(-S^2 \cos^2 \phi)(1 + S^2 \sin^2 \phi). \quad (24)$$

The detailed derivation has been given by Hughes (1965).

C. The Probe Pressure Ratio, R(S, D, α)

It is now possible to find the expression for the flux of molecules which enter the gage volume. If this quantity is denoted by $N_1(S, D, \alpha)$ then from Eqs. (6) and (7)

$$N_1(S, D, \alpha) = \pi r^2 \frac{n_1 C_{m_1}}{\pi^{1/2}} \int_0^{\pi/2} K(\phi, D)F(\phi, S, \alpha) \, d\phi. \tag{25}$$

The flux of those molecules that originate in the gage volume and pass out the inlet is given by

$$N_2(0, D, 0) = \pi r^2 \frac{n_2 C_{m_2}}{\pi^{1/2}} \int_0^{\pi/2} K(\phi, D)F(\phi, 0, 0) \, d\phi. \tag{26}$$

The integral on the right-hand side of Eq. (26) can be evaluated as $\frac{1}{2}W(D)$ where

$$W(D) = 1 - a(D)\psi(D) - [1 - 2a(D)]\zeta(D) \tag{27}$$

and where ψ and ζ are given in Eq. (5).

Since for equilibrium,

$$N_1(S, D, \alpha) = N_2(0, D, 0), \tag{28}$$

then Eqs. (25) and (26) lead to

$$\frac{n_2 C_{m_2}}{n_1 C_{m_1}} = \frac{2}{W(D)} \int_0^{\pi/2} K(\phi, D)F(\phi, S, \alpha) \, d\phi. \tag{29}$$

From the ideal gas law, $P = nm\mathcal{R}T$ (where m is the molecular mass) and the fact that $C_m = (2\mathcal{R}T)^{1/2}$, the left-hand side of Eq. (29) is seen to be precisely R. Finally, then,

$$R(S, D, \alpha) = \frac{2}{W(D)} \int_0^{\pi/2} K(\phi, D)F(\phi, S, \alpha) \, d\phi, \tag{30}$$

where $W(D)$ is given by Eq. (27), $K(\phi, D)$ is given by Eq. (18), and $F(\phi, S, \alpha)$ is given by Eq. (22), Eq. (23), or Eq. (24).

It is worth noting that for the orifice probe $(D \to \infty)$, $W(D) \to 1$ and $K(\phi, D) \to 1$ and so, from Eq. (2), F must fulfil the condition

$$R(S, \infty, \alpha) = 2 \int_0^{\pi/2} F(\phi, S, \alpha) \, d\phi = \chi(S \cos \alpha). \tag{31}$$

Another important conclusion, valid for large speed ratios, $(S > 10)$, may be drawn from Eq. (30). From the physical significance of F, it is to be expected that for large values of S, F will be effectively zero except in the neighborhood of $\phi = \alpha$. In the integration of $K \times F$ then, the function F has the property that it "punches out" the value of K at $\phi = \alpha$ much after the concept of the δ-function. As an approximation the following relation may be written. From Eqs. (30) and (31),

$$R(S, D, \alpha)_{S>10} \cong \frac{K(\alpha, D)}{W(D)} \chi(S \cos \alpha). \qquad (32)$$

It is emphasized that Eq. (32) is only valid for large S. It also becomes a weak approximation for very long tubes at zero angle of attack and for very short tubes at 90° angle of attack.

Equation (32) does serve to demonstrate that for tubes of finite length, the quantity R does not depend solely on $S \cos \alpha$ as is the case for an orifice probe, but has an additional dependence on α through K. For long tubes and high speed ratios then, the probe indicates a pressure considerably less than that corresponding to the component of speed ratio normal to the tube inlet. It may be shown, in fact, from Eq. (30) that this property is found for all $S > 0$, $\alpha > 0$, and finite D. From Eq. (30),

$$R(S \cos \alpha, D, 0) = \frac{2}{W(D)} \int_0^{\pi/2} K(\phi, D)F(\phi, S \cos \alpha, 0) \, d\phi. \qquad (33)$$

Since

$$2 \int_0^{\pi/2} F(\phi, S, \alpha) \, d\phi = 2 \int_0^{\pi/2} F(\phi, S \cos \alpha, 0) \, d\phi = \chi(S \cos \alpha), \qquad (34)$$

then the weighting properties of $K(\phi, D)$ will be the determining factor. From purely physical arguments, K decreases monotonically with increasing ϕ, and since $F(\phi, S, \alpha)$ tends to peak at $\phi = \alpha$, we see that

$$\frac{R(S \cos \alpha, D, 0)}{R(S, D, \alpha)} > 1. \qquad D \text{ finite}, \quad \alpha > 0, \quad S > 0. \qquad (35)$$

In particular, for $\alpha = 90°$, and since $R(0, D, 0) = 1$,

$$R(S, D, 90°) < 1 \qquad (D \text{ finite}), \qquad (36)$$

a result which has important implications for any experimental determination of static pressure. For $S > 10$, it may be seen from Eq. (32) that, at $\alpha = 90°$,

$$R(S, D, 90°)_{S>10} \cong \frac{K(90°, D)}{W(D)} \chi(0) = \frac{a(D)}{W(D)}, \qquad (37)$$

a result which could have been demonstrated directly from the physical significance of $a(D)$ and $W(D)$.

Again, from Eq. (37), and letting $D \to 0$ we obtain, for an infinitely long tube at 90° angle of attack and for $S > 10$,

$$\lim_{S \to \infty} R(S, 0, 90°) = \lim_{D \to 0} a(D)/W(D) = \tfrac{1}{2}. \qquad (38)$$

D. The Infinitely Long Tube

For the infinitely long impact tube $(D \to 0)$ it may be seen from Eq. (30) that

$$R(S, 0, \alpha) = \lim_{D \to 0} \left\{ [2/W(D)] \int_0^{\pi/2} K(\phi, D) F(\phi, S, \alpha) \, d\phi \right\}, \tag{39}$$

from which, Eq. (18),

$$R(S, 0, \alpha) = 2 \lim_{D \to 0} \frac{D}{W(D)} \left\{ \lim_{D \to 0} \int_0^{\tan^{-1} D} \frac{K_2(\phi, D)}{D} F(\phi, S, \alpha) \, d\phi \right.$$
$$\left. + \lim_{D \to 0} \int_{\tan^{-1} D}^{\pi/2} \frac{K_1(\phi, D)}{D} F(\phi, S, \alpha) \, d\phi \right\}. \tag{40}$$

Now the function $a(D)$ is given by Eq. (51) in Section III,A. From this expression, and Eq. (27), the following limits can be found:

$$\lim_{D \to 0} [a(D)/D] = \tfrac{2}{3}, \qquad \text{whence} \qquad \lim_{D \to 0} [W(D)/D] = \tfrac{4}{3},$$

and it can also be shown that (see Hughes, 1965)

$$\lim_{D \to 0} \int_0^{\tan^{-1} D} \frac{K_2(\phi, D)}{D} F(\phi, S, \alpha) \, d\phi = 0. \tag{41}$$

The following expression has therefore been demonstrated to be valid for the infinitely long impact tube:

$$R(S, 0, \alpha) = \tfrac{1}{2} \chi(S \cos \alpha) + (2/\pi) \int_0^{\pi/2} \cot \phi \, F(\phi, S, \alpha) \, d\phi. \tag{42}$$

It was found in Section II,B that analytic expressions for F are available for two values of α namely, $0°$ and $90°$. Accordingly, attempts were made to integrate Eq. (42) for these two cases. Although the case at $90°$ did not meet with any success, the case at $0°$ could be treated further by analytic means.

When attention is restricted to the impact tube at zero angle of attack, Eq. (22) may be substituted into the right-hand side of Eq. (42). Integrating yields the following result:

$$R(S, 0, 0) = (S\pi^{-1/2} + \tfrac{1}{2})\chi(S) + \tfrac{1}{2}(1 + \text{erf } S). \tag{43}$$

For $S > 5$, Eq. (43) may to a good approximation be written as

$$R(S, 0, 0) = 2S^2 + \pi^{1/2} S + 1. \tag{44}$$

The limiting case in which the speed ratio is increased indefinitely can also be treated. To avoid difficulty in interpreting the ratio

$$R(S, D, \alpha) = (P_2/P_1)(T_1/T_2)^{1/2}$$

it is desirable to form the ratio of the pressure in the gage volume behind a tube and the pressure in the gage volume behind an orifice probe at the same angle of attack. This ratio will be denoted by Ψ, viz.,

$$\Psi(S, D, \alpha) = P_2/P_{2\,orifice}.$$

The flux of incident molecules down a tube at an angle of attack α reduces to (see Eq. (6))

$$N_1(\infty, D, \alpha) = n_1 U \pi r^2 \cos \alpha \, K(\alpha, D), \tag{45}$$

and the flux of molecules from the gage volume which reach the inlet is

$$N_2(0, D, 0) = (n_2 C_{m_2}/2\pi^{1/2})\pi r^2 W(D). \tag{46}$$

Since, for equilibrium, $N_1 = N_2$,

$$n_2 C_{m_2} = 2\pi^{1/2} \cos \alpha \, \frac{K(\alpha, D)}{W(D)} \, n_1 U. \tag{47}$$

Since Eq. (47) when applied to an orifice probe gives the result $n_2 C_{m_2} = 2\pi^{1/2} \cos \alpha \cdot n_1 U$, the expression for Ψ becomes

$$\Psi(\infty, D, \alpha) = \frac{K(\alpha, D)}{W(D)}. \tag{48}$$

Note that this result is in accordance with Eq. (32).

As previously noted in Eq. (37), the infinite speed ratio case at 90° angle of attack is given by

$$\Psi(\infty, D, 90°) = \frac{a(D)}{W(D)}. \tag{49}$$

For an infinitely long impact tube in an infinite speed ratio flow one obtains, from Eq. (48),

$$\Psi(\infty, 0, \alpha) = \lim_{D \to 0} \frac{K(\alpha, D)}{W(D)}$$

$$= \tfrac{1}{2} + \pi^{-1} \cot \alpha. \tag{50}$$

III. Presentation of Numerical Data

In Section II the properties of free molecule impact tubes have been studied within an analytical framework in terms of three basic parameters, viz., S, D, α. This section presents the numerical results obtained by solving these relations on the IBM 7090 electronic computer of the University of Toronto, Institute of Computer Science.

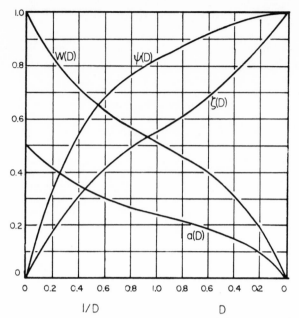

FIG. 4. Auxiliary functions versus nondimensional probe diameter.

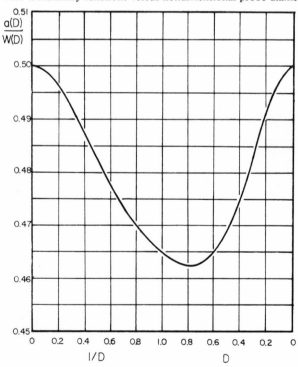

FIG. 5. Ratio of $a(D)$ and $W(D)$ versus nondimensional probe diameter.

Each of the three parameters was allowed to vary over a wide range; calculations were made for the values of S, D, α given in Table I and for each combination possible.

TABLE I

S		D		α (deg)	
0.0	1.25	0.0	1.25	0	50
0.05	1.5	0.05	1.5	10	60
0.1	2.0	0.1	2.0	20	70
0.2	3.0	0.2	3.0	30	80
0.3	5.0	0.3	5.0	40	90
0.5	10	0.5	10		
0.75	20	0.75	20		
1.0	∞	1.0	∞		

A. Preliminary Calculations

Short preliminary programs were written to evaluate the functions $a(D)$, $W(D)$. The functions $a(D)$ was calculated according to the following relation (Clausing, 1932)

$$a(D) = \frac{A_1 A_2 [3A_1 - 9 - 7^{1/2}D^2(A_2 - 7^{1/2})]}{A_1 A_2 (3 - 7^{1/2}D)(A_1 + A_2 D) + A(7A_1 D - 9A_2)}, \tag{51}$$

where

$$A_1 = (9 + A^2 D^2)^{1/2}, \qquad A_2 = (7 + A^2)^{1/2}, \qquad A = 3 + 7^{1/2}D,$$

and $W(D)$ is given by Eq. (27). Curves of $a(D)$, $W(D)$, $\psi(D)$, and $\zeta(D)$ are shown in Fig. 4 and the ratio $a(D)/W(D)$ is plotted in Fig. 5.

The function $\chi(y)$ was evaluated according to Eq. (2). It is useful to note that $\chi(y) \cong 2\pi^{1/2}y$ to within 0.01 % for $y \geqslant 3$.

Equation (18) was used to calculate the function $K(\phi, D)$. The interval $(0, \pi/2)$ was divided into 32 $(= 2^5)$ intervals for this computation. From Eq. (18), $K(\phi, D)$ is continuous at $\phi = \tan^{-1} D$ although the first and higher derivatives are not.

B. Calculation of $F(\phi, S, \alpha)$ and $R(S, D, \alpha)$

A general computer program was written which generated
(1) $K(\phi_i, D_j)$, $(i = 1, ..., 129)$, $(j = 1, ..., 14)$, from Eq. (18)
(2) $F(\phi_i, S_k, \alpha)$, $(k = 1, ..., 14)$, by a Simpson's Rule integration of Eq. (22).
It was found that 128 intervals in θ yielded satisfactory accuracy.

(3) $R(S_k, D_j, \alpha)$, by a combination of Simpson's Rule and trapezoidal approximation. This procedure served to integrate Eq. (30) numerically.

Slightly modified programs, which replaced the inner integration for $F(\phi, S, \alpha)$ with the relations given by Eqs. (23) and (24) were used for $\alpha = 0°$

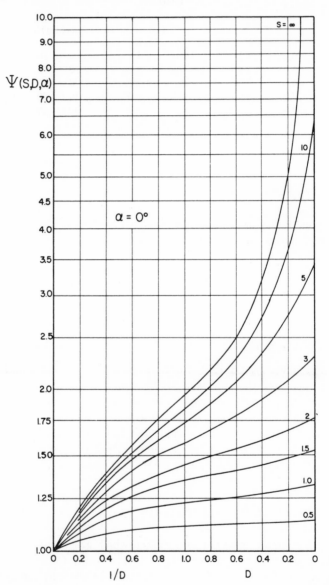

FIG. 6(a)-(f). Reduced pressure ratio as a function of nondimensional probe diameter.

and 90°, respectively. The limiting cases, $D \to 0$ and $S \to \infty$, discussed in Section II,D were programmed according to Eqs. (42) and (48), respectively.

C. Graphical Representation of Data

The "reduced" probe pressure ratio $\Psi(S, D, \alpha)$ is presented in the figures. This function has the advantage that the trends can be more readily portrayed graphically if the basic orifice probe dependence on S and α is removed as follows:

$$(P_2/T_2^{1/2})(T_1^{1/2}/P_1) = R(S, D, \alpha)$$

$$(P_2/T_2^{1/2})_{\text{orifice}}(T_1^{1/2}/P_1) = R(S, \infty, \alpha) = \chi(S \cos \alpha).$$

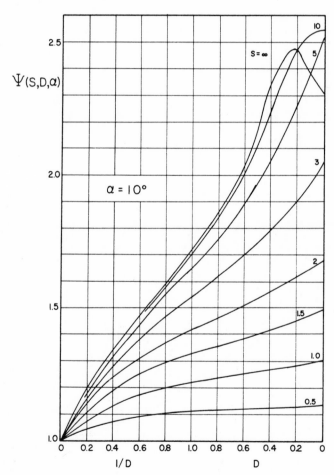

FIG. 6(b)

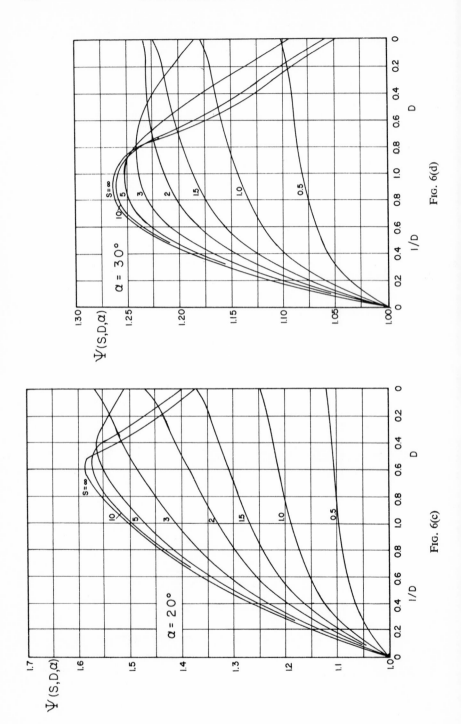

FIG. 6(c)

FIG. 6(d)

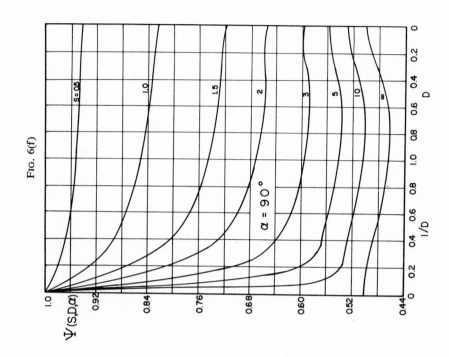

Fig. 6(f)

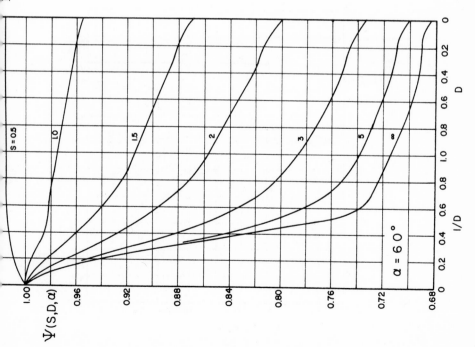

Fig. 6(e)

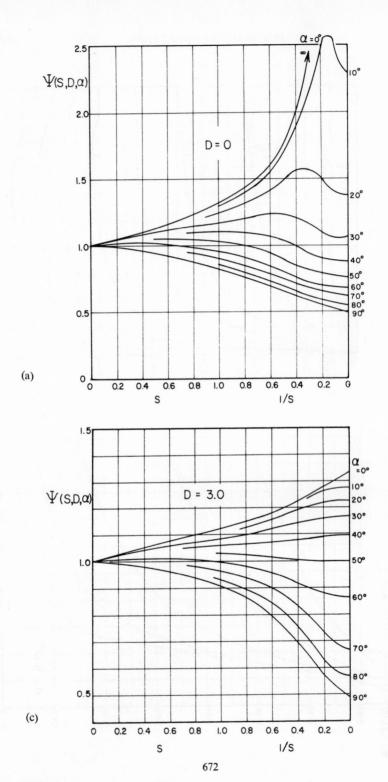

(a)

(c)

If equal gage temperatures are assumed in the two cases $(T_2 = T_{2, \text{orifice}})$, then

$$\frac{P_2}{P_{2, \text{orifice}}} = \frac{R(S, D, \alpha)}{\chi(S \cos \alpha)} = \Psi(S, D, \alpha). \tag{52}$$

In Figs. 6–8 the function $\Psi(S, D, \alpha)$ is displayed from several points of view. In Fig. 6 the effect of the tube length is shown. Note that for these curves Ψ is proportional to $R(S, D, \alpha)$ since S and α are constant along them. Figure 7 shows the dependence (in addition to the orifice probe dependence) on speed ratio for a specified tube and angle of attack. Finally, in Fig. 8, the change in gage volume pressure (over and above the cosine dependence of the orifice probe) is demonstrated when a particular tube is rotated under specific flow conditions.

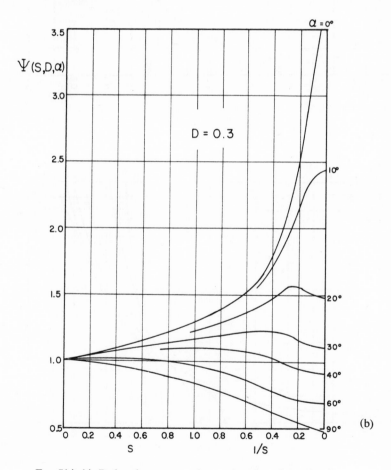

Fig. 7(a)–(c). Reduced pressure ratio as a function of speed ratio.

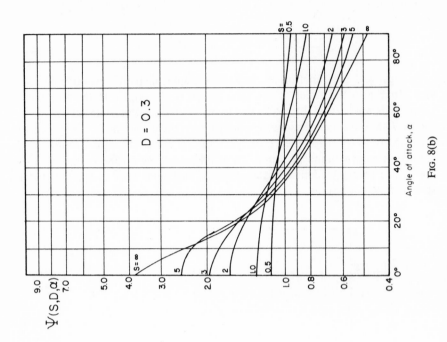

FIG. 8(b)

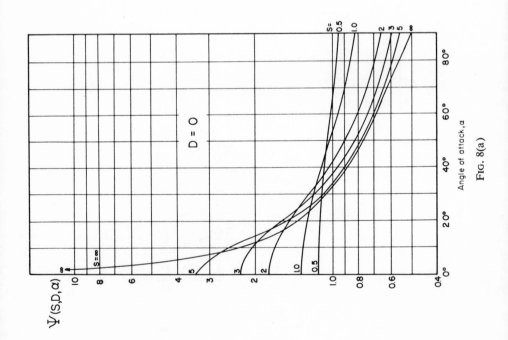

FIG. 8(a)

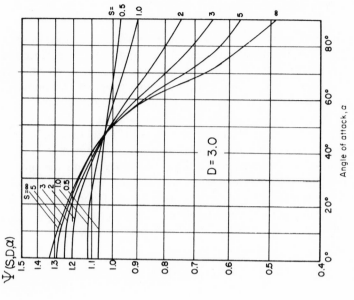

FIG. 8(d)

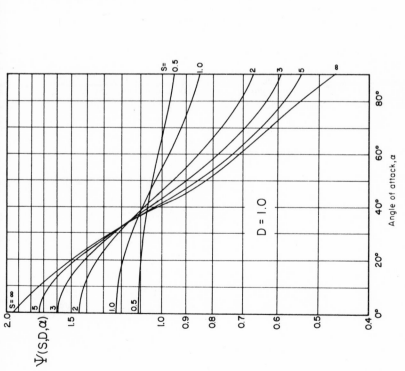

FIG. 8(c)

FIG. 8(a)–(d). Reduced pressure ratio a function of angle of attack.

IV. Concluding Remarks

The results computed in this report agree with those obtained by de Leeuw and Rothe (1963) for the impact tube at zero angle of attack. Since the same assumptions were made in both analyses, this agreement is to be expected and is really only a verification of the computer program. A summary of the limitations of the theory is given by de Leeuw and Rothe (1963).

One limitation on the analysis which bears special emphasis derives from the assumption of diffuse reflection from the tube wall. This assumption may not be entirely justified for small angles of attack and large values of S. Under these circumstances, the average incident molecule strikes the tube wall at high speed and at a shallow angle of incidence, and a tendency toward specular reflection may occur. Since this situation favors an increase in the flux of molecules down the tube toward the gage volume, a higher value of gage pressure than that predicted by theory may be expected.

REFERENCES

Clausing, P. (1932). *Ann. Physik* **12**, 961.

de Leeuw, J. H., and Rothe, D. E. (1963). *AIAA J.* **1**, 220. Also: Inst. of Aerophys., Univ. of Toronto UTIA Rept. 88.

Harris, E. L., and Patterson, G. N. (1958). UTIA Rept. 52 Inst. of Aerophys., Univ. of Toronto.

Hughes, P. C. (1965). Inst. for Aerospace Studies, Univ. of Toronto UTIAS Rept. 101.

Patterson, G. N. (1956). Inst. of Aerophys., Univ. of Toronto, UTIA Rept. 41.

Pond, H. L. (1962). *J. Aerospace Sci.* **29**, 917.

On the Internal Flow of Rarefied Gases[1]

YAU WU[2]

New York University, New York, New York

An attempt has been made to solve internal flow problems in the free and nearly free molecular regimes and higher order transition flows. In free-molecule flow, a matrix method has been introduced to solve a Fredholm integral equation for the surface collision density and the transmission probabilities. In nearly free-molecule flow and higher order transition flows, a successive approximation method has been proposed which is based on an iteration scheme of the Boltzmann equation and a series expansion to the solution of the integral equation for the surface collision density with the nondimensional collision frequency as its expansion parameter. The solution of the free-molecule flow serves as the zeroth-order approximation for both the iteration process and the series expansions. A set of integral equations and the associated iteration of Boltzmann equation form the governing equations for the free-molecule flow, nearly free-molecule flow and higher order transition flows. The integral equations which are transformed into matrix equations by finite-difference approximations have been solved successively. An internal flow through two parallel plates in the free and nearly free-molecular regimes has been calculated based on the BGK equation according to the proposed method.

I. Introduction

During recent years, the problem of internal flow in the field of rarefied gas dynamics has been a reviving subject. In the free-molecule flow regime, a Monte Carlo method has been applied for a short duct flow by Davis *et al.* (1961) and for a flat plate cascade flow by Kruger, and Shapiro (1961); a matrix-probability theory and a Markov chain model have been proposed

[1] This work has been supported by the Office of Naval Research under Contract N-onr-285(53), and is a portion of a dissertation submitted to the New York University for the degree of Doctor of Philosophy in Aeronautics and Astronautics.

[2] *Present address:* Department of Aerospace and Mechanical Sciences, Gas Dynamics Laboratory, Princeton University, Princeton, New Jersey.

by Wu (1961, 1964b), and a variational method has been used by De Marcus (1961) for the problem of flow through long and short tubes. However, in the regimes of nearly free-molecule flow and higher order transition flows, internal flow problems have not been treated directly from the Boltzmann equation and the given boundary conditions (i.e., reflection laws) without assuming an arbitrary distribution function or a linearized distribution function on the boundary (Ziering, 1961; Cercignani, 1963; Takao, 1961).

It is the purpose of this paper to present a method for internal flow problems in the regimes of free-molecule flow, nearly free-molecule flow and higher order transition flows (Wu, 1964a). In order to obtain a rigorous solution in these regimes, one has to solve the Boltzmann equation and the integral equation for surface collision density simultaneously. These two equations are coupled through the law for diffuse reflection. An integral equation for the surface collision density in general transition flow has been proposed. A series expansion method has been suggested by using the free-molecule flow-solution as its zeroth order approximation and a non-dimensional collision frequency as its expansion parameter. Based on a proposed iteration procedure for the Boltzmann equation, a set of integral equations for surface collision density has been obtained which governs the solutions of free-molecule flow, nearly free-molecule flow, and higher order transition flows. The integral equations which are transformed into matrix equations by finite-difference approximations have been solved successively. A plane Poiseuille flow has been solved for both free and nearly free-molecule flows based on the BGK equation (Bhatnagar et al., 1954) according to the proposed method.

II. Free-Molecule Flow

Free-molecule flow is the regime of extremely low density, in which the mean free path of the molecule is much greater than the characteristic dimension of the system, so that the collisions between molecules in the gas are negligible as compared with the collisions between gas molecules and the surfaces. In the vicinity of the surfaces the probability of no collision at a distance d is proportional to $e^{-d/\lambda}$; therefore, the collisions between impinging and reflected molecules can be neglected. However, we can not neglect the intermolecular collisions at a distance which is approximately equal to a mean free path. It is generally assumed that the distribution function of the incident stream is undisturbed by the re-emitted molecules from the surfaces of the body. Therefore, the mass, momentum, and energy transfer from the body can be evaluated by treating the flows of incident and reflected molecules separately.

A. Liouville Equation

In the free-molecule flow regime the velocity distribution function satisfies the Liouville equation, which is the Boltzmann equation in absence of collision. Therefore, the governing equation for free-molecule flow is a linear first order hyperbolic partial differential equation in phase space, i.e.;

$$\frac{\partial f}{\partial t} + \mathbf{v}\frac{\partial f}{\partial \mathbf{x}} = 0. \tag{2.1}$$

If the distribution function of molecules leaving the boundary is known *a priori* and is independent of the incident flow, the solution can be expressed for an initial-boundary value problem, i.e.,

$$f(\mathbf{v}, \mathbf{x}, t) = f(\mathbf{v}, \mathbf{x} - \mathbf{v}(t - t_0), t_0), \tag{2.2}$$

where t_0 is the value at which $\mathbf{x} - \mathbf{v}(t - t_0)$ intersects the boundary whenever this yields a result $t_0 > 0$.

B. Integral Equation for Surface Collision Density

In internal flow or in external flow about nonconvex bodies, the distribution function of molecules leaving the surface is not known. In steady state flow, one may define the normalized collision density $N(S_0)$ at point S_0 on the surface as the fraction of molecules leaving the surface per unit area per unit time for each molecule emitted from an open section for the same unit area and unit time. The normalized collision density is to be found from a Fredholm integral equation which expresses the fact that the rate of incident molecules on a surface element of the wall in the system is equal to the rate of departure.

$$N(S_0) = N_0(S_0) + \int_{S_{0'}} N(S_0')T(S_0', S_0)\, dS_0', \tag{2.3}$$

where $N(S_0)$ is normalized collision density at the point S_0 on the surface $N_0(S_0)$ is the probability that a molecule emitted from an open section per unit time will collide at the point S_0 on the surface directly without intermediate collisions, and $T(S_0', S)_0$ is the probability that a molecule which has suffered a diffuse reflection at a point S_0' on the surface will arrive at the point S_0 on the surface.

For actual calculations, the linearity of the normalized integral equation allows the solutions to any other problems to be synthesized from the normalized solution. Therefore, the free molecule flow from upstream and from downstream in any given initial condition can be treated independently and the solution can be obtained by superposing two separate flows.

By using the diffuse reflection law $T(S_0', S_0)$ and $N_0(S_0)$ are real and continuous function of S_0' and S_0 in the domain of integration, so that the solution of the Fredholm integral equation of the second kind can be obtained by the successive substitution method (see Mikhlin, 1957), i.e.,

$$N(S_0) = N_0(S_0) + \int_{S_0'} N_0(S_0')T(S_0', S_0)\, dS_0' +$$

$$+ \int_{S_0'} T(S_0', S_0) \int_{S_0''} N_0(S_0'')T(S_0'', S_0')\, dS_0''\, dS_0'$$

$$+ \cdots \int_{S_0'} T(S_0', S_0) \int_{S_0''} T(S_0'', S_0') \cdots \int_{S_0^m} N_0(S_0^m)T(S_0^m, S_0^{m-1})$$

$$+ dS_0^m \cdots dS_0' + R_{m+1}(S_0). \tag{2.4}$$

According to the existence and uniqueness theorem,
if

$$\int_{S_0} |T^2(S_0', S_0)|\, dS_0 \leqslant C_1, \qquad C_1 = \text{const}, \tag{2.5}$$

and

$$\int_{S_0} \int_{S_0'} |T^2(S_0', S_0)|\, dS_0\, dS_0' \leqslant 1, \tag{2.6}$$

then the limit of successive approximation is the unique solution of Eq. (2.3).

C. Diffuse Reflection Law and Boundary Conditions

For completely diffusely reflecting surfaces, the kernel $T(S_0', S_0)$ is symmetric and can be expressed in the form,

$$T(S_0', S_0) = \frac{\cos \phi_1, \cos \phi_2}{\pi l^2}, \tag{2.7}$$

where ϕ_1 is the acute angle between the normal at S_0 and the line l joining S_0 and S_0', and ϕ_2 is the similar angle corresponding to point S_0'.

At a surface element, dS_0 the distribution function $f_+(v, S_0)$ from the surface, for a steady state condition with fully diffuse reflection law, is a function of the surface collision density and the temperature of the surface. Thus,

$$f_+(\mathbf{v}, S_0) = \frac{1}{2\pi} \left(\frac{m}{KT_{S_0}}\right)^2 \exp\left\{-\left(\frac{m}{2KT_{S_0}}\right)|\mathbf{v}|^2\right\} M_0 N(S_0), \tag{2.8}$$

where $N(S_0)$ satisfies

$$N(S_0) = -\frac{1}{M_0} \int_{-\infty}^{\infty} dv_1 \int_{-\infty}^{\infty} dv_2 \int_{0}^{\infty} v_3 f_+(\mathbf{v}, S_0) \, dv_3, \qquad (2.9)$$

in which M_0 is the total number of molecules entering the system per unit time, i.e.,

$$M_0 = n_0 (KT/2m\pi)^{1/2} A. \qquad (2.10)$$

Equation (2.8) is the boundary condition to be used in Eq. (2.2) together with the given initial condition in the external regions to determine the distribution function everywhere. In the direction of the solid angle which intersects the surface, the distribution function opposite to the solid angle is,

$$f(\mathbf{v}, \mathbf{x}) = \frac{1}{2\pi} \left(\frac{m}{KT_{S_0}}\right)^2 \exp\left\{-\left(\frac{m}{2KT_{S_0}}\right)|\mathbf{v}(\mathbf{x} - \mathbf{v}(t - t_0))|^2\right\} M_0 N(S_0), \quad (2.11)$$

in which $\mathbf{v}$ is parallel to $(\mathbf{x} - S_0)$ and $\mathbf{v}(t - t_0) = (\mathbf{x} - S_0)$. In the direction of the solid angle which intersects the open sections, the distribution function opposite to the solid angle is the same Maxwellian distribution function as that in the external regions. From the known distribution function, one can calculate the mass, momentum, and energy transfer rates in any internal flow problems or external flow problems with nonconvex surfaces.

D. Matrix Method

In most geometrically complicated problems, it is impossible to describe the functions $N_0(S_0)$ and $T(S_0, S_0')$ in analytic form. Therefore, most of the integral equations can not be solved explicitly. Even in some simple internal flow problems, the successive approximation method is not quite successful, not only because of the complicated functions $N_0(S_0)$ and $T(S_0', S_0)$ and its successive integrations, but also owing to the slow convergence of the method.

In order to introduce a simplified method for practical purposes, one may divide the surface of the system into finite surface elements and define the matrix $[N_{0j}]$ as the probability that a molecule entering the system per unit time will collide on the jth surface element ΔS_{0j}; the matrix $[T_{ij}]$ as the probability that a molecule leaving the surface elements ΔS_{0i} after a diffuse reflection will be intercepted by the surface element ΔS_{0j} and the matrix $[N_i]$ as the collision density on a surface element ΔS_{0i}. Therefore, Eq. (2.4) can be written in a matrix form,

$$[N_j] = [N_{0i}]\{[I_{ij}] + [T_{ij}] + [T_{ij}]^2 + [T_{ij}]^3 + \cdots\}. \qquad (2.12)$$

since the series $\{[I_{ij}] + [T_{ij}] + [T_{ij}]^2 + [T_{ij}]^3 + \cdots\}$ is a Neumann matrix series and is equal to $\{[I_{ij}] - [T_{ij}]\}^{-1}$ if it is a convergent series, we have therefore

$$[N_j] = [N_{0i}]\{[I_{ij}] - [T_{ij}]\}^{-1}. \tag{2.13}$$

By transforming the integral equation into a matrix equation directly by a finite difference approximation, Eq. (2.3) becomes

$$[N_j] = [N_{0j}] + [N_i][T_{ij}],$$

or $\hspace{8cm}$ (2.14)

$$[N_i]\{[I_{ij}] - [T_{ij}]\} = N_{0j}].$$

If the matrix $\{[I_{ij}] - [T_{ij}]\}$ is nonsingular, then the inverse matrix exists. Multiplying the equation by the inverse matrix, the solution is obtained, i.e.,

$$[N_j] = [N_{0i}]\{[I_{ij}] - [T_{ij}]\}^{-1}. \tag{2.15}$$

Since the matrix $[N_{0j}]$ is given from the known initial conditions and the geometry of the system and the transition matrix $[T_{ij}]$ can be evaluated from the diffuse reflection law and geometry of the system, the collision density matrix $[N_i]$ for any internal flow problems with complicated geometry can be solved from the normalized matrix equation. The actual collision density at points S_0 on the surface, i.e., $M_0 N(S_0)$, is a function of temperature and density of the external regions.

In order to evaluate the free-molecule flux through the system which connects a gas in equilibrium and at rest at one end with a vacuum at the other, one must first find the transmission probabilities $P_{A \to A}$ and $P_{A \to B}$ which satisfy the following equations.

$$P_{A \to B} = P_{0\,A \to B} + \int_{S_0} P(S_0, B)N(S_0)\,dS_0, \tag{2.16}$$

and

$$P_{A \to A} = 1 - P_{A \to B}, \tag{2.17}$$

where $P_{A \to B}$ and $P_{A \to A}$ denote the transmission probabilities that a molecule entering the system from entrance A will either pass through the system and exit at B or return to A respectively; $P_{0\,A \to B}$ denotes the transmission probability that a molecule entering the system from entrance A will pass through the system without intermediate collisions with the surface; and $P(S_0, B)$ denotes the transmission probability that a molecule suffering a diffuse reflection from surface at point S_0 will pass through the exit B without intermediate collisions.

By dividing the entrance, exit and the solid boundary into m, n, and r elements, respectively, Eq. (2.16) can be written in a matrix form, i.e.,

$$P_{A \to B} = \frac{1}{m} \sum_{A_i} \sum_{B_j} [P_{0\,A_i \to B_j}] + \sum_{B_j} [N_i][P_{i \to B_j}], \tag{2.18}$$

and $P_{A \to A} = 1 - P_{A \to B}$, where $P_{A i \to B j}$ denotes the transmission probability matrix that a molecule entering the system from A_i will pass through the system and exit at B_j, $P_{0\ A i \to B j}$ denotes the transmission probability matrix that a molecule entering the system from A_i will pass through the system and exit at B_j without intermediate collisions; $P_{i \to B j}$ denotes the transmission probability matrix that a molecule suffering a diffuse reflection from surface element $S_{0 i}$ will pass through the section element B_j without intermediate collisions; and the summation signs $\Sigma_{A i}$ and $\Sigma_{B j}$ represent the sum of all elements and column of the matrix, respectively.

This method can be extended to a specular-diffuse reflection system and is applicable to external flow problems provided that the interaction between the molecules is negligibly small (Wu, 1961).

III. Nearly Free-Molecule Flow and Higher Order Transition Flows

In the previous section, the Liouville equation for free-molecule flow and the Fredholm integral equation of the second kind for surface collision density have been discussed. Now, let us examine whether a method to treat the Boltzmann equation, as well as the associated integral equation for the surface collision density in the transition regime can be found such that a combined iteration procedure is possible, beginning with the free-molecule flow solution as the zeroth order approximation. The first approximation should give us a solution of nearly free-molecule flow where intermolecular collisions are still infrequent but not negligible and the higher order approximations should give us the asymptotic solutions in the regime of transition flows.

A. Boltzmann Equation and Its Iteration Process

The Boltzmann equation can be written in the form

$$\frac{\partial f}{\partial t} + \mathbf{v} \cdot \frac{\partial f}{\partial \mathbf{x}} = \iiint d\mathbf{v}_1 \iint d\omega\, v_r G(v_r, \phi) f(\mathbf{v}', \mathbf{x}) f(\mathbf{v}_1', \mathbf{x})$$

$$- f(\mathbf{v}, \mathbf{x}) \iiint d\mathbf{v}_1 \iint d\omega v_r G(v_r, \phi) f(\mathbf{v}_1, \mathbf{x}), \quad (3.1)$$

$\mathbf{v}_1$ is the velocity of a molecule with which the molecule of velocity $\mathbf{v}$ Collides; $\mathbf{v}_1'$ and $\mathbf{v}'$ are the velocities of two molecules before collision, which give one molecule of velocity $\mathbf{v}_1$ after collision; $\mathbf{v}_r$ is the relative velocity of two colliding molecules with velocities $\mathbf{v}_1$ and $\mathbf{v}$, respectively; and $G(\mathbf{v}_r, \phi)$ is the collision cross section. Considering a coordinate fixed on one molecule and a parallel beam of molecules moving with $\mathbf{v}_r$ relative to this fixed scattering molecule, the proportion of the molecules that cross unit cross section of the beam, and are scattered into solid angle $d\omega$ about a direction at an angle ϕ with the direction of the beam is $G(\mathbf{v}_r, \phi)\, d\omega$.

For steady state flow, the Boltzmann equation can be written in the form,

$$\mathbf{v}\cdot\partial f/\partial \mathbf{x} = -Df + P, \tag{3.2}$$

where D is the absorption term for the total number of molecules lost in unit time from unit volume of a beam of molecules in $d\mathbf{v}$ about $\mathbf{v}$ due to intermolecular collision, i.e.,

$$D = D(f, \mathbf{v}, \mathbf{x}) \equiv \int\!\!\int\!\!\int d\mathbf{v}_1 \int\!\!\int d\omega\, v_r G(v_r, \phi) f(\mathbf{v}_1, \mathbf{x}), \tag{3.3}$$

and P is the emission term for the total number of molecules gained in unit volume of the beam in unit time by intermolecular collisions, i.e.,

$$P = P(f, \mathbf{v}, \mathbf{x}) \equiv \int\!\!\int\!\!\int d\mathbf{v}_1 \int\!\!\int d\omega\, v_r G(v_r, \phi) f(\mathbf{v}_1', \mathbf{x}) f(\mathbf{v}', \mathbf{x}). \tag{3.4}$$

In steady state flow, the Boltzmann equation can be rearranged in a form for a specific group of molecules having velocity vector in $d\mathbf{v}$ about $\mathbf{v}$,

$$\frac{df}{ds} + \frac{D}{v}f = \frac{P}{v}, \tag{3.5}$$

where,

$$D = D(f, \mathbf{v}, s); \qquad P = P(f, \mathbf{v}, s),$$

and

$$\frac{df}{ds} = \frac{1}{v}(\mathbf{v}\cdot\nabla f). \tag{3.6}$$

If the integral function $D = D^0, P = P^0$ are known *a priori* and independent of f, then Eq. (3.5) becomes a linear first order differential equation with V as a parameter,

$$\frac{df}{ds} + \frac{D^0}{v}f = \frac{P^0}{v}, \tag{3.7}$$

where $D^0 = D^0(\mathbf{v}, \mathbf{S})$ and $P^0 = P^0(\mathbf{v}, \mathbf{S})$. By integrating it with respect to S, one may obtain the solution

$$f(\mathbf{v}, \mathbf{S}) = C(\mathbf{v}, \mathbf{S}_1) \exp\left(-\int_{S_1}^{S} \frac{P^0}{v}\, dS'\right) + \int_{S_1}^{S} \frac{P^0}{v} \exp\left(-\int_{S_1}^{S} \frac{D^0}{v}\, dS''\right) dS'. \tag{3.8}$$

If f is prescribed at S_1, then the constant $C(\mathbf{v}, S_0)$ will be equal to $f(\mathbf{v}, S_1)$ and $f(\mathbf{v}, S) = f(\mathbf{v}, S_1 + |S - S_1| \, (\mathbf{v}/v)$. Therefore, for the given $\mathbf{v}$, the solution f along a path from S_1 to S is known if f is prescribed at S_1 and functions D^0 and P^0 are given along the path S.

Let D^0 and P^0 be the free-molecule flow solution, i.e., $D^0 = D(f^0, \mathbf{v}, S)$ and $P^0 = P(f^0, \mathbf{v}, S)$, where f^0 is the distribution function in free molecule flow. According to Eq. (3.7), one may obtain $f^{(1)}$ as the first iteration of the distribution function from the free-molecule flow solution (Willis, 1958). i.e.,

$$f^{(1)}\left(\mathbf{v}, S_1 + |S - S_1| \frac{\mathbf{v}}{v}\right) = f(\mathbf{v}, S_1) \exp\left(- \int_{S_1}^{S} \frac{D^0}{v} \, dS'\right) +$$

$$+ \int_{S_1}^{S} \frac{P^0}{v} \exp\left(- \int_{S_1}^{S} \frac{P^0}{v} dS''\right) dS'. \qquad (3.9)$$

For the transition flow in the vicinity of the free-molecular region, the only successive approximation to the solution of the Boltzmann equation can be evaluated by an iteration process if D^0, P^0 and $f^0(\mathbf{v}, S)$ in free-molecule flow are known and $f(\mathbf{v}, S_1)$ is an invariant during the process while intermolecular collisions are introduced Thus,

$$f^{(N+1)}\left(\mathbf{v}, S_1 + |S - S_1| \frac{\mathbf{v}}{v}\right) = f(\mathbf{v}, S_1) \exp\left(- \int_{S_1}^{S} \frac{D^{(N)}}{v} \, dS'\right) +$$

$$+ \int_{S_1}^{S} \left[\frac{P^{(N)}}{v} \exp\left(- \int_{S_1}^{S} \frac{D^{(N)}}{v} \, dS''\right)\right] dS', \qquad (3.10)$$

in which $D^{(N)} = D^{(N)}(f^{(N)}, \mathbf{v}, S)$ and $P^{(N)}(f^{(N)}, \mathbf{v}, S)$.

For internal flow problems, this iteration process can not be applied without knowing $f(\mathbf{v}, S_1)$ at each process. Since the function $f(\mathbf{v}, S_1)$ is not an invariant during the successive iterations, an iteration process of the Boltzmann equation is proposed as follows;

$$f^{(N+1)}\left(\mathbf{v}, S_1 + |S - S| \frac{\mathbf{v}}{v}\right) = f^{(N)}(\mathbf{v}, S_1) \exp\left(- \int_{S_1}^{S} \frac{D^{(N)}}{v} \, dS'\right) +$$

$$+ \int_{S_1}^{S} \frac{P^{(N)}}{v} \exp\left(- \int_{S_1}^{S} \frac{D^{(N)}}{v} dS''\right) dS'. \qquad (3.11)$$

The distribution function for each iteration process at S_0, i.e., $f^{(N)}(\mathbf{v}, S_1)$, can be described from the known external regions (both inlet and exit) or in terms of the collision density $N^{(N)}(S_0)$ at the surface S_0 on the solid boundary according to the diffuse reflection law, i.e.,

$$f^{(N)}(\mathbf{v}, \mathbf{S}_1) = f_+^{(N)}(\mathbf{v}, \mathbf{S}_0) = \frac{1}{2\pi}\left(\frac{m}{KT_{S_0}}\right)^2 \exp\left\{\frac{m}{2KT_{S_0}}\mathbf{v}^2\right\} M_0 N^{(N)}(S_0), \quad (3.12)$$

in which T_{S_0} is the temperature of the surface at S_0 and $N^{(N)}(S_0)$ is the Nth approximation to the surface collision density $N(S_0)$ in transition regime.

B. Integral Equation for Surface Collision Density in Transition Flow

Since $f^{(N)}(\mathbf{v}, S_0)$ is dependent on the Nth approximation to the collision density $N(S_0)$ in transition flow, it is necessary to propose an integral equation for the surface collision density $N(S_0)$ in transition flow as follows:

$$N(S_0) = N_0(S_\infty, S_0, f) + \int_{S_0'} N(S_0')T(S_0', S_0, f)\, dS_0'. \quad (3.13)$$

In this equation $N(S_0)$ is the surface collision density at S_0' $N_0(S_\infty, S_0, f)$ is the initial collision density at the surface S_0 on the boundary which is defined as the proportion of the molecules entering the system in unit time that arrive at the surface S_0 from the entrance along a straight path, emission and absorption of molecules taking place along the path due to intermolecular collisions. And $T(S_0', S_0, f)$ denotes the proportion of molecules, emitted from the surface at S_0' per unit area per unit time that will arrive at S_0 on the surface along a straight path, again with emission and absorption of molecules taking place along the path due to intermolecular collisions.

C. Series Expansion Method for Surface Collision Density

In free-molecule flow, the integral equation for the surface collision density reduces to the Fredholm integral equation of the second kind, i.e.,

$$N^{(0)}(S_0) = N_0^{(0)}(S_0) + \int_{S_0'} N^{(0)}(S_0')T^{(0)}(S_0', S_0)\, dS_0', \quad (3.14)$$

in which superscript (o) represents the quantities in free-molecule flow. As shown in the previous section, this integral equation can be solved by the matrix method. Since the solution for free-molecule flow can be obtained and should serve as the zeroth order approximation to the transition flow problem, one may develop a series expansion method for the transition flow problem by considering the solution of the integral equation in terms of its dependence on the parameter v, the collision frequency or a dimensionless parameter $\mu \equiv vd/\bar{C}$. Let us assume that N, N_0, and T possess series expansions in powers of μ as follows:

$$N(S_0) = N^{(0)}(S_0) + \mu N^{(1)}(S_0, f^{(0)}) + \mu^2 N^{(2)}(S_0, f^{(I)}) + \\ + \mu^3 N^{(3)}(S_0, f^{(II)}) + \cdots ,$$

$$N_0(S_0) = N_0^{(0)}(S_0) + \mu N_0^{(1)}(S_0, f^{(0)}) + \mu^2 N_0^{(2)}(S_0, f^{(I)}) + \\ + \mu^3 N_0^{(3)}(S_0, f^{(II)}) + \cdots , \quad (3.15)$$

$$T(S_0', S_0, f) = T^{(0)}(S_0', S_0) + \mu T^{(1)}(S_0', S_0, f^{(0)}) + \mu^2 T^{(2)}(S_0', S_0, f^{(I)}) + \\ + \mu^3 T^{(3)}(S_0', S_0, f^{(II)}) + \cdots ,$$

where $f^{(0)}$ can be obtained from $N^{(0)}(S_0)$ according to Eq. (2.11). By using the first iteration of the Boltzmann equation from free-molecule flow, $N_0^{(1)}(S_0, f^{(0)})$ and $T^{(1)}(S_0, S_0, f^{(0)})$ can be determined from Eqs. (3.16) and (3.17). $N^{(1)}(S_0, f^{(0)})$ is the first perturbation of collision density for the nearly free-molecule flow; $N^{(n)}$, $N_0^{(n)}$, $T^{(n)}$ are higher order terms of the series expansions and $N_0^{(N)}$, $T^{(N)}$ can be determined from the $(N\text{-}1)$th order approximations as follows:

$$N_{0\,i \to j}^{(N)} = \left\{ \frac{\displaystyle\int_0^\infty f_j^{(N)} v_s \, dv_s}{\displaystyle\int_0^\infty f_i^{(N-1)} v_s \, dv_s} \right\} N_{0\,i \to j}^{(N-1)}, \quad (3.16)$$

and

$$T_{i \to j}^{(N)} = \left\{ \frac{\displaystyle\int_0^\infty f_j^{(N)} v_s \, dv_s}{\displaystyle\int_0^\infty f_i^{(N-1)} v_s \, dv_s} \right\} T_{i \to j}^{(N-1)}, \quad (3.17)$$

in which,

$$N_{0\,i \to j}^{(N)} = \sum_{n=0}^{N} u^n N_{0\,i \to j}^{(n)}; \qquad T_{i \to j}^{(N)} = \sum_{n=0}^{n} \mu^n T_{i \to j}^{(n)}. \quad (3.18)$$

Substituting Eq. (3.15) into Eq. (3.13) and collecting terms in the same power of μ, one obtains a series of integral equations for various orders of perturbation. The zeroth order equation is the integral equation for the surface collision density in the regime of free-molecule flow, i.e.,

$$N^{(0)}(S_0) = N_0^{(0)}(S_0) + \int_{S_0'} T^{(0)}(S_0', S_0) N(S_0') \, dS_0'. \quad (3.19)$$

The corresponding first order equation is

$$N^{(1)}(S_0) = N_0^{(1)}(S_0, f^{(0)}) + \int_{S_0'} [T^{(1)}(S_0', S_0, f^{(0)}) N^{(0)}(S_0') + \\ + T^{(0)}(S_0', S_0) N^{(1)}(S_0', f^{(0)})] \, dS_0'. \quad (3.20)$$

Similarly, the integral equations for higher order perturbation may be found as follows:

$$N^{(2)} = N_0^{(2)} + \int_{S_0'} [T^{(0)}N^{(2)'} + T^{(1)}N^{(1)'} + T^{(2)}N^{(0)'}] \, dS_0',$$

$$\vdots$$

$$N^{(n)} = N_0^{(n)} + \int_{S_0'} \sum_{m=0}^{n} [T^{(m)}(S_0', S_0, f^{(M-1)})N^{(n-m)}(S_0', f^{(N-M-1)})] \, dS_0'.$$

$$(3.21)$$

These equations can be arranged in the following forms:

$$N^{(1)} = \left\{ N_0^{(1)} + \int_{S_0'} T^{(1)}N^{(0)'} \, dS_0' \right\} + \int_{S_0'} T^{(0)}N^{(1)'} \, dS_0',$$

$$N^{(2)} = \left\{ N_0^{(2)} + \int_{S_0'} [T^{(1)}N^{(1)'} + T^{(2)}N^{(0)'}] \, dS_0' \right\} + \int_{S_0'} T^{(0)}N^{(2)'} \, dS_0',$$

$$\vdots \qquad\qquad (3.22)$$

$$N^{(n)} = \left\{ N_0^{(m)} + \int_{S_0'} \sum_{m=1}^{n} [T^{(m)}(S_0', S_0, f^{(m-1)})N^{(n-m)'} + \right.$$

$$\left. + (S_0', f^{(N-M-1)})] \, dS_0' \right\} + \int_{S_0'} T^{(0)}N^{(n)'} \, dS_0'.$$

Since each solution of an integral equation is dependent on the solutions of previous equations and the successive iterations of the Boltzmann equation, one can solve them by the matrix method successively, thus,

$$[N_j]^{(1)} = \{[N_{0i}]^{(1)} + [T_{ij}]^{(1)}[N_i]^{(0)}\}\{[I_{ij}] - [T_{ij}]^{(0)}\}^{-1},$$

$$[N_j]^{(2)} = \{[N_{0i}]^{(2)} + [T_{ij}]^{(1)}[N_j]^{(1)} + [T_{ij}]^{(2)}[N_j]^{(0)}\}\{[I_{ij}] - [T_{ij}]^{(0)}\}^{-1},$$

$$\vdots \qquad\qquad (3.23)$$

$$[N_j]^{(n)} = \{[N_{0i}]^{(n)} + \sum_{m=1}^{n} [T_{ij}]^{(m)} [N_j]^{(n-m)}\}\{[I_{ij}] - [T_{ij}]^{(0)}\}^{-1}$$

Therefore, the successive approximations for the surface collision density matrix in the transition flow will be

$$[N_j]^{(N)} = \sum_{n=0}^{N} \mu^n [N_j]^{(n)} = \sum_{n=0}^{N} [\mu^{(n)}\{[N_{0i}]^{(n)} + \sum_{m=1}^{n} [T_{ij}]^{(m)}[N_j]^{n-m}\} .$$

$$\times \{[I_{ij}] - [T_{ij}]^{(0)}\}^{-1}].$$

$$(3.24)$$

D. BGK Equation and Its Iteration Process

A kinetic model for the Boltzmann equation introduced simultaneously by Welander (1954); Bhatnagar, *et al.* (1954) is based on the assumption that the molecules scattered into the beam of molecules come from collisions between molecules in Maxwellian motion. Then ff_1 is equal to $f_e f_{e1}$ or $f_e f_{e1}$ according to the summational invariants. Hence, $P(\mathbf{v}, \mathbf{x}) = \eta_m n(\mathbf{x}) f_0(\mathbf{v}, \mathbf{x})$ and $D(\mathbf{v}, \mathbf{x}) = \eta_m n(\mathbf{x})$ for the Maxwellian molecules. The Boltzmann equation under this assumption becomes the BGK equation, i.e.,

$$\frac{\partial f}{\partial t} + \mathbf{v} \cdot \frac{\partial f}{\partial \mathbf{x}} = \eta_m n(\mathbf{x})(f_e - f) = D(\mathbf{x})(f_e - f). \tag{3.25}$$

If $D(\mathbf{x})$ is replaced by the mean value over the range of $\mathbf{x}$, then Eq. (3.25) becomes

$$\frac{\partial f}{\partial t} + \mathbf{v} \cdot \frac{\partial f}{\partial \mathbf{x}} = v(f_e - f), \tag{3.26}$$

where $v(= \bar{D})$ is the collision frequency.

The BGK equation shares several important properties with the Boltzmann equation. The moments of the collision term vanish and the H-theorem holds. The solution approaches to a local Maxwellian distribution in thermal equilibrium and to free-molecule flow at zero collision frequency.

In steady state flow, the BGK equation can be re-arranged in a form for a specific group of molecules having a velocity vector in $d\mathbf{v}$ about $\mathbf{v}$,

$$df/dS + vf = vf_e. \tag{3.27}$$

An iteration scheme can be set up based on the same principle described in the previous section, i.e.,

$$f^{(1)}\left(\mathbf{v}, S_1 + |S - S_1|\frac{\mathbf{v}}{v}\right) = f^{(0)}(\mathbf{v}, S_1) \exp\left[-\frac{v(S - S_1)}{v}\right] +$$
$$+ \int_{S1}^{S} \frac{vf_e^{(0)}}{v} \exp\left(-\frac{v(S - S')}{v}\right) dS', \tag{3.28}$$

and

$$f^{(N+1)}\left(\mathbf{v}, \mathbf{S}_1 + |\mathbf{S} - \mathbf{S}_1|\frac{\mathbf{v}}{v}\right) = f^{(N)}(\mathbf{v}, \mathbf{S}_1) \exp\left[-\frac{v(S - S_1)}{v}\right] +$$
$$+ \int_{S1}^{S} \frac{vf_e^{(N)}}{v} \exp\left(-\frac{v(S - S')}{v}\right) dS', \tag{3.29}$$

in which $f^{(0)}(S_1, v)$ and $f_0^{(0)}$ are the functions in the free-molecular regime, $f_e^{(N)}$ is the N-th approximation of the local Maxwellian distribution function and $f^{(N)}(S_1, v)$ is the Nth approximation of the distribution function at S_1 and satisfies Eq. (3.12).

IV. Free and Nearly Free-Molecule Flow through Two Parallel Plates

A. Free-Molecular Regime

(1) Consider the free-molecule flow through two infinitely wide parallel plates which are connected by two large containers A and B (Fig. 1). Both

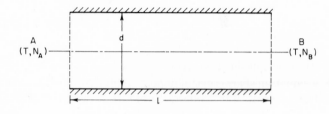

FIG. 1. Two-dimensional parallel plates.

containers and the channel are filled with a rarefied gas whose mean free path is much greater than the dimension of the plates. Assume uniform temperature throughout the system and known density and velocity distributions in both regions A and B.

We neglect intermolecular collision in the channel and assume that molecules hitting the boundaries of the channel will reflect diffusely with a Maxwellian distribution corresponding to the temperature of the surface. If each plate is divided into sixteen elements and each section at the ends of the channel is divided into four elements, then the following quantities can be defined: $[N_{A_i}S_j]^{(0)}$ is the initial transmission probability matrix for a molecule issuing with an Maxwellian distribution from the end section element A_i and striking the surface element j, $[T_{ij}]^{(0)}$ is the transmission probability matrix for a molecule emitted from the surface element i and striking the surface element according to the diffuse reflection law, $[N_{S_iB_j}]^{(0)}$ is the final transmission probability matrix for a molecule emitted from the surface element i and passing through the end section element B_j according to the diffuse reflection law and $[N_{A_iB_j}]^{(0)}$ is the transmission probability matrix for a molecule issuing with the Maxwellian distribution from the end section element A_i and passing through the end section B_j without intermediate collisions with the channel boundaries. All these matrices are described in Section IV, C.

According to the matrix method in free-molecule flow, one obtains the distribution matrix $[M_{ij}]$,

$$[M_{ij}] = \{[I_{ij}] - [T_{ij}]^{(0)}\}^{-1}, \tag{4.1}$$

and the surface collision density matrix,

$$[N_{ik}]^{(0)} = [N_{A_iS_j}]^{(0)} [M_{jk}]. \tag{4.2}$$

Therefore, the transmission probability that a molecule emitted from region A will be transmitted to region B is

$$[P_{A_i \to B_k}]^{(0)} = [N_{A_iB_k}]^{(0)} + [N_{ij}]^{(0)}[N_{S_jB_k}]^{(0)}, \tag{4.3}$$

or

$$P_{A \to B}^{(0)} = \frac{1}{m}\left(\sum_{A_i} \sum_{B_k} \left[P_{A_i \to B_k} \right]^{(0)} \right).$$

Similarly, the transmission probability in the opposite direction can be obtained,

$$[P_{B_i \to A_k}]^{(0)} = [N_{B_iA_k}]^{(0)} + [N_{ij}]^{(0)}[N_{S_jA_k}]^{(0)}, \tag{4.4}$$

or

$$P_{B \to A}^{(0)} = \frac{1}{n}\left(\sum_{B_i} \sum_{A_k} \left[P_{B_i \to A_k} \right] \right).$$

A reciprocal transmission probability theorem which has been proved by Wu (1961) shows that $P_{A \to B} = P_{B \to A}$ for identical velocity distributions and end section areas at the entrance and exit.

(2) Let us consider a free-molecule flow through two parallel plates connecting two large containers, let the density in region A be N_A and the density in region B be $0.8 N_A$. From the fundamental solutions in Section IV, A, 1, one can obtain the solution by the superposition method. The surface collision density and the distribution function in the system can be evaluated by superposing independent upstream and downstream free-molecule flows. Therefore, one obtains the surface collision density,

$$[N_{ik}]^{(0)} = \{[N_{A_iS_j}]^{(0)} + 0.8[N_{B_iS_j}]^{(0)}\}[M_{jk}], \tag{4.5}$$

and the transmission coefficients R and Q,

$$R^{(0)} = P^{(0)}_{A \to B} + 0.8 P^{(0)}_{B \to B}, \tag{4.6}$$

$$Q^{(0)} = P^{(0)}_{A \to A} + 0.8 P^{(0)}_{B \to A}, \tag{4.7}$$

where R is the number of molecules which cross the end section B from the channel when one molecule enters the channel from region A in unit time and 0.8 molecule enters the channel from region B in unit time. Q is the number of molecules which cross the end section A from the channel when one molecule enters the channel from region A in unit time and 0.8 molecule enters the channel from region B in unit time. Therefore, the net flux of the molecules through the channel can be defined as the ratio of the net through flow to the incident flux at the upstream side of the channel.

B. Nearly Free-Molecular Regime

In the nearly free-molecular regime for the example of Section IV, A, 2, the successive approximation method can be applied by employing the BGK equation (Krook model). The surface collision density (Fig. 2) initial transmission probability matrix and the transition matrix for free-molecule flow serve as the zeroth order approximations. It has been observed that the surface

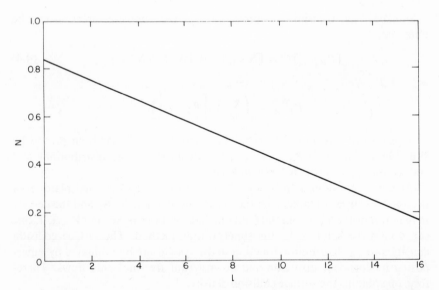

FIG. 2. Collision density distribution of free-molecule flow through two parallel plates ($N_A = N_A$, $N_B = 0$).

collision density and the density in the channel are linearly distributed through-out the system and the mean velocity of the gas is much less than the mean molecular speed. Therefore, the local Maxwellian distribution function in the emission term of the BGK equation can be described as a linear function along an arbitrary path in the system and the mean gas velocity in distribution function can be neglected because the effect of the mean gas velocity on the scattered molecules in any free path within the system is extremely small com-pared with that due to the molecular speed of the Maxwellian distribution.

The surface collision density in nearly free-molecule flow is

$$[N_i]^{(1)} = [N_i]^{(0)} + \mu[N_i]^{(1)}, \tag{4.9}$$

in which

$$[N_k]^{(1)} = \{[N_{0_i}]^{(1)} + [T_{ij}]^{(1)}[N_j]^{(0)}\}[M_{ik}]. \tag{4.10}$$

From the free molecule flow solution, f_e can be described as a linear function along an arbitrary path from i to j, i.e.,

$$f_e^{(0)} = f_i^{(0)} + (f_j^{(0)} - f_i^{(0)}) \frac{S' - S}{S - S_1}. \tag{4.11}$$

The distribution function along a path with given initial and final distribution

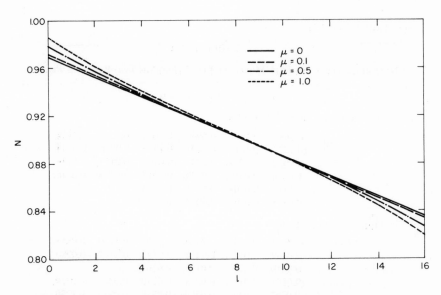

FIG 3. Collision density distribution of free and near-free-molecule flow through two parallel plates ($N_A = N_A$, $N_B = 0.8N_A$).

function can be written in the form

$$f_S = f_j^{(1)} = f_i^{(0)} \exp\left\{-\frac{v(S-S_1)}{v}\right\} + \int_{S_1}^{S} \frac{vf_i^{(0)}}{v} \exp\left\{-\frac{v(S-S')}{v}\right\} dS'$$

$$+ \int_{S_1}^{S} \frac{v(f_j^{(0)} - f_i^{(0)})}{v} \exp\left\{-\frac{v(S-S')}{v}\right\} \frac{S'-S}{S-S_1} dS'$$

$$= f_i^{(0)} \exp\left\{-\frac{v(S-S_1)}{v}\right\} + \frac{vf_i^{(0)}}{v} \int_{S_1}^{S} \exp\left\{-\frac{v(S-S_1)}{v}\right\} dS'$$

$$+ \frac{v(f_j^{(0)} - f_i^{(0)})}{v} \frac{1}{S-S_1} \int_{S_1}^{S} \exp\left\{-\frac{v(S-S_1)}{v}\right\}(S'-S_1) \, dS'.$$

$$(4.12)$$

Substituting Eq. (4.12) into Eqs. (3.16) and (3.17), one obtains $N_0^{(l)}{}_{i\to j}$ and $T_{ij}^{(l)}$ in which $N_0^{(l)}{}_{i\to j} = N_0^{(0)}{}_{i\to j} + \mu N_0^{(1)}{}_{i\to j}$ and $T_{ij}^{(l)} = T_{i\to j}^{(0)} + \mu T_{i\to j}^{(1)}$.

By integrating along the paths from surface elements i to surface elements j and by substituting $[N_{0i}]^{(1)}$ and $[T_{ij}]^{(1)}$ into Eq. (3.23), $[N_j]^{(1)}$ is obtained. According to Eq. (3.24), the surface collision density in the nearly free-molecule flow has been evaluated (Fig. 3). The transmission coefficients R and Q in the nearly free-molecular regime have also been calculated.

C. Numerical Solutions

See Tables I and II.

TABLE I

NUMERICAL DATA FOR FREE-MOLECULE FLOW THROUGH TWO PARALLEL PLATES

(a) $N_A = N_A$; $N_B = 0$

(i) Initial transmission probability matrix

$$[N_{AiSj}] = \begin{bmatrix} 0.3081, & 0.1392, & 0.0940, & 0.0668, & 0.0567, & 0.0448, \\ 0.1237, & 0.1810, & 0.1497, & 0.1039, & 0.0726, & 0.0534, \\ 0.0322, & 0.0264, & 0.0237, & 0.0193, & 0.0157, & 0.0136, \\ 0.0440, & 0.0319, & 0.0220, & 0.0212, & 0.0179, & 0.0146, \\ 0.0116, & 0.0104, & 0.0094, & 0.0083 \\ 0.0121, & 0.0103, & 0.0095, & 0.0087 \end{bmatrix}$$

(ii) Final transmission probability matrix

$$[N_{SiA}] = [0.4391, \quad 0.3249, \quad 0.2350, \quad 0.1720, \quad 0.1270, \quad 0.0955,$$
$$0.0749, \quad 0.0589, \quad 0.0474, \quad 0.0392, \quad 0.0329, \quad 0.0280,$$
$$0.0240, \quad 0.0208, \quad 0.0183, \quad 0.0161].$$

$$[N_{SiB}] = [0.0161, \quad 0.0183, \quad 0.0208, \quad 0.0240, \quad 0.0280, \quad 0.0329,$$
$$0.0392, \quad 0.0474, \quad 0.0589, \quad 0.0749, \quad 0.0955, \quad 0.1270,$$
$$0.1720, \quad 0.2350, \quad 0.3249, \quad 0.4391]$$

TABLE I—*continued*

(iii) Transition probability matrix

$$[T_{ij}] = \begin{bmatrix} a & b & c & d & \cdots & o & p \\ b & a & b & c & \cdots & & \cdot \\ c & b & a & & \cdots & & \cdot \\ d & c & & & \cdots & & \\ \cdot & \cdot & & & \cdots & & \\ \cdot & \cdot & & & \cdots & & c \\ \cdot & \cdot & & & \cdots & & b \\ p & o & & & & & a \end{bmatrix}$$

in which,

$[a, b, c, d, e, \cdots, p] = [0.1218, 0.1142, \quad 0.0899, \quad 0.0630,$
$\quad 0.0450, \quad 0.0315, \quad 0.0206, \quad 0.0160, \quad 0.0115, \quad 0.0082,$
$\quad 0.0063, \quad 0.0049, \quad 0.0040, \quad 0.0032, \quad 0.0025, \quad 0.0022]$

(iv) Surface collision density

$[N_i] = [0.81421, \quad 0.77292, \quad 0.74206, \quad 0.68889, \quad 0.64985,$
$\quad 0.60817, \quad 0.56538, \quad 0.52208, \quad 0.47963, \quad 0.44126,$
$\quad 0.39917, \quad 0.35634, \quad 0.31265, \quad 0.26899, \quad 0.22468,$
$\quad 0.18039]$

(v) Number densities

$N(a) = [0.83702, \quad 0.77569, \quad 0.73362, \quad 0.69377, \quad 0.65497,$
$\quad 0.61621, \quad 0.57759, \quad 0.53927, \quad 0.50090, \quad 0.46254,$
$\quad 0.42420, \quad 0.38555, \quad 0.34676, \quad 0.30791, \quad 0.26798,$
$\quad 0.25576, \quad 0.16396]$

$N(b) = [0.83952, \quad 0.78101, \quad 0.73693, \quad 0.69536, \quad 0.65551,$
$\quad 0.61654, \quad 0.57784, \quad 0.53917, \quad 0.50090, \quad 0.46262,$
$\quad 0.42394, \quad 0.38420, \quad 0.34619, \quad 0.30627, \quad 0.26457,$
$\quad 0.20030, \quad 0.17146]$

$N(c) = [0.78984, \quad 0.75182, \quad 0.71337, \quad 0.67479, \quad 0.63623,$
$\quad 0.59747, \quad 0.55906, \quad 0.52026, \quad 0.48157, \quad 0.44275,$
$\quad 0.40433, \quad 0.36555, \quad 0.32695, \quad 0.28832, \quad 0.24981,$
$\quad 0.21172]$

(vi) Transmission probabilities

$P_{A \to B} = .40076$
$P_{A \to A} = .59924$

(b) $N_A = N_A; \quad N_B = 0.8 N_B$

(i) Surface collision density

$[N_i] = [0.96472, \quad 0.95635, \quad 0.94797, \quad 0.93960, \quad 0.93122, \quad 0.92285$
$\quad 0.91447, \quad 0.90610, \quad 0.89772, \quad 0.88935, \quad 0.88097, \quad 0.97260,$
$\quad 0.86422, \quad 0.85555, \quad 0.84747, \quad 0.83910]$

(ii) Transmission coefficients

$Q = 0.920$
$R = 0.880$

TABLE II

NUMERICAL DATA FOR NEARLY FREE-MOLECULE FLOW THROUGH TWO PARALLEL PLATES

$$\langle N_A = N_A; \quad N_B = 0.8 N_A \rangle$$

(i) Surface collision densities $[N_i]^{(1)}$

$\mu = 0.1$,

[0.96612,   0.95759,   0.94892,   0.94039,   0,93184,
0.92334,   0.91486,   0.90634,   0.89795,   0.88943,
0.88096,   0.87245,   0.86390,   0.85563,   0.84664,
0.83806]

$\mu = 0.5$,

[0.97171,   0.96255,   0.95270,   0.94353,   0.93430,
0.92529,   0.91642,   0.90731,   0.89883,   0.88974,
0.88089,   0.87187,   0.80260,   0.85475,   0.84331,
0.83391]

$\mu = 1.0$,

[0.97869,   0.96875,   0.95743,   0.94746,   0.93738
0.92772,   0.91837,   0.90851,   0.89993,   0.89014,
0.88080,   0.87114,   0.86097,   0.85364,   0.83914,
0.82872]

(ii) Transmission coefficients Q, R

$\mu = 0.1$	$Q = 0.92110$	$R = 0.87884$
$\mu = 0.5$	$Q = 0.92760$	$R = 0.87310$
$\mu = 1.0$	$Q = 0.93573$	$R = 0.86592$

D. Discussion

In the free-molecular regime, the surface collision density along the channel in this example has been calculated and found to be linearly distributed. This gives some justification for the assumption of a linearized surface collision density in many internal flow problems. In the regime of nearly free-molecule flow, the surface collision density is no longer a linear function along the system. The transmission coefficient R decreases (or Q increases) as the collision frequency μ increases. This implies that, for a given pressure gradient (or density gradient) in this internal flow system, the mass flow (or volume flow) will decrease when the collision frequency μ is increasing. However, one can not determine where the minimum mass flow will be in the solution for nearly free-molecule flow. In order to locate the minimum mass flow for the same pressure gradient, one has to solve the surface collision density and transmission coefficients in higher order transition flow.

ACKNOWLEDGMENT

The author is grateful to Professors C. K. Chu, L. Arnold and H. Grad for many stimulating discussions.

REFERENCES

Bhatnagar, P. L., Gross, E. P., and Krook, M. (1954). *Phys. Rev.* **94**, 511.

Cercignani, C. (1963). In "Rarefied Gas Dynamics" (J. A. Laurmann, ed.), Vol. II, pp. 92–101. Academic Press, New York

Davis, D. H., Levenson, L. L., and Milleron, M. (1961). In "Rarefied Gas Dynamics" (L Talbot, ed.), pp. 99–116. Academic Press, New York.

DeMarcus, W. C. (1961). In "Rarefied Gas Dynamics" (L. Talbot, ed.), pp. 161–168. Academic Press, New York.

Kruger, C. H., and Shapiro, A. H. (1961). In "Rarefied Gas Dynamics" (L. Talbot, ed.) pp. 117–140. Academic Press, New York.

Mikhlin, S. G. (1957). "Integral Equations." Macmillan (Pergamon), New York.

Takao, K. (1961). In "Rarefied Gas Dynamics" (L. Talbot, ed.), pp. 465–474. Academic Press, New York.

Welander, P. (1954). *Arkiv Fysik* **7**, No. 44.

Willis, D. R. (1958). Rept. No. 442. Princeton Univ., Princeton, New Jersey.

Wu, Y. (1961). In "Rarefied Gas Dynamics" (L. Talbot, ed.) pp. 141–160. Academic Press, New York.

Wu, Y. (1964a). Rept. No. NYU-AA-64-1. New York Univ., New York.

Wu, Y. (1964b). Rept. No. 711. Princeton Univ., Princeton, New Jersey.

Ziering, S. (1961). In "Rarefied Gas Dynamics" (L. Talbot, ed.), pp. 451–465. Academic Press, New York.

Subject Index

Accommodation coefficients, 605

Bhatnagar-Gross-Krook equation
  for Couette flow, 97
  for free jet flow, 126
  for leading edge flow, 396
    modified equation for nearly-free molecule flow, 442
  for nearly-free molecule flow, 298, 315, 442, 692
  for propagation of sound, 2, 26, 51
  for Rayleigh's problem, 332ff.
  for shock structure, 105, 140ff., 182ff.
  for shock tube problem, 78
Bimodal method, 354ff.
Boltzmann equation
  Maxwell molecule shock tube problem, 79
  for strong shock structure, 161ff.
Boundary layer, 417, 467ff., 505, 574ff., 592ff.

Collision integral, 280, 372
Cone, 508ff., 574ff.
Couette flow, 97, 291, 354, 370
Cylinder, 312, 326, 433

Discrete ordinate technique, 370ff.
Drag
  cylinder, 312ff., 326ff., 433ff., 444ff.
  flat strip, 433ff., 444ff.
  optimization, 630ff.
  sphere, 433ff.
  wire mesh, 444ff.

Electron beam technique
  attenuation method, 253, 267, 539
  large angle scattering, 241

Equilibrium cylinder temperature, 438

Flat plate
  leading edge flow, 112ff., 394ff., 416ff., 487ff., 508ff., 540, 592ff.
  with steps, 574ff.
Free molecule experiments
  cylinder drag, 435
  flat strip drag, 435
Free molecule theory
  for conical tubes, 641ff.
  for flat plate leading edge, 394ff.
  for impact probe at angle of attack, 653ff.
  for shapes with minimum drag, 630ff.
  for shock tube problem, 74
Free jet flow, 125ff., 621ff.
Frozen flow, 125ff.

Heat transfer
  hypersonic flat plate flow, 416ff., 490
  hypersonic wedge flow, 467ff.
Hypersonic flow
  cone flow, 508ff.
  Couette flow, 291
  leading edge, 487ff., 508ff., 535ff.
  stagnation point flow, 543
  wedge flow, 467ff.

Impact probe, 653ff.
Internal flow
  between flat plates, 677ff.
  conical tubes, 641ff.
  experiments in ducts, 548ff.
  impact probe, 653ff.

Knudsen layer, 123

699